Differential and Difference Equations

It is proper in philosophy to consider the similar,
even in things far distant from each other.

Aristotle

DIFFERENTIAL

AND DIFFERENCE

EQUATIONS

LOUIS BRAND

M.D. Anderson Professor of Mathematics
University of Houston

John Wiley & Sons, Inc., New York · London · Sydney

To my wife

Preface

The title of this book calls for a word of explanation. In my student days at Harvard I was greatly impressed by a course given by Maxime Bôcher on linear differential equations of the second order in which he pointed out the far-reaching analogies between linear differential and difference equations.* It was in this course that he made a remarkable piece of mathematical deduction, for he pointed out that an unpublished (and lost) paper of Charles Sturm, "On the Distribution of Heat in a Series of Vases," must inevitably have led Sturm to the discovery of his famous theorem on the location of roots in an algebraic equation. The Sturmian sequences used in this theorem are the solutions of certain difference equations.

In this book these analogies have been systematically developed; there is a close correspondence not only between the *basic theorems* but also in *methods of procedure*. Thus the methods of "undetermined coefficients" and "variation of parameters" are precisely parallel in both cases. In each case a solution in closed form is possible only when a particular solution of the homogeneous equation is known; and then the general solutions have the same structure.

For equations with constant coefficients the analogies are even more striking and extend to the operational methods of solution. To the *exponential shift*

$$f(D)e^{ax}X = e^{ax}f(D+a)X$$

there corresponds the *power shift*

$$f(E)a^xX = a^xf(aE)X;$$

---

* Professor Bôcher distinguished between the difference equation

$$\Delta^2y(x) + p(x)\,\Delta y(x) + q(x)\,y(x) = r(x)$$

and the equivalent recurrence relation

$$y(x+2) + [p(x) - 2]\,y(x+1) + [q(x) - p(x) + 1]\,y(x) = r(x).$$

The conditions $y(0) = \alpha$, $\Delta y(0) = \beta$, in the former become $y(0) = \alpha$, $y(1) = \alpha + \beta$, in the latter.

and, just as the operational formula

$$(D - a)^{-1} = e^{ax} D^{-1} e^{-ax}$$

constitutes almost all of the theory of linear differential equations with constant coefficients, so does

$$(E - a)^{-1} = a^{x-1} \Delta^{-1} a^{-x}$$

constitute the corresponding theory of difference equations.

Transform methods of solution are also closely parallel. The Laplace transform for differential equations corresponds to the Maclaurin transform (or more closely to the Laurent transform) for difference equations. Just as the operational calculus of Mikusiński arrives at the Laplace transformation formulas through a division algebra in which the convolution of functions plays the role of multiplication and the multiplicative unit is the Dirac delta function, so also is a corresponding operational calculus due to Elias (and developed independently by the author) available for the solution of difference equations and in which the analog of convolution is the Cauchy product of sequences and the multiplicative unit is the "unit sequence" $\{1, 0, 0, \ldots\}$. In both of these operational calculi questions of convergence do not arise because the improper Laplace integral is bypassed in Mikusiński's calculus of functions and the convergence of series to a generating function is bypassed in the corresponding calculus of sequences. Thus, in solving equations by these operational methods, we need not be concerned whether the solution functions satisfy certain convergence criteria, for they are not germane to the problem. Moreover, functions, such as e^{t^2}, which have no Laplace transform, or sequences, such as $\{n!\}$, which have no generating function, can still be dealt with by these new operational methods.

In this chapter dealing with the solution of differential equations in series the use of the operator $\vartheta = xD$, instead of D, not only illuminates the problem but is also a great labor-saving device. A series is *known* only when the coefficient of its general term is known, and this is always the case when the coefficients satisfy a two-term recurrence relation. Differential equations that can be put in the form

$$f(\vartheta)y + x^s g(\vartheta)y = 0$$

have two-term recurrence relations which yield their solutions with a minimum of labor. This form also reveals the indicial equation $f(\lambda) = 0$ and the "skip number" s by which the powers in the series advance. In addition, this form leads easily to solutions that are valid for large x. The hypergeometric, confluent hypergeometric, Legendre, Chebyshev, Laguerre, Hermite, and Bessel equations are all of the foregoing type, and the corresponding series or polynomial solutions are readily found. In the Sturm-Liouville systems the recurrence relations between the orthogonal functions lead to generating functions by means of a standard technique, which gives another example of the interplay between differential and difference equations.

The numerical solution of differential equations also depends on the solution of difference equations; and the spurious or parasitic solutions that may arise in forming extended tables are precisely those unstable solutions of the difference equation that are extraneous to the problem.

In dealing with stability the criteria of Routh-Hurwitz and the more recent direct method of Liapunov are both developed and illustrated with linear and nonlinear examples. A detailed treatment of this important matter would be out of place in an introductory book, especially since several excellent books on the subject are now available.

At the start I mentioned a course of Professor Bôcher. I must add that in all the years since then I have never heard more flawless or more elegant exposition. He was a mathematician and indeed an artist; for him mathematics was truly an art. I shall never forget one great lecture that he gave on Haar's sensational paper on the analogies between general Sturm-Liouville series and Fourier series, which extended even to Gibbs' phenomenon. At one point he paused, turned to the class, and said: "Gentlemen, I have often been asked what constitutes great mathematics; this proof of Haar which I have just given is Great Mathematics." On occasion some important parts of mathematics seem as dull as ditchwater, but with Maxime Bôcher there was always the excitement of discovery, an elegance of presentation, and the consummate art of a master.

Even in the most elementary parts of differential equations, theorems that the student first encounters in "advanced" calculus, continually intrude. I have then consistently given references to my *Advanced Calculus* because, naturally, I am most familiar with its contents. Other excellent works covering the same ground are listed in the final bibliography. Several of the French titles have long been admired for the elegance and clarity of their exposition.

Finally, I wish to express my grateful appreciation for the contribution of the Taft Fund toward typing the manuscript. I am also indebted to Mrs. Anne Hagedorn for her efficient and painstaking help in this regard, to my wife for her assistance with the proofs, and to the editorial and production staff of the publisher for the care they have bestowed upon this book.

LOUIS BRAND

University of Houston,
May 1966

Contents

Chapter 11. Mikusiński's Operational Calculus 517

Chapter 12. Existence and Uniqueness Theorems 561

My passion is for lucidity.
I don't mean simple-mindedness.
If people can't understand it, why write it?

PHYLLIS MCGINLEY
Time, June 15, 1965

CHAPTER 1

Differential Equations
of the First Order

1. DEFINITIONS

A *differential equation* is an equation involving functions of one or more independent variables and certain of their derivatives. A differential equation is called *ordinary* if there is but one independent variable, *partial* if there are two or more independent variables. The *order* of a differential equation is the order of the highest derivative it contains.

In the following ordinary differential equations x is the *independent variable* and $y(x)$, a function of x, is the *dependent variable*:

$$\text{(1)} \qquad x\frac{dy}{dx} + y = 3x^2,$$

$$\text{(2)} \qquad \left(\frac{dy}{dx}\right)^2 - 4y + 0,$$

$$\text{(3)} \qquad x^2\frac{d^2y}{dx^2} - 2x\frac{dy}{dx} + 2y = 0,$$

$$\text{(4)} \qquad 2x^2\frac{d^2y}{dx^2} - \left(\frac{dx}{dy}\right)^2 = 0.$$

Equations (1) and (2) are of the first order, (3) and (4) of the second.

The pair of *simultaneous equations* of the first order

$$\text{(5)} \qquad \frac{dx}{dt} - y = 0, \qquad \frac{dy}{dt} + x = 0,$$

are also ordinary; t is now the independent variable and the dependent variables x and y are functions of t.

1

The following *partial differential equations*

(6) $$x\frac{\partial z}{\partial x} + y\frac{\partial z}{\partial y} = 2z,$$

(7) $$\frac{\partial^2 z}{\partial x^2} + \frac{\partial^2 z}{\partial y^2} = 0$$

are, respectively, of the first and second orders; z is regarded as a function of two independent variables x, y.

A functional relation between the dependent and independent variables which satisfies the differential equation is said to be a *solution* of the equation. A differential equation is completely solved when *all* of its solutions are known. For example $y = x^2$ is a solution of (1); for then

$$xy' + y = 2x^2 + x^2 = 3x^2.$$

We shall see later that *all* solutions of (1) are given by

(1)' $$y = x^2 + \frac{C}{x},$$

where C is an arbitrary constant. Consequently we call (1)' the *general solution* of (1) whereas $y = x^2$ is merely a *particular* solution corresponding to the value $C = 0$ of the arbitrary constant.

The function $y = x^2$ is also a particular solution of (2), because $(2x)^2 - 4x^2 = 0$. In this case we shall see that the general solution is

(2)' $$y = x^2 + Cx + \frac{C^2}{4},$$

where C is an arbitrary constant.

Again, $y = x^2$ is a particular solution of (3); for $2x^2 - 4x^2 + 2x^2 = 0$. We shall find that the general solution is

(3)' $$y = C_1 x + C_2 x^2,$$

where C_1 and C_2 are arbitrary constants. When $C_1 = 1$, $C_2 = 0$, we obtain the particular solution $y = x$.

Finally, $y = x^2$ is evidently a solution of (4). The general solution in this case proves to be

(4)' $$y = \frac{2x}{C_1} - \frac{2}{C_1{}^2}\log(1 + C_1 x) + C_2,$$

where C_1 and C_2 are arbitrary constants. Unlike the previous cases, (4)' does *not* include the particular solution $y = x^2$. But when $C_2 = 0$, y approaches x^2 as C_1 approaches zero, for in the immediate neighborhood of the origin we can write

$$\log(1 + C_1 x) = C_1 x - \tfrac{1}{2}C_1{}^2 x^2 + \tfrac{1}{3}C_1{}^3 x^3 - \cdots,$$
$$y = x^2 - \tfrac{2}{3}C_1 x^3 + \cdots,$$

when $C_2 = 0$. Thus in an extended sense (4)′ still includes $y = x^2$.

Although a solution of an nth-order equation containing n independent* arbitrary constants is usually called its "general solution", the word *general*, however, must not be taken in the sense of *complete*. Indeed some differential equations have solutions which are not obtainable by giving special values to the arbitrary constants of the general solution. Such solutions are called *singular*. For example, the equation

(8) $$y'^2 - xy' + y = 0$$

has the general solution $y = Cx - C^2$, and the singular solution $y = x^2/4$ not contained therein.

It is important to note the exact *interval* on which the solution of a differential equation is valid. Thus the solution x^2 of equation (1) is valid for all real x; however, the solution $1/x$ is valid only on the open intervals $0 < x < \infty$ or $-\infty < x < 0$. When solutions are given as infinite series, the interval of convergence is paramount.

PROBLEMS

1. Show that

$$x = C_1 \cos t + C_2 \sin t, \qquad y = C_2 \cos t - C_1 \sin t$$

are solutions of equations (5).

2. Show that $y'' + n^2 y = 0$ has the solutions

$$y = A \cos nx + B \sin nx \quad \text{and} \quad y = C \cos(nx - D),$$

where A, B, C, D are arbitrary constants.

3. If $f(y/x)$ is an arbitrary function of y/x, prove that $z = x^2 f(y/x)$ satisfies (6). Show that this solution includes the particular solutions $z = x^2$, $z = xy$, $z = y^2$.

4. Verify that $z = \log(x^2 + y^2)$ and $z = \tan^{-1}(y/x)$ are particular solutions of (7).

5. Show that all the tangents to the parabola $y = x^2/4$ forming the singular solution of (8) are included in the lines forming the general solution.

6. Show that the differential equation $yy' + x = 0$ has no solutions that cross the x-axis and that its solution curves are the semicircles

$$y = \sqrt{C^2 - x^2} \quad \text{and} \quad y = -\sqrt{C^2 - x^2},$$

exclusive of the points $x = \pm C$.

---

* The constants are *independent* when each may be varied independently of the others.

7. Show that
$$y = \cos \log |x| \quad \text{and} \quad y = \sin \log |x|$$
are solutions of the equation $x^2 y'' + xy' + y = 0$ over any interval $a \leq x \leq b$ in which a and b have the same sign.

8. Show that
$$y = e^{x^2} \int_0^x e^{-t^2} \, dt + C e^{x^2}$$
is a solution of $y' - 2xy = 1$ for any constant value of C. [Cf. *Advanced Calculus*, § 119.]

2. EXPLICIT, IMPLICIT, AND PARAMETRIC SOLUTIONS

An ordinary differential equation of the first order may be written

(1)
$$F(x, y, y') = 0,$$

a notation that indicates that x, y, and $y' = dy/dx$ are connected by a functional relation. The function $y = \varphi(x)$ is an explicit solution of (1) when

(2)
$$F[x, \varphi(x), \varphi'(x)] \equiv 0$$

on the interval under consideration.

A relation $f(x, y) = 0$ is said to be an *implicit solution* of (1) when it determines one or more functions $y = \varphi(x)$ which satisfy (2). It is frequently difficult or impossible to solve $f(x, y) = 0$ for y. Nevertheless we can test the solution by obtaining y by implicit differentiation*:

$$\frac{\partial f}{\partial x} + \frac{\partial f}{\partial y} y' = 0, \qquad y' = -\frac{f_x}{f_y}.$$

Then, if

$$F(x, y, -f_x/f_y) \equiv 0$$

identically or by virtue of the relation $f(x, y) = 0$, $f(x, y) = 0$ is an implicit solution of (1).

The pair of equations

(3)
$$x = f(t), \qquad y = g(t)$$

---

* We shall often use subscripts to denote partial derivatives:
$$f_x = \frac{\partial f}{\partial x}, \qquad f_y = \frac{\partial f}{\partial y}.$$

is said to be a parametric solution of (1) when these functions, along with

$$\frac{dy}{dx} = \frac{dy/dt}{dx/dt} = \frac{g'(t)}{f'(t)},$$

reduce (1) to an identity in t:

$$F(f, g, g'/f') \equiv 0.$$

PROBLEMS

1. Show that $(x - C)^2 + y^2 = C^2$ is an implicit solution of

$$x^2 - y^2 + 2xyy' = 0$$

in the region $x > 0$, $y > 0$.

2. Show that $y = x(1 + \log |y|)$ is an implicit solution of

$$(x^2 - xy)y' + y^2 = 0$$

in the region $x > 0$, $x > y$.

3. Show that the equation $f(y') = x$ has the parametric solution

$$x = f(t), \qquad y = \int tf'(t)\, dt + C.$$

4. Show that the equation $f(y') = y$ has the parametric solution

$$x = \int t^{-1}f'(t)\, dt + C, \qquad y = f(t).$$

5. Show that the equation $y = xy' + f(y')$ has the general solution

$$y = Cx + f(C),$$

and the parametric (singular) solution

$$x = -f'(t), \qquad y = -tf'(t) + f(t).$$

3. INTEGRAL CURVES

If a differential equation of the first order is of the first degree in y', we may solve it for y' and write

(1) $y' = f(x, y).$

Then each particular solution $y = y(x)$ of (1) represents a plane curve whose slope at the point (x, y) is $f(x, y)$. Each such curve is called an *integral curve*, and the equation is solved when all of its integral curves are known.

A family of curves depending on a single parameter is often spoken of as a "single infinity of curves" and symbolized as "∞^1 curves." Similarly, "∞^2 curves" means an infinitude of curves depending on *two* independent parameters. Thus the equations

$$y = cx, \qquad \frac{x}{c_1} + \frac{y}{c_2} = 1, \qquad (x - c_1)^2 + (y - c_2)^2 = c_3{}^2$$

represent ∞^1 straight lines, ∞^2 straight lines, and ∞^3 circles, respectively.

A one-parameter family of curves is represented by an equation

(2) $$\varphi(x, y, C) = 0$$

containing a single arbitrary constant C. On differentiating (2) with respect to x, we have

(3) $$\frac{\partial \varphi}{\partial x} + \frac{\partial \varphi}{\partial y} y' = 0,$$

where, in general, $\partial \varphi / \partial x$ and $\partial \varphi / \partial y$ involve C. On eliminating C between (2) and (3), we obtain a relation

(4) $$F(x, y, y') = 0,$$

which expresses a property common to all the curves represented by (2) when C has any constant value. Equation (4), which is at least as general as (2), is called the *differential equation of the family*, and (2) is often called the *general integral* of this differential equation. In some cases, however, curves not included in (2) will also satisfy (4), so that the *general* integral is not necessarily *complete* (see Ex. 3).

If equation (2) is solved for C, giving $f(x, y) = C$, the corresponding differential equation is given at once by differentiation with respect to x:

(5) $$\frac{\partial f}{\partial x} + \frac{\partial f}{\partial y} y' = 0.$$

Example 1. The differential equation of the family of concentric circles about the origin $x^2 + y^2 = C$ is $x + yy' = 0$. This states that the tangent to a circle is perpendicular to the radius through the point of contact; for their respective slopes, $-x/y$ and y/x, have the product -1.

Example 2. The differential equation of the parabolas $y^2 = Cx$ is found by eliminating C between $y^2 = Cx$ and $2yy' = C$; this gives

$$2xy' - y = 0 \quad \text{or} \quad y' = \frac{y}{2x}.$$

This shows that the portion of any tangent between the point of contact and the x-axis is bisected by the y-axis.

Example 3. The family of circles of radius 1 with centers on the x-axis is given by $(x - C)^2 + y^2 = 1$. Differentiation gives $2(x - C) + 2yy' = 0$, and on eliminating C we obtain

$$y^2 y'^2 + y^2 = 1$$

as their differential equation. Its integral curves include the circles and *also the two lines* $y = \pm 1$, tangent to the circles.

Example 4. Find the differential equation of the family of confocal conics with foci at $(k, 0)$ and $(-k, 0)$:

(i)
$$\frac{x^2}{C^2} + \frac{y^2}{C^2 - k^2} = 1.$$

On differentiating (i) we have

$$\frac{x}{C^2} + \frac{yy'}{C^2 - k^2} = 0.$$

Therefore we have the equal ratios

$$\frac{x}{C^2} = \frac{-yy'}{C^2 - k^2} = \frac{x + yy'}{k^2}.$$

Hence

(ii)
$$\frac{x^2}{C^2} = x\,\frac{x + yy'}{k^2}, \qquad \frac{y^2}{C^2 - k^2} = -\frac{y}{y'}\,\frac{x + yy'}{k^2},$$

and on substituting from (ii) in (i), we have

$$\left(x - \frac{y}{y'}\right)\left(\frac{x + yy'}{k^2}\right) = 1$$

or

(iii)
$$xyy'^2 + (x^2 - y^2 - k^2)y' - xy = 0.$$

The line $y = 0$ is obviously an integral curve of (iii) but is not a member of the family of conics (i). Note that we tacitly assume $y' \neq 0$ in (ii).

Example 5. Find the differential equation of the 2-parameter family of unit circles

(i)
$$(x - a)^2 + (y - b)^2 = 1.$$

We must now differentiate twice to obtain three equations from which to eliminate *two* parameters a, b:

(ii)
$$(x - a) + (y - b)y' = 0,$$

(iii)
$$1 + y'^2 + (y - b)y'' = 0.$$

From (iii) and (ii) we find

$$y - b = -\frac{1 + y'^2}{y''}, \qquad x - a = \frac{(1 + y'^2)y'}{y''},$$

and substitution in (i) gives the differential equation of the *second* order:

(iv)　　　$\dfrac{(1 + y'^2)^2}{y''^2}(1 + y'^2) = 1$　or　$(1 + y'^2)^3 - y''^2 = 0$.

Equation (iv) is another way of characterizing the family of circles (i); it states that these curves all have the curvature

$$\kappa = \frac{|y''|}{(1 + y'^2)^{3/2}} = 1.$$

PROBLEMS

Find the differential equations of the following families of curves.

1. The parabolas $y^2 = Cx$.

2. All conics of eccentricity e with the y-axis as directrix and focus $(C, 0)$ on the x-axis.

3. The tangents to the parabola $y = x^2$. Show that their envelope $y = x^2$ also satisfies the differential equation.

4. The normals to the parabola $y = x^2$. Show that their envelope $2(2y - 1)^3 = 27x^3$ also satisfies the differential equation.

5. All circles through the points $(1, 0)$ and $(-1, 0)$. What line satisfies the equation?

6. All unit circles with their centers $(C, 0)$ on the x-axis. Show that their envelope, $y = \pm 1$, also satisfies the differential equation.

7. $y = f(x) + Cg(x)$.

8. $y^n = f(x) + Cg(x)$.

9. $y = \dfrac{f(x) + Cg(x)}{h(x) + Ck(x)}$.

10. Show that the 3-parameter family of circles

$$(x - a)^2 + (y - b)^2 = r^2$$

has the differential equation of the *third* order:

$$y'''(1 + y'^2) - 3y'y''^2 = 0.$$

What property of the circles does this equation state?

11. Show that the 5-parameter family of conics

$$Ax^2 + 2Bxy + Cy^2 + 2Dx + 2Ey + F = 0,$$

for which $C \neq 0$, has the differential equation of the *fifth* order:

$$[(y'')^{-2/3}]''' = 0 \quad \text{or} \quad 9\,(y'')^2 y^\text{v} - 45\,y''y'''y^\text{iv} + 40(y''')^3 = 0.$$

[Set $C = 1$ (no loss in generality), solve for

$$y = ax + b \pm \sqrt{cx^2 + 2dx + e},$$

and show that $(y'')^{-2/3}$ is a quadratic polynomial in x.]

12. If $B^2 = AC$ in Problem 10, the conics become a 4-parameter family of parabolas which have a differential equation of the *fourth* order:

$$[(y'')^{-2/3}]'' = 0 \quad \text{or} \quad 3\,y''y^\text{iv} - 5\,(y'')^2 = 0.$$

[In Problem 11, $c = 0$ in the equation for y.]

4. LINEAL ELEMENTS

A *lineal element* is a point with a line through it. Thus a lineal element in the xy-plane may be designated by three numbers, the two coordinates (x, y) of its point and the slope p of its line. The determination of a lineal element by three *independent* numbers or coordinates (x, y, p) is briefly expressed by saying there are ∞^3 lineal elements in a plane.

A plane curve Γ, $\varphi(x, y) = 0$, defines ∞^1 lineal elements; their points P are on Γ, their lines tangent to Γ at P. This set of lineal elements is called a *curve union*; their coordinates (x, y, p) satisfy

(1) $$\varphi(x, y) = 0, \qquad \varphi_x + \varphi_y p = 0.$$

If Γ is a straight line, p is the same for all elements of the union.

A point $P(a, b)$ in the plane also defines ∞^1 lineal elements; their points are P, their lines pass through P. This set of lineal elements is called a *point union*; their coordinates satisfy

(2) $$x = a, \qquad y = b, \qquad p \text{ arbitrary.}$$

In general, a single infinity of lineal elements is given by expressing the coordinates as functions of a single variable. The question whether such a set forms a union is answered by the following

Theorem. *The set of lineal elements*

(3) $$x = x(t), \qquad y = y(t), \qquad p = p(t)$$

forms a union when and only when

(4) $$dy - p \, dx = 0.$$

PROOF. The set (3) will be a union along the curve $x = x(t)$, $y = y(t)$, when and only when

$$p(t) = \frac{y'(t)}{x'(t)} = \frac{dy}{dx} \, ;$$

and (3) will be a point union when and only when $x(t)$ and $y(t)$ are constants; then $dx = dy = 0$. In both cases (4) holds good.

Consider now the first-order differential equation

(5) $$F(x, y, p) = 0$$

where $p = dy/dx$. This sets up one relation between the ∞^3 lineal elements (x, y, p) of the plane. Hence ∞^2 lineal elements satisfy (5); they form its *direction field*. The problem of solving a differential equation consists in finding all the point and curve unions in its direction field.

In the direct solution of a differential equation, point unions are usually neglected. But when the equation is solved by means of a transformation of its lineal elements, unions of one type may transform into unions of the other type; then both types of unions must be considered to obtain a complete solution.

When p enters (5) to the first degree only, p is a single-valued function of x, y:

(6) $$p = f(x, y).$$

Then at any point $P(x, y)$, p is determined by (6); and if we imagine a moving point $P(x, y)$ departing from $P_0(x_0, y_0)$ and always moving in the direction imposed by the slope $p = f(x, y)$, it will trace out a curve union in the direction field of (6). Thus it appears that a curve union of (6) will pass through a given initial point P_0. We shall see later under what conditions this is rigorously true, and how the unicity of the solution through P_0 may be assured.

The curves $f(x, y) = C$ are called the *isoclines* of the differential equation $y' = f(x, y)$. When a suitably spaced set of isoclines of a differential equation has been drawn, an approximate solution curve may be found by drawing segments with an intermediate slope between adjacent isoclines. This may be done as follows. If an integral curve cuts an isocline $f(x, y) = C_1$ at P_1, draw segments of slopes C_1 and C_2 through P_1 to meet the adjacent isocline $f(x, y) = C_2$ at the points A and B; then the midpoint of the arc AB may be taken as P_2. The starting point P_0 is given by the initial conditions and the foregoing process is continued from point to point. The broken line (*Cauchy polygon*) so obtained suggests the solution curve which it approaches as the isoclines are more and more closely spaced.

Consider, for example, the equation

$$y' = x^2 + y^2.$$

The isoclines are the circles $x^2 + y^2 = C$; they are numbered with their C-values in Fig. 4a. The zero isocline reduces to the point $(0, 0)$. The integral curve through the origin has a horizontal point of inflection there, for $y'(0) = y''(0) = 0$ from the equation; it cuts each isocline at the slope given by its C-number. The curve is obviously symmetrical about the origin.

Example 1. The differential equation

$$x + yy' = 0$$

has the lineal element at P perpendicular to OP; for the slopes, $-x/y$ and y/x are negative reciprocals. Hence the lineal elements at a distance r from the

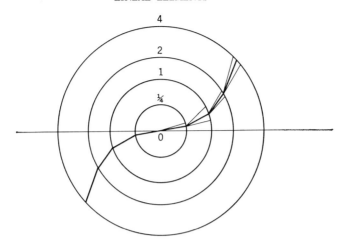

Fig. 4a   Isoclines of $y' = x^2 + y^2$ and Cauchy polygon through the origin.

origin belong to the circle $x^2 + y^2 = r^2$. Besides this family of curve unions the direction field also includes the point union $x = 0$, $y = 0$, y' arbitrary, at the origin. The isoclines are the straight lines $x + Cy = 0$ through the origin.

Example 2. The isoclines of the equation

$$y' = y - x$$

are the family of parallel lines $y - x = C$ of slope 1. The isocline $y - x = 1$ is also an integral curve.

The direction field in Fig. 4b clearly shows that the line $y = x + 1$ is an integral curve and suggests that all integral curves approach this line asymptotically as $x \to -\infty$.

We shall see later that all integral curves are given by

$$y = x + 1 + Ce^x.$$

They are divided into two sets ($C > 0$ and $C < 0$) by the line $y = x + 1$ ($C = 0$).

Sketch the integral curve through the origin, $y = x + 1 - e^x$, by adding the ordinates of $y = x + 1$ and $y = -e^x$. Was it correctly suggested by the direction field?

Example 3. The equation

$$y = y'x + y'^2$$

is satisfied by the lineal elements of the ∞^1 lines (isoclines)

$$y = Cx + C^2$$

and also by the single curve union $4y + x^2 = 0$ enveloped by these lines. Verify this and illustrate with a sketch.

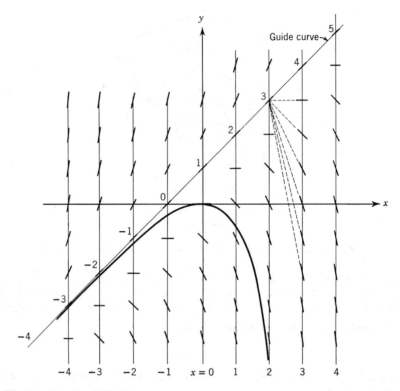

Fig. 4b   Direction field of $y' = y - x$. Integral curves: $y = x + 1, y = x + 1 - e^x$. Lineal element at (x, y) passes through point marked x on guide curve.

Example 4. The equation

$$y - 2 = y'(x - 1)$$

is satisfied by the curve unions formed by the ∞^1 lines (isoclines)

$$y - 2 = C(x - 1)$$

through the point $(1, 2)$ and also by the point union

$$x = 1, \qquad y = 2, \qquad p \text{ arbitrary.}$$

Example 5. For linear equations such as

(i) $y' + f(x)y = g(x),$

the direction field is readily constructed from a *guide curve* which is found as follows. The lineal element of (i) at the point (x, y) lies on the line

$$Y - y = [g(x) - f(x)y](X - x);$$

since this passes through the point

(ii) $$X = x + \frac{1}{f(x)}, \qquad Y = \frac{g(x)}{f(x)}$$

which depends only on x, all lineal elements which have the same x pass through the point (ii). With x as parameter, the guide curve has the parametric equations (ii). If x-values are marked on points of this curve, then all lineal elements for which $x = c$ pass through the c-point of the guide curve. Thus the lineal elements on any vertical may be rapidly constructed.

In Example 2, $f(x) = -1, g(x) = -x, X = x - 1, Y = x$, and the guide curve is the line $Y = X + 1$. Its basic property shows that all of its points have lineal elements along the line, so that it is clearly an integral curve (Fig. 4b).

PROBLEMS

Draw isoclines of the following equations and sketch the integral curve through the origin.

1. $y' = x + y$.
2. $y' = x^2 - y^2$.
3. $y' = y - x^2$.
4. $y' = x^2 + y^2 - 1$.
5. $(x - y)y' = x + y$; show that the integral curves are spirals about the origin—a point union.
6. Show that the guide curve for the equation $(x^2 + 1)y' + y = x$ is the parabola $Y^2 + Y - X + 1 = 0$ and construct the direction field.
7. Find the guide curves in Problems 1 and 3.

5. SOLUTION BY QUADRATURES

The solution of the special differential equation

(1) $$\frac{dy}{dx} = f(x), \qquad a \leqq x \leqq b,$$

is of fundamental importance in the Calculus. If $F(x)$ is an *antiderivative* of $f(x)$, that is

$$\frac{dF}{dx} = f(x), \qquad a \leqq x \leqq b,$$

$y = F(x)$ is a particular solution of (1). All solutions of (1) are then given by

(2) $$y = F(x) + \text{const.}$$

PROOF. If $G(x)$ denotes any solution of (1), let $\varphi(x) = G(x) - F(x)$. Then

$$\varphi'(x) = G'(x) - F'(x) = f(x) - f(x) = 0$$

in (a, b). From the mean-value theorem (*Advanced Calculus* p. 113),

$$\varphi(x) - \varphi(a) = (x - a)\varphi'(\xi) = 0, \qquad a < \xi < x \leqq b,$$

and hence $\varphi(x) = \varphi(a)$, a constant. Thus any solution $G(x)$ of (1) has the form (2).

All antiderivatives of $f(x)$ are denoted by $\int f(x)\, dx$, the *indefinite integral* of $f(x)$. A *table of integrals* gives the antiderivatives of functions arranged by classes, but the antiderivatives of many functions such as

$$\sqrt{1 + x^3}, \quad e^{-x^2}, \quad \frac{e^x}{x}, \quad \frac{1}{\log x}, \quad \sin x^2, \quad \sqrt{\sin x}$$

will not appear, since they cannot be expressed in terms of the elementary functions in finite form—that is, without use of limiting operations such as infinite series or infinite products.

Although a good table of integrals is useful, the basic techniques of integration by substitution, by parts, and by partial fractions must always be kept in mind. Thus we have

$$\int f(x)\, dx = \int f\{\varphi(t)\}\, \varphi'(t)\, dt, \qquad x = \varphi(t);$$

and if u and v are functions of x,

$$\int u\, dv = uv - \int v\, du;$$

or, in terms of definite integrals,

$$\int_a^b f(x)\, dx = \int_\alpha^\beta f\{\varphi(t)\}\, \varphi'(t)\, dt, \qquad a = \varphi(\alpha),\, b = \varphi(\beta);$$

$$\int_a^b u(x)v'(x)\, dx = u(x)v(x)\Big|_a^b - \int_a^b v(x)u'(x)\, dx$$

(*Advanced Calculus* §§ 122–123.) When $f(x)/g(x)$ is a *proper* rational function [deg. $f(x) <$ deg. $g(x)$], it may be expressed as a sum of *partial fractions* whose denominators are factors of $g(x)$; this algebraic problem is dealt with in books on algebra or the calculus.

The short table of integrals with additive constant omitted, given on page 15 is particularly useful. Since a large amount of "practical" integration is accomplished by means of formulas (1) to (7), they should be memorized.

Various other first-order equations may be solved by integrations or *quadratures* (the word refers to the use of integrals in obtaining areas). Hence we often speak of "integrating" a differential equation in order to obtain its solutions. This is by no means always possible. In fact, relatively few first-order differential equations can be solved by quadratures. Many that can be solved in this manner are readily recognizable. This chapter deals with a number of such types.

The most comprehensive table of definite integrals is that of D. Bierens de Haan, *Nouvelles Tables d'Intégrales Définies*, Stechert, New York, 1937 (the corrected 1867 edition).

Table 5

Basic Indefinite Integrals

1. $\int u^n \, du = \dfrac{u^{n+1}}{n+1}$ $(n \neq -1)$.

2. $\int \dfrac{du}{u} = \log |u|$ $(u \text{ real}).$*

3. $\int e^u \, du = e^u$.

4. $\int \sin u \, du = -\cos u$.

5. $\int \cos u \, du = \sin u$.

6. $\int \sinh u \, du = \cosh u$.

7. $\int \cosh u \, du = \sinh u$.

8. $\int \dfrac{du}{a^2 + u^2} = \dfrac{1}{a} \tan^{-1} \dfrac{u}{a}$, $-\tfrac{1}{2}\pi \leqq \tan^{-1} \leqq \tfrac{1}{2}\pi$.

9. $\int \dfrac{du}{a^2 - u^2} = \dfrac{1}{a} \tanh^{-1} \dfrac{u}{a} = \dfrac{1}{2a} \log \dfrac{a+u}{a-u}$.

10. $\int \dfrac{du}{\sqrt{a^2 - u^2}} = \sin^{-1} \dfrac{u}{a}$, $-\tfrac{1}{2}\pi \leqq \sin^{-1} \leqq \tfrac{1}{2}\pi$.

11. $\int \dfrac{du}{\sqrt{u^2 + a^2}} = \sinh^{-1} \dfrac{u}{a} = \log (u + \sqrt{u^2 + a^2})$.

12. $\int \dfrac{du}{\sqrt{u^2 - a^2}} = \cosh^{-1} \dfrac{u}{a} = \log (u + \sqrt{u^2 - a^2})$, $0 \leqq \cosh^{-1}$.

---

* In the field of complex numbers, log u is correct, but when restricted to the real field the arguments of log should be absolute values as in 2. However, absolute value bars are usually omitted as in 9, 11, and 12. In higher mathematics *log* always means a *natural* logarithm (base e); some writers use *ln* to avoid any possible misunderstanding.

6. EXACT EQUATIONS

An equation of the first order and first degree in y' may be written

(1) $$P(x, y) + Q(x, y)y' = 0$$

or, upon multiplying by dx,

(2) $$P(x, y)\, dx + Q(x, y)\, dy = 0.$$

We shall assume that P and Q are continuous and have continuous first partial derivatives in a region $\mathscr{R}$ of the xy-plane which includes the point (x_0, y_0).

Equation (1) or (2) is said to be *exact* when there exists a function $u(x, y)$ such that

(3) $$\frac{\partial u}{\partial x} = P(x, y), \qquad \frac{\partial u}{\partial y} = Q(x, y).$$

Then

$$P\, dx + Q\, dy = \frac{\partial u}{\partial x}\, dx + \frac{\partial u}{\partial y}\, dy = du,$$

a perfect differential.

When (1) is exact, we have from (3)

$$\frac{\partial P}{\partial y} = \frac{\partial^2 u}{\partial y\, \partial x}, \qquad \frac{\partial Q}{\partial x} = \frac{\partial^2 u}{\partial x\, \partial y}.$$

By hypothesis, $\partial P/\partial y$ and $\partial Q/\partial x$ are continuous; hence the mixed derivatives on the right are equal.* Thus for (1) to be an exact equation it is *necessary* that

(4) $$\frac{\partial P}{\partial y} = \frac{\partial Q}{\partial x}.$$

Conversely, when P and Q satisfy this condition, the equation $P\, dx + Q\, dy = 0$ is exact. To prove this we shall construct a function $u(x, y)$ which satisfies both equations (3). We first integrate $\partial u/\partial x = P(x, y)$ partially with regard to x, holding y constant; we thus obtain

(5) $$u(x, y) = \int_{x_0}^{x} P(x, y)\, dx + f(y),$$

---

* **Theorem.** If the partial derivatives $f_x(x, y)$ and $f_y(x, y)$ exist in some neighborhood of the point (a, b) and $f_{xy}(x, y)$ is continuous at (a, b), then $f_{yx}(a, b)$ exists and

$$f_{yx}(a, b) = f_{xy}(a, b).$$

Advanced Calculus, p. 163, Theorem 1.

where $f(y)$, an arbitrary function of y, plays the part of the constant of integration. Any number x_0 for which $P(x_0, y)$ is defined may be chosen as the lower limit.

The function $u(x, y)$ in (5) satisfies $\partial u/\partial x = P$. We shall now choose $f(y)$ so that $\partial u/\partial y = Q$. To this end, differentiate (5) partially with respect to y. Since $\partial P/\partial y$ is continuous the derivative of the integral may be found by differentiating under the integral sign.* We thus obtain

$$\frac{\partial u}{\partial y} = \int_{x_0}^{x} P_y(x, y)\, dx + f'(y) = \int_{x_0}^{x} Q_x(x, y)\, dx + f'(y),$$

in view of (4). In this equation we now put

$$\frac{\partial u}{\partial y} = Q(x, y), \qquad \int_{x_0}^{x} Q_x(x, y)\, dx = Q(x, y) - Q(x_0, y),$$

and, after canceling $Q(x, y)$, find that

$$0 = -Q(x_0, y) + f'(y).$$

Hence u will satisfy *both* equations (3) when $f'(y) = Q(x_0, y)$; that is, when

$$f(y) = \int Q(x_0, y)\, dy,$$

an indefinite integral of $Q(x_0, y)$. With this value of $f(y)$, (5) gives the desired solution of equations (3):

(6) $$u(x, y) = \int_{x_0}^{y} P(x, y)\, dx + \int Q(x_0, y)\, dy.$$

In practice, x_0 is chosen so that the indefinite integral is simplified as much as possible. If $P(x, y)$ does not become infinite as $x \to 0$, the choice $x_0 = 0$ is usually advantageous.

In the foregoing solution we began with $\partial u/\partial x = P$ and integrated with respect to x. If we had begun with $\partial u/\partial y = Q$ and integrated with respect to y, we should have found

(7) $$u = \int_{y_0}^{y} Q(x, y)\, dy + \int P(x, y_0)\, dx,$$

where y_0 is any number for which $Q(x, y_0)$ is defined.

---

* **Theorem.** If $f(x, y)$ and $f_y(x, y)$ are continuous in a region $\mathscr{R}$ of the xy-plane, then

$$\frac{\partial}{\partial y} \int_a^b f(x, y)\, dx = \int_a^b f_y(x, y)\, dx.$$

Advanced Calculus, § 133.

Both (6) and (7) give a function $u(x, y)$ which satisfies equations (3); it is determined to an additive constant implied by the indefinite integral. This fact is readily verified by direct differentiation.

When (1) is exact, its solutions $y(x)$ make $u[x, y(x)] = C$; for

$$P + Qy' = 0 \quad \text{implies} \quad \frac{\partial u}{\partial x} + \frac{\partial u}{\partial y} \frac{dy}{dx} = \frac{du}{dx} = 0.$$

Conversely, all functions $y(x)$ that satisfy $u(x, y) = C$ are solutions of (1); for

$$\frac{du}{dx} = \frac{\partial u}{\partial x} + \frac{\partial u}{\partial y} \frac{dy}{dx} = 0 \quad \text{implies} \quad P + Qy' = 0.$$

Theorem. *If $P(x, y)$ and $Q(x, y)$ have continuous first partial derivatives, the equation*

$$P \, dx + Q \, dy = 0$$

will be exact when and only when $P_y = Q_x$. All of its solutions $y(x)$ then satisfy the equation

(8) $$\int_{x_0}^{x} P(x, y) \, dx + \int Q(x_0, y) \, dy = C.$$

If the second integral in (8) is taken between the limits y_0 and y, the left member will vanish when $x = x_0$, $y = y_0$. Hence the integral curve of $P \, dx + Q \, dy = 0$ which passes through the point (x_0, y_0) is given by

(9) $$\int_{x_0}^{x} P(x, y) \, dx + \int_{y_0}^{y} Q(x_0, y) \, dy = 0.$$

Example 1. The equation

$$\frac{xy + 1}{y} \, dx + \frac{2y - x}{y^2} \, dy = 0$$

is exact since

$$\frac{\partial}{\partial y} \left(x + \frac{1}{y} \right) = \frac{\partial}{\partial x} \left(\frac{2}{y} - \frac{x}{y^2} \right) = -\frac{1}{y^2}.$$

Its solutions satisfy (8) with $x_0 = 0$:

$$\int_0^x \left(x + \frac{1}{y} \right) dx + \int \frac{2}{y} \, dy = C,$$

$$\frac{1}{2} x^2 + \frac{x}{y} + 2 \log |y| = C.$$

Or we may use (7) with $y_0 = 1$:

$$\int_1^y \left(\frac{2}{y} - \frac{x}{y^2} \right) dy + \int (x + 1) \, dx = C,$$

$$\left[2 \log |y| + \frac{x}{y} \right]_{y=1}^y + \frac{1}{2} x^2 + x = C,$$

which again gives the preceding result.

Example 2. The equation

$$\frac{dy}{dx} + \frac{ax + by + h}{bx + cy + k} = 0$$

may be written

$$(ax + by + h) \, dx + (bx + cy + k) \, dy = 0.$$

This is an exact equation for

$$\frac{\partial}{\partial y} (ax + by + h) = \frac{\partial}{\partial x} (bx + cy + k) = b.$$

Hence its solutions satisfy

$$\int_0^x (ax + by + h) \, dx + \int (cy + k) \, dy = C,$$

$$\tfrac{1}{2} ax^2 + bxy + hx + \tfrac{1}{2} cy^2 + ky = C.$$

Example 3. The equation

$$\left(1 - \frac{x}{x^2 + y^2} \right) dx + \frac{x^2}{y(x^2 + y^2)} \, dy = 0$$

is exact since

$$P_y = Q_x = \frac{2xy}{(x^2 + y^2)^2}.$$

Its solutions satisfy (8) with $x_0 = 0$:

$$\int_0^x \left(1 - \frac{x}{x^2 + y^2} \right) dx = \left[x - \frac{1}{2} \log (x^2 + y^2) \right]_{x=0}^x = C,$$

$$x - \tfrac{1}{2} \log (x^2 + y^2) + \log |y| = C.$$

If we use (7), the solution is not so simple:

$$\int_1^y \frac{x^2}{y(x^2 + y^2)} \, dy + \int \left(1 - \frac{x}{x^2 + 1} \right) dx = C.$$

The first integral is evaluated by using partial fractions; thus

$$\int_1^y \left(\frac{1}{y} - \frac{y}{x^2 + y^2} \right) dy = \log |y| - \tfrac{1}{2} \log (x^2 + y^2) + \tfrac{1}{2} \log (x^2 + 1)$$

and again we obtain the preceding result.

PROBLEMS

Prove exact and integrate in two ways.

1. $(x^2 - y^2)\, dx + (y^3 - 2xy)\, dy = 0.$

2. $\left(\dfrac{x^2}{y} - \dfrac{y^2}{x}\right) dx - \left(\dfrac{x^3}{3y^2} + 2y \log x\right) dy = 0.$

3. $(7r - 2 \cos \theta)\, dr + 2r \sin \theta\, d\theta = 0.$

4. $\dfrac{4y^2 - 2x^2}{4xy^2 - x^3}\, dx + \dfrac{8y^2 - x^2}{4y^3 - x^2 y}\, dy = 0.$

5. $\dfrac{dx}{\sqrt{x^2 + y^2}} + \left(1 - \dfrac{x}{\sqrt{x^2 + y^2}}\right) \dfrac{dy}{y} = 0.$

6. $\dfrac{2xy - 1}{y}\, dx + \dfrac{x + 3y}{y^2}\, dy = 0.$

7. $\dfrac{(1 + y^2)\, dx + (1 + x^2)\, dy}{(1 - xy)^2} = 0.$

8. $e^{-x} \sin y\, dx - (y + e^{-x} \cos y)\, dy = 0;$ $y = 0$ when $x = 0.$

9. $(ye^{xy} + 2x)\, dx + (xe^{xy} - 2y)\, dy = 0;$ $y = 2$ when $x = 0.$

10. $(2r + \sin \theta + \cos \theta)\, dr$
$\qquad\qquad + r(\cos \theta - \sin \theta)\, d\theta = 0;$ $r = 1$ when $\theta = 0.$

11. $3x^2 y^{-1}\, dx + (y^2 - x^3 y^{-2})\, dy = 0;$ $y = 1$ when $x = 1.$

12. $\left(\dfrac{1}{x^2} + \dfrac{2x^2}{y^3}\right) dy - 2\left(\dfrac{x}{y^2} + \dfrac{y}{x^3}\right) dx = 0;$ $y = -1$ when $x = -1.$

13. $\left(\dfrac{2}{x^3} - \dfrac{y}{x^2}\right) dx + \left(y + \dfrac{1}{x}\right) dy = 0;$ $y = 1$ when $x = 2.$

14. $\left(\dfrac{1}{x} + \dfrac{y}{x^2}\right) dx - \dfrac{1}{x}\, dy = 0;$ $y = 1$ when $x = -1.$

7. SEPARABLE EQUATIONS

In the equation

(1) $$P(x)\, dx + Q(y)\, dy = 0,$$

we say that the *variables are separated*. The integrals of this exact equation $(P_y = Q_x = 0)$ are given by (6.8), and here we may omit the limits x_0, x since Q is independent of x:

(2) $$\int P(x)\, dx + \int Q(y)\, dy = C.$$

Both integrals are indefinite and all constants of integration may be combined in C.

An integral curve through the point (x_0, y_0) is given by

$$(3) \qquad \int_{x_0}^{x} P(x)\, dx + \int_{y_0}^{y} Q(y)\, dy = 0.$$

The variables may be separated in the more general equation

$$(4) \qquad X(x)\, Y_1(y)\, dx + X_1(x)\, Y(y)\, dy = 0$$

in which both coefficients are products of a function of x by a function of y. If we assume that $X_1 Y_1 \neq 0$ in a region $\mathcal{R}$, we can divide (4) by $X_1 Y_1$ and convert it into the exact equation

$$(5) \qquad \frac{X}{X_1}\, dx + \frac{Y}{Y_1}\, dy = 0$$

in which the variables are separated. The equation

$$(6) \qquad \int \frac{X}{X_1}\, dx + \int \frac{Y}{Y_1}\, dy = C$$

comprises the integrals of (4) for which $X_1 Y_1 \neq 0$. We must now examine (4) to see if some solutions are lost as a consequence of this condition. If $X_1(a) = 0$, the line $x = a$ (for which $dx = 0$) is obviously an integral curve of (4). Similarly, if $Y_1(b) = 0$, the line $y = b$ (for which $dy = 0$) is also an integral curve. All such lines, given by the roots of $X_1(x) = 0$, $Y_1(y) = 0$, which are not included in (6) for any value of C, must be adjoined to (6) to obtain the complete solution of (4).

Example 1. Solve the equation

$$\frac{dy}{dx} = a - by$$

if $y = 0$ when $x = 0$.

This equation is separable and the required solution is given by

$$\int_{0}^{y} \frac{-b\, dy}{a - by} = -b \int_{0}^{x} dx.$$

For the first integral to exist, $a - by$ must not vanish in the range of integration; hence $a - by$ must keep the same sign as a, the value of $a - by$ at the lower limit. Then $(a - by)/a$ is positive and

$$\log \frac{a - by}{a} = -bx, \qquad \frac{a - by}{a} = e^{-bx},$$

$$y = \frac{a}{b}(1 - e^{-bx}).$$

Example 2. Solve the equation

(7)
$$\frac{dx}{dt} = k(a - x)(b - x), \qquad a > b > 0,$$

if $x = 0$ when $t = 0$.

The equation is separable; and since

$$\frac{1}{(a - x)(b - x)} = \frac{1}{a - b}\left\{\frac{1}{b - x} - \frac{1}{a - x}\right\},$$

the required solution is given by

$$\int_0^x \frac{dx}{b - x} - \int_0^x \frac{dx}{a - x} = (a - b)k \int_0^t dt.$$

Since a and $a - x$, b, and $b - x$, must keep the same sign (see Ex. 1)

$$\log \frac{a - x}{a} - \log \frac{b - x}{b} = (a - b)kt,$$

(8)
$$\log \frac{b(a - x)}{a(b - x)} = (a - b)kt.$$

To express x as a function of t we put (8) in the form

$$\frac{b(a - x)}{a(b - x)} = e^{(a-b)kt}$$

and obtain

(9)
$$x = ab \frac{e^{(a-b)kt} - 1}{ae^{(a-b)kt} - b}.$$

Since $a - b > 0$, we see that $x \to b$ as $t \to \infty$.

When $a = b$, the solution of (7) for which $x = 0$ when $t = 0$ is given by

$$\int_0^x \frac{dx}{(a - x)^2} = k \int_0^t dt,$$

(10)
$$\frac{1}{a - x} - \frac{1}{a} = kt,$$

(11)
$$x = \frac{ka^2t}{1 + kat}.$$

Example 3. The equation

$$(1 + y^2)\, dx + (1 + x^2)\, dy = 0$$

or

$$\frac{dx}{1 + x^2} + \frac{dy}{1 + y^2} = 0$$

gives on integration

$$\tan^{-1} x + \tan^{-1} y = c.$$

We may remove the inverse tangents by taking the tangent of both members and using the formula for $\tan (\alpha + \beta)$; thus

$$\frac{x + y}{1 - xy} = \tan c = C.$$

No real solutions are given by $1 + x^2 = 0, 1 + y^2 = 0$.

Example 4. Find all the curves whose arcs are proportional to the angle they subtend at the origin.

Using polar coordinates r, θ, we have for the element of arc

$$ds^2 = r^2 \, d\theta^2 + dr^2.$$

Hence the prescribed property $s = k\theta$ is expressed by the differential equation $ds/d\theta = k$ or

(i) $$r^2 + \left(\frac{dr}{d\theta}\right)^2 = k^2.$$

If we choose the positive sense of θ so that $dr/d\theta$ is positive, $dr/d\theta = \sqrt{k^2 - r^2}$; hence

$$\frac{dr}{\sqrt{k^2 - r^2}} = d\theta \quad (k \neq r), \qquad \sin^{-1}\frac{r}{k} = \theta + c,$$

(ii) $$r = k \sin (\theta + c).$$

These solutions represent all circles of diameter k passing through the origin.

In obtaining (ii) we excluded the case $r = k$; obviously this is also a solution of (i) which is not included in (ii) for any value of c. For any given k, the complete solution consists of the family of circles (ii) and the circle $r = k$ about the origin.

PROBLEMS

1. $\dfrac{dy}{dx} = \dfrac{(2x - 1)y}{x}$. Solve for y.

2. $\dfrac{dy}{dx} = \dfrac{xy}{1 + x^2}$. Find y if $y = 1$ when $x = 0$.

3. $\dfrac{dy}{dx} = -ky^2$. Find y and the constant k if $y = a$ when $t = 0$, $y = b$ when $t = 1$.

4. $\dfrac{dy}{dx} = \dfrac{y}{(x - 1)(x - 2)}$. Find y if $y = 1$ when $x = 3$.

5. $\dfrac{dy}{dx} - \dfrac{y}{x} = y$. Solve for y.

6. $(y^2 - 1) \, dx + xy(1 - x) \, dy = 0$.

7. $2xy(1 - y^2) \, dx + (1 + x^2)(1 + y^2) \, dy = 0$.

8. $\dfrac{dy}{dx} = \dfrac{y}{2 + e^x}$.

9. $(1 - y^2)\, dx + (1 - x^2)\, dy = 0$.

10. $\dfrac{dx}{dt} = kx(a - x)$.   Find x if $x = \frac{1}{2}a$ when $t = 0$.

11. $(1 + x^2)y' = \sqrt{1 - y^2}$.   Obtain solution free from transcendental functions.

12. $\sqrt{x - 1}\, y' + \sqrt{y - 1} = 0$.   Find an integral curve through the point $(2, 2)$.

13. $y' = 5 - 2y$.   Find y if $y = 2$ when $x = 0$.

14. $y' + \dfrac{y}{x} = 2xy$.   Solve for y.

15. $x^2 y' - (x - 1)y = 0$.   Solve for y.

16. $x^2 e^x y' + (x + 1)y^2 = 0$.   Solve for y.

17. $(1 - x^2)y' = 1 - y^2$.   Find all solutions such that $y = 1$ when $x = 1$.

8. MULTIPLIERS

The function $\mu(x, y)$ is said to be a *multiplier* (or an *integrating factor*) of the differential equation

(1) $$P(x, y)\, dx + Q(x, y)\, dy = 0$$

if the equation

(2) $$\mu P\, dx + \mu Q\, dy = 0$$

is exact. Then if $\mu \neq 0$ in the region in which $P(x, y)$ and $Q(x, y)$ are defined, the integrals of (2) are precisely the integrals of (1).

From (4.4) we know that (2) will be exact when and only when

(3) $$\frac{\partial}{\partial x}(\mu Q) = \frac{\partial}{\partial y}(\mu P),$$

that is, when μ satisfies the partial differential equation

(4) $$Q\frac{\partial \mu}{\partial x} - P\frac{\partial \mu}{\partial y} = \left(\frac{\partial P}{\partial y} - \frac{\partial Q}{\partial x}\right)\mu.$$

Any particular solution of (4) will be a multiplier of (1). For example, if (1) is exact, $P_y - Q_x = 0$, and we may take $\mu = 1$.

We shall now prove two fundamental theorems concerning multipliers. The relation $u(x, y) = C$ is said to be an integral of (1) provided the values of y' computed from

$$\frac{\partial u}{\partial x} + \frac{\partial u}{\partial y} y' = 0 \quad \text{and} \quad P + Qy' = 0$$

are the same; that is, if

(5)
$$\frac{u_x}{P} = \frac{u_y}{Q}$$

is an identity. If we denote these equal ratios by μ, we have

$$\mu(P \, dx + Q \, dy) = u_x \, dx + u_y \, dy = du.$$

Since the factor μ converts (1) into an exact equation $du = 0$, we have the following theorem.

Theorem 1. *If $u(x, y) = C$ is an integral of $P \, dx + Q \, dy = 0$,*

$$\mu = \frac{u_x}{P} = \frac{u_y}{Q}$$

is a multiplier.

This theorem shows that the existence of an integral of (1) implies the existence of a multiplier. We shall now show that if a single multiplier of (1) is known, an infinite number of others may be found.

Theorem 2. *If the multiplier μ converts $P \, dx + Q \, dy = 0$ into $du = 0$, and $f(u)$ is any continuous function of u, then $\mu f(u)$ is also a multiplier.*
    PROOF. Let $F(u) = \int f(u) \, du$; then

$$\mu f(u)(P \, dx + Q \, dy) = f(u) \, du = \frac{dF}{du} du = dF.$$

In the case of a separable equation

(6)
$$X(x) \, Y_1(y) \, dx + X_1(x) \, Y(y) \, dy = 0,$$

the multiplier $1/X_1 Y_1$ is obvious. The use of this multiplier implies that $X_1 Y_1 \neq 0$. All linear factors of $X_1 Y_1 = 0$ (of the type $x = a$ or $y = b$) are also solutions of (5) and must be added to the general solution

(7)
$$\int \frac{X}{X_1} \, dx + \int \frac{Y}{Y_1} \, dy = C$$

if they are not already included in (7) for particular values of C.

For example, the equation

$$y \, dx + x \, dy = 0$$

has the multiplier $1/xy$ and the general solution $xy = C$. When $C = 0$ this includes the particular solutions $x = 0$, $y = 0$ obtained from $xy = 0$.

Even when the variables are not separable, a multiplier can sometimes be found by recalling formulas such as

$$d(xy) = x \, dy + y \, dx, \qquad d\left(\frac{x}{y}\right) = \frac{y \, dx - x \, dy}{y^2}.$$

Thus the equation

(8) $$y \, dx - (x + y) \, dy = 0$$

has the multiplier $1/y^2$; for

$$\frac{y \, dx - x \, dy}{y^2} - \frac{y \, dy}{y^2} = d\left(\frac{x}{y} - \log |y|\right).$$

The general solution

$$\frac{x}{y} - \log |y| = C$$

does not include the singular solution $y = 0$. If $\log y$ is written instead of $\log |y|$, y is restricted to positive values and that part of the integral curve (plot it) below the x-axis is lost.

If equation (1) has a singular solution it will be included in $1/\mu = 0$; for the multiplier μ makes $\mu P \, dx + \mu Q \, dy$ an exact differential $dF(x, y)$ and (1) may be written

(1)' $$\frac{dF}{\mu} = 0.$$

Thus *all* solutions of (1) make $dF = 0$ or $1/\mu = 0$. Now $dF = 0$ supplies the general solution $F(x, y) = C$; hence any solution of (1) not included therein must make $1/\mu = 0$. For example, equation (8) has $1/y^2$ as multiplier and $y^2 = 0$ provides the singular solution $y = 0$.

When a solution of the first-order equation

(1) $$\frac{dy}{dx} = -\frac{P(x, y)}{Q(x, y)} = f(x, y)$$

is known, we can find its multipliers. The more difficult question as to the *existence* of solutions of (1) is dealt with in Chapter 12. For the present we state without proof a theorem that guarantees the *existence* and *unicity* of an integral curve of equation (1) through the point (x_0, y_0).

Existence and Uniqueness Theorem. *If $f(x, y)$ and $\partial f / \partial y$ are continuous in some closed region about the point (x_0, y_0), the initial value problem*

$$y'(x) = f(x, y), \qquad y(x_0) = y_0,$$

has a unique solution valid in some interval $x_0 - h_1 < x < x_0 + h_2$ about $x = x_0$.

The extent of the interval over which the solution is valid is considered in § 151. When the equation is linear this interval may be specified in advance (§ 16).

Example. The separable equation

(i) $2y\,dx + x\,dy = 0$

has $\mu = 1/xy$ as multiplier; for

$$\frac{1}{xy}(2y\,dx + x\,dy) = 2\frac{dx}{x} + \frac{dy}{y} = d(\log x^2 y).$$

Its general solution is $x^2 y = C$; and $1/\mu = xy = 0$ gives the particular solutions $x = 0$, $y = 0$, but they are not singular as both are included in the general solution for $C = 0$.

For any continuous function f, Theorem 2 shows that

$$\mu = \frac{1}{xy}f(x^2 y)$$

is a multiplier of (i). For example, we have the multipliers

$$\frac{1}{xy} \cdot x^2 y = x, \qquad \frac{1}{xy}\sqrt{x^2 y} = \frac{1}{\sqrt{y}}, \qquad \frac{1}{xy}(x^2 y)^2 = x^3 y.$$

In fact, it is easily shown that $x^{2n+1}y^n$ is a multiplier of (i) for any value of n.

9. MULTIPLIERS OF A GIVEN FORM

If a multiplier μ of the equation

(1) $P(x, y)\,dx + Q(x, y)\,dy = 0$

cannot be found by inspection, the *multiplier equation*

(2) $(\mu Q)_x = (\mu P)_y$

may disclose one. Thus the multipliers μ of (1) satisfy the *partial differential equation*

(3) $Q\mu_x - P\mu_y = (P_y - Q_x)\mu,$

a more advanced problem than the original *ordinary* equation. However a particular solution $\mu \neq 0$ of (3) is all we require.

If (1) admits a multiplier of the form $\mu = X(x)\,Y(y)$, we have from (3)

(4)
$$Q\frac{X_x}{X} - P\frac{Y_y}{Y} = P_y - Q_x.$$

Now if $P_y - Q_x$ can be put in the form

(5)
$$P_y - Q_x = Qg(x) - Ph(y),$$

we can satisfy (4) by putting

$$\frac{X_x}{X} = g(x), \qquad \frac{Y_y}{Y} = h(y);$$

and on integration,

$$\log X = \int g(x)\,dx, \qquad \log Y = \int h(y)\,dy,$$

(6)
$$X = \exp \int g(x)\,dx, \qquad Y = \exp \int h(y)\,dy.*$$

In particular, when $\mu = x^m y^n$, we have $X_x/X = m/x$, $Y_y/Y = n/y$, and (4) becomes

(7)
$$\frac{Q}{x}m - \frac{P}{y}n = P_y - Q_x.$$

If two numbers m, n satisfy (7), equation (1) has the multiplier $x^m y^n$.

We may also try to find a multiplier $\mu = \mu(v)$ where v is a *given* function of x and y. Equation (3) now becomes

$$Q\mu_v v_x - P\mu_v v_y = (P_y - Q_x)\mu,$$

(8)
$$\frac{\mu_v}{\mu} = \frac{P_y - Q_x}{Qv_x - Pv_y}.$$

Now if the right member is a function $f(v)$ of v alone, we have

$$\frac{\mu_v}{\mu} = f(v), \qquad \log \mu = \int f(v)\,dv;$$

hence

(9)
$$\mu = \exp \int f(v)\,dv \quad \text{if} \quad \frac{P_y - Q_x}{Qv_x - Pv_y} = f(v).$$

Some particular cases of (9) are given in the following table. If the quantity in the second column is a function $f(v)$ of the corresponding v in

---

* The notation exp u means e^u and is usually employed when the exponent is at all complicated. Note that $\exp(u + v) = (\exp u)(\exp v)$.

the first column, then

$$P\,dx + Q\,dy = 0 \quad \text{admits} \quad \mu = \exp \int f(v)\,dv$$

as multiplier.

Table 9

	v	$f(v)$
(10)	x	$(P_y - Q_x)/Q$
(11)	y	$(P_y - Q_x)/(-P)$
(12)	$x + y$	$(P_y - Q_x)/(Q - P)$
(13)	xy	$(P_y - Q_x)/(yQ - xP)$
(14)	$x^2 + y^2$	$(P_y - Q_x)/2(xQ - yP)$

Example 1. For the equation

$$(x^2 y + y + 1)\,dx + x(1 + x^2)\,dy = 0,$$

$P_y - Q_x = -2x^2.$ This suggests (10)

$$\frac{P_y - Q_x}{Q} = \frac{-2x^2}{x(1 + x^2)} = \frac{-2x}{1 + x^2} = f(x);$$

$$\int f(x)\,dx = \log\,(1 + x^2)^{-1}, \qquad \mu = (1 + x^2)^{-1}.$$

With this μ we get the exact equation

$$\left(y + \frac{1}{1 + x^2} \right) dx + x\,dy = 0$$

whose integral is

$$\int_0^x \left(y + \frac{1}{1 + x^2} \right) dx + 0 = xy + \tan^{-1} x = C.$$

Example 2. For the equation

$$2xy\,dx + (1 - x^2 - y^2)\,dy = 0$$

$P_y - Q_x = 4x.$ This suggests (11)

$$\frac{P_y - Q_x}{-P} = \frac{4x}{-2xy} = -\frac{2}{y} = f(y);$$

$$\int f(y)\,dy = \log y^{-2}, \qquad \mu = y^{-2}$$

The resulting exact equation

$$2\frac{x}{y}\,dx + \left(\frac{1 - x^2}{y^2} - 1 \right) dy = 0$$

has the integral

$$\int_0^x \frac{2x\,dx}{y} + \int \left(\frac{1}{y^2} - 1\right) dy = \frac{x^2}{y} - \frac{1}{y} - y = C$$

or

$$x^2 - y^2 - 1 = Cy.$$

Example 3. Since the preceding table gives no help with the equation

$$(xy^2 + y)\,dx - x \log x\,dy = 0, \quad x > 0,$$

let us test it for $\mu = X(x)\,Y(y)$. Condition (5) becomes

$$2(xy + 1) + \log x = -(x \log x)g(x) - y(xy + 1)h(y),$$

and is obviously satisfied by taking

$$g(x) = -\frac{1}{x}, \qquad h(y) = -\frac{2}{y}.$$

Since

$$\int g(x)\,dx = \log x^{-1}, \qquad \int h(y)\,dy = \log y^{-2},$$

$\mu = x^{-1}y^{-2}$; for the given equation implies $x > 0$. This multiplier yields the exact equation

$$\left(1 + \frac{1}{xy}\right) dx - \frac{\log x}{y^2}\,dy = 0,$$

whose integral is

$$\int_1^x \left(1 + \frac{1}{xy}\right) dx - 0 = C$$

or

$$x + \frac{1}{y} \log x = C - 1 = K.$$

Example 4. In Example 7.3 the separable equation

$$(1 + y^2)\,dx + (1 + x^2)\,dy = 0$$

was solved by using the multiplier $\mu = (1 + x^2)^{-1}(1 + y^2)^{-1}$. This involved the use of inverse trigonometric functions followed by a special device to remove them. A simpler procedure is available, however, for $P_y - Q_x = 2(y - x)$ suggests trying (13) in the table:

$$\frac{P_y - Q_x}{yQ - xP} = \frac{2(y - x)}{y(1 + x^2) - x(1 + y^2)} = \frac{2}{1 - xy}.$$

Because this is a function of $v = xy$,

$$\log \mu = 2 \int \frac{dv}{1 - v} = \log (1 - v)^{-2}, \qquad \mu = \frac{1}{(1 - xy)^2}.$$

This multiplier yields the exact equation

$$\frac{1 + y^2}{(1 - xy)^2}\,dx + \frac{1 + x^2}{(1 - xy)^2}\,dy = 0,$$

whose integral is

$$(1 + y^2) \int_0^x \frac{dx}{(1 - xy)^2} + y = C,$$

$$\frac{1 + y^2}{y(1 - xy)} - \frac{1 + y^2}{y} + y = \frac{x + y}{1 - xy} = C,$$

in agreement with Example 7.3.

Example 5. An equation such as

$$(2xy + y^3)\, dx + (3x^2 + xy^2)\, dy = 0,$$

involving only powers of x and y, frequently admits a multiplier $\mu = x^m y^n$. The condition (7) now reads

$$m(3x + y^2) - n(2x + y^2) = -4x + 2y^2$$

and can be satisfied by equating the coefficients of x and y^2 on both sides; thus

$$3m - 2n = -4, \qquad m - n = 2,$$

whence $m = -8$, $n = -10$; and $\mu = x^{-8}y^{-10}$. This multiplier yields the exact equation

$$(2x^{-7}y^{-9} + x^{-8}y^{-7})\, dx + (3x^{-6}y^{-10} + x^{-7}y^{-8})\, dy = 0,$$

whose integral is

$$\int_1^x (2x^{-7}y^{-9} + x^{-8}y^{-7})\, dx + \int (3y^{-10} + y^{-8})\, dy = C$$

or

$$-\tfrac{1}{3}x^{-6}y^{-9} - \tfrac{1}{7}x^{-7}y = C,$$

since all other terms cancel. Multiplying by $-21x^7y^9$ gives

$$7x + 3y^2 = Kx^7y^9.$$

It is not necessary to remember (or look up) condition (7). If we multiply the given equation by $x^m y^n$, apply the exactness condition, and then equate the coefficients of like terms, we get precisely the values of m and n given earlier. Try it on this example and also on Example 3.

PROBLEMS

Find multipliers for the following differential equations and solve them. The brackets, when present, indicate the type of multiplier.

1. $xy\, dx + (x^2 + y^2 + 1)\, dy = 0.$ $[\mu(y)]$.
2. $(x \sin y + y \cos y)\, dx + (x \cos y - y \sin y)\, dy = 0.$ $[\mu(x)]$.
3. $(2xy + 3)\, dx - x^2\, dy = 0.$ $[\mu(x)]$.
4. $(x^{n+1} + y^n)y' - x^n y = 0.$ $[\mu(y)]$.
5. $(y - y^2)\, dx + x\, dy = 0.$ $[x^m y^n]$.
6. $y^2\, dx + (x^2 - xy)\, dy = 0.$ $[x^m y^n]$.
7. $(x^2y + 2y^3)\, dx - (2x^3 + 3xy^2)\, dy = 0.$ $[x^m y^n]$.

8. (a) When $AD - BC \neq 0$, show that the equation

$$x^p(Ay\, dx + Bx\, dy) + y^q(Cy\, dx + Dx\, dy) = 0$$

always has a multiplier of the form $x^m y^n$.

(b) When $AD - BC = 0$, show that the equation may be written

$$(x^p + ky^q)(Ay\, dx + Bx\, dy) = 0.$$

9. If p and q are functions of x, the equation $(py - qy^n)\, dx + dy = 0$ admits a multiplier of the form XY; find it.

10. Solve the equations

(a) $x^2y(3y\, dx + 2x\, dy) + 4y\, dx + 3x\, dy = 0$.

(b) $(x^3 + y^4)\, dx - xy^2(2y + x^2)\, dy = 0$.

11. Solve the equation $(1 - y^2)\, dx + (1 - x^2)\, dy = 0$ by finding a multiplier which is a function of xy.

12. Solve the equation $(3xy + y^2)\, dx + (3xy + x^2)\, dy = 0$ by finding a multiplier which is a function of $x + y$.

13. Find a multiplier of $y' - x^2y = x^5$ and solve.

14. Prove that $(axy + by^2)\, dx + (axy + bx^2)\, dy = 0$ admits the multiplier $\mu = (x + y)^{a/b-2}$.

15. Find a multiplier and solve:

(a) $(2xy + x^2y + \frac{1}{3}y^3)\, dx + (x^2 + y^2)\, dy = 0$

(b) $(y^2 - x^2y)\, dx + x^3\, dy = 0$.

16. Prove that $P\, dx + Q\, dy = 0$ has the multiplier $(P^2 + Q^2)^{-1}$ if $P_x = Q_y$ and $P_y = -Q_x$.

10. TWO MULTIPLIERS

We first prove the following lemma.

Lemma. *If the equation*

(1) $$P(x, y)\, dx + Q(x, y)\, dy = 0$$

is exact and has a multiplier $\mu(x, y)$ other than a constant, then $\mu(x, y) = C$ is an integral.

PROOF. Since (1) is exact, $P_y = Q_x$; and since μ is a multiplier,

$$(\mu P)_y = (\mu Q)_x \quad \text{or} \quad P\mu_y = Q\mu_x.$$

On multiplying (1) by μ_y, we have

$$P\mu_y\, dx + Q\mu_y\, dy = Q(\mu_x\, dx + \mu_y\, dy) = Q\, d\mu = 0;$$

hence $\mu(x, y) = C$ is a solution of (1).

Two multipliers of an equation are said to be *independent* if their ratio is not a constant. We can now state the following theorem.

Theorem. *If λ and μ are independent multipliers of $P\, dx + Q\, dy = 0$, then $\mu/\lambda = C$ is an integral.*

PROOF. By hypothesis both equations

(2) $$\lambda P \, dx + \lambda Q \, dy = 0,$$

(3) $$\mu P \, dx + \mu Q \, dy = 0$$

are exact. Multiplying (2) by μ/λ converts it into (3), an exact equation. Hence the exact equation (2) has the multiplier μ/λ and therefore the integral $\mu/\lambda = C$ by the preceding lemma.

The theorem includes the lemma; for when (1) is exact we may take $\lambda = 1$.

To illustrate the theorem, consider the equation $x \, dy - y \, dx = 0$. It obviously admits the multipliers $\lambda = 1/xy$ and $\mu = 1/x^2$; hence $\mu/\lambda = y/x = C$ is an integral.

Example. The separable equation

$$(1 + y^2) \, dx + (1 + x^2) \, dy = 0,$$

with multipliers $\lambda = (1 + x^2)^{-1}(1 + y^2)^{-1}$ and (Ex. 9.4) $\mu = (1 - xy)^{-2}$, has the solution

$$\frac{\mu}{\lambda} = \frac{(1 + x^2)(1 + y^2)}{(1 - xy)^2} = \left(\frac{x + y}{1 - xy}\right)^2 + 1 = C$$

or

$$(x + y)/(1 - xy) = K.$$

11. COMPOUND INTEREST LAW

A sum of money x_0 drawing interest at the rate r per year* is compounded n times per year. The rate of interest for one interest period is r/n and at the end of one period the principal is

$$x_1 = x_0 + x_0 \frac{r}{n} = x_0\left(1 + \frac{r}{n}\right).$$

At the end of two interest periods the principal is

$$x_2 = x_1\left(1 + \frac{1}{n}\right) = x_0\left(1 + \frac{1}{n}\right)^2;$$

and at the end of p interest periods

(1) $$x_p = x_0\left(1 + \frac{r}{n}\right)^p.$$

---

* For example $r = 0.06$ when the rate is 6 per cent.

Hence at the end of t years or nt interest periods, the principal will amount to

$$x_{nt} = x_0\left(1 + \frac{r}{n}\right)^{nt}.$$

As n, the frequency of compounding, increases without limit, the principal at the end of t years approaches

(2) $$x = x_0 \lim_{n\to\infty}\left(1 + \frac{r}{n}\right)^{nt} = x_0 e^{rt};$$

for if we put $n = mr$,

$$\lim_{n\to\infty}\left(1 + \frac{r}{n}\right)^{n} = \lim_{m\to\infty}\left(1 + \frac{1}{m}\right)^{mr} = e^r,$$

In particular if $x_0 = 1$, $r = 1$ (100%), $x = e$ when $t = 1$ year; hence

> *One dollar at 100 per cent continuous compound interest*
> *will amount to e dollars at the end of one year.*

The increase of money under continuous compound interest may be simply expressed in a differential equation. Thus if the money amounts to x dollars at the end of t years, the interest in the next brief interval of dt years will be $dx = xr\,dt$ dollars; hence

(3) $$\frac{dx}{dt} = rx.$$

If $x = x_0$ when $t = 0$, we have

$$\int_{x_0}^{x}\frac{dx}{x} = r\int_0^t dt,$$

$$\log\frac{x}{x_0} = rt, \qquad x = x_0 e^{rt},$$

in agreement with (2).

In one year at simple interest of rate R one dollar becomes $1 + R$; whereas at the rate r, continuously compounded, one dollar becomes e^r. These rates produce equal yields when

(4) $$1 + R = e^r.$$

In the natural sciences the law of growth

(5) $$\frac{dx}{dt} = \pm kx \qquad (k > 0)$$

applies exactly (or approximately) in many important problems. In all such problems the *relative* rate of change $(dx/dt)/x$ is constant (or nearly constant). According as this constant is positive or negative, the variable x increases or decreases as time goes on. Thus in (5) the plus sign corresponds to a *growth problem*, the minus sign to a *decay problem*. The corresponding solutions are

$$(6,7) \qquad x = x_0 e^{kt}, \qquad x = x_0 e^{-kt},$$

where in both cases $k > 0$. All processes which conform to equation (5) are said to follow the *compound interest law* (Lord Kelvin).

If $x = x_1$ when $t = t_1$, we have from (6)

$$(8) \qquad e^{kt_1} = \frac{x_1}{x_0}, \qquad k = \frac{1}{t_1} \log \frac{x_1}{x_0}.$$

Thus the growth constant k is determined by the values of x at two different times.

Example 1. Continuous Investment. A man invests his savings of P dollars per year continuously at the rate $r(100r$ per cent). If the interest is compounded continuously, what will the savings amount to in t years?

If the savings amount to x dollars in t years, in the next brief interval of dt years they will increase by

$$dx = P \, dt \text{ (savings)} + rx \, dt \text{ (interest)}.$$

On integrating this separable equation under the conditions $x = 0$ when $t = 0$, we have

$$\int_0^x \frac{r \, dx}{P + rx} = r \int_0^t dt, \qquad \log \frac{P + rx}{P} = rt,$$

$$x = \frac{P}{r} (e^{rt} - 1).$$

Example 2. Bacterial Growth. The growth of bacteria in a culture with abundant food and in the absence of toxins follows very closely the compound interest law. In fact, the rate of increase of one-celled organisms, which reproduce by simple fission, would most likely be proportional to their number at any instant. If the bacterial count is x at time t, then

$$(i) \qquad \frac{dx}{dt} = kx, \qquad x = x_0 e^{kt},$$

where x_0 is the count at time zero. Thus if the bacteria in a culture double in 3 days,

$$2x_0 = x_0 e^{3k}, \qquad k = \tfrac{1}{3} \log 2.$$

Their number after t days is then

$$x = x_0 e^{t/3 \log 2} = x_0 2^{t/3}.$$

For the times $t = 0, 3, 6, 9, 12, \ldots$ the ratios $x/x_0 = 1, 2, 4, 8, 16, \ldots$; thus an arithmetic progression in t corresponds to a geometric progression in x.

Example 3. Radioactive Disintegration. Radioactive elements, such as uranium and radium, break down spontaneously into lighter elements. Rutherford and Soddy in 1902 stated the general law: *The rate of disintegration of radioactive elements is proportional to the number of atoms present; it is independent of their age and of the temperature and pressure.*

For example, radium (at. wt. 226) breaks down into radon (at. wt. 222) and helium (at. wt. 4). This change

$$_{88}Ra^{226} \rightarrow {_{86}}Rn^{222} + {_2}He^4,$$

where the subscripts denote *atomic numbers* or nuclear charges. This disintegration proceeds at such a rate that in 1620 years only one-half of the original radium atoms remain: the *half-life* of radium is 1620 years. The half-lives of various radioactive elements range from 16,500,000,000 years (thorium 232) to less than a millionth of a second (polonium 212).

If there are x atoms of a radioactive element present at time t,

$$\frac{dx}{dt} = -kx, \qquad x = x_0 e^{-kt},$$

where $x = x_0$ when $t = 0$. If the half-life is T,

$$\frac{1}{2} x_0 = x_0 e^{-kT}, \qquad k = \frac{1}{T} \log 2.$$

This law of decay is equivalent to the statement that, on the average, one out of n atoms disintegrates every year; that is

$$\frac{dx}{dt} = -\frac{x}{n}.$$

Since $k = 1/n$, we have the relation

$$T = n \log 2.$$

Of the x_0 atoms originally present at time $t = 0$, only $x = x_0 e^{-kt}$ remain after time t. The *average life* of an atom therefore is

$$\frac{1}{x_0} \int_0^{x_0} t \, dx = -k \int_\infty^0 t e^{-kt} \, dt = \left(t + \frac{1}{k} \right) e^{-kt} \Big|_\infty^0 = \frac{1}{k} = \frac{T}{\log 2}.$$

Ordinary carbon is $_6C^{12}$, but the radioactive isotope $_6C^{14}$ (carbon 14) is continually formed in the atmosphere by cosmic ray neutrons hitting nitrogen nuclei:

$$_0n^1 + {_7}N^{14} = {_1}H^1 + {_6}C^{14}.$$

Thus some CO_2 molecules (about 1 in 800 billion) contain C^{14} and these are continually being absorbed by growing plants. When the plant dies it stops taking up C^{14} and the amount present in the plant decays by expelling β-particles with a half-life of 5760 years.* The age of an object made of vegetable matter,

---

* This value is the result of recent experiments conducted at the National Bureau of Standards. With this value the Dead Sea Scrolls date from about 20 B.C.

such as wood or cotton, may then be measured by making a β-count per gram of carbon and comparing it with the β-count of carbon from a contemporary sample.

The volcano that formed Crater Lake in Oregon killed a tree whose charcoal gave a β-count of 44.5 per cent of the amount from "living" carbon; hence

$$0.445x_0 = x_0e^{-kt}, \qquad k = \frac{\log 2}{T} = \frac{0.6931}{5760} = 0.0001203.$$

The Crater Lake volcano therefore erupted about

$$t = \frac{-\log 0.445}{k} = \frac{0.8097}{0.0001203} = 6728 \text{ B.P.,}$$

that is, 6728 years before the present.

On the whole, radiocarbon dating has given results in accord with known historical facts. But when the β-count is small (say after 10,000 B.P.), the error may be considerable.

For longer periods of geologic time, the potassium-argon decay, of half-life 2.3×10^9 years, $_{19}K^{40} \rightarrow {}_{18}Ar^{40}$ with electron capture and emission of γ radiation, has proved useful and reliable. It has been applied to ancient feldspars and micas and also to meteorites, the latter showing ages of from 4.3 to 4.8 billion years.

Example 4. Newton's Law of Cooling. A body at temperature u is surrounded by a medium at temperature $v < u$. Newton's law states that the body will cool at a rate proportional to $u - v$; that is,

(i)
$$\frac{du}{dt} = -k(u - v), \qquad k > 0.$$

Problem 1. A body at 100° cools in air at 20°. If it cools to 60° in 15 minutes, how long will it take to cool to 25°?

SOLUTION. If the temperature of the air is regarded as constant, equation (i) becomes

(ii)
$$\frac{du}{dt} = -k(u - 20);$$

hence

$$\int_{100}^{60} \frac{du}{u - 20} = -k \int_0^{15} dt, \qquad k = -\frac{1}{15}\log\frac{40}{80} = \frac{\log 2}{15}.$$

If the body cools to 25° in t_1 minutes,

$$\int_{100}^{25} \frac{du}{u - 20} = -k \int_0^{t_1} dt = -kt_1,$$

$$t_1 = -\frac{1}{k}\log\frac{5}{80} = 15\frac{\log 16}{\log 2} = 15 \times 4 = 60 \text{ min.}$$

Problem 2. A body at 140° is placed in an insulated vessel containing water at 40°. Five minutes later the temperatures of the body and water are 110° and 50°. How long will it take for the body to cool to 75°?

Let the body and the water have masses of m and M grams; and let α be the specific heat of the body. Since the vessel is insulated, the calories of heat lost by the body are gained by the water. Thus if the temperatures of the body and the water at any time are u and v, respectively,

$$M(v - v_0) = m\alpha(u_0 - u).$$

From the given data

$$\frac{m\alpha}{M} = \frac{50 - 40}{140 - 110} = \frac{1}{3}, \qquad v = 40 + \frac{1}{3}(140 - u) = \frac{1}{3}(260 - u).$$

and equation (i) becomes

(iii) $$\frac{du}{dt} = -k\left\{u - \frac{260}{3} + \frac{u}{3}\right\} = -\frac{4k}{3}(u - 65).$$

This equation has the same form as (ii); the body and water reach thermal equilibrium when $du/dt = 0$, that is, when $u = 65°$. Putting $4k/3 = k'$, we now have

$$\int_{140}^{110} \frac{du}{u - 65} = -k' \int_0^5 dt = -5k', \qquad k' = -\frac{1}{5}\log\frac{45}{75} = \frac{1}{5}\log\frac{5}{3};$$

and if $u = 75°$ in t_1 minutes,

$$\int_{140}^{75} \frac{du}{u - 65} = -k' \int_0^{t_1} dt = -k't_1,$$

$$t_1 = -\frac{1}{k'}\log\frac{10}{75} = 5\frac{\log\frac{15}{2}}{\log\frac{5}{3}} = 5\frac{0.8751}{0.2219} = 19.72 \text{ min.}$$

In the calculation, we used common logarithms (base 10) instead of natural logarithms (base e), because the *ratio* of two logarithms is the same irrespective of their base.

Example 5. A condenser having the capacitance C is discharged through a resistance R. If q is the charge on the condenser, the potential difference between its plates is q/C. As the condenser is discharged, the current $i = dq/dt$ flows in the circuit and the potential drop across the resistance is $Ri = R\,dq/dt$ (Ohm's law). In a simple loop the sum of the electromotive forces is zero; hence

$$R\frac{dq}{dt} + \frac{q}{C} = 0 \quad \text{or} \quad \frac{dq}{dt} = -\frac{1}{RC}q.$$

The condenser discharge follows the compound interest law; and

$$q = q_0 e^{-t/RC}.$$

Example 6. Growth of Population. In a population of x organisms, let the birth and death rates be b and c. Then if b and c are constant, the population will change according to the equation

(i) $$\frac{dx}{dt} = (b - c)x.$$

If $x = x_0$ when $t = 0$,

$$x = x_0 e^{(b-c)t}.$$

Thus if $b > c$, the population will increase indefinitely, and if $b < c$, it will decrease and eventually die out. This simple conclusion, however, is not in accordance with statistics. A hypothesis that yields results in better agreement with observation is that both b and c are linear functions of x:

$$b = b_0 - rx, \qquad c = c_0 + sx, \qquad r, s > 0.$$

These imply that the birth rate drops and the death rate rises with increasing population. With these values (i) becomes

(ii) $$\frac{dx}{dt} = x(A - Bx), \qquad A = b_0 - c_0, \qquad B = r + s.$$

As $t \to \infty$,

$$x \to \frac{A}{B} \quad \text{if} \quad A > 0,$$

$$x \to 0 \quad \text{if} \quad A \leqq 0.$$

Thus $M = A/B$ is the saturation value of the given population.

Equation (ii) is the so-called *logistic equation* of Verhulst-Pearl. It may be written in the form

(iii) $$\frac{dx}{dt} = kx(M - x)$$

where $k = r + s > 0$. The population x grows at a rate proportional to both x and $M - x$, the amount it falls short of saturation. When $x = M$, the population remains stationary. Using partial fractions, (iii) may be written

$$\frac{-dx}{M - x} - \frac{dx}{x} = -Mk \, dt;$$

hence, on integration,

$$\log \frac{M - x}{x} = -Mkt + C.$$

To simplify this result, choose the origin of time so that $C = 0$; then $M - x = x$ or $x = \frac{1}{2}M$. Thus counting time from the point when the population is half saturated, we have

(iv) $$\frac{M - x}{x} = e^{-Mkt}, \qquad x = \frac{M}{1 + e^{-Mkt}}.$$

As $t \to \infty$, $x \to M$; and as $t \to -\infty$, $x \to 0$.

Pearl and Reed* gave a formula of this type for the population of the United States which is in good agreement with the decennial census from 1790 to 1950. Their formula was chosen to give a perfect fit for the years 1790, 1850, 1910; and as $t \to \infty$, $x \to$ about 197 million. As this saturation population is far too small, the formula will fall short of the mark in the future.

REFERENCES

Kostitzin, V. A., *Mathematical Biology*, Harrap, London, 1939.

Lotka, A. J., *Principles of Mathematical Biology*, Dover, New York, 1956.

Pearl, Raymond, *The Biology of Population Growth*, Knopf, New York, 1925.

Volterra, Vito, *Leçons sur la Théorie Mathématique de la Lutte pour la Vie*, Gauthier-Villars, Paris, 1931.

---

* *Proc. Nat. Acad. Sci.*, **6**, p. 275, 1920.

PROBLEMS

1. What will \$100 amount to in 10 years at 4% interest per year, if the interest is compounded
  (a) annually; (b) semiannually;
  (c) quarterly; (d) continuously?

2. How long will it take for a sum of money to double itself at 6% interest per year compounded continuously?

3. In how many years will a thousand dollars increase to a million at 6% interest per year compounded continuously?

4. Bacteria in a culture increase from 100,000 to 200,000 in 3 days. When will they number 1,000,000?

5. A body at 200° cools in air at 20°. If it cools to 100° in 10 minutes, when will its temperature be 40°?

6. In a chemical reaction $A \rightarrow B$, the rate at which A is being transformed into B is proportional to the amount of A still remaining. If x, the amount of A, is reduced from x_0 to x_1 in t_1 hours, find the amount x_2 after t_2 hours.

7. A mothball of radius r_0 sublimes at a rate proportional to the area of its surface. If its radius is r_1 after t_1 days, when will it disappear?

8. The water in a tank can dissolve, at most, 300 pounds of salt. If a large amount of salt is placed in the tank, the rate of solution is proportional to $300 - x$ when x pounds of salt are already dissolved. If 100 pounds of salt dissolve in one hour, how long before 200 pounds are dissolved?

9. A vessel of arbitrary shape contains a liquid which evaporates at a rate equal to the area exposed to air. If evaporation reduces the original depth y_0 of the liquid to y_1 in t_1 days, how long before the evaporation is complete?

10. A 3-lb piece of iron at 180° is plunged into an insulated vessel containing 10 pounds of water at 40°. If the specific heat of the iron is $\frac{1}{9}$, to what temperature will it eventually cool? Express the temperature u of the iron as a function of the time t.

11. A mass m of hot metal of specific heat α is plunged into a mass M of water in an insulated vessel. If the initial temperatures of metal and water are u_0 and v_0, show that the metal will eventually cool to the temperature

$$u_\infty = \frac{Mv_0 + \alpha m u_0}{M + \alpha m};$$

and that the rate of cooling is

$$\frac{du}{dt} = -k\left(1 + \alpha \frac{m}{M}\right)(u - u_\infty).$$

12. In a community of N people x have an infectious disease at time t. If the rate of infection is

$$\frac{dx}{dt} = kx(N - x) \quad \text{and} \quad x(0) = x_0 \neq 0,$$

show that

$$\frac{N}{x} = 1 + \left(\frac{N}{x_0} - 1\right)e^{-Nkt}.$$

What conclusion can be drawn as $t \rightarrow \infty$?

13. A piece of old charcoal gives a β-count of 64 whereas a similar recent sample gives a count of 512. How old B.P. (before the present) is the piece?

14. If the half-life of an element is exactly one day and 2^{30} atoms are present at noon January 1, how many will probably be present at noon on January 11? January 21? January 31?

12. FLOW OF FLUIDS

Problems in continuous flow, whether of gases, liquids, or such imponderables as heat and electricity, always lead to differential equations. In many cases the equation states that the change of a substance x in a certain interval is given by

$$dx = \text{input of } x - \text{output of } x.$$

Instead of change we may consider the *rate* of change and write

$$\frac{dx}{dt} = \text{input rate of } x - \text{output rate of } x.$$

We now illustrate with examples the setting up of such flow equations.

Example 1. Mixing of Gases. A stream of hydrogen is slowly passed into a 6-liter flask containing pure oxygen and the mixture passes out at the same rate. *The rate need not be uniform*, but it must be slow enough to ensure perfect mixing. How many liters of hydrogen must be passed in before the gases are in the proportion in which they occur in water (H_2O)?

After x liters of hydrogen have been passed in, let the flask contain y liters of hydrogen. Now pass in dx liters of hydrogen; then

Change of H in flask = input of H − output of H.

When dx liters of H flow in, dx liters of a gas mixture containing the fraction $y/6$ of H flow out; hence we must solve

$$dy = dx - \frac{y}{6} dx$$

under the conditions $y = 0$ when $x = 0$. When $y = 4$, the flask will contain H and O in the ratio 2:1; to find the corresponding value of x we have

$$\int_0^4 \frac{-\frac{1}{6} dy}{1 - y/6} = -\frac{1}{6} \int_0^x dx, \qquad \log\left(1 - \frac{y}{6}\right)\Big|_0^4 = -\frac{x}{6},$$

$$x = -6 \log \tfrac{1}{3} = 6 \log 3 = 6.5916 \text{ liters.}$$

Since we know nothing about the *rate* of flow, time does not enter the problem.

Example 2. In a tank are 100 gallons of brine containing 50 pounds of salt. Water runs in the tank at the rate of 3 gal/min and the brine runs out at the rate of 2 gal/min, the concentration being kept uniform by stirring. How much salt is in the tank at the end of one hour?

Let the tank contain x pounds of salt after t minutes of flow. Then the *rate* at which the salt in the tank changes is

$$\frac{dx}{dt} = \text{input rate} - \text{output rate}.$$

Since each minute of flow adds one gallon to the contents of the tank, the concentration of brine after t minutes is $x/(100 + t)$ lb/gal; hence we must solve

$$\frac{dx}{dt} = 0 - 2\frac{x}{100 + t}$$

under the conditions $x = 50$ when $t = 0$. After 60 minutes the corresponding x is given by

$$\int_{50}^{x} \frac{dx}{x} = -2\int_{0}^{60} \frac{dt}{100 + t},$$

$$\log\frac{x}{50} = -2\log\frac{160}{100} = \log\left(\frac{5}{8}\right)^2;$$

$$\frac{x}{50} = \frac{25}{64}, \qquad x = 19.53 \text{ lb.}$$

Example 3. Flow from a Orifice. When a liquid in a vessel escapes from a small orifice y feet below the surface, its average velocity in the orifice is $k\sqrt{y}$, where k is a constant that depends on the nature of the orifice and the liquid. If the area of the orifice is a square feet, the

$$\text{rate of outflow} = ak\sqrt{y} \text{ ft}^3/\text{sec.}$$

Hence if V cubic feet of liquid are in the tank after t seconds,

(i) $$\frac{dV}{dt} = \text{rate of inflow} - \text{rate of outflow.}$$

When V is expressed as a function of y (or dV given in terms of y and dy) this is a differential equation in y and t.

Problem 1. How long will it take to empty a full cylindrical water tank 10 feet in diameter and 16 feet high, through a 2-inch circular hole in the bottom? The constant $k = 4.8$.

Solution. Since $V = 25\pi y$ ft^3 and $a = \pi/144$ ft^2, we have from (i)

$$25\pi\frac{dy}{dt} = 0 - \frac{\pi}{144}4.8\sqrt{y} = -\frac{\pi}{30}\sqrt{y}.$$

Hence the time required to empty it is

$$t = -750\int_{16}^{0} y^{-1/2}\, dy = 750 \times 2y^{1/2}\Big|_{0}^{16} = 750 \times 8 \text{ sec} = 100 \text{ min.}$$

Problem 2. How long will it take to empty the same tank supported horizontally, through a 2-inch circular hole at its lowest point?

Solution. With the origin at the bottom, the equation of an end circle is

$$x^2 + (y - 5)^2 = 25 \quad \text{or} \quad x^2 + y^2 - 10y = 0.$$

Now

$$V = 16 \int_0^y 2x \, dy, \qquad dV = 32x \, dy = 32 \sqrt{10y - y^2} \, dy,$$

and (i) becomes

$$32 \sqrt{10y - y^2} \frac{dy}{dt} = 0 - \frac{\pi}{144} 4.8 \sqrt{y}.$$

The time required to empty the tank is now

$$t = -\frac{960}{\pi} \int_{10}^0 \sqrt{10 - y} \, dy = \frac{640}{\pi} (10 - y)^{3/2} \Big|_{10}^0 = \frac{6400 \sqrt{10}}{\pi} \text{ sec} = 6443 \text{ sec}$$

$$= 107.4 \text{ min.}$$

PROBLEMS

1. Brine containing 3 pounds of salt per gallon flows at the rate of 2 gal/min into a 100-gallon tank initially filled with fresh water, and the mixture (supposed uniform) flows out at the same rate. Find the amount of salt in the tank after one hour.

2. Fresh water flows at the rate of 3 gal/min into a tank holding 150 gallons of brine and the mixture flows out at the same rate. If the tank initially contained 50 pounds of salt, when will its salt content be reduced to 5 pounds?

3. A tank contains 100 gallons of brine with 80 pounds of salt. Fresh water flows in at the rate of 2 gal/min, and the mixture is pumped out at the rate of 3 gal/min. When will the tank contain 10 pounds of salt?

4. How long will it take to empty a full cylindrical tank 20 feet in diameter and 25 feet high, through a 2-inch circular hole in the bottom ($k = 4.8$),

     (a) when its axis is vertical?

     (b) when its axis is horizontal?

5. Two vertical tanks 8 feet in diameter and 16 feet high are connected by a short 2-inch pipe at the bottom. One tank is full of water, the other empty; how long will it take before both tanks are half full, if the average velocity in the pipe is $6.4 \, y_1 - y_2$?

6. A spherical tank 9 feet in diameter is full of water. How long will it take to empty it through a 2-inch circular hole in the bottom if $k = 4.8$?

7. A conical tank with axis vertical and apex downward is full of water. If it is 9 feet high and 10 feet in diameter at the top, how long will it take to empty it through a 1-inch circular hole at the apex. Take $k = 4.8$ and treat the hole as if it were at the exact vertex.

8. A tank, whose horizontal section $A(y)$ is a known function of the height y above the bottom, has an orifice of area a at the bottom. If it is filled with liquid to a height of h, show that it will empty in the time

$$t = \frac{1}{ka} \int_0^h \frac{A(y)}{\sqrt{y}} \, dy.$$

9. Water runs into a cylindrical tank 8 feet in diameter and 10 feet high at the rate of 0.3 ft³/sec and runs out through a circular 2-inch hole in the bottom ($k = 4.8$). If the tank was initially empty, how long will it take until the height of water is 4 feet? To what height will the water in the tank eventually rise?

13. LAW OF MASS ACTION

In an *irreversible* bimolecular reaction

$$A + B \rightarrow C + D,$$

let the number of gram molecules* of the reagents be as follows:

Time	A	$+$	B	$\rightarrow$	C	$+$	D
0	a		b		0		0
t	$a - x$		$b - x$		x		x

As for the amounts at time t, note that for each molecule of C or D formed, a molecule of A and B must disappear. The law of mass action now states that both C and D are formed at a rate proportional to the product of the active gram-molecular amounts of A and B; that is,

(1) $$\frac{dx}{dt} = k(a - x)(b - x),$$

where k is the *velocity constant* of the reaction. This equation under the given initial conditions ($x = 0$ when $t = 0$) is solved in Example 7.2, where both cases $a > b$ and $a = b$ are considered. When a pair of corresponding values of x and t are known, the velocity constant is given by (7.8) or (7.10).

If the given reaction is *reversible*,

$$A + B \rightleftharpoons C + D,$$

with the same gram-molecular amounts as before, C and D are formed at the rate $k_1(a - x)(b - x)$ and destroyed at the rate $k_2 x^2$; hence

(2) $$\frac{dx}{dt} = k_1(a - x)(b - x) - k_2 x^2,$$

where k_1 and k_2 are velocity constants of the forward and backward reaction. The reaction reaches equilibrium when $dx/dt = 0$, that is, when

$$f(x) = k_1(a - x)(b - x) - k_2 x^2 = 0.$$

---

* A gram molecule of A is the number of grams equal to the molecular weight of A. Thus a gram molecule of H_2O is $2 + 16 = 18$ grams.

If $k_1 \neq k_2$, $f(x)$ assumes the signs shown in the table:

x	$-\infty$		0	b	a		∞
$f(x)$	$k_1 - k_2$		$+$	$-$	$-$		$k_1 - k_2$

Therefore $f(x)$ has two real zeros, α and β. The one α between 0 and b is the equilibrium value of x; the other β is clearly inadmissible since $\beta > a$ or < 0 according as $k_1 - k_2$ is positive or negative. Since

$$f(x) = (k_1 - k_2)(\alpha - x)(\beta - x),$$

equation (2) now assumes the same form as (1), namely,

(3)
$$\frac{dx}{dt} = (k_1 - k_2)(\alpha - x)(\beta - x).$$

When α and β are known, (3) may be solved as in Example 7.2.

The rate at which a substance dissolves in a solvent is also governed by an equation of the form (1). Thus, if b pounds of solute are to be dissolved in V gallons of solvent, experiment has shown that after x pounds have been dissolved the rate of solution is proportional to
   (i) the amount $b - x$ still undissolved;
   (ii) the difference between the concentration s of a saturated solution and the present concentration x/V. This very reasonable law is expressed by the differential equation

(4)
$$\frac{dx}{dt} = k(b - x)\left(s - \frac{x}{V}\right) = \frac{k}{V}(a - x)(b - x)$$

where $a = sV$ is the total dissolvable solute.

Example. If $a \neq b$ in the irreversible reaction of the text, equation (1) may be written

$$\frac{dx}{a - x} - \frac{dx}{b - x} = k(b - a)\,dt,$$

and, on integration, between the limits 0 and x, 0 and t, we find

$$\log \frac{b(a - x)}{a(b - x)} = k(a - b)t,$$

whence

$$x = ab\,\frac{e^{k(a-b)t} - 1}{a e^{k(a-b)t} - b} = ab\,\frac{1 - e^{k(b-a)t}}{a - b e^{k(b-a)t}}.$$

If $b > a$, $x \to a$ as $t \to \infty$; and if $a > b$, $x \to b$ as $t \to \infty$. Interpret these results.

If $a = b$, equation (1) yields on integration between the limits used before,

$$\frac{1}{a-x} - \frac{1}{a} = kt.$$

We now find

$$x = a - \frac{a}{1 + akt} = \frac{a^2 kt}{1 + akt}.$$

Now $x \to a$ as $t \to \infty$.

PROBLEMS

1. The water in a tank can dissolve at most 300 pounds of salt. If 250 pounds of salt are placed in the tank, 100 pounds will dissolve in one hour. When will 200 pounds of salt be dissolved?

2. An inert material with 50 pounds of salt in its pores, when agitated with 50 gallons of water for one hour, loses one half its salt. How much salt would it lose if 100 gallons of water had been used? A saturated salt solution contains 3 pounds of salt per gallon.

3. If the reaction $A + B \to C + D$, $a = b = 2$ gram molecules, and $x = 1$ when $t = 30$ min. Find the velocity constant k and x when $t = 60$ min.

4. In the reaction $A + B \to C + D$, $a = b = 10$ gram molecules. After 50 minutes 5 gram molecules of A were left. At what time from the outset will A be reduced to 2 gram molecules?

5. In the reversible reaction $A \rightleftharpoons B$, the gram molecules of A and B at any time t are $a - x$ and x. If $x = \alpha$ at equilibrium, show that

$$\frac{dx}{dt} = (k_1 + k_2)(\alpha - x), \qquad x = \alpha(1 - e^{-(k_1+k_2)t}).$$

If there are 10, 7, 3 gram molecules of A after 0, 5, ∞ minutes, find k_1 and k_2.

6. In the reversible reaction

$$\text{acetic acid} + \text{alcohol} \rightleftharpoons \text{acetic ester} + \text{water},$$

$k_1/k_2 = 4$. At the start, acid and alcohol were present in equal gram-molecular amounts $(a = b)$. How many gram molecules of ester are present when the reaction reaches equilibrium?

7. In the reversible reaction of Problem 6 we have the following data:

t (Days)	Acid	+ Alcohol	$\rightleftharpoons$ Ester	+ Water
0	1	1	0	0
t	$1-x$	$1-x$	x	x
64	$\frac{3}{4}$	$\frac{3}{4}$	$\frac{1}{4}$	$\frac{1}{4}$
∞	$\frac{1}{3}$	$\frac{1}{3}$	$\frac{2}{3}$	$\frac{2}{3}$

Show that $k_1 = 4k_2$ and

$$\frac{dx}{dt} = 3k_2\left(\frac{2}{3} - x\right)(2 - x).$$

Find k_1 and k_2. When will $x = \frac{1}{2}$ gram molecule?

8. In the reversible reaction of Problem 6 we have the data:

Days	A	$+$	B	$\rightleftharpoons$	C	$+$	D
0	3		3		0		0
t	$3 - x$		$3 - x$		x		x
100	2		2		1		1
∞	1		1		2		2

Deduce the differential equation

$$\frac{dx}{dt} = 3k_2(6 - x)(2 - x).$$

When will $x = \frac{3}{2}$ gram molecules?

9. In a reversible reaction we have the data:

(a)

Days	A	$+$	B	$\rightleftharpoons$	C	$+$	D
0	3		1		0		0
t	$3 - x$		$1 - x$		x		x
20	$\frac{11}{4}$		$\frac{3}{4}$		$\frac{1}{4}$		$\frac{1}{4}$
∞	$\frac{9}{4}$		$\frac{1}{4}$		$\frac{3}{4}$		$\frac{3}{4}$

Deduce the differential equation

$$\frac{dx}{dt} = k_1(3 - 4x)$$

and find the value of k_1. When will $x = \frac{1}{2}$ gram molecule?

(b)

Days	A	$+$	B	$\rightleftharpoons$	C	$+$	D
0	3		3		0		0
t	$3 - x$		$3 - x$		x		x
10	2		2		1		1
∞					ξ		ξ

If k_1/k_2 is unchanged, deduce the differential equation

$$\frac{dx}{dt} = 3k_1(3 - 2x).$$

When will $x = \frac{3}{2}$ gram molecules? Find ξ and k_1.

10. In a reversible reaction we have the data:

Days	A	$+$	B	$\rightleftharpoons$	C	$+$	D
0	3		4		0		0
t	$3 - x$		$4 - x$		x		x
20	2		3		1		1
∞	1		2		2		2

Show that

$$\frac{dx}{dt} = k_2 (12 - x)(2 - x), \qquad 10 k_2 t = \log \frac{12 - x}{12 - 6x},$$

and find the value of k_2. When will $x = \frac{1}{2}$ gram molecule?

14. TANGENTS AND NORMALS

A property of a plane curve that refers to its tangent or normal may be expressed by a differential equation. Its integration leads to the equation of the curves having the property in question.

When the equation of a curve is given in rectangular coordinates, x, y, the slope of its tangent at the point (x, y) is given by the value of dy/dx at this point. Thus if the tangent to the curve makes an angle ψ with the positive x-axis,

$$(1) \qquad \text{Slope of tangent} = \tan \psi = \frac{dy}{dx} = y'.$$

When the equation of the curve is $f(x, y) = 0$,

$$(2) \qquad \frac{\partial f}{\partial x} + \frac{\partial f}{\partial y} y' = 0, \qquad y' = -\frac{f_x}{f_y},$$

where $f_x = \partial f/\partial x$.

Let X, Y denote the running coordinates along the tangent or normal to the curve at the point (x, y). Then the equation of its tangent at (x, y) is

$$(3) \qquad Y - y = y'(X - x);$$

and since the slope of the normal at (x, y) is $-1/y'$, the equation of the normal is

$$(4) \qquad Y - y = -\frac{1}{y'}(X - x).$$

When the equation of the curve is given in polar coordinates r, θ, the slope of the tangent *referred to a line from the pole through the point* of contact (Fig. 14a) is

$$(5) \qquad \tan \varphi = \frac{r}{r'}$$

where $r' = dr/d\theta$. Because, from the equations

$$x = r \cos \theta, \qquad y = r \sin \theta,$$

we have

$$\tan \psi = \frac{dy}{dx} = \frac{r' \sin \theta + r \cos \theta}{r' \cos \theta - r \sin \theta} = \frac{\tan \theta + r/r'}{1 - (r/r') \tan \theta};$$

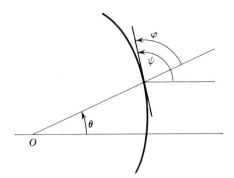

Fig. 14a

and since $\psi = \theta + \varphi$, the addition theorem for tangents shows that $\tan \varphi = r/r'$.*

Example 1. Find the curves whose normals pass through a fixed point (a, b).
  The normal to the curve at (x, y) has the slope $(y - b)/(x - a)$; hence the curves have the differential equation

$$-\frac{dx}{dy} = \frac{y - b}{x - a} \quad \text{or} \quad (x - a)\,dx + (y - b)\,dy = 0.$$

On integrating we have

$$(x - a)^2 + (y - b)^2 = C^2,$$

where C^2 is an arbitrary positive constant. The curves are circles about (a, b) as center.

Example 2. The part of every tangent to a curve between the point of tangency and the y-axis is bisected by the x-axis. Find all curves having this property.
  From (3) we see that the tangent cuts the y-axis at the point

$$X = 0, \qquad Y = y - xy';$$

and the x-axis at the point

$$X = x - \frac{y}{y'}, \qquad Y = 0.$$

Thus the point $(x - y/y', 0)$ is midway between (x, y) and $(0, y - xy')$; hence

$$x - \frac{y}{y'} = \frac{x + 0}{2}, \qquad 0 = \frac{2y - xy'}{2}.$$

Both equations give

$$\frac{dy}{dx} = 2\frac{y}{x} \quad \text{or} \quad \frac{dy}{y} - 2\frac{dx}{x} = 0;$$

---

* Or we may draw the x-axis through the point of contact; then $\theta = 0$, $\psi = \varphi$, and $\tan \psi = r/r'$.

and on integration we find

$$\log y - 2 \log x = \log \frac{y}{x^2} = \log C, \qquad \frac{y}{x^2} = C.$$

Therefore the parabolas $y = Cx^2$ with vertex at the origin and symmetric about the y-axis have the required property. Does the line $y = 0$ (corresponding to $C = 0$) have the property in question?

Example 3. The *equiangular spiral* is a curve that cuts all lines through a point 0 at a constant angle α.

Choose 0 as the pole of the coordinates r, θ; then the differential equation of the spiral is given by putting $\varphi = \alpha$ in (5):

$$\frac{dr}{d\theta} = (\cot \alpha)r.$$

Fig. 14b Section of *Nautilus pompilius*.

Hence r increases with θ according to the compound interest law and

$$r = r_0 e^{(\cot \alpha)\theta}.$$

This is the polar equation of a family of equiangular (or logarithmic) spirals; r_0, the value of r corresponding to $\theta = 0$, is the parameter of the family.

If a sea shell such as the pearly nautilus (*Nautilus pompilius*) is cut in two along its plane of symmetry, the equal halves display logarithmic spirals. Moreover the rear side of the operculum* of certain shells, such as *Turbo*, shows a beautiful spiral which indicates its law of growth.

15.   ORTHOGONAL TRAJECTORIES

Let the one-parameter family of curves

(1) $$\varphi(x, y, c) = 0$$

have the differential equation (cf. § 3):

(2) $$F(x, y, y') = 0.$$

The curves cutting the family (1) everywhere at right angles are called the *orthogonal trajectories* of (1). If X, Y, Y' are the coordinates and slope along a trajectory, at all points where it cuts a curve of the family (1), we have

$$X = x, \qquad Y = y, \qquad Y' = -\frac{1}{y'} \; ;$$

hence if we put

$$x = X, \qquad y = Y, \qquad y' = -\frac{1}{Y'}$$

in (2) we obtain the differential equation

(3) $$F\left(X, Y, -\frac{1}{Y'}\right) = 0$$

of the orthogonal trajectories. The general integral of (3), say

(4) $$f(X, Y, C) = 0,$$

will give their Cartesian equations.

For the sake of clearness we have used small and capital letters to distinguish the given curves from their trajectories. It is customary, however, to use small letters for both families. We then have the rule:

The differential equation of the orthogonal trajectories is obtained by replacing y' by $-1/y'$ in the differential equation of the given family.

---

* The plug which closes up the shell when the animal is within. It may be calcareous or horny; calcareous opercula are often called "cat's eyes."

Let the 1-parameter family of curves in polar coordinates

(5) $\varphi(\theta, r, c) = 0$

have the differential equation

(6) $F(\theta, r, r') = 0,$

where $r' = dr/d\theta$. The curve (1) through the point $P(\theta, r)$ has the slope r/r' relative to OP; for the orthogonal trajectory through P we have

$$\Theta = \theta, \qquad R = r, \qquad \frac{R}{R'} = -\frac{r'}{r};$$

hence if we put

$$\theta = \Theta, \qquad r = R, \qquad r' = -\frac{R^2}{R'}$$

in (6), we obtain the differential equation

(7) $$F\left(\Theta, R, -\frac{R^2}{R'}\right) = 0$$

of the orthogonal trajectories. The general integral of (7) will give their polar equations. Reverting in (7) to small letters, we have the rule applicable to polar coordinates:

The differential equation of the orthogonal trajectories is obtained by replacing r' by $-r^2/r'$ in the differential equation of the given family.

Note that the differential equation of the given 1-parameter family of curves must be *free from the parameter*. Consider, for example, the family of circles tangent to the y-axis at the origin:

$$(x - a)^2 + y^2 = a^2 \quad \text{or} \quad x^2 + y^2 = 2ax.$$

Differentiation gives $x + yy' = a$; but this is *not* the differential equation of the family since it still contains a. Elimination of a between the two equations yields

$$y^2 - x^2 = 2xy\frac{dy}{dx}.$$

When dy/dx is replaced by $-dx/dy$, we get

$$x^2 - y^2 = 2xy\frac{dx}{dy}$$

for the differential equation of the trajectories, and its one-parametric solution will give their Cartesian equation. In this case, however, integration is not necessary, for the second differential equation may be obtained from the first by interchanging x and y. Its solution is therefore the given equation with x and y interchanged:

$$x^2 + (y - a)^2 = a^2 \quad \text{or} \quad x^2 + y^2 = 2ay.$$

This represents a family of circles tangent to the x-axis at the origin.

Example 1. The family of parabolas

$$y^2 = cx$$

has the differential equation

$$2xy' - y = 0 \qquad \text{(Ex. 3.2).}$$

For the orthogonal trajectories

$$-\frac{2x}{y'} - y = 0 \quad \text{or} \quad 2x + yy' = 0.$$

The integral of this separable equation,

$$2x^2 + y^2 = C,$$

represents a family of ellipses that cut the parabolas at right angles.

Example 2. The family of circles tangent to the y-axis at the origin is given by

$$r = c \cos \theta \qquad (c = \text{diameter}).$$

Their differential equation is

$$\frac{r'}{r} = -\frac{\sin \theta}{\cos \theta}.$$

Replacing r' by $-r^2/r'$ we obtain the differential equation

$$\frac{r}{r'} = \frac{\sin \theta}{\cos \theta} \quad \text{or} \quad \frac{dr}{r} = \frac{\cos \theta}{\sin \theta} \, d\theta$$

for the orthogonal trajectories. The integral

$$\log r = \log \sin \theta + \log C \quad \text{or} \quad r = C \sin \theta$$

represents a family of circles tangent to the x-axis at the origin. These two families of circles cut at right angles.

Example 3. A family of curves has the differential equation

(i) $$P(x, y)y'^2 + Q(x, y)y' + R(x, y) = 0.$$

Two curves of this family pass through each point (x, y) for which the equation gives real and distinct values of y', say y_1' and y_2'. The product of these roots $y_1'y_2' = R/P$; and if $R/P = -1$, the curves will cut at right angles. Thus a necessary and sufficient condition that the integral curves of equation (8) form two orthogonal sets is that

(ii) $$P + R = 0.$$

The two sets of curves form a *self-orthogonal* system.

For example, the system of confocal conics

(iii) $$\frac{x^2}{C^2} + \frac{y^2}{C^2 - k^2} = 1   \text{(Ex. 3.3)}$$

has the differential equation

$$xyy'^2 + (x^2 - y^2 - k^2)y' - xy = 0,$$

and since $P + R = xy - xy = 0$, the curves are orthogonal; they consist of ellipses $(C > k)$ and hyperbolas $(C < k)$. As $C \to k$ from above or below, the ellipses and hyperbolas approach the double line $y = 0$, which is obviously a solution of the differential equation.

PROBLEMS

In Problems 1 to 12 find the orthogonal trajectories of the given curves (parameter c).

1. The hyperbolas: $x^2 - y^2 = cx$.
2. The ellipses: $2x^2 + 3y^2 = c$.
3. The hyperbolas: $xy = c$.
4. The hyperbolas: $x^2 + 2xy - y^2 = c$.
5. The parabolas: $y^2 = 2(c - x)$.
6. The curves: $x^2 + y^2 = cx^2y^2$.
7. The cardioids: $r = c(1 - \cos\theta)$.
8. The parabolas: $r = c/(1 - \cos\theta)$.
9. The equiangular spirals: $r = ce^{\theta \cot\alpha}$.
10. The spirals of Archimedes: $r = c\theta$.
11. The cissoids: $r = a\sin\theta\tan\theta$.
12. The strophoids: $r = a(\sec\theta + \tan\theta)$.
13. Show that the orthogonal trajectories of the generalized parabolas $y = cx^n$ are the central conics $x^2 + ny^2 = C$.
14. Show that the family of parabolas $y^2 + 2cx = c^2$ is self-orthogonal.
15. Show that the family of parabolas $x^2 = 4a(y + a)$ is self-orthogonal.
16. When a family of curves is cut by another family at a constant angle $\alpha \neq \pi/2$, we have *oblique trajectories*. At a point of intersection let the tangents of the two families have inclinations of φ and $\varphi + \alpha$ to the x-axis. Then if the given family has the differential equation (2), prove that the α-trajectories have the differential equation

$$F\left(x, y, \frac{y' - \tan\alpha}{1 + y'\tan\alpha}\right) = 0.$$

17. Find the α-trajectories of the family of straight lines $y = cx$. [The d.e. has the multiplier $1/(x^2 + y^2)$.]
18. Find the differential equation (1) of the cardioids $r = c(1 + \cos\theta)$ and (2) of their orthogonal trajectories. Prove that (2) becomes (1) on making the change of variable $\theta = \pi - \varphi$. Interpret this result geometrically.
19. Prove that the circles $x^2 + y^2 = ax$ cut the circles $x^2 + y^2 = by$ at right angles.

20. The function $f(z) = u(x, y) + iv(x, y)$ of the complex variable $z = x + iy$ has a unique derivative when and only when the Cauchy-Riemann equations $u_x = v_y, u_y = -v_x$ are satisfied. Show that the two families of curves $u(x, y) = a$, $v(x, y) = b$ cut at right angles at all points where $f'(z) \neq 0$. (Cf. *Advanced Calculus*, p. 195.)

21. Solve Problem 19 by considering the function $1/z$.

22. Both $f(z) = z^2, f'(z) = 2z$ are zero when $z = 0$. Do the curves $u(x, y) = 0$ and $v(x, y) = 0$ cut at right angles? Explain.

CHAPTER 2

Important Types
of First-Order Equations

16. LINEAR EQUATION

The equation

(1) $$P_0(x)\frac{dy}{dx} + P_1(x)y = R(x)$$

is said to be *linear in y*. This equation will be exact when

$$\frac{dP_0}{dx} = \frac{\partial}{\partial y}(P_1 y - R) = P_1.$$

Then (1) may be written

$$\frac{d}{dx}(P_0 y) = R$$

and an integration gives the general solution.

If (1) is not exact, it admits a multiplier $\mu(x)$, a function of x alone. Such a multiplier must satisfy the equation

$$\frac{d}{dx}(\mu P_0) = \mu P_1.$$

On division by μP_0 we have

$$\frac{d(\mu P_0)}{\mu P_0} = \frac{P_1}{P_0}\,dx;$$

hence

$$\log \mu P_0 = \int \frac{P_1}{P_0}\,dx, \qquad \mu P_0 = \exp \int \frac{P_1}{P_0}\,dx.$$

We therefore have

Theorem 1. *The linear equation*

(1) $$P_0(x)y' + P_1(x)y = R(x)$$

admits the multiplier

(2) $$\mu(x) = \frac{1}{P_0} \exp \int \frac{P_1}{P_0} \, dx$$

over any interval in which $P_0 \neq 0$; and multiplication by μ converts it into the exact equation

(3) $$\frac{d}{dx}(\mu P_0 y) = \mu R.$$

From (3) we obtain the general solution of (1):

$$\mu P_0 y = \int \mu R \, dx + C \quad \text{or} \quad y = \frac{1}{\mu P_0} \int \mu R \, dx + \frac{C}{\mu P_0}.$$

The general solution of the linear equation (1) thus has the structure

(4) $$y = Cu(x) + f(x).$$

When $R = 0$, $f(x) = 0$, and $Cu(x)$ gives *all* solutions of the reduced equation

(5) $$P_0(x)y' + P_1(x)y = 0.$$

When $C = 0$, we obtain the function *zero* (whose graph is the line $y = 0$) as a trivial solution of (5); then $f(x)$ is a particular solution of (1).

If $y_1(x)$ is any particular solution of (1), $y - y_1$ is a solution of (5) and therefore is included in $Cu(x)$. We therefore have

Theorem 2. *The general solution of the linear equation (1) is obtained by adding any particular solution to the general solution of the reduced equation (5):*

(6) $$y = Cu(x) + y_1(x).$$

For example, the equation $y' + y = 2$ obviously has the function 2 as a particular solution; and since e^{-x} is a solution of $y' + y = 0$, the general solution is $y = Ce^{-x} + 2$.

A characteristic feature of the *linearity* of the reduced equation is that all of its solutions, $Cu(x)$, are obtained from one, $u(x)$. Thus all solutions of (5) have essentially the same functional behavior.

In § 8 we stated an existence theorem for the first-order equation $y' = f(x, y)$. When $f(x, y)$ is linear in y, this theorem is readily proved and the interval in which the solution is valid may be specified.

Theorem 3 (Existence and Uniqueness). *Let the functions $p(x)$, $q(x)$ be continuous in the interval $a < x < b$ containing the point x_0 in its interior. Then for each real number y_0, the initial value problem*

(7) $$y' + p(x)y = q(x), \qquad y(x_0) = y_0,$$

has the unique solution

(8) $$y(x) = \frac{1}{\mu(x)} \int_{x_0}^{x} \mu(t)q(t)\, dt + \frac{y_0}{\mu(x)}, \qquad a < x < b,$$

where

(9) $$\mu(x) = \exp \int_{x_0}^{x} p(t)\, dt.$$

PROOF. The multiplier $\mu(x)$ and $\mu'(x) = p(x)\mu(x)$ are continuous in the interval (a, b). Since $\mu(x)$ is always positive, multiplying equation (7) by $\mu(x)$ yields

$$\frac{d}{dx}(\mu y) = \mu q,$$

an equation *with the same solutions*. *All* solutions of this equation are given by

$$\mu(x)y(x) = \int_{x_0}^{x} \mu(t)q(t)\, dt + C.$$

Because $\mu(x_0) = 1$, the condition $y(x_0) = y_0$ requires that $C = y_0$. Hence the unique solution of the initial value problem (7) is

(10) $$y(x) = \frac{1}{\mu(x)} \int_{x_0}^{x} \mu(t)q(t)\, dt + \frac{y_0}{\mu(x)}.$$

Because $\mu'(x) = p(x)\mu(x)$,

$$y'(x) = q(x) - \frac{p(x)}{\mu(x)} \int_{x_0}^{x} \mu(t)q(t)\, dt - y_0 \frac{p(x)}{\mu(x)}.$$

Evidently $y(x)$ and $y'(x)$ are continuous in (a, b), and a direct check shows that both differential equation and initial condition are satisfied.

An important consequence of this theorem is that the singularities of the solution of a linear equation can occur only at the points at which the coefficient functions (p, q) are singular. This does not mean, however, that the solution *must* have singularities at these points. For example, the solution of

$$y' + \frac{y}{x} = 2, \qquad y(1) = 1,$$

is $y = x$ and this has no singularity at $x = 0$, where $p = 1/x$ is singular.

Example 1. In the initial value problem

$$y' - 2xy = 1, \qquad y(0) = 1,$$

the linear equation admits the multiplier

$$\mu = \exp \int (-2x)\, dx = e^{-x^2}.$$

On multiplying the equation by e^{-x^2}, we have

$$\frac{d}{dx}(e^{-x^2}y) = e^{-x^2}, \qquad e^{-x^2}y = \int_0^x e^{-x^2}\, dx + C.$$

The initial condition now gives $C = e^0 \cdot 1 = 1$, so that

$$y = e^{x^2} \int_0^x e^{-x^2}\, dx + e^{x^2}.$$

The integral cannot be expressed in terms of the elementary functions, but the *error function*

$$\operatorname{erf} x = \frac{2}{\sqrt{\pi}} \int_0^x e^{-x^2}\, dx$$

has been tabulated.* Thus the solution may be written

$$y = e^{x^2}(\tfrac{1}{2}\sqrt{\pi}\operatorname{erf} x + 1).$$

Example 2. The linear equation

$$x \frac{dy}{dx} - 4y + 2x^2 + 4 = 0$$

admits the multiplier

$$\mu = \frac{1}{x} \exp \int \frac{-4}{x}\, dx = \frac{1}{x} \exp \log x^{-4} = x^{-5}.$$

This converts it into the exact equation

$$x^{-4}\, dy + [2x^{-3} + 4(1 - y)x^{-5}]\, dx = 0$$

whose integral is

$$x^{-4} \int_0^y dy + \int (2x^{-3} + 4x^{-5})\, dx = C; \qquad (6.7)$$

hence

$$x^{-4}y - x^{-2} - x^{-4} = C$$

or

$$y = Cx^4 + x^2 + 1.$$

When $C = 0$ we obtain the simplest particular solution $y_1 = x^2 + 1$; and Cx^4 is the general solution of the reduced equation $xy' - 4y = 0$.

---

* Cf. ref 13, pp. 128—132.

Example 3. The linear equation

(i)
$$\frac{dy}{dt} + y = 0$$

admits the multiplier e^t and has the general solution $y = Ce^{-t}$.
The nonlinear equation

(ii)
$$\frac{dy}{dt} + y - y^2 = 0$$

is separable,

$$\frac{dy}{y} + \frac{dy}{1 - y} + dt = 0,$$

and we find its general solution to be

$$y = \frac{K}{K + e^t}$$

To compare these solutions let us choose the constants C and K so that $y(0) = a$; then $C = a$, $K = a/(1 - a)$ and the solutions of (i) and (ii) become

$$y_1 = ae^{-t}, \qquad y_2 = \frac{ae^{-t}}{1 - a + ae^{-t}},$$

in which we interpret t as the time. When $a = 0$ both y_1 and y_2 have the equilibrium value $\{0\}$; when $a = 1$, $y_1 = e^{-t}$ but y_2 has the equilibrium value $\{1\}$.*
The linear equation (i) has a single equilibrium solution $y = 0$ and all of its solutions approach this as $t \to \infty$. But the nonlinear equation (ii) has two equilibrium solutions $y = 0$ and $y = 1$, and the behavior of its solutions depends on their initial value a. If $a < 1$, $y_2 \to 0$ as $t \to \infty$; but if $a > 1$, y_2 becomes infinite for the finite value $t = \log a/(a - 1)$. Whereas *all* solutions of a linear equation have common properties, the solutions of nonlinear equations behave in diverse ways which depend on the initial conditions and the structure of the equation itself. Thus there is a certain danger in replacing a nonlinear equation by its linear approximation to simplify it; for on eliminating the difficulties we may also eliminate essential phenomena of the problem under investigation.

PROBLEMS

1. Find multipliers of the following equations:

(a) $y' + 2xy = R(x)$,

(b) $xy' - y = R(x)$,

(c) $y' \cos x + y \sin x = R(x)$,

(d) $y' \sin x + y \cos x = R(x)$,

(e) $x^2 y' + (1 - x)y = R(x)$,

(f) $e^x y' - y = R(x)$,

(g) $t \log t \, \dfrac{dx}{dt} + x = R(t)$,

(h) $y^2 \dfrac{dx}{dy} - x = R(y)$.

---

* $\{0\}$ and $\{1\}$ denote constant *functions*; cf. § 136.

Solve the following initial value problems:

2. $y' + 2xy = x$, $y(0) = 1$.

3. $y' + y = \sin x$, $y(0) = 1$.

4. $(t + 2) dx + (3x - t) dt = 0$, $x(0) = 1$.

5. $y' + y + x + x^2 + x^3 = 0$, $y(0) = 1$.

6. $\dfrac{dx}{dt} - x = (2t - 1)e^{t^2}$, $x(0) = 2$.

In the following problems predict the interval in which the solution is valid from Theorem 3 and compare with the interval of validity of the actual solution.

7. $(1 - x^2)y' - y = 0$, $y(0) = 1$.

8. $(1 - x^2)y' - xy = 1$, $y(0) = 0$.

9. $2xy' + y = x$; find a solution valid for all x.

10. If exp x is *defined* as the solution of $y' - y = 0$, $y(0) = 1$, prove that exp $(a + x) = (\exp a)(\exp x)$.

In problems 11 and 12 predict the interval in which the solution is valid and compare with the actual solution.

11. $(1 + x^2)y' + 2xy - 4x^3 = 0$, $y(0) = -1$.

12. $x(x^2 - 1)y' + 2(2x^2 - 1)y + 4x^2 = 0$, $y(1) = 0$.

Show that the solution is valid in any closed interval in which $x \neq 0$.

13. Solve the initial value problems

(i) $y' + y = 0$, $y(0) = a$,

(ii) $y' + y + y^3 = 0$, $y(0) = a$,

and contrast their solutions for different values of a. Find the equilibrium solutions in each case.

14. The lineal elements of the linear equation

$$y' + p(x)y = q(x)$$

at all points of abscissa λ pass through the point

$$x = \lambda + \frac{1}{p(\lambda)}, \qquad y = \frac{q(\lambda)}{p(\lambda)} \qquad \text{(Ex. 4.5).}$$

Construct the direction field of $xy' + y = 2x$ from its guide curve. Show that the guide curve yields a solution valid for all x.

15. Find the guide curve and direction field for $xy' - y = \sqrt{x}$. Find the solution for which $y(4) = 0$.

16. In the linear equation $u' + p(x)u = 0$, $p(x)$ is continuous in the interval $a \leq x \leq b$. Prove that a solution that is zero at any point of the interval must be identically zero.

If $u(x)$ is a nonzero solution of $u' + p(x)u = 0$, prove that the initial value problem

$$y' + p(x)y = q(x), \qquad y(a) = 0$$

has the unique solution

(11) $y_1(x) = \displaystyle\int_a^x \frac{u(x)}{u(t)} q(t) \, dt$.

Use this formula to solve Problem 15.

17. $(2x + 4)\,dy = \tan y\,dx$ is separable and linear in x. Find two multipliers and solve (cf. §10).

18. A tank contains a mixture of 50 gallons of alcohol and 100 gallons of water. A mixture of equal parts of alcohol and water flows in at the rate of 2 gal/min and the liquid in the tank, kept uniform by stirring, flows out at the rate of 1 gal/min. How much alcohol in the tank after 30 minutes?

19. When the emf $E \sin \omega t$ volts is applied to a circuit containing a resistance of R ohms and an inductance of L henrys in series, the current i varies according to

$$L\frac{di}{dt} + Ri = E \sin \omega t.$$

If $i = 0$ when $t = 0$, show that

$$i = \frac{E}{Z} \sin(\omega t - \alpha) + \frac{E}{Z} \sin \alpha \exp\left(-\frac{Rt}{L}\right) \text{ amperes,}$$

where the *impedance* Z and the *phase angle* α are defined by

$$R = Z \cos \alpha, \qquad \omega L = Z \sin \alpha \qquad \text{(Fig. 16a).}$$

20. When the emf $E \sin \omega t$ volts is applied to a circuit containing a resistance of R ohms and a capacitance of C farads in series, the current i varies according to

$$Ri + \frac{1}{C}\int_0^t i\,dt = E \sin \omega t.$$

If $i = 0$ when $t = 0$, show that

$$i = \frac{E}{Z} \sin(\omega t + \alpha) - \frac{E}{Z} \sin \alpha \exp\left(-\frac{t}{CR}\right) \text{ amperes,}$$

where the *impedance* and *phase angle* α are defined by

$$R = Z \cos \alpha, \qquad 1/\omega C = Z \sin \alpha \qquad \text{(Fig. 16b).}$$

(a)   (b)

Fig.16 (a) Impedance in RL series circuit; (b) impedance in RC series circuit.

21. Show that the equation $y' = f(x, y)$ is linear or separable according as it admits a multiplier $\mu(x)$ or $\mu(y)$.

17. BERNOULLI EQUATION

The equation

$$(1) \qquad P_0(x)\frac{dy}{dx} + P_1(x)y = R(x)y^n, \qquad n \neq 0, 1,$$

is called a Bernoulli equation in y. The exponents $n = 0$ and 1 are excluded, for the equation is linear or separable in the respective cases.

If we multiply (1) by $(1 - n)y^{-n}$ and introduce the new dependent variable $v = y^{1-n}$, we have

(2) $$P_0(x) \frac{dv}{dx} + (1 - n) P_1(x)v = (1 - n) R(x).$$

This equation is linear in v and admits the multiplier (16.2) when P_1 is replaced by $(1 - n)P_1$; hence the Bernoulli equation (1) admits the multiplier

(3) $$\mu = \frac{1}{y^n P_0} \exp (1 - n) \int \frac{P_1}{P_0} \, dx.$$

The essential thing to remember is that the Bernoulli equation (1) admits a multiplier $\mu = y^{-n} X(x)$. When (1) is multiplied by this μ and the exactness condition applied, y^{-n} cancels out and X may be determined.

Example 1. The Bernoulli equation in y,

(i) $$x \frac{dy}{dx} - 3y + x^4 y^2 = 0,$$

has a multiplier $\mu = y^{-2} X(x)$; hence

$$\frac{\partial}{\partial x} (xy^{-2}X) = \frac{\partial}{\partial y} (x^4 - 3y^{-1})X = 3y^{-2}X.$$

Canceling y^{-2} gives

$$\frac{d}{dx} (xX) = 3X, \qquad \frac{(xX)'}{xX} = \frac{3}{x},$$

$$\log (xX) = \log x^3, \qquad X = x^2, \qquad \mu = x^2 y^{-2}.$$

This multiplier converts (i) into an exact equation

$$x^3 y^{-2} \, dy + (x^6 - 3x^2 y^{-1}) \, dx = 0,$$

whose integral is

$$x^3 \int_1^y y^{-2} \, dy + \int (x^6 - 3x^2) \, dx = C,$$

$$-\frac{x^3}{y} + x^3 + \frac{x^7}{7} - x^3 = C, \qquad (6.7)$$

$$\frac{x^7}{7} - \frac{x^3}{y} = C.$$

Example 2. The equation

(ii) $$(y^2 - 1) \, dx + (3x^2 - 2xy) \, dy = 0$$

is a Bernoulli equation in x (it has terms in dx/dy, x, x^2); it therefore has a multiplier $\mu = x^{-2} Y(y)$. To find Y we multiply (ii) by μ and use the exactness condition:

$$\frac{\partial}{\partial y} [x^{-2}(y^2 - 1) Y] = \frac{\partial}{\partial x} [(3 - 2x^{-1}y) Y] = 2x^{-2}y \, Y.$$

Canceling x^{-2} gives

$$\frac{d}{dy}[(y^2 - 1)Y] = 2y\,Y \quad \text{or} \quad (y^2 - 1)Y' = 0;$$

hence we may take $Y = 1$, $\mu = x^{-2}$. This multiplier converts (ii) into an exact equation

$$x^{-2}(y^2 - 1)\,dx + (3 - 2x^{-1}y)\,dy = 0$$

whose integral is

$$\int_0^y (3 - 2x^{-1}y)\,dy - \int \frac{dx}{x^2} = 3y - \frac{y^2}{x} + \frac{1}{x} = C. \qquad (6.7)$$

Example 3. The Bernoulli equation $y' + y = y^3$ has the multiplier

$$\mu = \frac{1}{y^3}\exp(-2)\int dx = \frac{e^{-2x}}{y^3}.$$

When written

$$dy + (y - y^3)\,dx = 0,$$

the equation is seen to be separable with the multiplier

$$\lambda = \frac{1}{y - y^3}.$$

Its solution (cf. § 10) is therefore

$$\frac{\mu}{\lambda} = \frac{e^{-2x}}{y^3}\frac{y - y^3}{1} = K \quad \text{or} \quad y^2 = \frac{1}{1 + Ke^{2x}}.$$

PROBLEMS

Find general solutions for the following equations:
1. $xy' + y = x^2y^2$.
2. $y' + y^2 = y/x$.
3. $4x^3y\,dx - (x^4 + y^2)\,dy = 0$.
4. $(y^2 - x^2y)\,dx + x^3\,dy = 0$.
5. $x^2y' - xy + y^3e^x = 0$.
6. $(y' - \frac{1}{2}y^2)\sin\theta - y\cos\theta = 0$.
7. $(1 - x^2)y' = xy + xy^2$.
8. $yy' + y^2 + 1 = 0$; find two multipliers (§10).
9. $(x^2 + x - y)\,dx - (x + 1)\,dy = 0$.
10. $x^2y' - xy = y^2$, $y(-1) = 1$.

18. RICCATI EQUATION

If P, Q, R are functions of x,

$$(1) \qquad\qquad \frac{dy}{dx} + Py^2 + Qy + R = 0$$

is called a *Riccati equation*. If y_1 is a particular solution of (1),

$$\frac{dy_1}{dx} + Py_1{}^2 + Qy_1 + R = 0;$$

on subtracting this equation from (1) we have

$$\frac{d}{dx}(y - y_1) + [P(y + y_1) + Q](y - y_1) = 0;$$

or, on putting $z = y - y_1$, we have

$$\frac{dz}{dx} + (2Py_1 + Q)z + Pz^2 = 0.$$

This is a Bernoulli equation with the multiplier $z^{-2} \exp -\int (2Py_1 + Q)\, dx$. Hence, if y_1 is a particular solution of the Riccati equation (1), it admits the multiplier

$$(2) \qquad \mu = \frac{1}{(y - y_1)^2} \exp \int -(2Py_1 + Q)\, dx.$$

If y_2 is a second particular solution, the Riccati equation also admits the multiplier

$$\lambda = \frac{1}{(y - y_2)^2} \exp \int -(2Py_2 + Q)\, dx.$$

The general solution of (1) is then given by $\lambda/\mu = \text{const}$ (§ 10). Since λ and μ are both positive, we can take the square root of both members and write the general solution in the form

$$(3) \qquad \frac{y - y_1}{y - y_2} \exp \int P(y_1 - y_2)\, dx = C.$$

When this equation is solved for y, we find that the general solution of the Riccati equation has the structure

$$(4) \qquad y = \frac{f(x) + Cg(x)}{h(x) + Ck(x)}.$$

(cf. Prob. 3.9). Conversely, any relation of this form leads to a Riccati equation on eliminating C between y and the equation for y'.

The Riccati equation (1) may be reduced to the form

$$(5) \qquad \frac{dz}{dx} + z^2 + \left(Q - \frac{P'}{P}\right)z + PR = 0$$

by the substitution $y = z/P$. Equations in this form are closely related to linear differential equations of the second order.

Theorem. *The Riccati equation*

$$(6) \qquad P_0(x)(z' + z^2) + P_1(x)z + P_2(x) = 0$$

and the associated linear equation

$$(7) \qquad P_0(x)u'' + P_1(x)u' + P_2(x)u = 0$$

have corresponding solutions which satisfy the equations

$$(8) \qquad u(x) = \exp \int z(x)\, dx, \qquad z(x) = \frac{u'(x)}{u(x)}.$$

PROOF. From (8) we have

$$u' = z \exp \int z(x)\, dx = zu,$$

$$u'' = z'u + zu' = (z' + z^2)u,$$

hence

$$P_0u'' + P_1u' + P_2u = [P_0(z' + z^2) + P_1z + P_2]u.$$

Thus any solution $z(x)$ of (6) corresponds to a solution $u(x) = \exp \int z(x)\, dx$ of (7). Conversely, any solution $u(x) \neq 0$ of (7) corresponds to a solution $z(x) = u'(x)/u(x)$ of (6).

If u_1 and u_2 are particular solutions of (7) whose ratio is not a constant, the general solution of (7) is known to be $u = C_1u_1 + C_2u_2$ (§ 28). The general solution of (6) is then

$$y = \frac{u'}{u} = \frac{C_1u_1' + C_2u_2'}{C_1u_1 + C_2u_2},$$

which involves but one essential constant, say C_2/C_1.

To solve a Riccati equation a particular solution, y_1, should be sought. This is usually accomplished by a trial substitution of a function with disposable constants, such as ax^b or $ax + b$. The choice of the trial function depends on the nature of the equation. If a particular solution can not be found by trial (which is nearly always the case), we may transform the Riccati equation to the associated linear equation of the second order (as in Ex. 1); any solution of this equation corresponds to a solution of the Riccati equation.

When y_1 is known, the Riccati equation admits the multiplier (2) and its solution depends on quadratures. No systematic method of solution other than this is known and we must usually resort to approximate methods or expansions in power series.

Count Jacopo Riccati (1676–1754) studied the special Riccati equation

$$(9) \qquad y' + ay^2 = bx^m \qquad (a, b, m \text{ constant}).$$

When $y = z/a$, (9) becomes $z^1 + z^2 = abx^m$.

Daniel Bernoulli showed in 1724 that (9) can be integrated in "closed" form by means of elementary functions when

$$(10) \qquad m = \frac{-4k}{2k \pm 1}, \qquad k = 0, 1, 2, \ldots, \uparrow \infty(m = -2),$$

and in 1841 Liouville showed that these were the only cases in which this is possible [cf. A. R. Forsyth, ref. 26, pp. 184–187].

Example. To solve the Riccati equation

$$(i) \qquad y' - e^{-x}y^2 - y - e^x = 0, \qquad (P = -e^{-x})$$

make the transformation $y = z/P = -e^x z$. This gives

$$-e^x(z' + z) - e^x z^2 + e^x z - e^x = 0,$$

or

$$(ii) \qquad z' + z^2 + 1 = 0.$$

The associated linear equation

$$(iii) \qquad u'' + u = 0$$

obviously has the particular solutions $u_1 = \cos x$, $u_2 = \sin x$. Hence (ii) has the particular solutions

$$z_1 = \frac{u_1'}{u_1} = -\tan x, \qquad z_2 = \frac{u_2'}{u_2} = \cot x;$$

thus (i) has the particular solutions

$$y_1 = e^x \tan x, \qquad y_2 = -e^x \cot x.$$

We may now obtain the general solution of (i) from (3). Since

$$\exp \int P(y_1 - y_2) = \exp \int (-\tan x - \cot x)\, dx \, \exp\left(\log\frac{\cos x}{\sin x}\right) = \cot x,$$

the general solution of (i) is

$$(iv) \qquad \frac{y - e^x \tan x}{y + e^x \cot x} \cot x = C.$$

We shall see later that the general solution of (iii) is

$$u = C_1 \cos x + C_2 \sin x;$$

hence the general solutions of (ii) and (iii) are $z = u'/u$ and

$$(v) \qquad y = \frac{u'}{Pu} = e^x \frac{C_1 \sin x - C_2 \cos x}{C_1 \cos x + C_2 \sin x}.$$

Let the reader show that (v) agrees with (iv). From (v) we have $y = y_1$ when $C_2 = 0$, $y = y_2$ when $C_1 = 0$.

PROBLEMS

Find two particular solutions and the general solution of the following equations.

1. $y' + e^{-x}y^2 - y - e^x = 0$ (try ae^{bx}).

2. $y' - xy^2 - \dfrac{y}{x} + x^3 = 0$ (try ax^b).

3. $x^2(y' + y^2) + xy - 1 = 0$.

4. $y' = k(a - y)(b - y)$, $a \neq b$.

Find the solution for which $y(0) = 0$ (Ex. 7.2).

5. $(1 - x^2)y' + y^2 - 1 = 0$.

6. $y' = (x + y)^2 - 2$ (try $x + y = a$).

7. Find a multiplier for $y' = y^2 + xy + x - 2$.

8. Find a multiplier for $y' = y^2 - y \sin x + \cos x$.

9. Find the general solution: $y' + y^2 - 3y + 2 = 0$.

10. If $u(x)$ is any solution of

$$u'' + \left(Q - \frac{P'}{P}\right)u' + PRu = 0,$$

show that $y = u'(x)/Pu(x)$ is a solution of (1).

11. If y_1, y_2, y_3 are three different solutions of (1), use (3) to prove that the general solution is

$$\frac{y - y_1}{y - y_2} = C\frac{y_3 - y_1}{y_3 - y_2}.$$

12. Solve Problem 5 by finding three particular solutions.

13. $y' = 1 + y^2 - x^2$; find the solution for which $y(0) = 1$.

14. Show that the substitution $y = z/a$ reduces (9) to $z' + z^2 = abx^m$ and find the associated linear equation.

15. Solve $y' + y^2 + (2x + 1)y + x^2 + x + 1 = 0$ (try $y = ax + b$).

16. Solve $y' + 2y^2 = x^{-2}$ (try $y = ax^b$).

19. HOMOGENEOUS EQUATIONS

A function $f(x, y)$ is said to be *homogeneous of degree n* when

(1) $f(tx, ty) = t^n f(x, y)$

for every positive value of t.* For example, the functions

$$2x^2 + xy - y^2, \qquad \sin\frac{y}{x + y}, \qquad \frac{1}{\sqrt{x^2 + y^2}}, \qquad \frac{2}{xy^2}$$

are homogeneous of degree 2, 0, -1, -3, respectively. If we put $t = 1/x$

---

* *Advanced Calculus*, § 81.

in (1), we have for any homogeneous function of degree n

(2)
$$f(x, y) = x^n f\left(1, \frac{y}{x}\right).$$

In particular, we see that a homogeneous function of degree zero ($n = 0$) is a function of y/x (or x/y) alone.

The differential equation

(3)
$$P(x, y)\,dx + Q(x, y)\,dy = 0$$

is called *homogeneous* when $P(x, y)$ and $Q(x, y)$ are homogeneous functions of the same degree. If we apply (2) to these functions, (3) becomes

(4)
$$x^n P\left(1, \frac{y}{x}\right) dx + x^n Q\left(1, \frac{y}{x}\right) dy = 0.$$

This suggests introducing the variable $v = y/x$. Then

$$y = vx, \qquad dy = v\,dx + x\,dv,$$

and (4) becomes

(5)
$$x^n [P(1, v) + vQ(1, v)]\,dx + x^{n+1} Q(1, v)\,dv = 0.$$

This equation is separable (§ 7) and obviously admits the multiplier

(6)
$$\mu = \frac{1}{x^{n+1}[P(1, v) + vQ(1, v)]} = \frac{1}{xP(x, y) + yQ(x, y)}$$

which separates the variables of (5) provided $xP + yQ \neq 0$.

If $xP + yQ = 0$, the first term of (5) is zero and (5) becomes

(7)
$$x^{n+1} Q(1, v)\,dv = xQ(x, y)\,dv = 0.$$

The multiplier $\mu = 1/xQ$ converts (7) into the exact equation $dv = 0$; and this has $v = C$, that is, $y = Cx$, for its general solution.

These results are summarized in the following theorem.

Theorem. *The homogeneous equation $P\,dx + Q\,dy = 0$ is changed into*
   (a) *a separable equation by the substitution $y = vx$;*
   (b) *an exact equation by the multiplier*

$$\mu = \frac{1}{xP + yQ} \quad \text{if} \quad xP + yQ \neq 0;$$

$$\mu = 1/xQ \qquad \text{if} \quad xP + yQ = 0$$

and then $y = Cx$ is the general solution.
   Singular solutions, if any, will be included in $1/\mu = 0$.

Example 1. $(x + y) dx + (y - x) dy = 0.$

1° Write the equation

$$y' = \frac{x + y}{x - y} \quad \text{and put} \quad y = vx.$$

Then

$$v + x\frac{dv}{dx} = \frac{1 + v}{1 - v} \quad \text{or} \quad x\frac{dv}{dx} = \frac{1 + v^2}{1 - v}.$$

Separate variables and integrate:

$$\frac{dv}{1 + v^2} - \frac{v\,dv}{1 + v^2} - \frac{dx}{x} = 0.$$

$$\tan^{-1} v - \tfrac{1}{2}\log(1 + v^2) - \log x = C,$$

that is,

(i)
$$\tan^{-1}\frac{y}{x} - \tfrac{1}{2}\log(x^2 + y^2) = C.$$

2° Since $x(x + y) + y(y - x) = x^2 + y^2$, the equation has the multiplier $\mu = 1/(x^2 + y^2)$. The exact equation

$$\frac{x + y}{x^2 + y^2}\,dx + \frac{y - x}{x^2 + y^2}\,dy = 0$$

has the integral (§ 6)

$$\int_0^x \frac{x\,dx}{x^2 + y^2} + y\int_0^x \frac{dx}{x^2 + y^2} + \int \frac{dy}{y} = K,$$

(ii)
$$\tfrac{1}{2}\log(x^2 + y^2) + \tan^{-1}\frac{x}{y} = K,$$

since $\log y$ cancels. The integrals (i) and (ii) are equivalent since $\tan^{-1} x/y = \tfrac{1}{2}\pi - \tan^{-1} y/x$.

Example 2. $(\sqrt{x^2 + y^2} + y)\,dx - x\,dy = 0$ has a multiplier whose reciprocal

$$\mu^{-1} = x(\sqrt{x^2 + y^2} + y) - yx = x\sqrt{x^2 + y^2}.$$

Multiply by μ to get the exact equation

$$\frac{\sqrt{x^2 + y^2} + y}{x\sqrt{x^2 + y^2}}\,dx - \frac{dy}{\sqrt{x^2 + y^2}} = 0.$$

To integrate this we begin with the second term which permits the use of the lower limit $y_0 = 0$. Thus, from (6.7) we have

$$\int \frac{dx}{x} - \int_0^y \frac{dy}{\sqrt{x^2 + y^2}} = \text{const},$$

$$\log x - \log\frac{y + \sqrt{x^2 + y^2}}{x} = \log C, \quad\quad (C > 0),$$

$$\frac{x^2}{y + \sqrt{x^2 + y^2}} = C,$$

$$x^2 - Cy = C\sqrt{x^2 + y^2}.$$

On squaring, this gives $x^4 - 2Cx^2y = C^2x^2$; that is,

(i) $\qquad\qquad\qquad\qquad x^2 - 2Cy = C^2 \quad \text{or} \quad x = 0.$

The solution $x = 0$ is not singular for it is included in the general solution ($C = 0$). Since $1/\mu = 0$ also gives $x = 0$, there is no singular solution.

If $C > 0$, $y = (x^2 - C^2)/2C$ is a solution; for remembering that $\sqrt{\ }$ denotes the *positive* root,

$$\sqrt{x^2 + \frac{(x^2 - C^2)^2}{4C^2}} + \frac{x^2 - C^2}{2C} = \frac{x^2 + C^2}{2C} + \frac{x^2 - C^2}{2C} = \frac{x^2}{C} = xy'.$$

If $C < 0$, the left member equals

$$-\frac{x^2 + C^2}{2C} + \frac{x^2 - C^2}{2C} = -C$$

and (i) is not a solution. Thus (i) is the general solution only when $C \geqq 0$.

PROBLEMS

1. $(x^2 + y^2)\, dx + xy\, dy = 0.$
2. $y^2\, dx + (x^2 - xy)\, dy = 0.$
3. $(x - 2y)\, dx + (2x - y)\, dy = 0.$
4. $x\, dy - y\, dx = \sqrt{x^2 + y^2}\, dx.$
5. $(3x - y)\, dx + (x - 3y)\, dy = 0.$
6. $(x^2 - xy + y^2)\, dx + (x^2 - xy)\, dy = 0.$
7. $(xe^{y/x} + y)\, dx - x\, dy = 0.$
8. $(x + \sqrt{y^2 - xy})\, dy - y\, dx = 0.$
Find two multipliers and solve problems 9 and 10 without integration:
9. $(x^2y - y^3)\, dx + (3x^3 - 5xy^2)\, dy = 0.$
10. $(xy + y^2)\, dx + x^2\, dy = 0.$
11. Solve if $y = 1$ when $x = -1$: $\quad \dfrac{dy}{dx} = \dfrac{x + y}{x}.$
12. Solve if $y = 1$ when $x = 0$: $\quad x^{n-1}y\, dx - (x^n + y^n)\, dy = 0.$

20. ISOBARIC EQUATIONS

The ideas of dimensional analysis are sometimes useful in dealing with differential equations. If we regard the variables x and y as having the dimensions L^1 and L^k relative to some unit L, then $y' = dy/dx$ has the dimensions L^{k-1} and both y/x^k and y'/x^{k-1} are dimensionless (i.e., pure numbers). Since the unit in question is immaterial for our purpose, we say that x and y have the "weights" 1 and k and write

$$\text{wt } x = 1, \qquad \text{wt } y = k, \qquad \text{wt } y' = k - 1, \qquad \text{wt } \frac{y}{x^k} = 0.$$

Since $x^m y^n$ has the dimensions $L^m L^{kn} = L^{m+kn}$, wt $(x^m y^n) = m + kn$. Functions such as e^u, $\sin u$, $\log u$ have zero weight when wt $u = 0$. But if wt $u \neq 0$, these functions can not be regarded as having a definite weight, for their Maclaurin expansions contain terms of different weights.

A differential equation is said to be *isobaric* (Greek *isos* equal, *barus* heavy) if all of its terms have the same weight when the weights of its variables are suitably chosen. In particular, an isobaric equation in which both variables have the same weight (e.g., 1) is *homogeneous* (Greek *homos*, same, *genos* kind).

A simple test will show whether an equation is isobaric or not. To test

$$(y^2 - 3x^2 y)\, dx + x^3\, dy = 0,$$

for example, let wt $x = 1$, wt $y = k$; then its terms have the weights $2k + 1$, $3 + k$, $3 + k$, respectively. Hence the equation will be isobaric when

$$2k + 1 = 3 + k \quad \text{or} \quad k = 2.$$

Thus, when wt $x = 1$, wt $y = 2$, the equation is isobaric, each term having the weight 5.

Consider now the equation

(1) $$P(x, y)\, dx + Q(x, y)\, dy = 0,$$

which is isobaric when wt $x = 1$, wt $y = k$. If we write $y = z^k$, $dy = kz^{k-1}\, dz$, and

$$\text{wt } y = k \cdot \text{wt } z, \qquad \text{wt } z = 1.$$

Hence, when y is replaced by z^k, (1) becomes a homogeneous equation

(2) $$P(x, z^k)\, dx + kz^{k-1} Q(x, z^k)\, dz = 0$$

in x and z; for wt $x = $ wt $z = 1$. From § 19 we now have the following results.

First, the substitution $z = vx$ will change (2) into a separable equation; since $y = z^k$, the substitution

(3) $$y = wx^k \qquad (w = v^k)$$

will change (1) into a separable equation.

Second, since (2) admits the multiplier

$$\mu = \frac{1}{xP(x, z^k) + kz^k Q(x, z^k)},$$

(1) admits the multiplier

(4) $$\mu = \frac{1}{xP(x, y) + kyQ(x, y)}$$

when $xP + kyQ \neq 0$; and, when $xP + kyQ = 0$, (1) has the general solution $w = C$, that is, $y = Cx^k$.

Example 1. If wt $x = 1$, wt $y = k$, the terms of the equation

(i) $(xy^2 - y)\, dx + x\, dy = 0$

have the weights $2 + 2k$, $k + 1$, $k + 1$; hence when $2 + 2k = k + 1$ or $k = -1$, each term of (i) will have the weight 0. The substitution

$$y = \frac{v}{x}, \qquad y' = \frac{xv' - v}{x^2}$$

yields the separable equation

$$\frac{v^2}{x} - \frac{v}{x} + \frac{xv' - v}{x} = 0,$$

$$x\frac{dv}{dx} + v^2 - 2v = 0,$$

$$\frac{dv}{v(v-2)} + \frac{dx}{x} = 0, \qquad \frac{dv}{v-2} - \frac{dv}{v} + 2\frac{dx}{x} = 0.$$

Integrating, we have

$$\log(v - 2) - \log v + 2\log x = \log C,$$

$$\frac{x^2(v - 2)}{v} = C.$$

Putting $v = xy$ gives the general solution

(ii) $\dfrac{x(xy - 2)}{y} = C.$

As an isobaric equation with wt $y = -1$, (i) admits the multiplier

$$\mu = \frac{1}{x(xy^2 - y) - xy} = \frac{1}{xy(xy - 2)}.$$

But (i) is also a Bernoulli equation,

$$xy' - y = -xy^2,$$

and therefore admits the multiplier (17.3) with $P_0 = x$, $P_1 = -1$, $n = 2$:

$$\lambda = \frac{1}{y^2 x}\exp\int\frac{dx}{x} = \frac{1}{y^2}.$$

Hence $\lambda/\mu = C$ is an integral (§ 10), in agreement with (ii).

Of course (i) may be made exact by using λ or μ and integrated by the method of § 6. Thus, with $\lambda = 1/y^2$, we obtain the exact equation

$$\left(x - \frac{1}{y}\right)dx + \frac{x}{y^2}\,dy = 0,$$

whose integral is

$$\int_0^x \left(x - \frac{1}{y} \right) dx = \frac{x^2}{2} - \frac{x}{y} = C.$$

There are no singular solutions, for when $C = 0$ we have $xy = 2$ and $x = 0$, and as $C \to \infty$ we have $y = 0$. These are precisely the results obtained by putting $1/\mu = 0$.

Example 2. If wt $x = 1$, wt $y = k$, the terms of the equation

(i) $2xy \, dx + (2x^2 - 3y) \, dy = 0$

have the weights $2 + k$, $2 + k$, $2k$; hence, when $k = 2$, each term of (i) will have the weight 4. Thus (i) has a multiplier μ whose reciprocal

$$\mu^{-1} = 2x^2 y + 2y(2x^2 - 3y) = 6y(x^2 - y).$$

Dividing (i) by $y(x^2 - y)$ converts it into the exact equation

$$\frac{2x}{x^2 - y} \, dx + \frac{2x^2 - 3y}{y(x^2 - y)} \, dy = 0$$

whose integral is

$$\int_0^x \frac{2x \, dx}{x^2 - y} + 3 \int \frac{dy}{y} = \text{const},$$

$$\log \frac{x^2 - y}{-y} + 3 \log y = \log C,$$

(ii) $(y - x^2)y^2 = C.$

There are no singular solutions.

Equation (i) also admits the multiplier $\lambda = y$. Hence $\lambda/\mu = C$ is an integral, in agreement with (ii).

PROBLEMS

   1. $(x^2 - 2y^3) \, dx + 3xy^2 \, dy = 0.$
   2. $(x - y^2) \, dx + (y^3 - 2xy) \, dy = 0.$
   3. $2xy \, dx + (2x^2 - 3y) \, dy = 0.$
   4. $(x^2 y^2 + y) \, dx + (2x^3 y - x) \, dy = 0.$
   5. $x \, dy + (x^4 y^2 - 3y) \, dx = 0.$
Solve the Riccati equations as isobaric:
   6. $dy/dx = y^2 + 1/4x^2.$
   7. $dy/dx = \frac{1}{2}y^2 + y/x - 1/2x^2.$
Find two multipliers and solve problems 8, 9, and 10 without integration:
   8. $(y^2 - x^2 y) \, dx + x^3 \, dy = 0.$
   9. $2(xy + x^3) \, dx + (x^2 + y) \, dy = 0.$
   10. $(x + 2x^2 y) \, dy + (2y + 3xy^2) \, dx = 0.$
Solve problems 11 and 12 as isobaric and as Bernoulli equations:
   11. $(y^2 - x^2 y) \, dx + x^3 \, dy = 0.$
   12. $2xy \, dx + (2x^2 - 3y) \, dy = 0.$
   13. Prove isobaric, find a multiplier, and solve:

$$yf(xy) \, dx + xg(xy) \, dy = 0.$$

14. Do the same for the equation (due to Euler):

$$y(1 + xy)\, dx + x(1 - xy)\, dy = 0.$$

15. Show that the special Riccati equation (cf. § 18)

$$y' + ay^2 = bx^{-2}$$

is isobaric and find a multiplier μ. Solve it when $a = 2$, $b = 1$, and $x, y > 0$.

21. POINT TRANSFORMATIONS

A differential equation

(1) $$F\left(x, y, \frac{dy}{dx}\right) = 0$$

may often be simplified or reduced to a standard form by introducing new variables u, v by means of the equations

(2) $$u = f(x, y), \qquad v = g(x, y).$$

Geometrically, we regard (2) as a *point transformation*, for it transforms points (x, y) of the xy-plane to points (u, v) of the uv-plane. We shall assume that the Jacobian

(3) $$J = \frac{\partial(u, v)}{\partial(x, y)} = \begin{vmatrix} u_x & u_y \\ v_x & v_y \end{vmatrix} \neq 0$$

over a region R of the xy-plane. There is then no functional relation between u and v; for this would imply $J \equiv 0$.* Moreover, if the point (u_1, v_1) corresponds to (x_1, y_1) we can solve equations (2) uniquely for x, y in the neighborhood of x_1, y_1.† We thus obtain the inverse transformation

(4) $$x = h(u, v), \qquad y = k(u, v).$$

A curve in the xy-plane transforms into a curve in the uv-plane; and at corresponding points their slopes dy/dx and dv/du are related by the equation

(5) $$\frac{dy}{dx} = \frac{y_u\, du + y_v\, dv}{x_u\, du + x_v\, dv} = \frac{y_u + y_v(dv/du)}{x_u + x_v(dv/du)}.$$

By means of (4) and (5) we can now transform the differential equation (1) into another

(6) $$G\left(u, v, \frac{dv}{du}\right) = 0.$$

---

* *Advanced Calculus*, p. 180.
† *Advanced Calculus*, § 85.

If (6) can be integrated to give

(7) $$\varphi(u, v, C) = 0,$$

we obtain a solution of (1) on replacing u and v by their values (2) in terms of x and y.

Thus the Bernoulli equation

$$P_0 \frac{dy}{dx} + P_1 y = R y^n \qquad (n \neq 1)$$

is transformed by

$$u = x, \qquad v = y^{1-n}$$

into the linear equation

$$P_0 \frac{dv}{dx} + (1 - n)P_1 v = (1 - n)R.$$

Again, the homogeneous equation

$$\frac{dy}{dx} + f\left(\frac{y}{x}\right) = 0$$

is transformed by

$$u = x, \qquad v = \frac{y}{x}$$

into the separable equation

$$v + x \frac{dv}{dx} + f(v) = 0.$$

In these cases only one variable is changed. However, a change of both variables is often of service, as in a change from rectangular to polar coordinates:

$$x = r \cos \theta, \qquad y = r \sin \theta.$$

The equation

(8) $$\frac{dy}{dx} = f\left(\frac{ax + by + c}{\alpha x + \beta y + \gamma}\right)$$

may always be integrated by a point transformation. There are two cases to consider

1. $$D = \begin{vmatrix} a & b \\ \alpha & \beta \end{vmatrix} \neq 0.$$

Make the point transformation

(9) $$x = u + h, \qquad y = v + k;$$

then $dy/dx = dv/du$ and

$$\frac{ax + by + c}{\alpha x + \beta y + \gamma} = \frac{au + bv + ah + bk + c}{\alpha u + \beta v + \alpha h + \beta k + \gamma}.$$

Since $D \neq 0$, the linear equations

$$ah + bk + c = 0, \qquad \alpha h + \beta k + \gamma = 0,$$

may be solved uniquely for h, k. With these values (8) becomes

(10) $$\frac{dv}{du} = f\left(\frac{au + bv}{\alpha u + \beta v}\right) = g\left(\frac{v}{u}\right).$$

This equation is homogeneous and may be integrated as in § 19.

Equations (9) may be interpreted as a translation of rectangular axes to the new origin (h, k), the point of intersection of the lines

$$ax + by + c = 0, \qquad \alpha x + \beta y + \gamma = 0.$$

When these lines are parallel, we have the second case:

2. $$D = \begin{vmatrix} a & b \\ \alpha & \beta \end{vmatrix} = 0.$$

We now put

(11) $$u = x, \qquad v = \frac{ax + by}{a} = \frac{\alpha x + \beta y}{\alpha};$$

these fractions are equal since $D = 0$. Now

$$\frac{dv}{dx} = 1 + \frac{b}{a}\frac{dy}{dx}$$

and (8) is reduced to

(12) $$\frac{dv}{dx} = 1 + \frac{b}{a}f\left(\frac{av + c}{\alpha v + \gamma}\right)$$

in which the variables are separable.

Example 1. Solve

(i) $$\frac{dy}{dx} = \frac{3x - y - 5}{-x + 3y + 7}.$$

The lines $3x - y - 5 = 0$, $-x + 3y + 7 = 0$ meet in the point $(1, -2)$. The change of variable

$$x = u + 1, \qquad y = v - 2$$

reduces (i) to the homogeneous equation

$$\frac{dv}{du} = \frac{3u - v}{-u + 3v}$$

or

$$(3u - v)\, du + (u - 3v)\, dv = 0.$$

Since this admits the multiplier μ whose reciprocal

$$\mu^{-1} = u(3u - v) + v(u - 3v) = 3(u^2 - v^2),$$

the equation

$$\frac{3u - v}{u^2 - v^2}\, du + \frac{u - 3v}{u^2 - v^2}\, dv = 0$$

is exact. Its integral is

$$\int_0^u \frac{3u - v}{u^2 - v^2}\, du + 3 \int \frac{dv}{v} = \log C,$$

$$2\int_0^u \frac{du}{u + v} + \int_0^u \frac{du}{u - v} + 3 \log v = \log C,$$

$$(u + v)^2 (v - u) = C.$$

Finally, on putting $u = x - 1$, $v = y + 2$, we have

$$(x + y + 1)^2 (y - x + 3) = C.$$

Example 2. Solve

$$\frac{dy}{dx} = \frac{2xy}{x^2 + y^2 - 1}.$$

From this proportion we deduce

$$\frac{dx + dy}{dx - dy} = \frac{(x + y)^2 - 1}{(x - y)^2 - 1}.$$

This suggests the substitution

$$u = x - y, \qquad v = x + y,$$

which transforms the equation into

$$\frac{dv}{du} = \frac{v^2 - 1}{u^2 - 1}.$$

The integral of this separable equation is

$$\frac{(u + 1)(v - 1)}{(u - 1)(v + 1)} = C \quad \text{or} \quad \frac{uv - 1}{v - u} = \frac{C + 1}{C - 1} = K.$$

Hence, in terms of the original variables,

$$x^2 - y^2 - 1 = 2Ky.$$

(Cf. Ex. 9.3).

PROBLEMS

Find the general solution of the following equations:

1. $y' = \dfrac{x + 2y + 2}{y - 2x + 6}$.

2. $y' = \dfrac{x + y - 1}{2x + 2y - 3}$.

3. $y' = \dfrac{x + 4y - 2}{4x - y + 9}$.

4. $y' = \dfrac{2x - 3y + 5}{1 - y}$.

5. $y' = \left(\dfrac{x - y + 3}{x - y + 1}\right)^2$.

6. Show that the equation $(x + y)\,dx - (x - y)\,dy = 0$ becomes $\dfrac{dr}{d\theta} = r$ in polar coordinates. What are the integral curves?

7. Using polar coordinates, reduce

$$y' = \frac{ax + by}{bx - ay} \quad \text{to} \quad \frac{dr}{d\theta} = \frac{b}{a}\,r$$

and solve.

8. Show that $dy/dx = f(x, y)$ becomes

$$\frac{dr}{d\theta} = r\,\frac{\cos\theta + y' \sin\theta}{y' \cos\theta - \sin\theta}$$

in polar coordinates provided y' is replaced by $f(r \cos\theta, r \sin\theta)$ (cf. § 14).

9. Show that the homogeneous equation $y' = f(y/x)$ becomes separable in polar coordinates.

22. SOLUTIONS IN SERIES

When a differential equation

(1) $$\frac{dy}{dx} = f(x, y)$$

is given, we first test it to see if it falls under any of the special cases we have previously discussed. If it does not (and this is the usual case), we may try to find a multiplier, or failing this, introduce new variables to bring it to a more manageable form. If all efforts fail, the reason may well be that the function defined by the differential equation is none of the elementary functions dealt with in the calculus; for we can hardly expect this very limited class of functions to satisfy a general relation such as (1). We must therefore use a more versatile method of representing functions than mere combinations of the elementary functions—the powers, the exponentials and logarithms, and the circular functions and their inverses.

A method of great versatility is the representation of functions by means of *power series*. Thus, if we seek a solution $y(x)$ of (1) such that $y = b$ when $x = a$, we may express $y(x)$ in a Taylor series about $x = a$:

(2)
$$y(x) = b + \sum_{n=1}^{\infty} \frac{y^{(n)}(a)}{n!} (x - a)^n.$$

Equation (1) gives $y'(a) = f(a, b)$, and by successive differentiation we can find in turn $y''(a)$, $y'''(a)$, etc. It is rarely possible to find a formula for $y^{(n)}(a)$ for all n, so that we really do not obtain an *infinite series* but rather a polynomial approximation for $y(x)$. In practical problems, however, this approximation may be very useful. The following examples illustrate the method.

The power series method also applies to equations of higher order (cf. Prob. 8).

Example 1. The separable equation

(i)
$$\frac{dy}{dx} = y^2 + 1, \qquad y(0) = 0,$$

has the solution $y = \tan x$ under the given condition. Let us attempt to satisfy (1) with the Macluarin series

$$y = \sum_{n=1}^{\infty} \frac{y^n(0)}{n!} x^n.$$

From (i) we have

$$y'' = 2yy', \qquad y''' = 2y'^2 + 2yy'', \qquad y^{iv} = 6y'y'' + 2yy''',$$
$$y^{v} = 6(y'')^2 + 8y'y''' + 2yy^{iv}, \ldots,$$

with increasing complication for higher derivatives. Since $y(0) = 0$, we find in turn

$$y'(0) = 1, \qquad y''(0) = 0, \qquad y'''(0) = 2, \qquad y^{iv}(0) = 0,$$
$$y^{v}(0) = 16, \qquad y^{vi}(0) = 0, \; y^{vii}(0) = 272, \ldots,$$

hence

$$y = x + \tfrac{1}{3}x^3 + \tfrac{2}{15} x^5 + \tfrac{17}{315} x^7 + \cdots,$$

the first four terms in the power series for $\tan x$. The general expression for $y^{(n)}(0)$, however, is not disclosed by this method, and we have no infinite series to test for convergence.

Let us write (i) as

$$\frac{dx}{dy} = \frac{1}{1 + y^2} = \sum_{n=0}^{\infty} (-1)^n y^{2n}, \qquad |y| < 1,$$

where $(1 + y^2)^{-1}$ is expanded into an infinite geometric series of ratio $-y^2$. We can now determine x by integrating this series term by term from $y = 0$ to any y in the interval $-1 < y < 1$:

$$x = \sum_{n=0}^{\infty} (-1)^n \frac{y^{2n+1}}{2n + 1}, \qquad |y| \leq 1.$$

This is indeed the series for $\tan^{-1} y$, valid when $|y| \leq 1$. Thus, even if we were ignorant of the function $\tan^{-1} y$, we would have a usable expression for the solution of (i), provided $|y| \leq 1$.

Example 2. The special Riccati equation (cf. § 18, (9) and (10))

(ii) $$\frac{dy}{dx} = y^2 + x, \qquad y(0) = 1,$$

in spite of its deceptive simplicity, has no solution in terms of the elementary functions, and none of our previous methods can be used to solve it in closed form. This lack of success is due to the fact that *Bessel functions* are needed to solve it.

We again assume a Maclaurin expansion for

$$y(x) = 1 + \sum_{n=0}^{\infty} \frac{y^{(n)}(0)}{n!} x^n$$

and compute successive derivatives as in Example 1:

$$y'' = 2yy' + 1, \qquad y''' = 2y'^2 + 2yy'', \qquad y^{\mathrm{iv}} = 6y'y'' + 2yy''',$$
$$y^{\mathrm{v}} = 6(y'')^2 + 8y'y''' + 2yy^{\mathrm{iv}}, \ldots,$$
$$y'(0) = 1, \qquad y''(0) = 3, \qquad y'''(0) = 8, \qquad y^{\mathrm{iv}}(0) = 34,$$
$$y^{\mathrm{v}}(0) = 186, \qquad y^{\mathrm{vi}}(0) = 1212, \ldots;$$

hence

$$y = 1 + x + \tfrac{3}{2}x^2 + \tfrac{4}{3}x^3 + \tfrac{17}{12}x^4 + \tfrac{31}{20}x^5 + \tfrac{101}{60}x^6 + \cdots.$$

Again, we have no knowledge of the general term and consequently only a polynomial approximation of the solution.

The substitution $y = -z$ reduces (ii) to the form

$$z' + z^2 + x = 0,$$

whose associated linear equation is

$$u'' + xu = 0.$$

Because of its linearity this is much easier to solve in series, as we shall see later on (cf. § 129, Prob. 4).

Example 3. The solution of the linear equation (§16)

(i) $$y' + y = e^{-x}, \qquad y(0) = 1,$$

is $y = (x + 1)e^{-x}$. We may also obtain a series solution, $y = \sum_{0}^{\infty} c_n x^n$, as follows. Replacing y, y' and e^{-x} by their series, we have

$$\sum_{n=0}^{\infty} n c_n x^{n-1} + \sum_{n=0}^{\infty} c_n x^n = \sum_{n=0}^{\infty} \frac{(-1)^n}{n!} x^n.$$

Equating the coefficients of x^n on both sides gives the difference equation

(ii) $$(n + 1)c_{n+1} + c_n = \frac{(-1)^n}{n!}.$$

Since $y(0) = c_0 = 1$, (ii) gives the values of $c_1, c_2, c_3, \ldots$, in turn by putting $n = 0, 1, 2, \ldots$; thus we find

$$c_1 = 0, \qquad c_2 = -\tfrac{1}{2}, \qquad c_3 = \tfrac{1}{3}, \qquad c_4 = -\tfrac{1}{8}, \qquad c_5 = \tfrac{1}{30}, \ldots.$$

Later we shall consider methods for solving difference equations. For this example, however, the solution is easily found, for on multiplying (ii) by $n!$ and writing $a_n = (-1)^n n! c_n$, we have

$$a_{n+1} - a_n = -1, \qquad a_0 = 1.$$

Now $a_1 = 0$, $a_2 = -1$, $a_3 = -2, \ldots$, and in general $a_n = 1 - n$; hence $c_n = (-1)^n (1 - n)/n!$ and

$$y = 1 + \sum_{n=1}^{\infty} (-1)^n \frac{1 - n}{n!} x^n.$$

The ratio test shows that this series converges for all x.

PROBLEMS

1. Find seven terms of the series solution of
$$y' = x^2 - y^2, \qquad y(0) = 1.$$

2. Show that the equation
$$y' = x^2 + y^2, \qquad y(0) = 0$$
may be satisfied by a series of the form
$$y = c_1 x^3 + c_2 x^7 + c_3 x^{11} + \cdots = \sum_{n=1}^{\infty} c_n x^{4n-1}.$$
Find the first three terms of the series.

3. Find a series solution for
$$y' - y = e^x + 1, \qquad y(0) = 1,$$
and show that $c_n = (n + 2)/n!$ when $n > 0$.

4. Find a series solution for
$$(x^2 - x)y' + (1 - 2x)y + x^2 = 0, \qquad y(2) = 0,$$
by computing $y'(2), y''(2), \ldots$.

5. Show that the equation
$$y' + 3x^2 y = 1, \qquad y(0) = 0,$$
may be satisfied by a series of the form
$$y = \sum_{n=0}^{\infty} c_n x^{3n+1}.$$

Obtain a recurrence relation connecting c_n and c_{n-1} and find five terms of the series.

6. Find a series solution, valid when $|x| < 1$, for

$$(1 + x)y' - 1 = 0, \qquad y(0) = 0.$$

7. In the linear equation

$$y' = P_1 y + Q_1$$

P_1 and Q_1 are functions of x. Prove that the higher derivatives have the form

$$y^{(n)} = P_n y + Q_n,$$

where P_n and Q_n satisfy the recurrence relations

$$P_{n+1} = P_n' + P_1 P_n, \qquad Q_{n+1} = Q_n' + Q_1 P_n.$$

8. For the problem

$$y'' - xy = 0, \qquad y(0) = 1, \qquad y'(0) = 0,$$

show that when $n \geq 2$

$$y^{(n)} = xy^{(n-2)} + (n - 2)y^{(n-3)}$$

and obtain the series solution.

9. Find the series solution of the problem

$$(1 - x^2)y' - xy = 1, \qquad y(0) = 0,$$

that is, find the general term of the series.

Assume that $y = \sum_{n=0}^{\infty} c_n x^{2n+1}$; the *reason* for this assumption is explained in chapter 10 (cf. Prob. 109.13).

10. With the same assumption as in Problem 9, find the series solution of

$$y' - xy = 1, \qquad y(0) = 0.$$

23. EQUATIONS OF HIGHER DEGREE IN y'

Write $dy/dx = p$ and let

(1) $$F(x, y, p) = 0$$

be an equation of the second degree in p.

Method 1. If (1) is solved for p, we obtain two equations of the first degree in x and y. Their general solutions constitute the general solution of (1).

Method 2. If (1) is solved for y, say

$$y = \varphi(x, p),$$

we have

$$p = \varphi_x + \varphi_p \frac{dp}{dx}$$

on differentiation with respect to x. If this first-order equation in x and p has the solution $x = f(p, C)$,

$$x = f(p, C), \qquad y = \varphi[f(p, C), p] = g(p, C)$$

are the parametric equations of the integral curves. The elimination of p between them yields their Cartesian equation.

Method 3. If (1) is solved for x, say

$$x = \varphi(y, p),$$

we have

$$\frac{1}{p} = \varphi_y + \varphi_p \frac{dp}{dy}$$

on differentiation with respect to y. If this first-order equation in y and p has the solution $y = f(p, C)$, then

$$y = f(p, C), \qquad x = \varphi[f(p, C), p] = g(p, C)$$

are the parametric equations of the integral curves. The elimination of p between them yields their Cartesian equation.

These methods obviously apply when the degree of (1) in p is greater than two. Thus if (1) is of the third degree in p, method 1 requires the solution of a cubic equation; then method 2 or 3 is usually preferable, especially when $F(x, y, p)$ is linear in x or y.

We illustrate these methods by solving

(2) $$xp^2 - 2yp - x = 0$$

in three ways.

Method 1. Solving (2) for p yields two homogeneous equations:

$$p = \frac{dy}{dx} = \frac{y \pm \sqrt{y^2 + x^2}}{x}.$$

Putting $y = vx$ (§ 19), we find

$$v + x \frac{dv}{dx} = v \pm \sqrt{v^2 + 1},$$

whence

$$\frac{dv}{\sqrt{v^2 + 1}} = \pm \frac{dx}{x},$$

$$\log (v + \sqrt{v^2 + 1}) = \log C \pm \log x.$$

With the *plus* sign,

$$v + \sqrt{v^2 + 1} = Cx, \qquad v^2 + 1 = (Cx - v)^2,$$

(3) $$C^2x^2 - 2Cy - 1 = 0.$$

With the *minus* sign,

$$v - \sqrt{v^2 + 1} = \frac{C}{x}, \qquad v^2 + 1 = \left(\frac{C}{x} + v\right)^2,$$

$$\frac{C^2}{x^2} + 2C\,\frac{y}{x^2} - 1 = 0,$$

(4) $$C^2 + 2Cy - x^2 = 0.$$

If we put $C = 1/K$ and multiply by $-K^2$, we again obtain (3).

Method 2. Solving (2) for y gives

$$2y = x\left(p - \frac{1}{p}\right).$$

We now *differentiate* this equation with respect to x; then

$$2p = p - \frac{1}{p} + x\left(1 + \frac{1}{p^2}\right)\frac{dp}{dx},$$

$$p + \frac{1}{p} = x\left(1 + \frac{1}{p^2}\right)\frac{dp}{dx},$$

$$\left(1 + \frac{1}{p^2}\right)\left(x\frac{dp}{dx} - p\right) = 0.$$

Since the first factor cannot vanish if p is real, we must have

$$\frac{dp}{p} - \frac{dx}{x} = 0, \qquad \log\frac{p}{x} = \log C$$

or $p = Cx$. If we substitute this value in (2) and divide out x, we again obtain (3).

Method 3. Solving (2) for x gives

$$x = \frac{2py}{p^2 - 1}.$$

We now differentiate with respect to y; then

$$\frac{1}{p} = \frac{2p}{p^2 - 1} - 2\frac{1 + p^2}{(p^2 - 1)^2}y\frac{dp}{dy},$$

$$\frac{1 + p^2}{p(p^2 - 1)} = 2\frac{1 + p^2}{(p^2 - 1)^2}y\frac{dp}{dy},$$

$$\frac{p^2 - 1}{p} = 2y\frac{dp}{dy}.$$

$$\frac{dy}{y} = \frac{2p\,dp}{p^2 - 1},$$

$$p^2 - 1 = Cy.$$

Using this to eliminate p from (2), we have

$$C^2x^2 = 4Cy + 4,$$

which again reduces to (3) when we put $C = 2K$. In this solution we have tacitly assumed that $p^2 \neq 1$. This is justified since (2) gives $y = 0$ when $p = \pm 1$, an impossibility since $y = 0$ implies $p = 0$.

Example 1. Consider the equation of the first degree in x and y:

(i) $\qquad\qquad y = xg(p) + f(p) \quad \text{where} \quad g(p) \neq p.$

Differentiate (1) with respect to x; then

(ii) $\qquad\qquad p = g(p) + [xg'(p) + f'(p)]\dfrac{dp}{dx}.$

1°. If the equation $p - g(p) = 0$ has the roots $p_1, p_2, \ldots$, then the lines

$$y = xg(p_i) + f(p_i), \quad i = 1, 2, \ldots,$$

are singular solutions of (i). For when $p = p_i$, then $dp/dx = 0$ and (ii) is satisfied.

2°. When $p - g(p) \neq 0$, equation (ii) is linear in x:

(iii) $\qquad\qquad \dfrac{dx}{dp} - \dfrac{g'(p)}{p - g(p)} x = \dfrac{f'(p)}{p - g(p)}.$

If we solve (iii) for $x = \varphi(p, C)$, the equations

$$x = \varphi(p, C), \qquad y = g(p)\varphi(p, C) + f(p)$$

represent the general solution in terms of the parameter p.

The case when $g(p) = p$ is treated in the next article.

Let us apply this method to the equation

$$y = x(1 + p) + p^2.$$

Differentiation with respect to x gives

$$p = 1 + p + (x + 2p)\dfrac{dp}{dx},$$

$$\dfrac{dx}{dp} + x = -2p.$$

With the multiplier $\mu = e^p$, we obtain

$$\dfrac{d}{dp}(e^p x) = -2pe^p,$$

$$e^p x = C - 2(p - 1)e^p,$$

and hence

$$x = Ce^{-p} - 2(p - 1), \qquad y = C(1 + p)e^{-p} + 2 - p^2.$$

There are no singular solutions.

Example 2. If equations of the type

$$F(x, p) = 0 \quad \text{or} \quad F(y, p) = 0$$

are not readily solved for either variable, we may sometimes find a parametric solution. Thus, if $x = f(t)$, $p = g(t)$ satisfy $F(x, p) = 0$, we have

$$dy = p \, dx = g(t)f'(t) \, dt$$

and integration gives y as a function of t.

Consider, for example, the equation

(i) $$x^3 + p^3 - 3xp = 0,$$

which is cubic in both x and p. If we put $p = tx$, we have

$$x^3 + t^3x^3 - 3tx^2 = 0,$$

whence we obtain the parametric solution

$$x = \frac{3t}{1 + t^3}, \qquad p = \frac{3t^2}{1 + t^3}.$$

Now

$$dy = p \, dx = \frac{3t^2}{1 + t^3} \cdot \frac{3(1 - 2t^3)}{(1 + t^2)^2} \, dt,$$

$$y = 3 \int \frac{1 - 2t^3}{(1 + t^3)^3} \, 3t^2 \, dt = \frac{3(1 + 4t^3)}{2(1 + t^3)^2} + C,$$

where the integral is evaluated by the substitution $u = 1 + t^3$. Thus

$$x = \frac{3t}{1 + t^3}, \qquad y = \frac{3(1 + 4t^3)}{2(1 + t^3)^2} + C$$

is a parametric solution of (i).

PROBLEMS

Find all solutions of the following equations.
1. $xyp^2 + (x + y)p + 1 = 0$.
2. $y + px = 3x^4p^2$.
3. $p^2 + xy^2p + y^3 = 0$.
4. $4xp^2 + 4yp - y^4 = 0$.
5. $y = 2px - p^2$.
6. $(1 + p^2)y = 2px$.
7. $ap = x\sqrt{1 + p^2}$.
8. $y\sqrt{1 + p^2} = a(x + py)$.
9. $y^2(p^2 - 1) = 1$.
10. $x = p^3 + 3p + 1$.
11. $p^3 - y^2(a - p) = 0$.
12. $xp^2 - 2yp + 4x = 0$.

24. CLAIRAUT'S EQUATION

The equation

(1) $$y = px + f(p)$$

is known as Clairaut's equation after the French mathematician Alexis Claude Clairaut (1713–1765). Since (1) is solved for y, we apply method 2 of the previous article. Thus differentiation with respect to x gives

$$p = p + [x + f'(p)]\frac{dp}{dx},$$

so that (1) is equivalent to two equations:

(2) $$\frac{dp}{dx} = 0,$$

(3) $$x + f'(p) = 0.$$

Equation (2) gives $p = c$; and on replacing p in (1) by c, we obtain the general solution

(4) $$y = cx + f(c).$$

Equations (1) and (3) give a solution of (1) in parametric form

(5) $$x = -f'(p), \qquad y = f(p) - pf'(p),$$

which is free from arbitrary constants. This is the singular solution if $f''(p) \neq 0.$* If p is eliminated between equations (4) we obtain its Cartesian equation.

The general solution (4) is a 1-parameter family of straight lines. We shall now show that

The lines forming the general solution of Clairaut's equation are the tangents to the curve which represents its singular solution provided $f''(p) \neq 0$.

PROOF. The slope of the curve (5) is

$$\frac{dy}{dx} = \frac{dy/dp}{dx/dp} = \frac{f'(p) - f'(p) - pf''(p)}{-f''(p)} = p,$$

at the point corresponding to a given parameter value p. Hence at the point of the curve where $p = c$, namely

(6) $$x = -f'(c), \qquad y = f(c) - cf'(c),$$

---

* If $f''(p) = 0$, $f'(p) = a$, $f(p) = ap + b$ and equations (5) represent a point $x = -a$, $y = b$. All linear elements through $(-a, b)$ satisfy the equation $y = px + ap + b$.

the equation of the tangent line is

$$Y - y = c(X - x),$$

where X, Y are the coordinates of any point on the tangent. On substituting the values of x and y, we reduce this to

$$Y = cX + f(c),$$

the same equation as (4). This line through the point (6) of the curve (5) is tangent to the curve at that point.

Example 1. The equation

(i) $$xp^3 - yp^2 + 1 = 0 \quad \text{or} \quad y = px + \frac{1}{p^2}$$

is Clairaut's equation. Differentiating with respect to x gives

$$\left(x - \frac{2}{p^3}\right)\frac{dp}{dx} = 0.$$

From $dp/dx = 0$ we get $p = c$ and the general solution

$$y = cx + \frac{1}{c^2}.$$

From $x - 2/p^3 = 0$ we get the singular solution

$$x = \frac{2}{p^3}, \qquad y = \frac{2}{p^2} + \frac{1}{p^2} = \frac{3}{p^2}.$$

Its Cartesian equation is found by eliminating p from these equations:

$$4y^3 = 27x^2.$$

Equation (i) may be solved equally well by solving it for x and differentiating with respect to y.

Example 2. The Clairaut equation

$$y = px + b - ap$$

has the general solution

$$y - b = C(x - a).$$

These lines "envelop" the point (a, b) which is indeed given by (5):

$$x = a, \qquad y = b, \qquad p \text{ arbitrary.}$$

The singular solution is now a *point union* of lineal elements (§ 4) instead of the usual curve union. In the theory of differential equations developed by the Norwegian mathematician Sophus Lie, both types of unions are regarded as legitimate solutions.

PROBLEMS

Find the general and singular solutions in problems 1 to 4.

1. $y = px + \sqrt{p^2 - 1}$.

2. $y = px + a\sqrt{p^2 + 1}$.

3. $y = px + ap/\sqrt{1 + p^2}$.

4. $py - p^2x = 1$.

5. Find the curve whose tangents are at a constant distance a from the origin.

6. The segment of each tangent to a curve included between the rectangular axes has a constant length a. Find the curve.

7. A tangent to a curve in the first quadrant forms a triangle with the rectangular axes which always has the same area k^2. What is the curve?

8. $p^2(x^2 - p) - 2pxy + y^2 = 0$.

9. Find the general solution of $F(y - px, p) = 0$. (Differentiate the equation with respect to x.)

10. Show that a Clairaut equation in y is also a Clairaut equation in x.

11. Show that the substitution $x^2 = u$ reduces

$$y = \tfrac{1}{2}px + f\left(\frac{p}{x}\right)$$

to a Clairaut equation. Find its general solution. Solve Problem 23.12 in this way.

12. Show that the substitution $y^2 = v$ reduces

$$ayp^2 + (2x - b)p - y = 0$$

to a Clairaut equation. Find its general solution.

13. Show that $y = yp^2 + 2px$ has no singular solution. (Let $y^2 = v$.)

25. SUMMARY

The equation

$$(1) \qquad\qquad P(x, y)\, dx + Q(x, y)\, dy = 0$$

is exact when and only when $P_y = Q_x$; then either

$$(2) \qquad\qquad \int_a^x P(x, y)\, dx + \int Q(a, y)\, dy = C$$

or

$$(3) \qquad\qquad \int_b^y Q(x, y)\, dy + \int P(x, b)\, dx = C$$

gives the general solution. The lower limits a, b may be chosen at pleasure as long as the integral remains proper.

If $P_y \neq Q_x$, equation (1) admits an infinity of multipliers μ which make it exact, and all satisfy $(\mu P)_y = (\mu Q)_x$ or

$$Q \frac{\partial \mu}{\partial x} - P \frac{\partial \mu}{\partial y} = (P_y - Q_x)\mu.$$

Important special cases of (1) together with their multipliers μ are given in the following list. Substitutions are also given which reduce the equation to a simpler form.

Type	Equation	Multiplier
(4) Separable	$P(x)Q_1(y)\,dx + P_1(x)Q(y)\,dy = 0$	$\dfrac{1}{P_1(x)\,Q_1(y)}$
(5) Isobaric	$P(x, y)\,dx + Q(x, y)\,dy = 0$	$\dfrac{1}{xP + kyQ}$

When wt $x = 1$, wt $y = k$, terms have the same weight.

When $k = 1$, equation is homogeneous.

(6) Linear in y	$P_0(x)y' + P_1(x)y = R(x)$	$\dfrac{1}{P_0} \exp \displaystyle\int \frac{P_1}{P_0}\,dx$
(7) Bernoulli in y	$P_0(x)y' + P_1(x)y = R(x)y^n$	$\dfrac{1}{y^n P_0} \exp(1 - n) \displaystyle\int \frac{P_1}{P_0}\,dx$

$v = y^{1-n} \ (n \neq 1) \longrightarrow$ linear equation in v.

(8) Riccati $y' + P(x)y^2 + Q(x)y + R(x) = 0$

If y_1 is a particular solution,

$y = y_1 + v \longrightarrow$ Bernoulli equation in v.

$y = y_1 + \dfrac{1}{w} \longrightarrow$ Linear equation in w.

In brief: If a first-order equation is exact, integrate it; if not exact, try to find a multiplier. If none can be found, attempt a series solution or use approximate numerical methods (chapter 14).

If λ and μ are independent multipliers of (1), its general solution is $\lambda/\mu = C$. When $\lambda = x^m y^n$ is a multiplier of (1) independent of μ, $\mu = Cx^m y^n$ is the general solution.

To solve $F(x, y, p) = 0$,   of degree 2 in p:

Method 1. Solve for p and integrate each equation.

Method 2. Solve for $y = \varphi(x, p)$, differentiate with respect to x, and solve the equation in x, p. Parametric solution

$$x = f(p, C), \qquad y = \varphi(f, p) = g(p, C).$$

Method 3. Solve for $x = \psi(y, p)$, differentiate with respect to y, and solve equation in y, p. Parametric solution:

$$y = f(p, C), \qquad x = \psi(f, p) = g(p, C).$$

Clairaut's form: $\qquad\qquad y = px + f(p).$

Use method 2:

$$[x + f'(p)]\frac{dp}{dx} = 0.$$

(i) $y = Cx + f(C)$; general solution.

(ii) $x = -f'(p)$, $y = f(p) - pf'(p)$; parametric singular solution. The lines (i) are tangent to the curve (ii).

PROBLEMS

1. If the equation

$$\frac{dy}{dx} + f(x, y) = 0$$

admits a multiplier of the form

(i) $\mu = \mu(x)$ $\qquad\qquad f(x, y) = y\varphi(x) + \psi(x)$.
$\qquad\qquad\qquad\qquad\qquad\qquad$ Linear in y

(ii) $\mu = \mu(y)$ $\qquad\qquad f(x, y) = \varphi(x)/\psi(y)$.
$\qquad\qquad\qquad\qquad\qquad\qquad$ Separable equation

(iii) $\mu = x^m y^n$ $\qquad\qquad f(x, y) = \dfrac{m}{n+1}\dfrac{y}{x} + \varphi(x)y^{-n}$.
$\qquad\qquad\qquad\qquad\qquad\qquad$ Bernoulli in y

(iv) $\mu = X(x)Y(y)$ $\qquad f(x, y) = \dfrac{1}{\psi(y)}\left[\varphi_1(x)\displaystyle\int \psi(y)\, dy + \varphi_2(x)\right].$

[Proof of (iii). Multiply by $x^m y^n$ and apply exactness test:

$$mx^{m-1}y^n = x^m(ny^{n-1}f + y^n f_y), \qquad f_y + \frac{n}{y}f = \frac{m}{x}.$$

This equation is linear in f with y variable and x a constant parameter. Its multiplier is y^n; hence

$$y^n f = \frac{m}{x}\int y^n\, dy + \varphi(x) = \frac{m}{n+1}\frac{y^{n+1}}{x} + \varphi(x)$$

$$f(x, y) = \frac{m}{n+1}\frac{y}{x} + y^{-n}\varphi(x),$$

where $\varphi(x)$ is an arbitrary function of x.]

2. In Problem 8(a), § 9, show that $\mu = x^m y^n$ where

$$m + 1 = \frac{C(pB + qA)}{AD - BC}, \qquad n + 1 = \frac{B(pD + qC)}{AD - BC}.$$

CHAPTER 3

Linear Equations
of the Second Order

26. EXISTENCE THEOREM

In § 16 we obtained an explicit solution of the linear equation of the first order

$$P_0(x)y' + P_1(x)y = R(x)$$

by means of quadratures. Such an explicit solution is not possible for the general linear equation of the second order

(1) $$P_0(x)y'' + P_1(x)y' + P_2(x)y = R(x).$$

The functions $P_1(x)$ and $R(x)$ are defined over some interval $a \leq x \leq b$; and if $P_0(x) \neq 0$ over this interval, we may divide the equation by P_0 and reduce it to the form in which the leading coefficient is 1. When equation (1) is put in this form we may state

Theorem 1 (Existence and Uniqueness). *Let the functions $P(x)$, $Q(x)$, $R(x)$ in the linear equation*

(2) $$y'' + P(x)y' + Q(x)y = R(x)$$

be continuous in the interval $a < x < b$ containing the point x_0 in its interior. Then for each pair of real numbers y_0, y_0' there is one and only one solution $y(x)$ of (2) over $a < x < b$ such that

(3) $$y(x_0) = y_0, \qquad y'(x_0) = y_0'.$$

We defer the proof of this basic theorem (cf. § 159). For the present we assume its truth and examine its consequences. Note that when $y(x)$ is a *solution* of equation (2) in $a < x < b$, $y'(x)$ and $y''(x)$ must exist in this interval and hence $y(x)$ and $y'(x)$ are continuous there.* The equation itself then shows that y'' is also continuous.

---

* *Advanced Calculus*, p. 101.

A function which has a continuous derivative of order n (and therefore continuous derivatives of all lesser orders) is said to belong to class $\mathscr{C}^n$. A continuous function belongs to class $\mathscr{C}$. Classes $\mathscr{C}^1$ and $\mathscr{C}^2$ are usually written $\mathscr{C}'$ and $\mathscr{C}''$.

We shall call equation (2) *complete*, the associated equation with $R = 0$ *reduced*. In the left member of both equations we have the differential operator L defined by

(4)
$$L[y] \equiv y'' + Py' + Qy.$$

L is a *linear operator;* that is,

$$L[cu] = cL[u], \qquad L[u + v] = L[u] + L[v].$$

From these defining equations we have also

(5)
$$L[c_1u + c_2v] = c_1L[u] + c_2L[v].$$

We now have

Theorem 2. *If $u(x)$ and $v(x)$ are solutions of the reduced equation*

(6)
$$L[y] \equiv y'' + Py' + Qy = 0,$$

then

(7)
$$y(x) = c_1u(x) + c_2v(x)$$

with arbitrary constants c_1, c_2, is also a solution.

PROOF. If $L[u] = 0$ and $L[v] = 0$, (5) shows that

$$L[c_1u + c_2v] = 0.$$

When $v = ku$, the solution (7) reduces to $y = (c_1 + kc_2)u = Cu$, which has but one essential constant; but when v is not a multiple of u, we shall see in § 28 that *all* solutions of (6) are included in (7). Then (7) is the *general solution* of (6).

We can always bring equation (6) to the form

(8)
$$z'' + Sz = 0$$

by the change of dependent variable $y = wz$:

$$
\begin{array}{c|l}
Q & y = wz, \\
P & y' = w'z + wz', \\
1 & y'' = w''z + 2w'z' + wz''.
\end{array}
$$

By multiplying these equations by the quantity shown on the left and then adding them we find that

(9)
$$wz'' + (2w' + Pw)z' + (w'' + Pw' + Qw)z = 0.$$

If we choose w so that

$$2w' + Pw = 0, \qquad w = \exp\left(-\tfrac{1}{2}\int P\,dx\right),$$

the term in z' vanishes; and, because

$$w' = -\tfrac{1}{2}Pw, \qquad w'' = (-\tfrac{1}{2}P' + \tfrac{1}{4}P^2)w,$$

$$w'' + Pw' + Qw = (-\tfrac{1}{2}P' + \tfrac{1}{4}P^2 - \tfrac{1}{2}P^2 + Q)w,$$

we have the following

Theorem 3. *The change of variable*

$$y = z \exp\left(-\tfrac{1}{2}\int P\,dx\right)$$

transforms

$$y'' + Py' + Qy = 0 \quad into \quad z'' + (Q - \tfrac{1}{2}P' - \tfrac{1}{4}P^2)z = 0.$$

Example. Theorem 1 guarantees the existence and unicity of two solutions $u(x)$, $v(x)$ of the equation $y'' + y = 0$ which satisfy the conditions

$$u(0) = 1, \quad u'(0) = 0; \qquad v(0) = 0, \quad v'(0) = 1.$$

Since $P(x) = 0$ and $Q(x) = 1$ are continuous for all real x, the same is true for $u(x)$ and $v(x)$; moreover these functions are of class $\mathscr{C}''$ for all real x. What are these functions?

27. LINEAR DEPENDENCE

The n functions $f_1(x), f_2(x), \ldots, f_n(x)$ are said to be linearly dependent in an interval $I(a \leqq x \leqq b)$ if there are n constants $c_1, c_2, \ldots, c_n$, not all zero, such that

(1) $$c_1 f_1(x) + \cdots + c_n f_n(x) \equiv 0 \qquad in\ I.$$

If the functions $f_i(x)$ have derivatives of order $n - 1$ in I, we may differentiate (1) $n - 1$ times to obtain the equations

$$c_1 f_1'(x) + \cdots + c_n f_n'(x) \equiv 0,$$

(2) $$\cdots\cdots\cdots\cdots\cdots\cdots\cdots\cdots\cdots\cdots$$

$$c_1 f_1^{(n-1)}(x) + \cdots + c_n f_n^{(n-1)}(x) \equiv 0.$$

We may regard the system (1)–(2) as a set of n linear homogeneous equations in the unknowns $c_1, c_2, \ldots, c_n$ having the determinant

$$W(f_1, f_2, \ldots, f_n) = \begin{vmatrix} f_1 & f_2 & \cdots & f_n \\ f_1' & f_2' & \cdots & f_n' \\ \cdots & \cdots & \cdots & \cdots \\ f_1^{(n-1)} & f_2^{(n-1)} & \cdots & f_n^{(n-1)} \end{vmatrix}.$$

Now if the functions $f_i(x)$ are linearly dependent, the system (1)–(2) admits a solution $c_1, c_2, \ldots, c_n$ which does *not* consist of a set of zeros. But this can only be the case when $W(x) \equiv 0$.

The determinant (3) is called the Wronskian* of the n functions $f_1, f_2, \ldots, f_n$ which we assume to be differentiable $n - 1$ times. We may now state the important

Theorem 1. *A necessary condition that a set of functions be linearly dependent in an interval I is that their Wronskian vanish identically in I.*

Functions that are not linearly dependent are called *linearly independent*. The theorem therefore has the immediate

Corollary. *A sufficient condition that a set of functions be linearly independent in I is that their Wronskian does not vanish identically in I.*†

$W \equiv 0$ is *not* a *sufficient* condition for linear dependence. For example, let $f_1 = x^3, f_2 = |x|^3$ over the interval $-1 \leq x \leq 1$; then $W \equiv 0$ over the entire interval (proof?); but if

$$c_1 x^3 + c_2 |x|^3 \equiv 0 \qquad \text{over } I,$$

we have $c_1 + c_2 = 0$ when $x = 1$, $-c_1 + c_2 = 0$ when $x = -1$; hence $c_1 = c_2 = 0$.

This example also shows that $W \not\equiv 0$ is *not necessary* for linear independence. In brief,

$$\text{linear dependence implies} \quad W \equiv 0,$$
$$W \not\equiv 0 \quad \text{implies linear independence,}$$

but neither implication can be reversed.

For *two* functions, however, it is easy to prove the more complete

Theorem 2. *If the differentiable functions $f(x)$ and $g(x)$ are linearly dependent in an interval I, $W(f, g) \equiv 0$ over I.*

Conversely, if $W(f, g) \equiv 0$ over I and one function is never zero in I, then $f(x)$ and $g(x)$ are linearly dependent in I.

PROOF. The first part is included in Theorem 1, but an independent proof is simple. Let $c_1 f + c_2 g \equiv 0$ and $c_2 \neq 0$ in I; then if $k = -c_1/c_2$,

$$g(x) = kf(x) \quad \text{and} \quad W(f, g) = \begin{vmatrix} f & kf \\ f' & kf' \end{vmatrix} = 0.$$

---

* After the Polish mathematician H. Wronski (1778–1853).

† The logical principle involved: if $\mathscr{C}$ is a necessary condition for a property $\mathscr{P}$, then not-$\mathscr{C}$ is a sufficient condition for not-$\mathscr{P}$.

Conversely, let $W(f, g) \equiv 0$ and $f(x) \neq 0$ in I; then

$$\frac{W(f, g)}{f^2} = \frac{fg' - gf'}{f^2} = \left(\frac{g}{f}\right)' = 0 \quad \text{and} \quad \frac{g}{f} = c.$$

Thus $cf - 1 \cdot g \equiv 0$ in I and the functions are linearly dependent.

Example 1. The functions $1, x, x^2, \ldots, x^n$ are linearly independent in any interval I; for the polynomial $c_0 + c_1 x + \cdots + c_n x^n$ has at most n zeros in I and can not be identically zero unless all constants $c_i = 0$.

Example 2. A simple determinant reduction shows that the functions

$$u = e^{ax} \cos bx, \qquad v = e^{ax} \sin bx$$

or

$$v = e^{ax} \cosh bx, \qquad v = e^{ax} \sinh bx$$

have the Wronskian $W(u, v) = be^{2ax}$. Therefore both sets are linearly independent if $b \neq 0$.

PROBLEMS

Compute W for the following functions:
1. e^x, xe^x.
2. $e^x, x^2 e^x$.
3. $x^2, x, 1$.
4. $x, x + 1, x + 2$.
5. e^{ax}, e^{bx}, e^{cx} (a, b, c different).
6. $1, x, e^x, xe^x$.
7. $a_i x^2 + b_i x + c_i$ ($i = 1, 2, 3$).

Prove that $W = 2\Delta$ where $\Delta = \begin{vmatrix} a_1 & a_2 & a_3 \\ b_1 & b_2 & b_3 \\ c_1 & c_2 & c_3 \end{vmatrix}$.

8. $a_i u + b_i v + c_i w$ ($i = 1, 2, 3$).
Prove that $W = W(u, v, w)\Delta$ (see Prob. 7).
9. If λ is a differentiable function of x, prove that
(a) $W(u, v + w) = W(u, v) + W(u, w)$;
(b) $W(\lambda u, \lambda v) = \lambda^2 W(u, v)$;
(c) $W(u, \lambda u) = \lambda' u^2$.
10. If n functions are linearly independent in an interval I, prove that the functions of any subset are linearly independent in I.

28. THE REDUCED EQUATION

Let $u(x)$ and $v(x)$ be solutions of the reduced equation

(1) $$y'' + Py' + Qy = 0$$

on an interval $a \leqq x \leqq b$ in which $P(x)$ and $Q(x)$ are continuous; then

$$u'' + Pu' + Qu = 0,$$
$$v'' + Pv' + Qv = 0.$$

Multiply these equations by $-v$ and u, respectively, and add them; then

(2) $$(uv'' - vu'') + P(uv' - vu') = 0.$$

The Wronskian of u and v is

$$W = uv' - vu' \quad \text{and} \quad \frac{dW}{dx} = uv'' - vu'';$$

hence from (2)

(3) $$\frac{dW}{dx} + PW = 0.$$

This linear equation in W admits the multiplier

(4) $$\mu = \exp \int P \, dx. \qquad (16.2)$$

and on multiplying equation (3) by μ it becomes

$$\frac{d}{dx}(\mu W) = 0.$$

On integrating we get $\mu W = C$, or

(5) $$W = C \exp \left(-\int P \, dx \right),$$

an equation known as *Abel's identity.** If we take the integral in (5) between the limits x_0 and x we have $W(x_0) = c \exp(0) = C$. Writing W_0 for $W(x_0)$, Abel's identity now becomes

(6) $$W = W_0 \exp \left(-\int_{x_0}^{x} P(t) \, dt \right).$$

If $W_0 = 0$, $W(u, v) \equiv 0$; and if $W_0 \neq 0$, $W(u, v) \neq 0$. We may now prove

Theorem 1. *The Wronskian of two solutions of the reduced equation is either identically zero or never zero, according as the solutions are linearly dependent or independent.*

PROOF. We know that $W(u, v) = 0$ is a necessary condition for the linear dependence of u and v; we now show that it is also sufficient. If $u = 0$ throughout $[a, b]$, u and v are linearly dependent. If $u(x) \neq 0$ at some point, there is a subinterval I containing this point in which $u(x) \neq 0$.†

---

* Published in 1827 by the Norwegian mathematician Niels H. Abel (1802–1829).
† *Advanced Calculus*, Theorem 45.2.

Then u and v are linearly dependent in I (Theorem 27.2), say $c_1u + c_2v = 0$. Then $c_1u + c_2v$ is a solution of the reduced equation which, with its derivative $c_1u' + c_2v'$, vanishes in I. The existence theorem now affirms that the only solution with this property is identically zero throughout $[a, b]$. Thus u and v are linearly dependent in this interval.

Contrast this theorem with Theorem 2 of the preceding article. When the functions are solutions of equation (1), the mere vanishing of their Wronskian at any point is *necessary and sufficient* for their linear dependence; and for independent solutions the Wronskian is never zero. This is a special case of an analogous property of the solutions of a reduced linear equation of the nth order.

If only one solution $u(x)$ of equation (1) is known, Abel's identity enables us to find a second solution $v(x)$, independent of $u(x)$, by quadratures. For on dividing (5) by u^2 we have

$$\frac{uv' - vu'}{u^2} = \frac{C}{u^2} \exp\left(-\int P\,dx\right).$$

Since the left member is $(u/v)'$ we have on integration

(7) $$\frac{v}{u} = C\int \frac{e^{-\int P\,dx}}{u^2}\,dx + C'.$$

Thus when $C = 1$, $C' = 0$ we get the particular solution

(8) $$v = u\int \frac{e^{-\int P\,dx}}{u^2}\,dx.$$

With $C = 1$ (5) becomes

(9) $$W(u, v) = e^{-\int P\,dx} \neq 0,$$

where $\int P\,dx$ is the same antiderivative used in (8). Thus u and v are linearly independent.

Example 1. The linear equation

(i) $$(x^2 + 2x - 1)y'' - 2(x + 1)y' + 2y = 0$$

obviously has the solution $u = x + 1$. To find a second solution, divide the equation by $x^2 + 2x - 1$ to find P; thus

$$P = -\frac{2(x + 1)}{x^2 + 2x - 1}, \qquad -\int P\,dx = \log(x^2 + 2x - 1),$$

and from (8)

$$v = (x + 1)\int \frac{x^2 + 2x - 1}{(x + 1)^2}\,dx = (x + 1)\int\left[1 - \frac{2}{(x + 1)^2}\right]dx$$

$$= (x + 1)\left(x + \frac{2}{x + 1}\right) = x^2 + x + 2.$$

Instead of taking $v = x^2 + x + 2$, a simpler second solution is $v - u = x^2 + 1$. The general solution of (i) is therefore

$$y = c_1(x + 1) + c_2(x^2 + 1).$$

We can now prove the fundamental

Theorem 2. *If $u(x)$ and $v(x)$ are linearly independent solutions of the reduced equation* (1) *in an interval I, every solution of the equation in this interval is included in*

(10) $$y(x) = c_1 u(x) + c_2(vx)$$

when the constants are suitably chosen

PROOF. Let $y(x)$ be any solution of (1); and let $y(x_0) = k$, $y'(x_0) = k'$. Choose c_1 and c_2 so that

$$c_1 u(x_0) + c_2 v(x_0) = k$$
$$c_1 u'(x_0) + c_2 v'(x_0) = k'.$$

This is always possible since these linear equations in c_1, c_2 have as their determinant the Wronskian W_0 of u and v computed at x_0 and $W_0 \neq 0$ since u and v are linearly independent. With these values of c_1 and c_2 the two solutions of (1)

$$c_1 u(x) + c_2 v(x) \quad \text{and} \quad y(x)$$

have the same values k and their derivatives have the same value k' at the point x_0. But the existence theorem of § 26 states that there is only *one* solution of (1) taking on these values at x_0, thus proving (10).

Any pair of linearly independent solutions of (1) is called a *solution basis* of the equation. If $u(x)$, $v(x)$ form a solution basis of (1), *all* solution bases of this equation are given by

(11) $$U = \alpha u + \beta v, \qquad V = \gamma u + \delta v, \qquad \begin{vmatrix} \alpha & \beta \\ \gamma & \delta \end{vmatrix} \neq 0.$$

All bases of (1) must have this structure and

$$W(U, V) = \begin{vmatrix} \alpha u + \beta v & \gamma u + \delta v \\ \alpha u' + \beta v' & \gamma u' + \delta v' \end{vmatrix} = \begin{vmatrix} u & v \\ u' & v' \end{vmatrix} \begin{vmatrix} \alpha & \gamma \\ \beta & \delta \end{vmatrix}$$

on using row-column multiplication as with matrices. Thus $W(u, v) \neq 0$ implies $W(U, V) \neq 0$ if and only if $\alpha\delta - \beta\gamma \neq 0$.

If $W(u, v) \neq 0$, the equation

(12) $$W(y, u, v) = 0$$

is a linear differential equation of the second order having u and v as independent solutions; for when $y = u$ or v two columns of $W(y, u, v)$ are the same and reduce it to zero.

We may now restate Theorem 2 in the following form:

Theorem 3. *If $y(x)$, $u(x)$, $v(x)$ are three functions for which*

(13) $$W(y, u, v) = 0 \quad and \quad W(u, v) \neq 0,$$

then $y(x)$ is linearly dependent on $u(x)$ and $v(x)$: $y = c_1 u + c_2 v$.

The conditions (13) are not only sufficient for the linear dependence of y, u, v but also guarantee that the constant multiplying y is not zero.

Two functions cannot have a common zero in an interval in which their Wronskian $W \neq 0$; for $W = 0$ at a common zero.

Theorem 4. *In any interval in which the functions $u(x)$, $v(x)$, $u'(x)$, $v'(x)$ are continuous and $W(u, v) \neq 0$, the zeros of $u(x)$ and $v(x)$ separate each other.*

PROOF. Let a and b be consecutive zeros of $u(x)$. Then if $v(x) \neq 0$ when $a < x < b$, the function $f(x) = u(x)/v(x)$ continuous in $a \leq x \leq b$ and vanishes at $x = a$ and $x = b$. Hence by Rolle's theorem

$$f'(x) = \frac{vu' - uv'}{v^2} = -\frac{W(u, v)}{v^2}$$

must vanish between a and b, an impossibility since $W \neq 0$ by hypothesis. Thus $v(x)$ has at least *one* zero between a and b; but it cannot have *two*, for the preceding argument shows that $u(x)$ would then vanish between them—an impossibility since a and b are *consecutive* zeros of $u(x)$. Thus between consecutive zeros of $u(x)$ or $v(x)$ there is just one zero of $v(x)$ or $u(x)$, respectively; that is, the zeros of $u(x)$ and $v(x)$ *separate* each other.

The functions $u = \cos x$ and $v = \sin x$ for which $W = 1$ admirably illustrate this separation theorem.

Example 2. By Theorem 3 the equation

$$\begin{vmatrix} y & x & x^2 \\ y' & 1 & 2x \\ y'' & 0 & 2 \end{vmatrix} = x^2 y'' - 2xy' + 2y = 0$$

has the solution basis $u = x$, $v = x^2$ in any finite interval $0 < a \leq x \leq b$ where $W(x, x^2) = x^2 \neq 0$. Now u and v have a common zero at $x = 0$, but there $W = 0$ and Theorem 4 does not apply. In the differential equation both $P = -2/x$ and $Q = 2/x^2$ become infinite at $x = 0$. Note also that there is no *unique* solution for which $y(0) = y'(0) = 0$, for both $y = 0$ and $y = x^2$ fulfill this condition.

Example 3. Let $u(x)$, $v(x)$ be the solutions of $y'' + y = 0$ defined by

$$u(0) = 1, \quad u'(0) = 0; \quad v(0) = 0, \quad v'(0) = 1 \quad \text{(Ex. 26).}$$

They are linearly independent, for at $x = 0$, $W(u, v) = \begin{vmatrix} 1 & 0 \\ 0 & 1 \end{vmatrix} = 1$. Both $u'(x)$ and $v'(x)$ also satisfy $y'' + y = 0$ and must be linear combinations of u and v. Thus

$$u'(x) = a_1 u(x) + a_2 v(x),$$
$$u''(x) = a_1 u'(x) + a_2 v'(x) = -u(x).$$

Put $x = 0$ and use the initial conditions; then $a_1 = 0$, $a_2 = -1$ and hence $u'(x) = -v(x)$. In similar fashion we find $v'(x) = u(x)$.

Since $u(x + a)$ is also a solution of $y'' + y = 0$, we have

$$u(x + a) = b_1 u(x) + b_2 v(x), \qquad u'(x + a) = b_1 u'(x) + b_2 v'(x);$$

when $x = 0$, $b_1 = u(a)$, $b_2 = u'(a) = -v(a)$; hence

$$u(x + a) = u(x)u(a) - v(x)v(a)$$

which is the addition theorem for $u = \cos x$. Similarly we find

$$v(x + a) = v(x)u(a) + u(x)v(a),$$

the addition theorem for $v = \sin x$. The periodicity of $u(x)$ and $v(x)$ easily follows from the phase-plane analysis of $y'' + y = 0$ (Ex. 47.4).

PROBLEMS

Given the solution $u(x)$, find a second solution of the following equations.

1. $x^2 y'' - xy' + y = 0$, $u = x$.
2. $(x^2 - x)y'' + (x - 2)y' - y = 0$, $u = x - 2$.
3. $xy'' - (2x - 1)y' + (x - 1)y = 0$, $u = e^x$.
4. $(x + 2)y'' - (2x + 5)y' + 2y = 0$, $u = e^{2x}$.
5. $(1 - x^2)y'' - xy' + y = 0$, $u = x$.
6. $(x^2 - x)y'' + (3x - 1)y' + y = 0$, $u = (x - 1)^{-1}$.
7. $(x^2 + x)y'' + (1 + 5x)y' + 3y = 0$, $u = (1 - x)^{-3}$.
8. $x(x - 2)y'' + 2(x - 1)y' - 2y = 0$, $u = 1 - x$.
9. $x(x + 1)y'' + (x - 1)y' - y = 0$, $u = (1 + x)^{-1}$.
10. $xy'' - y' - 4x^3 y = 0$, $u = e^{x^2}$.
11. Find a linear second-order equation satisfied by

     (a) x and x^2;   (b) $x + 1$ and $x^2 + 1$;   (c) x and e^{2x}.

12. If $u(x)$ and $U(x)$ are nontrivial solutions of $y'' + Py' + Qy = 0$ such that $u(a) = 0$, $U(a) = 0$, prove that

$$U(x) = ku(x), \qquad k = U'(a)/u'(a).$$

13. In Example 3 prove that $u^2(x) + v^2(x) = 1$. Show that this also follows from Abel's identity (3).

14. If $u(x)$, $v(x)$ are solutions of $y'' - y = 0$ for which $u(0) = 1$, $u'(0) = 0$, $v(0) = 0$, $v'(0) = 1$, find $u'(x)$, $v'(x)$, $u(x + a)$, $v(x + a)$.

15. If $u(x)$, $v(x)$, $w(x)$ are solutions of $y''' + y = 0$ which satisfy $u(0) = 1$, $u'(0) = 0$, $u''(0) = 0$; $v(0) = 0$, $v'(0) = 1$, $v''(0) = 0$; $w(0) = 0$, $w'(0) = 0$, $w''(0) = 1$; prove without solving the equation that $u'(x) = -w(x)$, $v'(x) = u(x)$, $w'(x) = v(x)$. Show that $W = u^3 - v^3 + w^3 + 3uvw = 1$.

16. Using (8), give a direct proof of (9).

29. THE COMPLETE EQUATION

Let $y(x)$ denote any solution of the complete equation

(1) $y'' + Py' + Qy = R.$

Then if $y_1(x)$ is another solution,

$$y_1{}'' + Py_1{}' + Qy_1 = R,$$

and on subtraction we have

$$(y - y_1)'' + P(y - y_1)' + Q(y - y_1) = 0.$$

Thus $y(x) - y_1(x)$ is a solution of the reduced equation and must be included in its general solution $c_1u(x) + c_2v(x)$ (Theorem 28.2); hence

(2) $$y(x) = c_1u(x) + c_2v(x) + y_1(x).$$

The content of this equation is stated in the fundamental

Theorem. *The general solution of the complete equation is the sum of the general solution of the reduced equation and any particular solution of the complete equation.*

The part $c_1u(x) + c_2v(x)$ is called the *complementary function*; it contains the arbitrary constants and may be written down as soon as a solution basis of the reduced equation is known. Any particular solution of (1) may be chosen as $y_1(x)$; in general, the simpler the better. But in some problems the determination of c_1 and c_2 is simplified by choosing $y_1(x)$ to satisfy certain conditions. This will be apparent in later developments.

For example, consider the equation

$$y'' + y = x.$$

The reduced equation $y'' + y = 0$ obviously has the solution basis $u = \cos x$, $v = \sin x$ whose Wronskian $W = 1$. Moreover $y_1 = x$ is clearly a solution of the complete equation; hence its general solution is

$$y = c_1 \cos x + c_2 \sin x + x.$$

When one solution $u(x)$ is known, a second $v(x)$, independent of $u(x)$, is given by (28.8), and the complementary function is determined We shall now assume that a solution basis $u(x)$, $v(x)$ of the reduced equation is known and turn our attention to finding a particular solution $y_1(x)$ of

(3) $$y'' + Py' + Qy = R.$$

In fact, we shall obtain that specific solution which satisfies the conditions

(C_0) $$y(x_0) = 0, \qquad y'(x_0) = 0.$$

The function $u(x)$ satisfies the equation

(4) $$u'' + Pu' + Qu = 0.$$

Multiply (3) by $u(x)$, (4) by $-y(x)$, and add the equations; then

$$uy'' - yu'' + P(uy' - yu') = Ru$$

or, since

$$uy'' - yu'' = \frac{d}{dx}(uy' - yu'),$$

(5) $$(uy' - yu')' + P(uy' - yu') = Ru.$$

This is a linear equation of the first order in $uy' - yu'$ and admits the multiplier

(6) $$\lambda(x) = \exp \int_{x_0}^{x} P(t)\, dt.$$

On multiplication by λ, (3) becomes

$$\frac{d}{dx}[\lambda(uy' - yu')] = \lambda Ru.$$

Integrate this equation from x_0 to x; then if $y(x_0) = y'(x)_0 = 0$, we have

(7) $$\lambda(uy' - yu') = \int_{x_0}^{x} \lambda(t)R(t)u(t)\, dt$$

where t is the variable of integration.

The function $v(x)$ satisfies the equation

(4)′ $$v'' + Pv' + Qv = 0;$$

and the same process used before yields the analog of (7), namely

(7)′ $$\lambda(vy' - yv') = \int_{x_0}^{x} \lambda(t)R(t)v(t)\, dt.$$

Equations (7) and (7)′ are called *first integrals* of (3). From these we now eliminate y' by multiplying (7) by $v(x)$, (7)′ by $-u(x)$ and adding the resulting equations. We thus obtain on the left

(L) $$\lambda(uv' - vu')y = \lambda Wy = W_0 y$$

by Abel's identity

(8) $$W = W_0 \exp\left(-\int_{x_0}^{x} P(t)\, dt\right) = \frac{W_0}{\lambda}$$ (28.6);

and on the right

(R) $$\int_{x_0}^{x} \lambda(t)\, R(t)[u(t)\, v(x) - v(t)\, u(x)]\, dt,$$

in which $u(x)$, $v(x)$ are constant during integration with respect to t. On putting $\lambda(t) = W_0/W(t)$ in the integral and canceling $W_0 \neq 0$ from the equation $(L) = (R)$, we obtain the desired solution of (3):

$$(9) \qquad y_1(x) = \int_{x_0}^{x} \frac{R(t)}{W(t)} \begin{vmatrix} u(t) & v(t) \\ u(x) & v(x) \end{vmatrix} dt.$$

It is easy to verify that $y_1(x)$ satisfies the initial conditions C_0: It is obvious that $y_1(x_0) = 0$; and from the rule for differentiating an integral* we get

$$y_1'(x) = \frac{R(x)}{W(x)} \begin{vmatrix} u(x) & v(x) \\ u(x) & v(x) \end{vmatrix} + \int_{x_0}^{x} \frac{R(t)}{W(t)} \begin{vmatrix} u(t) & v(t) \\ u'(x) & v'(x) \end{vmatrix} dt$$

in which the first term is zero and the second vanishes when $x = x_0$.

Note that when the solution $y_1(x)$ given by (9) is used in the general solution (2), the constants c_1, c_2 needed to satisfy the initial value problem

$$y(x_0) = \alpha, \qquad y'(x_0) = \alpha'$$

are, in view of (C_0), determined from

$$c_1 u(x_0) + c_2 v(x_0) = \alpha,$$
$$c_1 u'(x_0) + c_2 v'(x_0) = \alpha'.$$

For its historical interest we give another derivation of (9) due to Lagrange,† by a process known as the *variation of parameters*. We attempt to satisfy (3) by an expression of the form

$$(10) \qquad y = A(x)u(x) + B(x)v(x)$$

in which the functions A and B are to be determined. Then

$$(11) \qquad y' = Au' + Bv'$$

just as if A and B were constants, provided that we impose a *first* condition

$$(i) \qquad A'u + B'v = 0$$

on A and B. Differentiate (11) to give

$$(12) \qquad y'' = Au'' + Bv'' + A'u' + B'v'.$$

Now multiply (10) by Q, (11) by P, and add the resulting equations to (12). Then, if

$$L[y] = y'' + Py' + Qy,$$

---

* *Advanced Calculus*, § 133.

† Joseph Louis Lagrange (1736–1813) did important work in differential equations, but is especially known for his fundamental treatise on mechanics, *Mécanique Analytique*, one of the first thoroughgoing applications of the calculus.

we have

$$L[y] = AL[u] + BL[v] + A'u' + B'v'.$$

But $L[u] = 0$, $L[v] = 0$; and if (10) is to satisfy $L[y] = R$, we must impose the *second* condition on A and B:

(ii) $A'u' + B'v' = R.$

The linear equations (i) and (ii) may now be solved for $A'(x)$ and $B'(x)$. This is always possible since their determinant is the non-zero Wronskian $W(u, v)$. We thus find

$$A' = -\frac{vR}{W}, \qquad B' = \frac{uR}{W}$$

and on integration between x_0 and x

$$A(x) = -\int_{x_0}^{x} \frac{R(t)}{W(t)} v(t)\, dt, \qquad B(x) = \int_{x_0}^{x} \frac{R(t)}{W(t)} u(t)\, dt.$$

Substitution of these values in (10) again yields the solution (9).

Example 1. $y'' + y = \tan x.$

The reduced equation $y'' + y = 0$ admits the solution basis $u = \cos x$, $v = \sin x$ whose Wronskian $W = 1$. Now (9) gives the particular integral

(i) $\qquad y_1 = \int_0^x \tan(t) \begin{vmatrix} \cos t & \sin t \\ \cos x & \sin x \end{vmatrix} dt$

$$= \sin x \int_0^x \sin t\, dt - \cos x \int_0^x \frac{\sin^2 t}{\cos t}\, dt$$

$$= \sin x (1 - \cos x) - \cos x\, \{\log(\sec x + \tan x) - \sin x\};$$

Thus

$$y_1 = \sin x - \cos x \log(\sec x + \tan x)$$

and $y_1(0) = 0$, $y_1'(0) = 0$ as required. Because the term $\sin x$ in y_1 may be assimulated into the complementary function, the general solution is

$$y = c_1 \cos x + c_2 \sin x - \cos x \log(\sec x + \tan x).$$

Note that (i) may be written

$$y_1 = \int_0^x \tan t \sin(x - t)\, dt.$$

This formula is a special case of another general expression for y_1 which we derive in the next chapter (§ 39).

Example 2. $(x + 1)y'' + xy' - y = (x + 1)^2.$

The reduced equation has the obvious solution $u = x$; and from (28.8) a second solution is

$$v = x \int \frac{(x + 1)e^{-x}}{x^2}\, dx = x\frac{e^{-x}}{x} = e^{-x}.$$

To find the solution for which $y(0) = y'(0) = 0$, we must first divide the equation by $x + 1$ to make the leading coefficient 1; then $R(x) = x + 1$. Since

$$W(u, v) = \begin{vmatrix} x & e^{-x} \\ 1 & -e^{-x} \end{vmatrix} = -(x + 1)e^{-x}$$

we have from (9)

$$y_1 = -\int_0^x e^t \begin{vmatrix} t & e^{-t} \\ x & e^{-x} \end{vmatrix} dt$$

$$= x \int_0^x dt - e^{-x} \int_0^x te^t \, dt$$

$$= x^2 - e^{-x}[(x - 1)e^x + 1].$$

Thus

$$y_1 = x^2 - x + 1 - e^{-x},$$

and $y_1(0) = 0$, $y_1'(0) = 0$ as required. The general solution is therefore

$$y = c_1 x + c_2 e^{-x} + x^2 + 1$$

for the terms $-x - e^{-x}$ may be assimilated in the complementary function.

PROBLEMS

Find y_1 such that $y_1(x_0) = y_1'(x_0) = 0$.
1. $y'' + y = \sec^3 x$; $x_0 = 0$.
2. $y'' - y = \sinh x$; $x_0 = 0$.
3. $y'' + 2y' + y = e^{-x} \log x$; $x_0 = 1$.
4. $y'' + y = \cot x$; $x_0 = \frac{1}{2}\pi$.
5. $y'' + y = \sec x$; $x_0 = 0$.
6. $(x - 1)y'' - xy' + y = (x - 1)^2$, $x_0 = 0$.
7. Show that the solution of $y'' = f(x)$ for which $y(x_0) = y'(x_0) = 0$ is

$$y_1(x) = \int_{x_0}^x f(t)(x - t) \, dt.$$

8. Show that the solution of $y''' = f(x)$ for which $y(x_0) = y'(x_0) = y''(x_0) = 0$ is

$$y_1(x) = \frac{1}{2} \int_{x_0}^x f(t)(x - t)^2 \, dt.$$

[See § 30 for the generalization of equation (9) to linear equations of order greater than 2.]

9. If the equation (1) has the particular solutions y_1, y_2, y_3 for which

$$\begin{vmatrix} y_1 & y_2 & y_3 \\ y_1' & y_2' & y_3' \\ 1 & 1 & 1 \end{vmatrix} \neq 0,$$

show that its general solution is

$$y = c_1(y_2 - y_1) + c_2(y_3 - y_1) + y_1;$$

and the equation itself may be written $W(y - y_1, y_2 - y_1, y_3 - y_1) = 0$.

10. If y_1 and y_2 are solutions of the linear equations

$$L[y] = R_1 \quad \text{and} \quad L[y] = R_2,$$

respectively, show that $y_1 + y_2$ is a solution of the equation

$$L[y] = R_1 + R_2.$$

30. SUMMARY AND GENERALIZATION

The general solution of the complete equation

(1) $$L[y] = y'' + P(x)y' + Q(x)y = R(x)$$

has the structure

(2) $$y(x) = c_1 u(x) + c_2 v(x) + y_1(x),$$

where $u(x)$ and $v(x)$ form a solution basis of the reduced equation $L[y] = 0$ and $y_1(x)$ is any particular solution of the complete equation. If $P(x)$, $Q(x)$, $R(x)$ are continuous in an interval $[a, b]$ in which x_0 is an interior point, c_1 and c_2 can be determined to give the unique solution of (1) (guaranteed by the existence theorem) for which $y(x_0) = y_0$, $y'(x_0) = y_0'$, two arbitrarily specified values. The graph of this solution is the *integral curve* through the point (x_0, y_0) with the slope y_0'.

The Wronskian $W(u, v)$ satisfies the differential equation

(3) $$W' + PW = 0,$$

which on integration yields *Abel's identity*

(4) $$W = C \exp\left(-\int P(x)\,dx\right).$$

When $u(x)$ is known, (4) determines a second solution $v(x)$ of (2) linearly independent of $u(x)$; in fact, $W(u, v) = e^{-\int P\,dx} \neq 0$.

The particular solution (29.7) of (1) for which

(C₀) $$y(x_0) = y'(x_0) = 0$$

may be written

(5) $$y_1(x) = \int_{x_0}^{x} H(x,t)R(t)\,dt,$$

where

(6) $$H(x, t) = \frac{1}{W(t)} \begin{vmatrix} u(t) & v(t) \\ u(x) & v(x) \end{vmatrix}.$$

Regarded as a function of x, $H(x, t)$ satisfies the reduced equation

(7) $$L[H(x, t)] = 0$$

and also

(8)
$$H(x, t)\Big|_{t=x} = 0, \qquad H'(x, t)\Big|_{t=x} = 1.$$

These basic results may be generalized to the complete linear equation of order n. We shall sketch a parallel treatment for the third-order equation

(1)′
$$L[y] = y''' + P_1(x)y'' + P_2(x)y' + P_3(x)y = R(x),$$

which exhibits all the essential ideas. The general solution of (1)′ has the structure

(2)′
$$y(x) = c_1u(x) + c_2v(x) + c_3w(x) + y_1(x),$$

where $u(x)$, $v(x)$, $w(x)$ form a solution basis of the reduced equation $L[y] = 0$ and $y_1(x)$ is any particular solution of the complete equation. If the functions $P_i(x)$, $R(x)$ are continuous in an interval in which x_0 is an interior point, c_1, c_2, c_3 can be determined to give the unique solution (guaranteed by an existence theorem) for which $y(x_0)$, $y'(x_0)$, $y''(x_0)$ take on arbitrarily specified values.

Recalling the method of differentiating a determinant, we have

$$W(x) = \begin{vmatrix} u & v & w \\ u' & v' & w' \\ u'' & v'' & w'' \end{vmatrix}, \qquad W'(x) = \begin{vmatrix} u & v & w \\ u' & v' & w' \\ u''' & v''' & w''' \end{vmatrix}.$$

Since $L[u] = 0$,

$$u''' = -P_1u'' - P_2u' - P_3u$$

with similar equations for u and w. In the determinant for $W'(x)$ replace the last row by these values, and add to this row P_3 times row 1 and P_2 times row 2; we then obtain

(3)′
$$W'(x) = \begin{vmatrix} u & v & w \\ u' & v' & w' \\ -P_1u'' & -P_1v'' & -P_1w'' \end{vmatrix} = -P_1W,$$

a linear equation which on integration yields *Abel's identity*

(4)′
$$W = C \exp\left(-\int P_1 \, dx\right).$$

The particular solution of (1)′ for which

$(C_0)′$
$$y(x_0) = y'(x_0) = y''(x_0) = 0$$

is given by

$$(5)' \qquad\qquad y_1(x) = \int_{x_0}^{x} H(x, t)R(t)\, dt$$

where, in analogy with (6), we conjecture that

$$(6)' \qquad H(x, t) = \frac{1}{W(t)} \begin{vmatrix} u(t) & v(t) & w(t) \\ u'(t) & v'(t) & w'(t) \\ u(x) & v(x) & w(x) \end{vmatrix}.$$

We proceed to justify this conjecture.

Regarded as a function of x, $H(x, t)$ satisfies the reduced equation

$$(7)' \qquad\qquad L[H(x, t)] = 0$$

and also

$$(8)' \qquad H(x, t)\Big|_{t=x} = 0, \qquad H'(x, t)\Big|_{t=x} = 0, \qquad H''(x, t)\Big|_{t=x} = 1.$$

Moreover, the rule for differentiating an integral* now gives

$$y_1'(x) = [H(x, x)R(x) = 0] + \int_{x_0}^{x} H'(x, t)R(t)\, dt,$$

$$y_1''(x) = [H'(x, x)R(x) = 0] + \int_{x_0}^{x} H''(x, t)R(t)\, dt,$$

$$y_1'''(x) = [H''(x, x)R(x) = R(x)] + \int_{x_0}^{x} H'''(x, t)R(t)\, dt.$$

These equations and $(7)'$ show that

$$L[y_1] = R(x) + \int_{x_0}^{x} L[H(x, t)]R(t)\, dt = R(x).$$

Thus $y_1(x)$ satisfies the complete equation $(1)'$ and also the initial conditions $(C_0)'$; for the integrals vanish when $x = x_0$. Our conjectural solution $(5)'$ is thereby justified.

In view of the developments in the next article we may regard $H(x, t)$ as a *Green's function* for the 1-endpoint problem.

Example 1. Green's Function for the system

$$(i) \qquad\qquad y' + P(x)y = R(x): \qquad y(a) = 0.$$

in which $P(x)$, $R(x)$ are continuous in an interval $a \leqq x \leqq b$.

Let $u(x) \neq 0$ be any solution of the reduced equation $u' + Pu = 0$; then

$$(ii) \qquad\qquad y_1(x) = \int_{a}^{x} \frac{u(x)}{u(t)} R(t)\, dt$$

---

* *Advanced Calculus*, § 133.

is the unique solution of the above system. Obviously $y(a) = 0$; and

$$y_1'(x) = \frac{u(x)}{u(x)} R(x) + \int_a^x \frac{u'(x)}{u(t)} R(t)\, dt$$

and since $u'(x) = -P(x)u(x)$, we have

$$y_1' = R(x) - P(x)y_1.$$

Thus the function

(iii) $$H(x, t) = u(x)/u(t)$$

plays the role of Green's function for the system (i). Since all solutions of $u' + Pu = 0$ are constant multiples of any particular solution, $H(x, t)$ is unaltered by another choice for $u(x)$.

Example 2. Cantilever Beam. Consider a loaded cantilever beam of length c clamped horizontally at its left end (Fig. 30). The elastic curve it assumes under its load has the differential equation

(i) $$y'' = M(x)/EI$$

where $M(x)$ is the moment function at a distance x from the left end, and EI is a constant (cf. § 74). Moments computed from loads to the left (right) of the

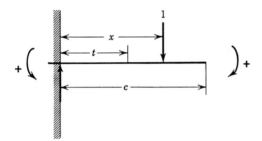

Fig. 30   Cantilever beam.

section are positive (negative) when counterclockwise and downward deflections are positive. A unit load at the section x produces a positive restraining moment x at the support and an upward reaction of 1. The moment function it generates at a distance t is therefore

(ii) $$H(x, t) = \begin{cases} x - t, & 0 \leq t \leq x \\ 0, & x \leq t \leq c. \end{cases}$$

The notation $H(x, t)$ is justified by the fact that it is the Green's function for the system

(iii) $$y'' = R(x): \qquad y(0) = y'(0) = 0.$$

For if we choose $u = 1$, $v = x$ as a basis for $y'' = 0$, $W = 1$ and

$$H(x, t) = \begin{vmatrix} 1 & t \\ 1 & x \end{vmatrix} = x - t.$$

Thus the deflection of the beam at any section x from the left support is given by

(iv)
$$y(x) = \frac{1}{EI} \int_0^c H(x, t)M(t)\, dt$$

where $H(x, t)$ is the moment function due to a unit downward load at the section x. This result is a special case of *Fränkel's formula* (cf. Ex. 31.3).

PROBLEMS

1. Deduce Abel's identity (4)′ for the linear equation of order n:
$$y^{(n)} + P_1 y^{(n-1)} + P_2 y^{(n-2)} + \cdots + P_n y = R.$$

2. Conjecture the solution $y_1(x)$, analogous to (5)′, for the equation above and justify it.

31. GREEN'S FUNCTION

So far we have considered the solution of a linear equation
$$L[y] = y'' + P(x)y' + Q(x)y = 0$$

with boundary conditions imposed at a single point. Such problems arise in the dynamics of a particle; the differential equation expresses the law of motion and the initial conditions state the position and velocity at a given instant. But there are problems with conditions imposed at two points, such as the deflection y of a loaded beam supported at both ends $x = a$, $x = b$; here we have the two end conditions, say $y(a) = \alpha$, $y(b) = \beta$.*
We shall now attempt to find a formula analogous to (30.5) which will give the solution of the system

(1)
$$L[y] = R(x): \qquad y(a) = 0, \qquad y(b) = 0$$

composed of a complete equation with two end conditions.
We first prove

Theorem 1. *If the functions $P(x)$, $Q(x)$ are continuous in the interval $a \leq x \leq b$, the system*

(2)
$$L[y] = 0: \qquad y(a) = \alpha, \qquad y(b) = \beta$$

will have a unique solution if and only if the system

(3)
$$L[y] = 0: \qquad y(a) = 0, \qquad y(b) = 0$$

is incompatible (i.e., has no solution other than $y = 0$).

---

* For a *cantilever beam*, however, we have 1-point conditions, say $y(a) = \alpha$, $y'(a) = \alpha'$.

PROOF. Let $u(x)$, $v(x)$ be a solution basis of $L[y] = 0*$; then every solution of this equation is included in

$$y(x) = c_1 u(x) + c_2 v(x)$$

by Theorem 28.3. In order to satisfy the conditions $y(a) = \alpha$, $y(b) = \beta$ of system (2) we must choose c_1 and c_2 so that

$$c_1 u(a) + c_2 v(a) = \alpha,$$
$$c_1 u(b) + c_2 v(b) = \beta.$$

These equations have a unique solution for c_1, c_2 if and only if the determinant

$$D = \begin{vmatrix} u(a) & v(a) \\ u(b) & v(b) \end{vmatrix} \neq 0.$$

When $\alpha = \beta = 0$, this condition requires $c_1 = c_2 = 0$ and yields the trivial solution $y = 0$ of system (3). Conversely, if system (3) has $y = 0$ as its sole solution, then $D \neq 0$ in order that the equations uniquely imply $c_1 = c_2 = 0$.

We turn now to system (1). The general solution of $L[y] = R(x)$ is

(4) $$y(x) = c_1 u(x) + c_2 v(x) + y_1(x)$$

where we choose $y_1(x)$ as particular solution; this is the solution of the system

$$L[y] = R(x), \qquad y(a) = 0, \qquad y'(a) = 0$$

given by (29.9). To satisfy the conditions $y(a) = y(b) = 0$ we must choose c_1 and c_2 to satisfy

(5) $$c_1 u(a) + c_2 v(a) = 0,$$
(6) $$c_1 u(b) + c_2 v(b) + y_1(b) = 0.$$

To simplify the formulas for c_1 and c_2, we now specify a basis such that

(7) $$u(a) = 0, \qquad u(b) \neq 0; \qquad v(b) = 0, \qquad v(a) \neq 0.$$

By Theorem 1 such a basis will surely exist if system (3) is incompatible. From (5) we now have $c_2 = 0$; and then from (6)

$$c_1 = -\frac{y_1(b)}{u(b)} = -\frac{1}{u(b)} \int_a^b H(b, t) R(t)\, dt \qquad (30.5)$$

---

* The existence theorem of § 26 implies the existence of a basis u, v; for example, we may specify u and v by the conditions

$$u(a) = 0, \qquad u'(a) = 1; \qquad v(a) = 1, \qquad v'(a) = 0;$$

then $W(a) = -1$ and the solutions are linearly independent.

where

$$H(b, t) = \frac{1}{W(t)} \begin{vmatrix} u(t) & v(t) \\ u(b) & 0 \end{vmatrix} = -\frac{u(b)v(t)}{W(t)};$$

thus

$$c_1 = \int_a^b \frac{v(t)}{W(t)} R(t)\, dt, \qquad c_2 = 0.$$

With these values (4) gives the desired solution of system (1). Splitting the integral for c_1 in two parts we have

$$y(x) = \int_a^x \frac{v(t)u(x)}{W(t)} R(t)\, dt + \int_x^b \frac{v(t)u(x)}{W(t)} R(t)\, dt$$

$$+ \int_a^x \frac{1}{W(t)} \begin{vmatrix} u(t) & v(t) \\ u(x) & v(x) \end{vmatrix} R(t)\, dt$$

or, on combining the first and third integrals,

$$(8) \qquad y(x) = \int_a^x \frac{u(t)v(x)}{W(t)} R(t)\, dt + \int_x^b \frac{v(t)u(x)}{W(t)} R(t)\, dt.$$

We now write (8) in the form

$$(9) \qquad y_2(x) = \int_a^b G(x, t) R(t)\, dt*$$

where

$$(10) \qquad G(x, t) = \begin{cases} \dfrac{u(t)v(x)}{W(t)}, & a \leqq t \leqq x, \\[2mm] \dfrac{v(t)u(x)}{W(t)}, & x \leqq t \leqq b \end{cases}$$

is defined as *Green's function*† for the system (1). We have thus proved

Theorem 2. *For any continuous functions $P(x)$, $Q(x)$, $R(x)$ in the interval $a \leqq x \leqq b$, and with a solution basis $u(x)$, $v(x)$ such that*

$$u(a) = 0 \quad (u(b) \neq 0), \qquad v(b) = 0 \quad (v(a) \neq 0),$$

the solution of the system

$$(1) \qquad L[y] = R(x): \qquad y(a) = 0, \qquad y(b) = 0,$$

---

* y_2 suggests the 2-point problem.

† Named for George Green (1793–1841), English mathematical physicist.

is given by

$$(9) \qquad y_2(x) = \int_a^b G(x, t)R(t)\, dt$$

where Green's function $G(x, t)$ is defined by (10) provided the system

$$(3) \qquad L[y] = 0: \qquad y(a) = 0, \qquad y(b) = 0$$

is incompatible.

That (8) satisfies system (1) may also be shown by direct calculation; the end conditions follow from (7), and $L[y] = R(x)$ follows from the rule for differentiating the integrals in (8).

Finally, we prove the more general

Theorem 3. *Under the conditions of Theorem 2, the solution of the system*

$$(11) \qquad L[y] = R(x): \qquad y(a) = \alpha, \qquad y(b) = \beta$$

is given by

$$(12) \qquad y(x) = \int_a^b G(x, t)R(t)\, dt + \alpha \frac{v(x)}{v(a)} + \beta \frac{u(x)}{u(b)}.$$

PROOF. From Theorem 2

$$L[y] = R(x) + 0 + 0 = R(x),$$
$$y(a) = 0 \;\; + \alpha + 0 = \alpha, \qquad y(b) = 0 \;\; + 0 + \beta = \beta.$$

If the system (3) has a solution other than $y = 0$, the point $x = b$ is said to be *conjugate* to the point $x = a$; then $D = u(a)v(b) - v(a)u(b) = 0$. If the equation

$$(13) \qquad u(a)v(x) - v(a)u(x) = 0$$

has no solutions other than $x = a$, there is no point conjugate to a; then system (3) is *always* incompatible and system (2) *always* has a unique solution.

For example, the system

$$y'' + y = 0: \qquad y(a) = 0, \qquad y(a + n\pi) = 0,$$

admits the solution $y = \sin (x - a)$ for all values of n and hence all points $x = a + n\pi$ are conjugate to a. On the other hand, in the system

$$y'' - y = 0: \qquad y(a) = 0, \qquad y(b) = 0,$$

there is no point conjugate to $x = a$; for we may take $u = \sinh x, \; v = \cosh x$; then equation (13) becomes

$$\sinh a \cosh x - \cosh a \sinh x = \sinh (a - x) = 0$$

and has no solution except $x = a$.

The condition $D \neq 0$ for the incompatibility of system (3) does not depend on the choice of a solution basis for $L[y] = 0$; for if another basis (cf. (28.10))

$$U = \alpha u + \beta v, \qquad V = \gamma u + \delta v, \qquad \begin{vmatrix} \alpha & \beta \\ \gamma & \delta \end{vmatrix} \neq 0,$$

is chosen, we also have

$$\begin{vmatrix} U(a) & V(a) \\ U(x) & V(x) \end{vmatrix} = \begin{vmatrix} u(a) & v(a) \\ u(x) & v(x) \end{vmatrix} \begin{vmatrix} \alpha & \gamma \\ \beta & \delta \end{vmatrix} \neq 0.$$

In forming Green's function (10) we may replace the basis u, v by another U, V such that $U(a) = 0$, $V(b) = 0$; then $U = \alpha u$, $V = \delta v$ (why?) and $W(U, V) = \alpha\delta W(u, v)$, so that $G(x, t)$ remains unaltered. Thus let us choose u and v so that $u(a) = v(b) = 0$, $u(b)$ and $v(a) > 0$. If the interval $a < x \leq b$ contains no point conjugate to a, we see from (13) that $u(x) \neq 0$ and therefore remains positive in this interval. Moreover $v(x) > 0$ for $a \leq x < b$ since a zero of v at x_1 would require a zero of u between x_1 and b by Theorem 28.4. With this choice of basis the numerators in $G(x, t)$ are positive, and since $W(t)$ has the sign of $W(a) = -v(a)u'(a)$, negative since $u'(a) > 0$, $G(x, t)$ remains negative in an interval $a < x < b$ which contains no point conjugate to a.

Example 1. There is no Green's function for the system

$$y'' + y = R(x), \qquad y(0) = 0, \qquad y(\pi) = 0.$$

For the system

$$y'' + y = 0, \qquad y(0) = 0, \qquad y(\pi) = 0$$

admits the non-zero solution $y = \sin x$.

Example 2. $y'' + y = 1$, $\quad y(0) = 0$, $\quad y(1) = 0$. The reduced system is incompatible (prove it!). We choose the basis

$$u = \sin x, \qquad v = \sin (x - 1)$$

in accordance with equations (7) and find

$$W(x) = \begin{vmatrix} \sin x & \sin (x - 1) \\ \cos x & \cos (x - 1) \end{vmatrix} = \sin 1,$$

$$G(x, t) = \begin{cases} \dfrac{\sin t \sin (x - 1)}{\sin 1}, & 0 \leq t \leq x, \\[2ex] \dfrac{\sin (t - 1) \sin x}{\sin 1}, & x \leq t \leq 1. \end{cases}$$

Equation (8) now gives

$$y_2(x) = \frac{\sin(x-1)}{\sin 1} \int_0^x \sin t \, dt + \frac{\sin x}{\sin 1} \int_x^1 \sin(t-1) \, dt$$

$$= \frac{\sin(x-1)(1-\cos x) + \sin x(\cos(x-1) - 1)}{\sin 1}$$

$$= 1 + \frac{\sin(x-1) - \sin x}{\sin 1}.$$

Example 3. *Fränkel's Formula.* Consider a loaded horizontal beam of length c simply supported at its ends (Fig. 31). The elastic curve it assumes under its load has the differential equation

(i) $$y'' = \frac{M(x)}{EI}$$

where $M(x)$ is the moment function at a distance x from the left end, and EI is a constant (cf. § 74). Moments computed from loads to the left (right) of the section are positive (negative) when counterclockwise and downward deflections are positive. A unit load at the section x produces upward reactions $(c-x)/c$, x/c at the supports and generates the negative moment function at a distance t:

(ii) $$G(x, t) = \begin{cases} -\dfrac{c-x}{c} t, & 0 \leq t \leq x \\[2mm] -\dfrac{x}{c}(c-t), & x \leq t \leq c. \end{cases}$$

The notation $G(x, t)$ for the moment function due to the unit load at section x

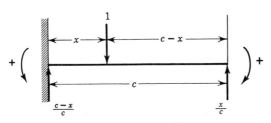

Fig. 31 Simply supported beam.

is justified by the fact that it is the Green's function for the system

(iii) $$y'' = R(x): \qquad y(0) = 0, \qquad y(c) = 0.$$

For if we choose $u = x$, $v = c - x$ as a basis for $y'' = 0$, we find $W(u, v) = -c$ and formula (10) gives precisely the result in (ii). Thus the deflection of the beam at any section x from the left support is given by

(iv) $$y(x) = \frac{1}{EI} \int_0^c G(x, t) \, M(t) \, dt$$

where $G(x, t)$ is the moment function due to a unit downward load at the section x. This result is known in the theory of elasticity as *Fränkel's Formula.*

PROBLEMS

1. Find the Green's function for the system

$$y'' + y = 0, \qquad y(0) = 0, \quad y(\tfrac{1}{2}\pi) = 0,$$

and solve it.

2. Solve the systems

(a) $y'' + y = 3 \sin 2t$, $y(0) = 0$, $y(\tfrac{1}{2}\pi) = 0$;

(b) $y'' + y = 3 \sin 2t$, $y(0) = \alpha$, $y(\tfrac{1}{2}\pi) = \beta$.

3. What is the smallest positive value of b for which the system

$$y'' + 2y' + 5y = 0, \qquad y(0) = 0, \quad y(b) = 0,$$

is incompatible?

4(a). Find the Green's function for the system

$$y'' + 2y' + 5y = 0, \qquad y(0) = 0, \qquad y(\tfrac{1}{4}\pi) = 0.$$

(b) Solve the system

$$y'' + 2y' + 5y = e^{-x}, \qquad y(0) = 0, \qquad y(\tfrac{1}{4}\pi) = 0.$$

5. Find the deflection at the point $x = a$ of a simple beam of length $c = a + b$ inches when loaded with P pounds at the point $x = a$. What is the deflection when $a = c/2$?

6. Find the deflection at the point $x = a$ of a simple beam of length $c = a + b$ inches when it carries a uniform load of w lb/in. Find the maximum deflection.

7. Prove the following properties of $G(x, t)$:

(a) $G(x, t)$ is continuous in the square $a \leqq x, t \leqq b$ in which it is defined;

(b) $\partial G/\partial x \big|_{x=t+} - \partial G/\partial x \big|_{x=t-} = -1$;

(c) $L[G(x, t)] = 0$ for each fixed value of t in the square except along the diagonal $x = t$;

(d) $G(a, t) = 0$, $G(b, t) = 0$.

8. Show that for any choice of two independent solutions $u(x)$, $v(x)$ of $L[y] = 0$ such that $u(a) = 0$, $v(b) = 0$, $G(x, t)$ is unaltered.

9. Show that the system

$$y'' - y = R(x): \qquad y(a) = 0, \qquad y(b) = 0$$

always has a Green's function. Find it and show that it is negative when $a < x, t < b$.

10. Obtain the Green's function for the system

$$(1 + x)y'' - xy' - y = x + 1: \qquad y(0) = 0, \qquad y(1) = 0,$$

and solve it.

32. EXACT EQUATIONS

A differential expression is said to be *exact* if it is the derivative of a differential expression of lower order. Thus if

(1) $$P_0 y'' + P_1 y' + P_2 y = \frac{d}{dx}(py' + qy)$$

the expression on the left is exact. Since the expression on the right is

$$py'' + (p' + q)y' + q'y$$

(1) implies that

$$P_0 = p, \qquad P_1 = p' + q, \qquad P_2 = q';$$

and these equations in turn imply that

(2) $$P_0'' - P_1' + P_2 = 0.$$

Conversely, equation (2) implies (1); for if $y(x)$ is a function with two derivatives,

$$P_0y'' + P_1y' + P_2y = P_0y'' + P_1y' + (P_1' - P_0'')y$$
$$= (P_0y' - P_0'y)' + (P_1y)'$$
$$= \frac{d}{dx}[P_0y' + (P_1 - P_0')y].$$

We therefore may state the

Theorem. *The differential expression $P_0y'' + P_1y' + P_2y$ is exact when and only when*

(2) $$P_0'' - P_1' + P_2 = 0;$$

and then

(3) $$P_0y'' + P_1y' + P_2y \equiv \frac{d}{dx}[P_0y' + (P_1 - P_0')y].$$

The *equation*

(4) $$P_0y'' + P_1y' + P_2y = R$$

is said to be exact when the expression $P_0y'' + P_1y' + P_2y$ is exact. Then (4) is equivalent to

$$\frac{d}{dx}[P_0y' + (P_1 - P_0')y] = R$$

and we have the first integral

$$P_0y' + (P_1 - P_0')y = \int R\, dx + C.$$

This linear equation of the first order may be integrated to give the general solution of (4).

Example 1. The equation

$$x^2y'' + xy' - y = x^3$$

is exact for $P_0'' - P_1' + P_2 = 2 - 1 - 1 = 0$, and, in view of (3), admits the first integral

$$x^2y' - xy = \tfrac{1}{4}x^4 + c,$$

or
$$y' - \frac{y}{x} = \frac{1}{4} x^2 + \frac{c}{x^2} .$$

This equation admits the multiplier $1/x$; and hence

$$\frac{d}{dx}\left(\frac{y}{x}\right) = \frac{1}{4} x + \frac{c}{x^3} ,$$

$$\frac{y}{x} = \frac{1}{8} x^2 - \frac{c}{2x^2} + c_2,$$

$$y = \frac{1}{8} x^3 + \frac{c_1}{x} + c_2 x.$$

Example 2. Find a solution u of

$$y'' + xy' + y = 0.$$

The equation is exact and

$$\frac{d}{dx} (y' + xy) = 0;$$

hence u may be taken as any function that satisfies

$$y' + xy = 0 \quad \text{or} \quad \frac{dy}{y} + x \, dx = 0.$$

A solution is

$$\log y = -\tfrac{1}{2}x^2 \quad \text{or} \quad y = e^{-x^2/2}.$$

Thus we may take

$$u = e^{-x^2/2}; \quad \text{and} \quad v = e^{-x^2/2} \int e^{x^2/2} \, dx \qquad (28.8)$$

is a second solution.

PROBLEMS

In Problems 1 to 4 prove that the equations are exact and find two independent solutions u and v.

1. $(x^2 + x)y'' + (x - 1)y' - y = 0.$
2. $(1 - x^2)y'' - xy' + y = 0.$
3. $(1 - x)y'' + xy' + y = 0.$
4. $x^2 y'' + (1 + 4x)y' + 2y = 0.$
5. If $P_1 = 2P_0'$, $P_2 = P_0''$, show that

$$P_0 y'' + P_1 y' + P_2 y = D^2(P_0 y).$$

In Problems 6 and 7, find the general solution.

6. $(x^2 + 3)y'' + 4xy' + 2y = e^{-x}.$
7. $(x^3 + 1)y'' + 6x^2 y' + 6xy = 3x.$
8. $(1 - x)y'' + xy' + y = 0.$ Find one solution.
9. $xy'' + y' = 16x^2.$ Find the solution $y(x)$ for which

$$y(1) = 2, \qquad y'(1) = 3.$$

10. $x^3 y'' + 2xy' - 2y = 0.$ Use an obvious particular solution to find the general solution.

33. ADJOINT EQUATION

If the equation

$$(1) \qquad P_0 y'' + P_1 y' + P_2 y = 0$$

is not exact, we may seek a multiplier $z(x)$ that will make it exact. Such a multiplier must satisfy the linear equation

$$(2) \qquad (P_0 z)'' - (P_1 z)' + P_2 z = 0, \qquad\qquad (31.2)$$

or, on performing the differentiations,

$$(3) \qquad Q_0 z'' + Q_1 z' + Q_2 z = 0$$

where

$$(4) \qquad Q_0 = P_0, \qquad Q_1 = 2P_0' - P_1, \qquad Q_2 = P_0'' - P_1' + P_2.$$

Equation (2) or (3) is called the *adjoint* of (1). Their coefficients P_i and Q_i are connected by equations (4), or by the equivalent equations

$$(5) \quad Q_0 = P_0, \qquad Q_1 - Q_0' = P_0' - P_1, \qquad 2Q_2 - Q_1' = 2P_2 - P_1'.$$

When Q and P are interchanged these equations remain unaltered; hence the relation between equations (1) and (2) is a reciprocal one: *Each equation is the adjoint of the other*. The *operators*

$$P = P_0 D^2 + P_1 D + P_2 \quad \text{and} \quad Q = Q_0 D^2 + Q_1 D + Q_2$$

are also called adjoint.

When an equation and its adjoint are the same, it is said to be *self-adjoint*. Then $Q_1 = P_1$, $Q_2 = P_2$; and equations (4) show that both conditions are fulfilled when

$$(6) \qquad P_1 = P_0'.$$

Therefore a self-adjoint equation may be written

$$(7) \qquad (P_0 y')' + P_2 y = 0.$$

The condition (6) shows that equation (1) will become self-adjoint after multiplication by a factor σ that satisfies the equation

$$\sigma P_1 = (\sigma P_0)' \quad \text{or} \quad \frac{(\sigma P_0)'}{\sigma P_0} = \frac{P_1}{P_0}.$$

Hence, on integration,

$$(8) \qquad \sigma = \frac{1}{P_0} \exp \int \frac{P_1}{P_0} \, dx.$$

With this value, the self-adjoint form of (1) is

$$(9) \qquad \sigma P_0 y'' + \sigma P_1 y' + \sigma P_2 y = 0.$$

Since (9) is self-adjoint its solutions are also its multipliers (or integrating factors). But since (9) is equation (1) multiplied by σ, the solutions of (1) *are* the solutions of (9). Hence the statement "the solutions of (9) are the multipliers of (9)" is equivalent to saying "σ times the solutions of (1) are the multipliers of (1)." But since the multipliers of (1) are the solutions of its adjoint (3), we have the

Theorem. *The solutions of*

$$(1) \qquad P_0 y'' + P_1 y' + P_2 y = 0$$

and its adjoint

$$(3) \qquad Q_0 z'' + Q_1 z' + Q_2 z = 0$$

correspond one-to-one through the relation $z = \sigma y$, *or*

$$(10) \qquad \frac{z}{y} = \sigma = \frac{1}{P_0} \exp \int \frac{P_1}{P_0}\, dx.$$

If z_1 and z_2 are linearly independent solutions of (3), the corresponding solutions of (1)

$$y_1 = \frac{z_1}{\sigma}, \qquad y_2 = \frac{z_2}{\sigma}$$

are also linearly independent, for it is easy to show that

$$W(y_1, y_2) = \frac{1}{\sigma^2} W(z_1, z_2).*$$

Since (1) is the adjoint of (3) it follows from (10) that

$$(11) \qquad \frac{y}{z} = \frac{1}{\sigma} = \frac{1}{Q_0} \exp \int \frac{Q_1}{Q_0}\, dx.$$

The foregoing theory shows that in order to solve (1) by making it an exact equation, we must first find a particular solution of (1). Thus again we are forced to the conclusion: *In order to solve* (1) *by quadratures a particular solution must be known.*

The linear operator P and its adjoint Q are related by the *Lagrange identity:*

$$(12) \qquad zP(y) - yQ(z) = \frac{d}{dx}\, [P_0(y'z - z'y) + (P_1 - P_0')yz].$$

---

* See Problem 27.9b.

PROOF. Using (2), the left member may be written

$$z[P_0 y'' + P_1 y' + P_2 y] - y[(P_0 z)'' - (P_1 z)' + P_2 z]$$
$$= (P_0 z)y'' - (P_0 z)''y + (P_1 z)y' + (P_1 z)'y$$
$$= D[(P_0 z)y' - (P_0 z)'y] + D(P_1 yz)$$
$$= D[P_0 zy' - P_0 z'y] + D[(P_1 - P_0')yz]$$

which is the right member of (12).

The Lagrange identity reveals a great deal of the theory of the linear equation of the second order. For the details see the author's paper "The Lagrange Identity as a Unifying Principle," *Am. Math. Monthly*, vol. 52, no. 9, Nov. 1945.

Example 1. The equation

(i) $$xy'' + 2y' + n^2 xy = 0$$

is not exact for $P_0'' - P_1' + P_2 = n^2 x$. The adjoint equation

$$(xz)'' - 2z' + n^2 xz = x(z'' + n^2 z) = 0$$

has the general solution

$$z = A \cos nx + B \sin nx.$$

The factor

$$\sigma = \frac{1}{x} \exp \int \frac{2}{x} \, dx = \frac{1}{x} x^2 = x.$$

Therefore the general solution of (i) is

$$y = \frac{z}{x} = A \frac{\cos nx}{x} + B \frac{\sin nx}{x}.$$

Example 2. The equation

(ii) $$xy'' + (2x - 1)y' + (x - 1)y = x^2 + 2x$$

when reduced, has for its adjoint

$$xz'' + (3 - 2x)z' + (x - 3)z = 0.$$

Since $x + (3 - 2x) + (x - 3) = 0$, it admits the solution e^x. Hence the multiplier e^x makes (ii) exact; and in view of (32.3)

$$\frac{d}{dx}[xe^x y' + (x - 2)e^x y] = (x^2 + 2x)e^x,$$

$$xe^x y' + (x - 2)e^x y = x^2 e^x + A.$$

This linear equation has the multiplier

$$\mu = \frac{1}{P_0} \exp \int \frac{P_1}{P_0} \, dx = \frac{1}{xe^x} \exp \int \left(1 - \frac{2}{x}\right) dx = \frac{e^x x^{-2}}{xe^x} = \frac{1}{x^3};$$

hence from (16.3)

$$\frac{d}{dx}\left(\frac{e^x}{x^2}y\right) = \frac{e^x}{x} + \frac{A}{x^3},$$

$$\frac{e^x}{x^2}y = \int \frac{e^x}{x}dx - \frac{A}{2x^2} + B.$$

Replacing $\dfrac{-A}{2}$ by A we have the general solution of (ii):

$$y = xe^{-x}\int \frac{e^x}{x}dx + Ae^{-x} + Bx^2e^{-x}.$$

Here the first term is a particular solution of (ii); e^{-x} and x^2e^{-x} are solutions of the reduced equation. All this is readily verified. Do it!

PROBLEMS

1. Find the adjoint of

$$(1 - x)y'' - y' + (1 + x)y = 0.$$

Compute the factor σ for this equation.

2. Solve by finding the adjoint equation:

$$xy'' + 2y' + xy = 0.$$

3. Solve by finding the adjoint equation:

$$x^2y'' + (3x^2 + 4x)y' + (2x^2 + 6x + 2)y = 0.$$

4. If z_1 and z_2 are linearly independent solutions of (3) whose Wronskian is W, prove that

$$y_1 = \frac{z_1}{P_0 W}, \qquad y_2 = \frac{z_2}{P_0 W}$$

are linearly independent solutions of (1) whose Wronskian is $1/P_0{}^2W$.
Verify this theorem by the results of Problem 3.

5. Using equations (5), prove that

$$\frac{1}{Q_0}\exp\int \frac{Q_1}{Q_0}dx = \frac{1}{\sigma}.$$

6. Form the adjoint of

$$x^2y'' + (4x - x^2)y' + (2 - 2x - 2x^2)y = 0.$$

Find two solutions z_1, z_2 of the adjoint and the corresponding solutions y_1, y_2 of the given equation.

7. Reduce $y'' + y'\tan x + y\cos x = 0$ to the self-adjoint form.

8. Reduce $xy'' - y' + x^3y = 0$ to the self-adjoint form and solve it.

9. Show that all multipliers of the form $z(x)$ of the linear equation of the first order

$$P_0y' + P_1y = 0 \quad \text{satisfy its adjoint} \quad (P_0z)' - P_1z = 0.$$

Prove the equation self-adjoint when $P_1 = \frac{1}{2}P_0'$.

34. FACTORABLE OPERATORS

The idea of exactness may be expressed in terms of operators. Thus if D denotes the operation d/dx, we may express the results of § 32 as follows:

The operator $P_0 D^2 + P_1 D + P_2$ can be factored into $D(pD + q)$ when and only when

$$P_0'' - P_1' + P_2 = 0; \quad \text{then} \quad p = P_0, \quad q = P_1 - P_0'.$$

An exact operator, therefore, is one that can be factored in a very simple way. This suggests the more general problem: can $P_0 D^2 + P_1 D + P_2$ be factored into two linear factors, say $(pD + q)(rD + s)$, where p, q, r, s are functions of x?

For the *equation*

(1) $$P_0 y'' + P_1 y' + P_2 y = 0$$

we may divide through by P_0 and consider the simpler problem of the factoring

(2) $$(D^2 + PD + Q) = (D + p)(D + q).$$

If $y(x)$ is an arbitrary operand $(D + q)y = y' + qy$ and

(3) $$(D + p)(D + q)y = y'' + (p + q)y' + (q' + pq)y.$$

Thus, if (2) holds, we must have

$$p + q = P, \quad q' + pq = Q.$$

Eliminating p from these equations we obtain the Riccati equation for q:

(4) $$q' + Pq - q^2 - Q = 0.$$

In order to solve this by quadratures we must know a particular solution (§ 18); and the problem of solving (1) again meets an obstacle.

The operators $D + p$ and $D + q$ do not in general commute; for when we interchange p and q in (3) we have

$$(D + q)(D + p)y = y'' + (q + p)y' + (p' + qp)y.$$

Thus $D + p$ and $D + q$ commute when and only when $p' = q'$ or $p - q = $ const.; in particular, they commute when p and q are constants.

Example. For the equation

(i) $$y'' - (1 + x^2)y = 0$$

we have $P = 0$, $Q = -1 - x^2$. Now the Riccati equation for q,

$$q' - q^2 + 1 + x^2 = 0$$

admits the obvious solution $q = -x$; since $p + q = 0$, $p = x$ and (i) becomes

$$(D + x)(D - x)y = 0.$$

This equation is satisfied when

$$y' - xy = 0 \quad \text{or} \quad y = e^{x^2/2} \, .$$

If we take $u = e^{x/2}$, a second solution is then $v = e^{x^2/2} \int e^{-x^2} \, dx$ (28.8).

PROBLEMS

1. Solve by factoring:

$$y'' + (1 - x^2)y = 0.$$

2. Prove that the equations

$$(D + p)(D + q)y = 0, \qquad (D - q)(D - p)y = 0,$$

are adjoint.

3. Prove that the operators $pD + q$ and $rD + s$ commute when and only when $pr' = rp'$, $ps' = rq'$.

If p and $r \neq 0$, these conditions give $r = ap$ and $s = aq + b$.

4. Solve by factoring

$$y'' - 2xy' + (x^2 - 1)y = 0.$$

Do the factors commute?

5. Prove the theorem (Jacobi):

If $y'' = f(x, y)$ has the first integral

$$y' = \varphi(x, y, C),$$

then $\partial\varphi/\partial C$ is a multiplier of the equation

$$dy - \varphi(x, y, C) \, dx = 0.$$

CHAPTER 4

$$\boxed{(D - a)^{-1} = e^{ax} D^{-1} e^{-ax}}$$

Linear Equations
with Constant Coefficients

35. COMPLETE AND REDUCED EQUATION

The differential equation

(1) $$a_0 y^{(n)} + a_1 y^{(n-1)} + \cdots + a_{n-1} y' + a_n y = \varphi(x)$$

is called a *complete* linear equation of the nth order in y. When $\varphi(x)$ is replaced by zero we obtain the corresponding *reduced* equation

(2) $$a_0 y^{(n)} + a_1 y^{(n-1)} + \cdots + a_{n-1} y' + a_n y = 0.$$

If D denotes the operation d/dx of taking a derivative, and D^2, D^3, etc. its repetitions, we may write (1) in the form

$$(a_0 D^n + a_1 D^{n-1} + \cdots + a_{n-1} D + a_n) y = \varphi(x),$$

or more compactly

(1)′ $$f(D)y = \varphi(x)$$

where $f(D)$ denotes the "polynomial" in D in the left member.

Consider now the polynomial

$$f(r) = a_0 r^n + a_1 r^{n-1} + \cdots + a_{n-1} r + a_n$$

in the complex variable r. It is a fundamental theorem that $f(r)$ may be expressed as a product of a_0 and n linear factors of the form $r - r_i$: thus

$$f(r) = a_0 (r - r_i)(r - r_2) \cdots (r - r_n),$$

where $r_1, r_2, \ldots, r_n$ are the n roots of the equation $f(r) = 0$. These roots may be real or complex, and some may be repeated. We shall always assume that the coefficients a_i in (1) are real; in this case the complex

127

roots of $f(r) = 0$ *always occur in conjugate pairs* $\alpha \pm \beta i$ where α and β are real. Such a complex pair corresponds to the linear factors

$$(D - \alpha - i\beta)(D - \alpha + i\beta)$$

or to the quadratic factor $(D - \alpha)^2 + \beta^2$ with real coefficients. Consequently $f(r)$ can always be expressed as a product of real linear and quadratic factors. Repeated factors correspond to multiple roots. Thus if

$$f(r) = 3(r + 2)r^2(r - 1)^3(r^2 + 1)^2,$$

$f(r) = 0$ is an equation of the tenth degree with the ten roots

$$-2, 0, 0, 1, 1, 1, i, i, -i, -i;$$

-2 is a simple root; 0, i, $-i$ are double roots; and 1 is a triple root. As another example, if $f(r) = r^3 - 1$,

$$f(r) = (r - 1)(r^2 + r + 1) = (r - 1)(r - \omega)(r - \omega^2);$$

the roots of $f(r) = 0$ are the three cube roots of 1:

$$1, \qquad \omega = \frac{-1 + i\sqrt{3}}{2}, \qquad \omega^2 = \frac{-1 - i\sqrt{3}}{2}.$$

Evidently the problem of factoring $f(r)$ into linear factors and the problem of finding the roots of the equation $f(r) = 0$ are essentially the same. When one is solved, the solution of the other is immediate.

We proceed to show that the general solution of the reduced equation

$$(2)' \qquad\qquad f(D)u = 0$$

may be written down as soon as the roots of its *characteristic equation*

$$(3) \qquad\qquad f(r) = 0$$

are known. But first we shall prove an identity known as the *exponential shift*.

PROBLEMS

Find the roots of the equation $f(r) = 0$ by factoring:

1. $f(r) = r^3 - 1$.
2. $f(r) = r^4 - 1$.
3. $f(r) = r^4 + 1$.
4. $f(r) = r^4 + 2r^2 + 1$.
5. $f(r) = r^3 - 2r^2 + 3r - 2$.
6. $f(r) = r^3 + 2r^2 - r - 2$.
7. $f(r) = r^3 - 5r - 2$.
8. $f(r) = r^3 + r^2 + r + 1$.
9. $f(r) = r^4 + 3r^2 + 2$.
10. $f(r) = r^4 + r^2 + 1$.
11. Prove that if a is a k-fold root of $f(x) = 0$, then

$$f(a) = f'(a) = \cdots = f^{(k-1)}(a) = 0.$$

12. If $f(r) = 0$ has real coefficients, prove that its complex roots occur in conjugate pairs.

[If $\bar{r}$ is the conjugate of r, show that the conjugates of r^n and $f(r)$ are r^n and $f(\bar{r})$.]

36. THE EXPONENTIAL SHIFT

If $f(D)$ is a polynomial in D and X a function of x,

(1) $$f(D)(e^{ax}X) = e^{ax}f(D + a)X.$$

PROOF. We first consider the case when $f(D) = D^k$. When $k = 1$ the rule for differentiating a product gives

(2) $$D(e^{ax}X) = e^{ax}DX + ae^{ax}X = e^{ax}(D + a)X$$

in agreement with (1). We use (2) as a start in mathematical induction. Assume that

(3) $$D^k(e^{ax}X) = e^{ax}(D + a)^k X;$$

then from (2)

$$\begin{aligned}
D^{k+1}(e^{ax}X) &= D\{e^{ax}(D + a)^k X\} \\
&= e^{ax}(D + a)\{(D + a)^k X\} \\
&= e^{ax}(D + a)^{k+1}X.
\end{aligned}$$

Thus if (3) is true for a given k, it is also true for $k + 1$; and since (3) is true when $k = 1$, it is true in general.

Since $f(D) = \sum_{k=0}^{n} a_{n-k}D^k$,

$$\begin{aligned}
f(D)(e^{ax}X) &= \sum_{k=0}^{n} a_{n-k}D^k(e^{ax}X) \\
&= e^{ax}\sum_{k=0}^{n} a_{n-k}(D + a)^k X \qquad \text{from (3)} \\
&= e^{ax}f(D + a)X,
\end{aligned}$$

and (1) is established.

Now the polynomial $f(D + a)$ of degree n has the Taylor expansion

$$f(a + r) = f(a) + \frac{f'(a)}{1!}r + \cdots + \frac{f^{(n)}(a)}{n!}r^n;$$

hence

$$f(D + a) = f(a) + \frac{f'(a)}{1!}D + \cdots + \frac{f^{(n)}(a)}{n!}D^n.$$

When $X = 1, f(D + a)1 = f(a)$, and the exponential shift (1) becomes

$$(4) \qquad f(D)e^{ax} = f(a)e^{ax}.$$

If $D^{-1}X$ denotes the antiderivative (or indefinite integral) of X; then $DD^{-1} = 1$, the identity operator. Similarly let the operator $(D + a)^{-1}$ be defined by

$$(5) \qquad (D + a)(D + a)^{-1} = 1.$$

With this definition the exponential shift also applies to the operator D^{-1}:

$$(6) \qquad D^{-1}(e^{ax}X) = e^{ax}(D + a)^{-1}X.$$

This means that D applied to the right-hand member will produce $e^{ax}X$; and indeed, from the exponential shift and (5),

$$D\{e^{ax}(D + a)^{-1}X\} = e^{ax}(D + a)(D + a)^{-1}X = e^{ax}X.$$

We shall call two operators *equivalent* (symbol =) when they produce the same result on any function to which they are applicable.* With this definition, (6), when multiplied by e^{-ax}, yields the important operational equation

$$(7) \qquad (D + a)^{-1} = e^{-ax}D^{-1}e^{ax}.$$

We shall usually use this in the form

$$(8) \qquad (D - a)^{-1} = e^{ax}D^{-1}e^{-ax}.$$

Thus $(D - a)^{-1}$ means:

Multiply by e^{-ax}, integrate, and then multiply by e^{ax}. We shall see that (7) contains virtually the entire theory of the linear differential equation with constant coefficients.

Applying $(D - a)^{-1}$ k times gives

$$(9) \qquad (D - a)^{-k} = e^{ax}D^{-k}e^{-ax};$$

for the intermediate factors $e^{-ax}e^{ax} = 1$.

Example 1. Linear equation of the first order $y' - ay = X$. The solution of $(D - a)y = X$ is

$$y = (D - a)^{-1}X = e^{ax}D^{-1}e^{-ax} \cdot X = e^{ax}\int e^{-ax}X \, dx,$$

an arbitrary constant c being added on integration. If $X = 0$ we obtain ce^{ax} as the solution of the reduced equation $y' - ay = 0$.

---

* See *Advanced Calculus* for the postulates governing an equivalence relation.

Example 2. $y'' + y' - 2y = e^x$. The operator $D^2 + D - 2 = (D + 2)(D - 1)$. The solution of

$$(D + 2)(D - 1)y = e^x$$

is

$$y = (D - 1)^{-1}(D + 2)^{-1}e^x$$

$$= e^x D^{-1}e^{-x} \cdot e^{-2x} D^{-1}e^{2x} \cdot e^x$$

$$= e^x D^{-1}e^{-3x} D^{-1}e^{3x}$$

$$= e^x D^{-1}e^{-3x}(\tfrac{1}{3}e^{3x} + c_1)$$

$$= e^x D^{-1}(\tfrac{1}{3} + c_1 e^{-3x})$$

$$= e^x \left(\frac{1}{3}x - \frac{c_1}{3} e^{-3x} + c_2 \right).$$

Since c_1 is arbitrary we may as well replace $-c_1/3$ by c_1; the solution is therefore

$$y = \tfrac{1}{3}xe^x + c_1 e^{-2x} + c_2 e^x.$$

This solution is also given by

$$y = (D + 2)^{-1}(D - 1)^{-1}e^x,$$

but the calculations (do them!) are not so simple.

Moral: A prospective integration (D^{-1}) should be performed last.

Example 3. $y'' - 2y' + y = \cos x$. Replace $\cos x$ by $e^{ix} = \cos x + i \sin x$ and solve

$$(D - 1)^2 Y = e^{ix}.$$

Using (9) we have

$$Y = e^x D^{-2}e^{-x} \cdot e^{ix}$$

$$= e^x D^{-2}e^{(i-1)x}$$

$$= e^x D^{-1}\left[\frac{e^{(i-1)x}}{i - 1} + c_1 \right]$$

$$= e^x \left[\frac{e^{(i-1)x}}{(i - 1)^2} + c_1 x + c_2 \right]$$

$$= \frac{e^{ix}}{-2i} + c_1 xe^x + c_2 e^x$$

where c_1 and c_2 are, arbitrary complex constants. The real part of Y,

$$y = -\tfrac{1}{2} \sin x + a_1 xe^x + a_2 e^x,$$

is the solution of the given equation. Its imaginary part

$$y = \tfrac{1}{2} \cos x + b_1 xe^x + b_2 e^x$$

is the solution of $y'' - 2y' + y = \sin x$.

Moral: It is sometimes easier to solve two related equations than one.

PROBLEMS

Find the general solutions for the following problems:

1. $y'' - 3y' + 2y = 0$.
2. $y'' - 4y = 0$.
3. $y'' + 2y' + y = 0$.
4. $y'' + y' = 1 + e^{-x}$.
5. $y'' + 3y' + 2y = 1$.
6. $y'' - y' - 2y = e^{-x} + e^{2x}$.
7. $y'' - 4y' + 4y = e^{2x}$.
8. $y'' - 4y' + 4y = \cosh x$.
9. $y'' - 2y' + y = e^x/x$.
10. $y'' + 2y + y = e^{-x} \log x$.
11. $(D - 1)^3 y = e^x + e^{2x}$.
12. $(D - 1)^2 y = xe^x + 7x - 2$.
13. $(D + 1)^3 y = 2 \cosh x$.
14. $(D - 1)^3 y = xe^x + x + 1$.
15. $(D - 1)^2 y = e^x \log x$.

37. THE REDUCED EQUATION

We next show how to obtain the general solution of the reduced equation

$$(1) \qquad\qquad f(D)u = 0$$

when the roots of the characteristic equation

$$(2) \qquad\qquad f(r) = 0$$

are known.

If (2) has the k-fold root a, $f(r)$ will contain $(r - a)^k$ as a factor. Then $f(D)$ will contain $(D - a)^k$ as a factor; and since the factors of $f(D)$ commute we may bring this factor to bear directly on u. Then (1) may be written

$$(1)' \qquad\qquad g(D)(D - a)^k u = 0.$$

Evidently any solution of

$$(3) \qquad\qquad (D - a)^k u = 0$$

will also be a solution of (1).

We now seek a solution of (3) of the form

$$(4) \qquad\qquad u = e^{ax} X$$

where X is a function of x to be determined. Substituting (4) in (3) and using the exponential shift, gives

$$e^{ax}(D + a - a)^k X = 0$$

or since $e^{ax} \neq 0$,

$$(5) \qquad\qquad D^k X = 0.$$

Therefore

$$X = D^{-k} 0 = P_{k-1}(x)$$

where $P_{k-1}(x)$ is a polynomial in x of degree $k - 1$ having k arbitrary constants for coefficients.

To see this clearly let $k = 3$; then

$$X = D^{-3}0 = D^{-2}C_1 = D^{-1}(C_1 x + C_2) = \tfrac{1}{2}C_1 x^2 + C_2 x + C_3$$

where we may as well replace $\tfrac{1}{2}C_1$ by C_1.

Corresponding to every real k-fold root a, we thus obtain a solution of (1) of the form:

(6) $$e^{ax}(C_1 x^{k-1} + C_2 x^{k-2} + \cdots + C_{k-1}x + C_k).$$

This discloses that

$$e^{ax}, \quad xe^{ax}, \quad x^2 e^{ax}, \ldots, x^{k-1}e^{ax}$$

are all particular solutions of (1). Moreover they are linearly independent solutions, since the functions

$$1, \quad x, \quad x^2, \ldots, x^{k-1}$$

are linearly independent. For if there were an *identity*

(7) $$a + bx + cx^2 + \cdots + hx^{k-1} \equiv 0$$

connecting them, this equation would admit *any* value of x as a root—an impossibility since equation (7) can have at most $k - 1$ distinct roots. Thus the existence of an identity such as (7) implies that the constants $a, b, c, \ldots, h$ are all zero.

In particular, for every *simple* root a of the characteristic equation, the reduced equation has the corresponding solution Ce^{ax}.

Next suppose that equation (2)—having *real* coefficients—has two k-fold conjugate complex roots $a + bi, a - bi$. For these roots the corresponding solutions of (1) are

(8) $$e^{(a+bi)x}P(x), \qquad e^{(a-bi)x}Q(x)$$

where $P(x)$ and $Q(x)$ are polynomials of degree $k - 1$, each containing k arbitrary constants. Now

$$e^{(a+bi)x} = e^{ax}(\cos bx + i \sin bx), \qquad e^{(a-bi)x} = e^{ax}(\cos bx - i \sin bx);$$

the sum of the solutions (8), which is also a solution of (1), may therefore be written

$$e^{ax}(P + Q) \cos bx + i(P - Q) \sin bx.$$

Now if $p(x)$ and $q(x)$ are arbitrary *real* polynomials of degree $k - 1$, choose

$$P = \tfrac{1}{2}(p - iq), \qquad Q = \tfrac{1}{2}(p + iq).$$

Then

$$P + Q = p, \qquad i(P - Q) = q,$$

and the solution corresponding to the k-fold complex roots $a \pm bi$ becomes

$$(9) \qquad e^{ax}\{p_{k-1}(x) \cos bx + q_{k-1}(x) \sin bx\}$$

in which we have restored the subscript $k - 1$ to indicate degree. Note that there are $2k$ real arbitrary constants in (9), k in each polynomial.

For a *simple* complex pair $a \pm bi$, the solution (9) reduces to

$$(10) \qquad e^{ax}(C_1 \cos bx + C_2 \sin bx).$$

We summarize these results in Table 37.

Table 37

Roots of $f(r) = 0$		Solution
Real	Simple	Ce^{ax}
a	k-fold	$e^{ax}P_{k-1}(x)$
Complex	simple	$e^{ax}(C_1 \cos bx + C_2 \sin bx)$
$a \pm ib$	k-fold	$e^{ax}\{P_{k-1}(x) \cos bx + Q_{k-1}(x) \sin bx\}$

The last entry includes all the others; for when $k = 1$, it reduces to the third; when $b = 0$, it reduces to the second; and when $b = 0$ and $k = 1$, it reduces to the first.

To obtain the general solution $y_0(x)$ of the differential equation $f(D)y = 0$ of order n:

(i) Find the roots of $f(r) = 0$;

(ii) Write the contributions of each root to the solution from the table above;

(iii) Add these contributions to get $y_0(x)$ which will then contain exactly n arbitrary constants.

Example 1. Consider an equation $f(D)u = 0$ of order ten; and let $f(r) = 0$ have the ten roots

$$-3, \quad 0, \quad 0, \quad 0, \quad \pm i, \quad 2 \pm 3i, \quad 2 \pm 3i.$$

They correspond respectively to the particular solutions:

$$C_1 e^{-3x}, \quad C_2 + C_3 x + C_4 x^2, \quad C_5 \cos x + C_6 \sin x,$$
$$e^{2x}(C_7 + C_8 x) \cos 3x, \quad e^{2x}(C_9 + C_{10}x) \sin 3x.$$

The general solution is the sum of these particular solutions and contains ten arbitrary constants.

Example 2. Find an operator $f(D)$ which nullifies the function

$$\varphi(x) = 4 - e^{3x} + 7xe^{-x} + 3e^{-x} \cos 2x,$$

that is, $f(D)\varphi(x) = 0$.

Solution. From the preceding table we obtain the factors of $f(D)$ which nullify the separate terms of $\varphi(x)$. Omitting the constant coefficients of the terms, we have:

Term	Roots	Factor
1	0	D
e^{3x}	3	$D - 3$
xe^{-x}	$-1, -1$	$(D + 1)^2$
$e^{-x} \cos 2x$	$-1 \pm 2i$	$(D + 1)^2 + 2^2 = D^2 + 2D + 5$

Thus $f(D) = D(D - 3)(D + 1)^2(D^2 + 2D + 5)$ is the *nullifying operator.*

PROBLEMS

Find the general solution for each of the following equations (cf. § 35, Problems 1–10).

1. $(D^3 - 1)y = 0.$ **2.** $(D^4 - 1)y = 0.$
3. $(D^4 + 1)y = 0.$ **4.** $(D^4 + 2D^2 + 1)y = 0.$
5. $(D^3 - 2D^2 + 3D - 2)y = 0.$ **6.** $(D^3 + 2D^2 - D - 2)y = 0.$
7. $(D^3 - 5D - 2)y = 0.$ **8.** $(D^3 + D^2 + D + 1)y = 0.$
9. $(D^4 + 3D^2 + 2)y = 0.$ **10.** $(D^4 + D^2 + 1)y = 0.$
11. $D(D + 1)^2(D^2 + 1)(D^2 + 2D + 2)y = 0.$
12. $(D - 1)^3(D^2 - 4D + 8)^2y = 0.$
Find a nullifying operator in Problems 13 to 15.
13. $x^2e^{3x} - x^3 \sin x + 2x + 3.$
14. $x \cos x + 3 \sin x + 4e^{-x} \cos x.$
15. $2x^3 + x - 3 + (x^2 + 2)e^{-2x} + 3 \sin 2x.$
16. Solve $y''' - 4y' = 0$ if $y(0) = 1$, $y'(0) = 0$, $y''(0) = 2.$
17. $y'' + 2by' + a^2y = 0.$
Show that the solution is

$$y = e^{-bx}\begin{cases} A \cosh \sqrt{b^2 - a^2}\,x + B \sinh \sqrt{b^2 - a^2}\,x & \text{(i)} \\ A + Bx & \text{(ii)} \\ A \cos \sqrt{a^2 - b^2}\,x + B \sin \sqrt{a^2 - b^2}\,x & \text{(iii)} \end{cases}$$

according as $b^2 \gtreqless a^2$. Deduce the solution (ii) from both (i) and (iii) by passing to the limit $a \to b$. $\left[\text{As } x \to 0, \quad \dfrac{\sinh x}{x} \quad \text{and} \quad \dfrac{\sin x}{x} \to 1.\right]$

38. EQUATION OF SECOND ORDER

The important equation of the second order with constant coefficients

$$(aD^2 + bD + c)y = 0$$

has the characteristic quadratic

$$ar^2 + br + c = 0.$$

Its roots may be real and distinct, real and equal, or conjugate complex.

Case 1. $b^2 - 4ac > 0$; the roots

$$\frac{-b \pm \sqrt{b^2 - 4ac}}{2a} = \alpha \pm \beta \text{ are real and distinct.}$$

Two independent solutions are

$$u_1 = e^{(\alpha + \beta)x}, \qquad v_1 = e^{(\alpha - \beta)x}.$$

It is often more convenient to take $u = \frac{1}{2}(u_1 + v_1)$ and $v = \frac{1}{2}(u_1 - v_1)$ as the independent solutions (§ 28); then

(1) $$u = e^{\alpha x} \cosh \beta x, \qquad v = e^{\alpha x} \sinh \beta x.*$$

Case 2. $b^2 - 4ac = 0$; there is a real double root $-b/2a = \alpha$. Two independent solutions are

(2) $$u = e^{\alpha x}, \qquad v = xe^{\alpha x}.$$

Case 3. $b^2 - 4ac < 0$; the roots

$$\frac{-b \pm i\sqrt{4ac - b^2}}{2a} = \alpha \pm i\beta \text{ are conjugate complex.}$$

Two independent solutions are

(3) $$u = e^{\alpha x} \cos \beta x, \qquad v = e^{\alpha x} \sin \beta x.$$

In the solution of a complete equation

(4) $$(D^2 + bD + c)y = \varphi(x)$$

in which $a = 1$, we shall use a solution $v(x)$ of the reduced equation which satisfies the conditions

(5) $$v(0) = 0, \qquad v'(0) = 1.$$

In the three cases we have respectively:

(1)′ $$v = \frac{1}{\beta} e^{\alpha x} \sinh \beta x,$$

(2)′ $$v = xe^{\alpha x},$$

(3)′ $$v = \frac{1}{\beta} e^{\alpha x} \sin \beta x.$$

---

* By definition, $\cosh x = \dfrac{e^x + e^{-x}}{2}$, $\quad \sinh x = \dfrac{e^x - e^{-x}}{2}$.

In the next article we shall see that the particular integral $y_1(x)$ of (4) which satisfies the conditions

$$y_1(x_0) = 0, \qquad y_1'(x_0) = 0$$

is given by

(6) $$y_1(x) = \int_{x_0}^{x} \varphi(t)v(x - t)\, dt.$$

The general solution of (4) is then

(7) $$y(x) = c_1u_1(x) + c_2u_2(x) + y_1(x).$$

39. THE PARTICULAR INTEGRAL

Theorem 1. *Let $v(x)$ be the solution of the reduced equation*

(1) $$y'' + by' + cy = 0$$

which satisfies the conditions

$$v(0) = 0, \qquad v'(0) = 1.$$

Then the solution $y_1(x)$ of the complete equation

(2) $$y'' + by' + cy = \varphi(x)$$

which satisfies the conditions

$$y_1(x_0) = 0, \qquad y_1'(x_0) = 0$$

is given by

(3) $$y_1(x) = \int_{x_0}^{x} \varphi(t)v(x - t)\, dt.$$

PROOF. Differentiate $y_1(x)$ in (3):*

$$y_1'(x) = \varphi(x)v(x - x) + \int_{x_0}^{x} \varphi(t)\frac{\partial}{\partial x} v(x - t)\, dt.$$

Now $v(0) = 0$; and if $\xi = x - t$

$$\frac{\partial}{\partial x} v(x - t) = \frac{\partial v}{\partial \xi}\frac{\partial \xi}{\partial x} = v'(x - t)$$

where $v'(x - t)$ denotes a derivative with respect to the argument $\xi = x - t$; hence

(4) $$y_1'(x) = \int_{x_0}^{x} \varphi(t)v'(x - t)\, dt;$$

---

* *Advanced Calculus*, § 133.

Differentiating again we have

(5) $$y_1''(x) = \varphi(x) + \int_{x_0}^{x} \varphi(t)v''(x-t)\, dt$$

since $v'(0) = 1$. Now multiply (3) by c, (4) by b, and add the resulting equations to (5). Then

(6) $$y_1'' + by_1' + cy_1 = \varphi(x);$$

for the integral

$$\int_{x_0}^{x} \varphi(t)\{v_0''(\xi) + bv'(\xi) + cv(\xi)\}\, dt = 0$$

since $v(x)$ is a solution of (1). Equation (6) shows that $y_1(x)$ satisfies the complete equation (2); and from (3) and (4) we have $y_1(x_0) = 0, y'(x_0) = 0$.

This theorem is readily generalized to apply to equation (35.1) of order n with $a_0 = 1$.

Theorem 2. *Let $v(x)$ be the solution of the reduced equation*

(7) $$y^{(n)} + a_1 y^{(n-1)} + \cdots + a_{n-1} y' + a_n y = 0$$

which satisfies the conditions

$$v(0) = v'(0) = \cdots = v^{(n-2)}(0) = 0, \qquad v^{(n-1)}(0) = 1.$$

Then the solution of the complete equation

(8) $$y^{(n)} + a_1 y^{(n-1)} + \cdots + a_{n-1} y' + a_n y = \varphi(x)$$

which satisfies the conditions

$$y(x_0) = y'(x_0) = \cdots = y^{(n-1)}(x_0) = 0,$$

is given by

(9) $$y_1(x) = \int_{x_0}^{x} \varphi(t)v(x-t)\, dt.$$

The proof follows the plan used in Theorem 1 and is left to the reader.

Example 1. The solution of the initial value problem

$$y'' + n^2 y = \varphi(x), \qquad y(0) = k, \qquad y'(0) = k'$$

is

$$y = k \cos nx + \frac{k'}{n} \sin nx + \frac{1}{n} \int_0^x \varphi(t) \sin n(x-t)\, dt;$$

for $v(x) = \dfrac{1}{n} \sin nx$ (38.3′) and the first two terms satisfy the initial conditions.

Example 2. The solution of the initial value problem

$$y'' + 2y' + y = \varphi(x), \qquad y(0) = k, \qquad y'(0) = k'$$

is

$$ke^x + (k - k')xe^x + \int_0^x \varphi(t)(x - t)e^{-(x-t)}\, dt$$

for $v(x) = xe^{-x}$ (38.2') and the first two terms satisfy the initial conditions. The integral may also be written

$$y_1 = \int_0^x \varphi(x - s)se^{-s}\, ds$$

by the change $t = x - s$, $dt = -ds$, in variable of integration. For example, if $\varphi(x) = e^{-x}$,

$$y_1 = \int_0^x e^{-(x-s)}se^{-s}\, ds = e^{-x}\int_0^x s\, ds = \tfrac{1}{2}x^2 e^{-x}.$$

Example 3. Solve the equation

(i) $$(D - a)^n y = \varphi(x).$$

Since $(r - a)^n = 0$ has the n-fold root a, the reduced equation has the general solution

(ii) $$y_0 = (c_1 + c_2 x + \cdots + c_k x^{n-1})e^{ax}. \qquad (\S 37)$$

The solution $x^{n-1}e^{ax}$ has the derivatives

$$D^k(x^{n-1}e^{ax}) = e^{ax}(D + a)^k x^{n-1}, \qquad k = 1, 2, \ldots, n - 1.$$

When $k < n - 1$, this contains x as a factor and vanishes when $x = 0$; when $k = n - 1$, the term independent of x is $e^{ax}(n - 1)!$ and the derivative becomes $(n - 1)!$ when $x = 0$. Thus we may take

$$v(x) = \frac{1}{(n - 1)!}\, x^{n-1}e^{ax}$$

and from (9) obtain the particular integral

(iii) $$y_1 = \frac{1}{(n - 1)!}\int_0^x \varphi(t)(x - t)^{n-1}e^{a(x-t)}\, dt,$$

or, making the change of variable $t = x - s$,

(iv) $$y_1 = \frac{1}{(n - 1)!}\int_0^x \varphi(x - s)s^{n-1}e^{as}\, ds.$$

The general solution $y = y_0 + y_1$.

PROBLEMS

Find the solution $v(x)$ of the reduced equation which satisfies the conditions $v(0) = 0$, $v'(0) = 1$, and the solution $y_1(x)$ of the complete equation for which $y_1(0) = y_1'(0) = 0$.

1. $y'' = e^{-x^2}$.
2. $y'' - 2y' = x$.
3. $y'' - 4y = 2$.
4. $y'' - 3y' + 2y = e^x$.
5. $y'' + 2y' + 2y = e^{-x}$.
6. $y'' + y = \sec^3 x$.
7. $y'' - (a + b)y' + aby = \varphi(x)$.
8. $y''' - 7y'' + 14y' - 8y = 1/x$, $\quad y(1) = y'(1) = 0$.
9. When $x_0 = 0$ show that (3) may be written

$$y_1(x) = \int_0^x \varphi(x - s)v(s)\, ds.$$

10. Use Problem 9 to find $y_1(x)$ for $(D + 1)^3 y = e^{-x}$.

40. METHOD OF UNDETERMINED COEFFICIENTS

Although the method of finding a particular integral given in § 38 is always applicable, it is usually simpler to use the following method when the right member $\varphi(x)$ of the complete equation

$$(1) \qquad\qquad f(D)y = \varphi(x)$$

consists of terms included in the table at the end of § 37. In this case we can always find an operator $g(D)$ which nullifies $\varphi(x)$, as explained in Example 37.2. Thus all solutions of the complete equation (1) are included in the general solution of

$$(2) \qquad\qquad g(D)f(D)y = g(D)\varphi(x) = 0,$$

a reduced equation of higher order. This determines the *form* of all particular solutions of (1).

Procedure

Let $f(r) = 0$ have m roots $r_1, r_2, \ldots, r_m$; construct from them the complementary function

$$(3) \qquad\qquad y_0 = c_1 u_1 + c_2 u_2 + \cdots + c_m u_m.$$

If $g(s) = 0$ has the n roots $s_1, s_2, \ldots, s_n$, the characteristic equation of (2)

$$g(s)f(r) = 0$$

has the $m + n$ roots $r_1, \ldots, r_m, s_1, \ldots, s_n$. From the set r, s, construct the general solution of (2); besides the terms in y_0 it will contain n *new* terms

(4) $$Av_1 + Bv_2 + \cdots + Kv_n.$$

That particular solution of (1) which does not contain the functions u_i in y_0 (which contribute nothing to $\varphi(x)$ since $f(D)u_i = 0$) is given by (4) when the "undetermined constants" $A, B, \ldots$ are properly chosen. To find them substitute

(5) $$y = Av_1 + Bv_2 + \cdots + Kv_n$$

in the left member of (1) and equate the coefficients of like functions on both sides. There are two cases.

Case 1. None of the roots r occur in the set s

In this case equation (5) is the general solution of $g(D)y = 0$. Then the functions v_i are those that occur in $\varphi(x)$ plus all those that result from them by repeated differentiation. (Ex. 1 and 2.)

Case 2. Some of the roots r occur in the set s

The set r, s now contains roots of higher multiplicity than either component set. From the set r, s, form the general solution of $g(D)f(D)y = 0$, discard all the functions u_i in y_0, and use the remaining functions v_i to get the proper form (5) of the particular solution.

Example 1. Solve the equation

$$y'' - 3y' + 2y = 2e^{-x} - x - \cos x.$$

From $r^2 - 3r + 2 = 0$, $r = 1, 2$. The roots of the operator that nullifies the right member: $s = -1, 0, 0, \pm i$. Since the set s has no roots in common with set r, we seek a particular solution of the form

$$\begin{array}{r|l}
2 & y = Ae^{-x} + B + Cx + D \cos x + E \sin x. \\
-3 & y' = -Ae^{-x} + C \quad\quad + E \cos x - D \sin x. \\
1 & y'' = Ae^{-x} \quad\quad\quad\quad - D \cos x - E \sin x.
\end{array}$$

The undetermined constants are A, B, C, D, E. In differentiating, put like functions in the same column. The equations are multiplied by the constants to the left of the line and added. On the left we have

$$2e^{-x} + x - \cos x;$$

and on the right

$$6Ae^{-x} + (2B - 3C) + 2Cx + (D - 3E) \cos x + (E + 3D) \sin x.$$

Equating coefficients of like functions gives five equations

$$6A = 2, \quad\quad 2B - 3C = 0, \quad\quad 2C = 1,$$
$$D - 3E = -1, \quad\quad E + 3D = 0;$$

whence
$$A = \tfrac{1}{3}, \qquad B = \tfrac{3}{4}, \qquad C = \tfrac{1}{2}, \qquad D = -\tfrac{1}{10}, \qquad E = \tfrac{3}{10}.$$

The particular integral
$$y_1 = \tfrac{1}{3}e^{-x} + \tfrac{3}{4} + \tfrac{1}{2}x - \tfrac{1}{10}\cos x + \tfrac{3}{10}\sin x$$

is the simplest possible; for it contains no functions in the complementary function
$$y_0 = c_1 e^x + c_2 e^{2x}.$$

The general solution $y = y_0 + y_1$.

Example 2. Solve the equation
$$y'' + y = x^2 + 2\sinh x.$$

From $r^2 + 1 = 0, r = \pm i$.
Since $2\sinh x = e^x - e^{-x}$, the roots of the operator that nullifies the right member are: $s = 0, 0, 0, 1, -1$. Since these differ from the r's, we seek a particular solution of the form

$$
\begin{array}{r|l}
1 & y = A + Bx + Cx^2 + De^x + Ee^{-x}. \\
0 & y' = B + 2Cx \qquad\quad + De^x - Ee^{-x}. \\
1 & y'' = 2C \qquad\qquad\quad + De^x + Ee^{-x}. \\
\hline
\end{array}
$$

$$x^2 + e^x - e^{-x} = (A + 2C) + Bx + Cx^2 + 2De^x + 2Ee^{-x}.$$

Equating coefficients:
$$A + 2C = 0, \qquad B = 0, \qquad C = 1, \qquad 2D = 1, \qquad 2E = -1;$$
hence
$$A = -2, \qquad B = 0, \qquad C = 1, \qquad D = \tfrac{1}{2}, \qquad E = -\tfrac{1}{2}.$$

The particular solution
$$y_1 = x^2 - 2 + \tfrac{1}{2}e^x - \tfrac{1}{2}e^{-x} = x^2 - 2 + \sinh x$$

is the simplest possible; for it contains no functions in the complementary function
$$y_0 = c_1 \cos x + c_2 \sin x.$$

The general solution $y = y_0 + y_1$.

Example 3. Solve the equation of Example 36.2:
$$y'' + y' - 2y = e^x.$$

From $r^2 + r - 2 = 0, r = 1, -2$.
The complementary function
$$y_0 = c_1 e^x + c_2 e^{-2x}.$$

The operator $D - 1$ nullifies e^x; hence $s = 1$. The reduced equation for the set $1, 1, -2$ has the solution
$$k_1 e^x + k_2 x e^x + k_3 e^{-2x}.$$

The second term is new; hence we seek a particular solution

$$
\begin{array}{r|l}
-2 & y = Axe^x. \\
1 & y' = A(x + 1)e^x. \\
1 & y'' = A(x + 2)e^x. \\
\hline
\end{array}
$$

$$e^x = 3Ae^x, \qquad A = \tfrac{1}{3}.$$

Note that we now obtain the *simplest* particular solution $y_1 = \frac{1}{3}xe^x$; and

$$y = c_1e^x + c_2e^{-2x} + \tfrac{1}{3}xe^x \qquad \text{(cf. Ex. 36.2.)}$$

Example 4. Solve the equation

$$y'' + y = x \cos x.$$

From $r^2 + 1 = 0$, $r = \pm i$; and

$$y_0 = c_1 \cos x + c_2 \sin x.$$

The operator that nullifies $x \cos x$ is $(D^2 + 1)^2$; hence $s = \pm i,\ \pm i$. The reduced equation for the set $\pm i,\ \pm i,\ \pm i$ has the solution

$$(k_1 + k_2 x + k_3 x^2) \cos x + (k_4 + k_5 x + k_6 x^2) \sin x.$$

The second, third, fifth and sixth terms are new; we therefore seek a particular solution of the form

$$
\begin{array}{l|l}
1 & y = (Ax + Bx^2) \cos x + (Cx + Dx^2) \sin x. \\
0 & y' = \{A + (2B + C)x + Dx^2\} \cos x + \{C + (2D - A)x - Bx^2\} \sin x. \\
1 & y'' = \{2(B + C) + (4D - A)x - Bx^2\} \cos x +. \\
  & \quad \{2(D - A) - (4B + C)x - Dx^2\} \sin x.
\end{array}
$$

Multiply the equations as shown and add them; then

$$x \cos x = \{2(B + C) + 4Dx\} \cos x + \{2(D - A) - 4Bx\} \sin x.$$

Hence

$$B + C = 0, \qquad 4D = 1, \qquad D - A = 0, \qquad B = 0;$$

and with $A = D = \frac{1}{4}$, $B = C = 0$, we have

$$y_1 = \tfrac{1}{4}(x \cos x + x^2 \sin x).$$

The general solution $y = y_0 + y_1$.

PROBLEMS

Find the complementary function y_0 and the simplest particular integral y_1.

1. $y'' - 2y' + y = \cos x$. (Ex. 36.3).   2. $3y'' + 2y' - 8y = 5 \cos x$.
3. $y'' - y = 1 - x - x^4$.   4. $y''' + y = 1 + x^2 + x^4$.
5. $y''' - 3y'' + 3y' - y = e^{-x}$.   6. $y'' + 2y' + 5y = x^2$.
7. $y'' + y = \cos x$.   8. $y'' + y = \sin x$.
9. $y'' - y = xe^x$.   10. $y'' + y' - 2y = e^x + e^{2x}$.
11. $y'' - y = xe^x$.   12. $y'' - 2y' + 2y = e^x \sin x$.
13. $y'' - y = x^2 - 2 \cos x$.   14. $y'' + y = x \cos x$.
15. $y'' + y = x \sin x$.
16. $y'' + 4y' + 13y = 4 \sin t - 12 \cos t$.
17. Solve Problem 16 under the conditions $y(0) = 0$, $y'(0) = -2$.

41. THE OPERATOR $1/f(D)$

If $f(D)$ is a polynomial in D, we shall denote any solution of the differential equation

$$f(D)y = \varphi(x) \quad \text{by} \quad y = \frac{1}{f(D)} \varphi(x).$$

Thus $f(D)$ nullifies $1/f(D)$:

(1) $$f(D) \frac{1}{f(D)} = 1, \quad \text{the identity operator.}$$

$f(D)$ and $1/f(D)$ do not commute; thus

$$D \cdot \frac{1}{D} x = D\left(\frac{x^2}{2} + c\right) = x, \qquad \frac{1}{D} \cdot Dx = \frac{1}{D} \cdot 1 = x + c.$$

Using this definition the exponential shift formulas

(2) $$f(D)e^{ax}X = e^{ax}f(D + a)X$$

(3) $$f(D)e^{ax} = f(a)e^{ax}$$

are also valid for $1/f(D)$:

(4) $$\frac{1}{f(D)} e^{ax}X = e^{ax} \frac{1}{f(D + a)} X,$$

(5) $$\frac{1}{f(D)} e^{ax} = \frac{e^{ax}}{f(a)}, \qquad f(a) \neq 0.$$

When $a = 0$, (5) becomes

(6) $$\frac{1}{f(D)} 1 = \frac{1}{f(0)}, \qquad f(0) \neq 0.$$

PROOFS. Apply $f(D)$ to (4) and use (2):

$$f(D)\left\{e^{ax} \frac{1}{f(D + a)} X\right\} = e^{ax}\left\{f(D + a) \frac{1}{f(D + a)}\right\}X = e^{ax}X.$$

Apply $f(D)$ to (5) and use (3):

$$f(D)\left\{\frac{e^{ax}}{f(a)}\right\} = \frac{1}{f(a)} f(a)e^{ax} = e^{ax}, \qquad f(a) \neq 0.$$

When $f(a) = 0$, $f(D)$ has $D - a$ as a factor, say

$$f(D) = (D - a)^k g(D), \qquad g(a) \neq 0.$$

Using (5) we have

$$\frac{1}{f(D)} e^{ax} = \frac{1}{(D-a)^k} \cdot \frac{1}{g(D)} e^{ax} = \frac{1}{(D-a)^k} \frac{e^{ax}}{g(a)};$$

and now from (4)

$$\frac{1}{g(a)} \frac{1}{(D-a)^k} e^{ax} = \frac{e^{ax}}{g(a)} \frac{1}{D^k} 1 = \frac{e^{ax}}{g(a)} \cdot \frac{x^k}{k!}$$

where $x^k/k!$ is the k-fold integral of 1 when constants are omitted; therefore

(7) $$\frac{1}{(D-a)^k g(D)} e^{ax} = \frac{x^k e^{ax}}{k!\, g(a)}, \qquad g(a) \neq 0.$$

These formulas are also applicable to

$$e^{ibx} = \cos bx + i \sin bx;$$

then

$$\frac{1}{f(D)} \cos bx = \mathrm{Re}\, \frac{1}{f(D)} e^{ibx}, \qquad \frac{1}{f(D)} \sin bx = \mathrm{Im}\, \frac{1}{f(D)} e^{ibx}.$$

For example, when a and b are positive,

$$\frac{1}{D^2 + a^2} e^{ibx} = \frac{e^{ibx}}{a^2 - b^2}, \qquad a \neq b;$$

$$\frac{1}{D^2 + a^2} e^{iax} = \frac{1}{(D-ai)(D+ai)} e^{iax} = \frac{1}{D-ai} \frac{e^{iax}}{2ai}$$

$$= \frac{e^{iax}}{2ai} \frac{1}{D} 1 = \frac{-ixe^{iax}}{2a};$$

hence

(8) $$\frac{1}{D^2 + a^2} \cos bx = \frac{\cos bx}{a^2 - b^2},$$

$$(a \neq b),$$

(9) $$\frac{1}{D^2 + a^2} \sin bx = \frac{\sin bx}{a^2 - b^2};$$

(10) $$\frac{1}{D^2 + a^2} \cos ax = \frac{x}{2a} \sin ax,$$

(11) $$\frac{1}{D^2 + a^2} \sin ax = -\frac{x}{2a} \cos ax.$$

Example 1. To find a particular integral of

$$(D^2 + 2D + 5)y = 3 + 2e^x - e^{-x}$$

we apply (5) to each term on the right:*

$$y_1 = \frac{3}{f(0)} + 2\frac{e^x}{f(1)} - \frac{e^{-x}}{f(-1)} = \frac{3}{5} + \frac{1}{4}e^x - \frac{1}{4}e^{-x}$$

or

$$y_1 = \tfrac{3}{5} + \tfrac{1}{2}\sinh x.$$

Example 2. A particular integral of

$$(D - 1)^2(D - 2)y = 2e^x$$

is

$$y_1 = \frac{2}{(D-1)^2}\frac{1}{D+2}e^x = \frac{2}{(D-1)^2}\frac{e^x}{3} \qquad \text{from (5)}$$

$$= \frac{2}{3}e^x\frac{1}{D^2}1 = \frac{2}{3}e^x \cdot \frac{x^2}{2} = \frac{1}{3}x^2e^x \qquad \text{from (4).}$$

Or we may use (7) directly with $g(D) = D + 2$:

$$y_1 = 2\frac{x^2e^x}{2!g(1)} = \frac{1}{3}x^2e^x.$$

Example 3. To find a particular integral of

$$(D^2 + 2D + 2)y = \cos x + 2\sin x,$$

we first apply $1/(D^2 + 2D + 2)$ to e^{ix}:

$$\frac{1}{D^2 + 2D + 2}e^{ix} = \frac{e^{ix}}{1 + 2i} = \frac{(1 - 2i)(\cos x + i\sin x)}{5}.$$

The real part plus twice the imaginary part gives

$$y_1 = \frac{\cos x + 2\sin x}{5} + 2\frac{\sin x - 2\cos x}{5}$$

$$= \frac{4\sin x - 3\cos x}{5} = \sin(x - \alpha)$$

where $\alpha = \tan^{-1}\tfrac{3}{4}$ (principal value!).

The method of undetermined coefficients gives this result with equal ease and less risk of error. Try it.

To find a particular solution of the differential equation

$$(1) \qquad\qquad f(D)y = P_k(x)$$

with a polynomial $P_k(x)$ of degree k on the right, we may use the following operational method. Let

$$f(D) = a_0 + a_1D + a_2D^2 + \cdots + a_nD^n;$$

---

* Note that

$$\frac{1}{f(D)}(\varphi_1 + \varphi_2) = \frac{1}{f(D)}\varphi_1 + \frac{1}{f(D)}\varphi_2. \text{ Proof?}$$

then there are two cases:

$$\text{(I)} \quad a_0 \neq 0; \qquad \text{(II)} \quad a_0 = 0.$$

In case I carry out the "long" division $1/f(D)$ in *ascending powers* of D until the remainder is of degree $> k$. The remainder will then have the form $g(D)D^{k+h}$ where h is a positive integer (usually 1). Then since

$$\text{dividend} = \text{divisor} \times \text{quotient} + \text{remainder}$$

we have the identity

$$(2) \qquad 1 = f(D)(b_0 + b_1 D + \cdots + b_k D^k) + g(D)D^{k+h}$$

where the quotient $b_0 + b_1 D + \cdots + b_k D^k$ is a polynomial whose degree $\leq k$. Thus the operator on the right in (2) has the same effect as multiplying by 1. Hence if we apply it to the polynomial $P_k(x)$, we get

$$f(D)(b_0 + b_1 D + \cdots + b_k D^k)P_k(x) = P_k(x),$$

since $D^{k+h}P_k(x) = 0$. But this equation states that

$$y(x) = (b_0 + b_1 D + \cdots + b_k D^k)P_k(x)$$

is a particular solution of (1).

Example 4. To find a particular solution of

$$(\text{i}) \qquad (D^2 + D + 1)y = x^3 + 2x + 3$$

we carry out the division

$$\frac{1}{1 + D + D^2} = 1 - D + D^3 - \frac{D^4 + D^5}{1 + D + D^2}$$

to obtain the operational identity

$$1 = (1 + D + D^2)(1 - D + D^3) - (1 + D)D^4.$$

Applying this to $x^3 + 2x + 3$, we see that

$$y = (1 - D + D^3)(x^3 + 2x + 3) = x^3 - 3x^2 + 2x + 7$$

is a particular solution of equation (i).

Example 5. To find a particular solution of

$$(\text{ii}) \qquad (D^3 - 2D + 1)y = x^3 + 2x^2 - x + 1,$$

we perform the division $1/(1 - 2D + D^3)$ by detached coefficients:

$$
\begin{array}{r|l}
1 + 0 + 0 + 0 + 0 + 0 + 0 & 1 - 2 + 0 + 1 \\
1 - 2 + 0 + 1 & \overline{1 + 2 + 4 + 7} \\
\cline{1-1}
2 + 0 - 1 + 0 & \\
2 - 4 + 0 + 2 & \\
\cline{1-1}
4 - 1 - 2 + 0 & \\
4 - 8 + 0 + 4 & \\
\cline{1-1}
7 - 2 - 4 + 0 & \\
7 - 14 + 0 + 7 & \\
\cline{1-1}
12 - 4 - 7. &
\end{array}
$$

Since the remainder $12D^4 - 4D^5 - 7D^6$ is of degree >3, the quotient $1 + 2D + 4D^2 + 7D^3$ yields the particular integral

$$y_1 = (1 + 2D + 4D^2 + 7D^3)(x^3 + 2x^2 - x + 1)$$
$$= x^3 + 8x^2 + 31x + 57.$$

In case II the constant term in $f(D)$ is absent; we may then write

$$f(D) = D^m g(D), \qquad g(0) \neq 0,$$

and obtain an operator from

$$\frac{1}{g(D)} = b_0 + b_1 D + \cdots + b_k D^k$$

as before. Then

$$y_1 = D^{-m}(b_0 + b_1 D + \cdots + b_k D^k)P_k(x)$$

where D^{-m} means m integrations without additive constants; for the terms arising from these constants are already in the complementary function.

Example 6. A particular integral of

$$D^2(D^2 + 1)y = x^3 + 2x + 3$$

is given by

$$y_1 = \frac{1}{D^2}\frac{1}{1 + D^2}(x^3 + 2x + 3).$$

Recalling that

$$\frac{1}{1 - r} = 1 + r + r^2 + \cdots + r^{n-1} + \frac{r^n}{1 - r},$$

we have

$$\frac{1}{1 + D^2} = 1 - D^2 + \frac{D^4}{1 + D^2}.$$

Since $D^4(x^3 - 2x + 3) = 0$, we have

$$y_1 = \frac{1}{D^2}(1 - D^2)(x^3 + 2x + 3)$$

$$= \frac{1}{D^2}(x^3 + 2x + 3 - 6x)$$

$$= \frac{1}{D^2}(x^3 - 4x + 3)$$

$$= \frac{1}{D}\left(\frac{1}{4}x^4 - 2x^2 + 3x\right),$$

$$y_1 = \frac{1}{20}x^5 - \frac{2}{3}x^3 + \frac{3}{2}x^2.$$

Example 7. To find a particular integral of

$$(D - 1)^2(D + 1)y = x^2 e^x$$

we first apply the exponential shift:

$$y_1 = \frac{1}{(D - 1)^2(D + 1)} x^2 e^x$$

$$= e^x \frac{1}{D^2(D + 2)} x^2$$

$$= \frac{e^x}{2} \frac{1}{D^2} \frac{1}{1 + \frac{1}{2}D} x^2.$$

At this point we expand $1/(1 + \frac{1}{2}D)$ into a geometric series, stopping at the term in D^2; thus

$$y_1 = \frac{1}{2} e^x \frac{1}{D^2} \left(1 - \frac{1}{2}D + \frac{1}{4}D^2\right) x^2$$

$$= \frac{1}{2} e^x \frac{1}{D^2} \left(x^2 - x + \frac{1}{2}\right)$$

$$= \frac{1}{2} e^x \frac{1}{D} \left(\frac{1}{3}x^3 - \frac{1}{2}x^2 + \frac{1}{2}x\right)$$

$$= \frac{1}{2} e^x \left(\frac{1}{12}x^4 - \frac{1}{6}x^3 + \frac{1}{4}x^2\right),$$

$$y_1 = \frac{1}{24} e^x(x^4 - 2x^3 + 3x^2).$$

PROBLEMS

Find a particular solution by operational methods. Paired problems (starred) should be solved together.

1. $(D - 1)^3 y = 1 + e^x + e^{2x} - e^{-x}$ 2. $(D^2 - 3D + 2)y = 2 \sinh x$
3. $(D^2 + 4D - 5)y = 4 \sin x$ *   4. $(D^2 + 4D - 5)y = 4 \cos x$
5. $(D^2 - 2D + 2)y = e^x \cos x$ *   6. $(D^2 - 2D + 2)y = e^x \sin x$
7. $(D^3 + D)y = 1 + e^{2x} + \cos x$ 8. $(D^3 + D)y = 2 + e^{-x} + \sin x$
9. $(D - 2)^2 y = 6x^2 e^{2x}$ 10. $(D^2 + 4D + 13)y = 6e^{2x} \cos 3x$
11. $(D^2 + 1)y = 2 \cos^2 x$ 12. $(D^3 - 1)y = \cosh x$
13. $(D^4 - 1)y = \cos x$ *   14. $(D^4 - 1)y = \sin x$
15. $(D^2 + 1)y = xe^{-x} \cos x$ *   16. $(D^2 + 1)y = xe^{-x} \sin x$
17. $(D^2 + D + 1)y = x^6$ 18. $(D^2 + 1)y = x^8$
19. $(D + 1)^3 y = e^{-x} + x^2$ 20. $(D^5 - 1)y = x^{10} + e^x$
21. $(D^2 + 1)y = f(x)$, a polynomial.

Show that a particular solution is

$$y = f(x) - f''(x) + f^{iv}(x) - f^{vi}(x) + \cdots$$

until the series terminates. Apply to Problem 18.

42. STABILITY

In the linear equation with constant real coefficients

(1) $$f(D)y = (a_0 D^n + a_1 D^{n-1} + \cdots + a_{n-1}D + a_n)y = 0,$$

let us regard the independent variable x as time. This equation is said to be *strictly stable* if every member of its solution basis is a *transient*; that is, every solution $\to 0$ as $x \to \infty$. An examination of the table at the end of § 37 shows that a solution basis consists of a set of functions of the form

$$e^{ax}x^j \cos bx, \qquad e^{ax}x^j \sin bx$$

where a is the real part of a root of the characteristic equation

(2) $$f(r) = a_0 r^n + a_1 r^{n-1} + \cdots + a_{n-1}r + a_n = 0$$

and j is zero or a positive integer. Each member of the basis $\to 0$ as $x \to \infty$ if $a < 0$;* then each root of (2) has a *negative real part*. Under these conditions every solution of (1) is bounded for $x \geqq 0$; for the basis functions are everywhere continuous and tend exponentially to zero as $x \to \infty$. Therefore we may state

Theorem 1. *The real equation* (1) *is strictly stable if every root of its characteristic equation has a negative real part.*

When this condition is fulfilled, all solutions of the complete equation

(3) $$f(D)y = \varphi(x)$$

will be bounded when the input $\varphi(x)$ is bounded. For the general solution of (3) is $y = y_0 + y_1$, where y_0 is a linear combination of the transient basis functions and y_1 a particular solution which may be taken as

$$y_1 = \int_0^x \varphi(t)v(x - t)\, dt \qquad (39.3);$$

and if $|\varphi(x)| < M$ for all $x \geqq 0$,

$$|y_1| < M \int_0^x |v(x - t)|\, dt < M \int_0^x |v(\tau)|\, d\tau$$

where $\tau = x - t$. Since $v(\tau)$ itself tends exponentially to zero, it is readily shown that the last integral is bounded. Thus if equation (1) is *strictly stable, the response to any bounded input $\varphi(x)$ is also bounded.*

If some functions of the solution basis are not transients but all of these are bounded for $x \geqq 0$, the equation is said to be *metastable*. This will be

---

* *Advanced Calculus*, § 66.

the case if all the multiple roots of (2) have negative real parts and when all simple roots ($j = 0$) have zero real parts ($a = 0$). Now, however, the response to *some* inputs $\varphi(x)$ is not bounded, namely, when $\varphi(x)$ contains a term which is a member of the solution basis of equation (1). For example, the equation $y'' + y = 0$ has the simple roots $\pm i$ with zero real parts and its solution basis $\cos x$, $\sin x$ is bounded. But the equation $y'' + y = \cos x$ with the bounded input $\cos x$ gives an unbounded response $\frac{1}{2}x \sin x$. [Cf. (41.10).]

We shall write equation (2) with $a_0 > 0$. This entails no loss in generality; for if $a_0 < 0$, we can multiply the equation by (-1). Now if all the roots of (2) have negative real parts, say $-\alpha$ or $-\alpha \pm i\beta(\alpha > 0)$, the left member of (2) is the product of factors of the type

$$x + \alpha \quad \text{or} \quad (x + \alpha - i\beta)(x + \alpha + i\beta) = x^2 + 2\alpha x + \alpha^2 + \beta^2$$

and all coefficients of (2) will be present and positive ($a_i > 0$). But if some of the simple roots have $\alpha = 0$, the corresponding factors are

$$x \quad \text{or} \quad (x - i\beta)(x + i\beta) = x^2 + \beta^2;$$

all coefficients that appear in (2) will then be positive but some may be missing ($a_i \geq 0$) due to the missing terms in the factors. We thus have the *necessary* conditions for a stable or metastable equation:

Theorem 2. *If equation* (1) *is strictly stable all coefficients of its characteristic equation must be present and positive* ($a_i > 0$); *if it is metastable, all non-zero coefficients must be positive* ($\alpha_i \geq 0$).

That these conditions are not sufficient is shown by Examples 1 and 2 below.

Necessary and sufficient conditions for stability were given by Adolph Hurwitz (1859–1919). To test the nth order equation (1), construct the n-rowed determinant

$$
(4) \quad D_n = \begin{vmatrix}
a_1 & a_3 & a_5 & a_7 & a_9 & \cdots & 0 \\
a_0 & a_2 & a_4 & a_6 & a_8 & \cdots & 0 \\
0 & a_1 & a_3 & a_5 & a_7 & \cdots & 0 \\
0 & a_0 & a_2 & a_4 & a_6 & \cdots & 0 \\
0 & 0 & a_1 & a_3 & a_5 & \cdots & 0 \\
& & & \cdot & & & \\
& & & \cdot & & & \\
& & & \cdot & & & \\
0 & 0 & 0 & 0 & 0 & \cdots & a_n
\end{vmatrix}, \quad a_i = 0 \quad \text{for} \quad i > n,
$$

whose elements are the coefficients a_i and zeros. Rows 1 and 2 contain all a_i of odd index and even index respectively. Rows 3 and 4 start with a zero followed by the elements of rows 1 and 2 respectively; rows 5 and 6 start with two zeros followed by the elements of rows 1 and 2 respectively; and so on. The principal diagonal contains the elements $a_1, a_2, \ldots, a_n$; and the last column consists of $n - 1$ zeros followed by a_n; thus

$$D_5 = \begin{vmatrix} a_1 & a_3 & a_5 & 0 & 0 \\ a_0 & a_2 & a_4 & 0 & 0 \\ 0 & a_1 & a_3 & a_5 & 0 \\ 0 & a_0 & a_2 & a_4 & 0 \\ 0 & 0 & a_1 & a_3 & a_5 \end{vmatrix}.$$

The *Hurwitz* sequence $D_1, D_2, \ldots, D_n$ is now formed from D_n by taking its principal minors of order $1, 2, \ldots, n$ in the upper left-hand corner. Thus for $n = 2$ and 3,

$$(5) \qquad D_1 = a_1, \qquad D_2 = \begin{vmatrix} a_1 & 0 \\ a_0 & a_2 \end{vmatrix};$$

$$(6) \qquad D_1 = a_1, \qquad D_2 = \begin{vmatrix} a_1 & a_3 \\ a_0 & a_2 \end{vmatrix}, \qquad D_3 = \begin{vmatrix} a_1 & a_3 & 0 \\ a_0 & a_2 & 0 \\ 0 & a_1 & a_3 \end{vmatrix}.$$

We now state the *Hurwitz stability criterion*:*

Theorem 3. *When* $a_0 > 0$, *a necessary and sufficient condition that equation* (1) *be strictly stable is that all members of its Hurwitz sequence be positive.*

If an equation is not strictly stable, it may still be metastable if its simple roots are 0 or $\pm\beta i$; but if these roots do not occur, the equation is *unstable*.

---

* For proof see J. V. Uspensky, *Theory of Equation*, McGraw-Hill, N.Y., 1948, appendix 3.

For a thorough treatment of the "Routh-Hurwitz Problem," see Gantmacher, ref. 6, vol. 2, chap. 15. In § 13 of Chapter 15 the simpler criteria of Liénard and Chipart are proved. These state that if $a_n, a_{n-2}, a_{n-4}, \ldots$ are all positive and *either* the D_i of odd index *or* of even index are positive, the roots of $f(r) = 0$ will have negative real parts. Thus if all coefficients a_i of $f(r)$ are positive (a necessary condition for stability) and $D_1, D_3, \ldots > 0$ or $D_2, D_4, \ldots > 0$, the equation (1) is strictly stable. Thus when all $a_i > 0$, $D_i > 0$ for odd i implies $D_i > 0$ for even i and vice versa. For example, if $n = 5$, the Liénard-Chipart conditions are

$$a_5, \qquad a_3, \qquad a_1 > 0; \qquad D_3, D_5 > 0 \quad or \quad D_2, D_4 > 0.$$

Thus the labor of computation is about cut in half.

To help decide this point we state

Theorem 4. *A necessary and sufficient condition that $f(r) = 0$ has a pair of roots of the same absolute value but opposite sign is that $D_{n-1} = 0$.* *

Consequently, when $D_{n-1} \neq 0$, no roots $\pm \beta i$ can occur; and if $a_n \neq 0$, there is no root 0. Since $D_n = a_n D_{n-1}$, if $D_n \neq 0$, neither $\pm \beta i$ nor 0 can be roots and the equation can not be metastable; hence

Theorem 5. *A necessary condition that equation* (1) *be metastable is that* $D_n = 0$.

Of course this condition is not sufficient.

Example 1. In the equation

(i) $$y''' + y'' + y' + y = 0$$

all $a_i = 1$. The Hurwitz sequence

$$D_1 = 1, \qquad D_2 = \begin{vmatrix} 1 & 1 \\ 1 & 1 \end{vmatrix} = 0, \qquad D_3 = \begin{vmatrix} 1 & 1 & 0 \\ 1 & 1 & 0 \\ 0 & 1 & 1 \end{vmatrix} = 0$$

shows that the equation is not stable. But the roots -1, $\pm i$ of its characteristic equation give the solution basis e^{-t}, $\cos t$, $\sin t$ whose members are bounded. Thus equation (i) is metastable. Note that $D_2 = 0$ guarantees an opposed pair of pure imaginary roots.

Example 2. The equation

(ii) $$y''' + y'' + 4y' + 30y = 0$$

has the Hurwitz sequence

$$D_1 = 1, \qquad D_2 = \begin{vmatrix} 1 & 30 \\ 1 & 4 \end{vmatrix} = -26, \qquad D_3 = \begin{vmatrix} 1 & 30 & 0 \\ 1 & 4 & 0 \\ 0 & 1 & 30 \end{vmatrix} = -780.$$

The equation is not stable or metastable ($D_3 < 0$); hence it is *unstable*. This example shows that an equation may be unstable even when all coefficients are present and positive.

PROBLEMS

1. Show directly that

$$a_0 y'' + a_1 y' + a_2 y = 0, \qquad a_0 > 0$$

is stable if $a_1, a_2 > 0$; and metastable if $a_1 > 0$, $a_2 = 0$ or $a_1 = 0$, $a_2 > 0$.

---

* F. R. Gantmacher, ref. 6, vol. 2, chap. 15, § 7. Theorem 4 is proved on p. 197.

2. Show directly that

$$a_0 y''' + a_1 y'' + a_2 y' + a_3 y = 0, \qquad a_0 > 0$$

is stable if $a_1, a_3 > 0$ and $a_1 a_2 > a_0 a_3$.

Test the following equations for stability.

   3. $(D^4 + 3D^3 + 3D^2 + 3D + 2)y = 0.$
   4. $(D^4 + 5D^3 + 10D^2 + 10D + 4)y = 0.$
   5. $(D^4 + D^3 + D^2 + D + 1)y = 0.$

43. EULER'S LINEAR EQUATION

If the operator $\vartheta = xD$ and $f(\vartheta)$ is a polynomial in ϑ, equations of the type

$$(1) \qquad\qquad f(\vartheta)y = \varphi(x)$$

are usually named for Euler, although they were originally solved by Johann Bernoulli about 1740. Later work on the equation was done by Euler and Cauchy. As usual with operators, ϑ^n means the operator xD applied n times; it does *not* mean $x^n D^n$.

Over a positive range of x, the change of independent variable $x = e^t$ will transform (1) into a linear equation with constant coefficients; for

$$(2) \qquad\qquad \vartheta = x\frac{d}{dx} = e^t \frac{dt}{dx}\frac{d}{dt} = e^t e^{-t}\frac{d}{dt} = \dot{D},$$

where $\dot{D}$ means d/dt, and (1) becomes

$$(3) \qquad\qquad f(\dot{D})y = \varphi(e^t).$$

If $y(t)$ is the general solution of (3), $y(\log x)$ is the general solution of (1).*

Theorem. *Every linear equation of the type*

$$(4) \qquad [a_0 x^n D^n + a_1 x^{n-1}D^{n-1} + \cdots + a_{n-1}xD + a_n]y = \varphi(x)$$

is an Euler equation.

  PROOF. Make the change of variable $x = e^t$; then

$$xD = \dot{D} \quad \text{or} \quad D = e^{-t}\dot{D}.$$

From the exponential shift

$$D^2 = e^{-t}\dot{D}(e^{-t}\dot{D}) = e^{-2t}(\dot{D} - 1)\dot{D},$$
$$D^3 = e^{-t}\dot{D} \cdot e^{-2t}(\dot{D} - 1)\dot{D} = e^{-3t}(\dot{D} - 2)(\dot{D} - 1)\dot{D};$$

and, by mathematical induction,

$$D^n = e^{-nt}\dot{D}(\dot{D} - 1)(\dot{D} - 2)\cdots(\dot{D} - n + 1).$$

---

* Over a negative range of x we put $x = -e^t$, then formula (2) still applies and (3) becomes $f(\dot{D})y = \varphi(-e^t)$,

Since $x^n = e^{nt}$ and $\dot{D} = \vartheta$, we have the fundamental relation between D and ϑ:

(5) $$x^n D^n = \vartheta(\vartheta - 1)(\vartheta - 2) \cdots (\vartheta - n + 1).$$

On substituting from (5) in (4), the bracket becomes a polynomial in ϑ for the coefficients are all constants.

The nth *factorial power* of x, written $x^{(n)}$, is defined as the product of n factors

$$x^{(n)} = x(x - 1)(x - 2) \cdots (x - n + 1).$$

With this notation* equation (5) becomes

(5)' $$x^n D^n = \vartheta^{(n)}.$$

For second-order equations we only need the special cases

(6) $$xD = \vartheta, \qquad x^2 D^2 = \vartheta(\vartheta - 1).$$

When t is the independent variable, the *exponential shift* formulas of § 36 become

(7) $$f(\dot{D})e^{at}T = e^{at}f(\dot{D} + a)T,$$
(8) $$f(\dot{D})e^{at} = e^{at}f(a).$$

Putting $e^t = x$, $\dot{D} = \vartheta$ and replacing the function $T(t)$ by $X(x)$, these become

(9) $$f(\vartheta)x^a X = x^a f(\vartheta + a)X,$$
(10) $$f(\vartheta)x^a = x^a f(a).$$

These *power shift* formulas will be extensively used in Chapter 10 in obtaining power series solutions of differential equations. They are also valid with the inverse operator $1/f(\vartheta)$, defined as in (41.1); thus from (10) we have

(11) $$\frac{1}{f(\vartheta)} x^a = \frac{x^a}{f(a)}, \qquad f(a) \neq 0.$$

Corresponding to

$$(\dot{D} - a)^{-1} = e^{at} \dot{D}^{-1} e^{-at}$$

we now have

(12) $$(\vartheta - a)^{-1} = x^a \vartheta^{-1} x^{-a}$$

where $\vartheta^{-1} = D^{-1} x^{-1}$, since

$$\vartheta \vartheta^{-1} = x D D^{-1} x^{-1} = x x^{-1} = 1.$$

---

* The definition of $x^{(n)}$ for all real n is given in § 78.

Thus we find

$$\vartheta^{-1}1 = D^{-1}x^{-1} = \log x$$
$$\vartheta^{-2}1 = D^{-1}(x^{-1}\log x) = \tfrac{1}{2}(\log x)^2$$

and in general

(13) $$\vartheta^{-n}1 = \frac{1}{n!}(\log x)^n.$$

To solve an Euler equation such as (4) use the relations (5) to convert it to the "theta-form" (1), put $x = e^t$ and solve the resulting equation (3), which is linear with constant coefficients; the inverse substitution $t = \log x$ then yields the solution of the original equation.

This change of independent variable may be avoided. After bringing the equation to the theta-form (1), find the roots of $f(r) = 0$. The solution of the reduced equation $f(\vartheta)y = 0$ may then be written down from the following table which is constructed from the table in § 37 by replacing x and e^{ax} by $\log x$ and x^a.

Table 43

Roots of $f(r) = 0$		Solution
Real simple	a	Cx^a
a k-fold		$x^a P_{k-1}(\log x)$
Complex simple		$x^a[C_1 \cos(b\log x) + C_2 \sin(b\log x)]$.
$a \pm ib$ k-fold		$x^a[P_{k-1}(\log x)\cos(b\log x) + Q_{k-1}(\log x)\sin(b\log x)]$.

The general solution of $f(\vartheta)y = 0$ is obtained by adding the contributions of all the roots of $f(r) = 0$ and contains exactly n arbitrary constants for an equation of order n. A particular solution of (1) must now be added to this complementary function. If $\varphi(x)$ is a sum of powers and exponentials (including the cosine and sine) this may be found by using the operational formulas above.

Both methods are illustrated in the following examples.

Example 1. $x^2y'' - xy' + y = x^2 + 2x + 3$.
Using (6), the left member becomes

$$[\vartheta(\vartheta - 1) - \vartheta + 1]y = (\vartheta - 1)^2 y.$$

If we put $x = e^t$, $\vartheta = \dot{D}$, the equation becomes

(i) $$(\dot{D} - 1)^2 y = e^{2t} + 2e^t + 3.$$

The general solution of (i) is

$$y = (c_1 + c_2 t)e^t + e^{2t} + t^2 e^t + 3;$$

and for the given equation
$$y = x(c_1 + c_2 \log x) + x^2 + x(\log x)^2 + 3.$$

The equation in x

(ii) $(\vartheta - 1)^2 y = x^2 + 2x + 3$

may also be solved directly. The double root 1 gives the complementary function
$$x(c_1 + c_2 \log x);$$

and the particular solution is

$$(\vartheta - 1)^{-2}(x^2 + 2x + 3) = x\vartheta^{-2}x^{-1}(x^2 + 2x + 3) \tag{12}$$

$$= x\vartheta^{-2}(x + 2 + 3x^{-1})$$

$$= x\left(\frac{x}{1^2} + 2\frac{(\log x)^2}{2} + 3\frac{x^{-1}}{(-1)^2}\right)$$

$$= x^2 + x(\log x)^2 + 3$$

on using (11) and (13).

Example 2. $4x^2 y'' + y = x^{1/2}.$
This equation has the theta-form

(i) $(2\vartheta - 1)^2 y = x^{1/2}.$

With $x = e^t$, $\vartheta = \dot{D}$, this becomes

$$(\dot{D} - \tfrac{1}{2})^2 y = \tfrac{1}{4} e^{t/2}.$$

The double root $\tfrac{1}{2}$ yields the complementary function
$$(c_1 + c_2 t)e^{t/2};$$

and a particular solution is given by the exponential shift:

$$y_1 = \frac{1}{4}\frac{1}{(D - \tfrac{1}{2})^2} e^{t/2} = \frac{e^{t/2}}{4}\frac{1}{D^2} 1 = \frac{t^2 e^{t/2}}{8}.$$

Dealing directly with (1), we have the corresponding results:

$$(c_1 + c_2 \log x)\sqrt{x},$$

$$y_1 = \frac{1}{4}\frac{1}{(\vartheta - \tfrac{1}{2})^2} x^{1/2} = \frac{x^{1/2}}{4}\frac{1}{\vartheta^2} 1 = \frac{1}{8} x^{1/2}(\log x)^2$$

from (13). The general solution of (i) is therefore

$$y = \sqrt{x}[c_1 + c_2 \log x + \tfrac{1}{8}(\log x)^2].$$

PROBLEMS

Find two independent solutions in Problems 1–8.
1. $x^2 y'' + xy' - y = 0.$ 2. $x^2 y'' - xy' - y = 0.$
3. $x^2 y'' + xy' + y = 0.$ 4. $x^2 y'' - xy' + y = 0.$
5. $x^2 y'' + 3xy' + y = 0.$ 6. $x^2 y'' - 2xy' + 2y = 0.$
7. $x^2 y'' + 5xy' + 13y = 0.$ 8. $xy'' + y' = 0.$

9. Solve Problem 1 when $y(1) = 2$, $y'(1) = 0$.
10. Solve Problem 8 when $y(-1) = 0$, $y'(-1) = 1$.
Find the general solution in Problems 11–12 when $x < 0$.
11. $4x^2 y'' - 4xy' + 3y = x + 3$.   **12.** $4x^2 y'' + 4xy' - y = x - x^{-1}$.
13. $x^2 y'' + xy' + y = \sin \log x$; solve when $x > 0$.
14. Show that the Euler equation

$$(\vartheta - a)^k g(\vartheta) y = bx^a, \qquad g(a) \neq 0,$$

has the particular integral

(14) $$y_1 = b \frac{x^a}{g(a)} \frac{(\log x)^k}{k!}$$ [Cf. § 41].

Solve Problems 15–16 using (14).
15. $x^2 y'' + 2xy' - 6y = 1 + x + x^{-1}$ **16.** $x^2 y'' - 2y = x^{-1} - x + 2x^2$.
17. Show that $\vartheta - a$ and $\vartheta - b$ are permutable operators.
18. Show that the adjoint of
$$(\vartheta - a)(\vartheta - b)y = 0 \quad \text{is} \quad (\vartheta + a + 1)(\vartheta + b + 1)y = 0.$$

44. SUMMARY

If $f(D)$ is a polynomial of degree n in D, the general solution of the complete equation

(1) $$(a_0 D^n + a_1 D^{n-1} + \cdots + a_n)y = f(D)y = \varphi(x)$$

has the form

(2) $$y(x) = y_0(x) + y_1(x).$$

Here $y_0(x)$, the *complementary function*, is the general solution of the reduced equation

(3) $$f(D)y = 0$$

and contains n arbitrary constants. When the n roots of the *characteristic equation*

(4) $$f(r) = 0$$

are known, y_0 may be expressed as a linear combination of n independent solutions of (3) given by Table 37, page 134. As shown by this table, y_0 involves only exponentials, cosines, sines, and powers.

Several methods are available to find a *particular integral* $y_1(x)$ of (1). If $\varphi(x)$ is composed of functions that appear in the table, the method of undetermined coefficients will give the simplest form of y_1—free of all functions that appear in y_0.

If $\varphi(x)$ is a sum of terms, the particular integral is the sum of the particular integrals for the separate terms. This fact enables one to use the most effective method for each term.

For exponential terms, use

(5) $$\frac{1}{f(D)} e^{ax} = \frac{e^{ax}}{f(a)} \quad \text{if} \quad f(a) \neq 0;$$

and if $f(D) = (D - a)^k g(D)$, use

(6) $$\frac{1}{f(D)} e^{ax} = \frac{x^k}{k!} \frac{e^{ax}}{g(a)} \quad \text{if} \quad g(a) \neq 0.$$

For $\cos bx$ or $\sin bx$, use these formulas on e^{ibx} and take the real or imaginary part, respectively, of the result.

For polynomials $P_k(x)$ of degree k in $\varphi(x)$, express $1/f(D)$ as a power series in D if $f(0) \neq 0$, and discard powers $> k$:

(7) $$\frac{1}{f(D)} = a_0 + a_1 D + \cdots + a_k D^k, \qquad a_0 = \frac{1}{f(0)}.$$

This may be done by long division or otherwise. The geometric series

$$\frac{1}{1 - D} = 1 + D + D^2 + \cdots$$

is often useful. But if $f(0) = 0$, write

$$f(D) = D^m g(D), \qquad g(0) \neq 0,$$

express $1/g(D)$ as a power series, and use

(8) $$\frac{1}{f(D)} = D^{-m}(b_0 + b_1 D + \cdots + b_k D^k), \qquad b_0 = \frac{1}{g(0)},$$

no constants being added in performing the m integrations D^{-m}. In either case the operator $1/f(D)$ applied to $P_k(x)$ will give y_1 with a minimum of labor.

For terms such as $e^{ax}x^m$, first shift e^{ax} by using

$$\frac{1}{f(D)} e^{ax}x^m = e^{ax} \frac{1}{f(D + a)} x^m$$

and then express the operator $1/f(D + a)$ as a series in D. If $f(a) = 0$, negative powers of D (integrations) will occur.

In any event, a particular integral is given by

(9) $$y_1(x) = \int_{x_0}^{x} \varphi(t)v(x - t)\, dt$$

provided $v(x)$ is a solution of the reduced equation for which

$$v(0) = v'(0) = \cdots = v^{(n-2)}(0) = 0, \qquad v^{(n-1)}(0) = 1/a_0.$$

The particular integral (9) satisfies the n conditions

$$y_1(0) = y_1'(0) = \cdots = y_1^{(n-1)}(0) = 0$$

and usually is not the simplest for it may contain functions that occur in the complementary function y_0.

Finally, the operational formula

(10) $$(D - a)^{-1} = e^{ax} D^{-1} e^{-ax}$$

enables one to write down the solution of equation (1) as soon as $f(D)$ is expressed as a product of linear factors:

(11) $$f(D) = (D - a)(D - b) \cdots .$$

Then the general solution of (1) is

(12) $$y(x) = (e^{ax} D^{-1} e^{-ax} \cdot e^{bx} D^{-1} e^{-bx} \cdots) \varphi(x)$$

when a constant is added in performing each of the n integrations D^{-1}. If these constants are omitted, we obtain a particular integral; and if $\varphi(x)$ is replaced by zero, we obtain the complementary function y_0.

Formula (12) requires n integrations *in series*—usually a laborious process. They may be replaced by n integrations *in parallel* by expressing $1/f(D)$ as a sum of partial fractions; but the process is still so tedious that this fact is mainly of theoretical interest. Nevertheless it is interesting that the entire theory of the equation $f(D)y = \varphi(x)$ resides in the single formula (10). This, moreover, is nothing other than the exponential shift:

$$(D - a)^{-1}1 = (D - a)^{-1} e^{ax} e^{-ax} = e^{ax} D^{-1} e^{-ax}.$$

For a k-fold root a we have

(13) $$(D - a)^{-k} = e^{ax} D^{-k} e^{-ax},$$

a nice result for a very special class of equations. But in general the instructions above follow the line of least resistance.

With such a plethora of methods one would imagine the subject closed. But this is not the case; for a popular and fashionable attack on equation (1) is afforded by the Laplace transform, whereby the solution of differential equations becomes an algebraic problem. This method supplies rigor to the Heaviside operational calculus and will be the subject of a later chapter. A method that uses the same transform formulas, but without any reference to convergence considerations, is the new operational calculus of the Polish mathematician Jan Mikusiński (ref. 12). The Laplace transform is the theme of Chapter 7; the Mikusiński calculus is sketched in Chapter 11.

CHAPTER 5

Systems of Equations

45. LINEAR SYSTEM OF TWO EQUATIONS

Consider the simultaneous equations

$$(1) \qquad f_1(D)x + g_1(D)y = \varphi_1(t),$$
$$(2) \qquad f_2(D)x + g_2(D)y = \varphi_2(t),$$

where $f_1(D), f_2(D), g_1(D), g_2(D)$ are polynomials in the operator $D = d/dt$ and t is the independent variable. If the determinant of the coefficients

$$\delta(D) = \begin{vmatrix} f_1(D) & g_1(D) \\ f_2(D) & g_2(D) \end{vmatrix}$$

is of degree n in D, we shall show that the general solution of the system (1, 2), in which x and y are expressed as functions of t, will contain exactly n essential arbitrary constants.

To prove this we shall show that if f_1 and f_2 are not zero we can reduce the system (1, 2) to an equivalent system having the same determinant δ, but in which x is lacking in one equation. If the degree of $f_2(D)$ does not exceed that of $f_1(D)$ divide $f_1(D)$ by $f_2(D)$; if quotient and remainder are $q(D)$ and $r(D)$, we have

$$f_1(D) = q(D)f_2(D) + r(D)$$

where $r(D)$ is of lower degree than $f_2(D)$. Now "multiply" (2) by the operator $q(D)$ and subtract the result from (1); this yields the equivalent system

$$(3) \qquad r(D)x + \{g_1(D) - q(D)g_2(D)\}y = \varphi_1(t) - q(D)\varphi_2(t),$$
$$(2) \qquad f_2(D)x + g_2(D)y = \varphi_2(t),$$

with the same determinant δ, but in which the degree of one coefficient of x has been lowered.* If the remainder $r(D)$ is not zero, this process

---

* The value of a determinant is not altered if the elements of one row are multiplied by the same quantity and subtracted from the corresponding elements of another row.

can be repeated until we arrive at a *triangular system*

(4) $$u(D)x + h(D)y = \psi_1(t)$$

(5) $$v(D)y = \psi_2(t)$$

having the determinant

$$\delta(D) = \begin{vmatrix} u(D) & h(D) \\ 0 & v(D) \end{vmatrix} = u(D)v(D).$$

If $u(D)$ and $v(D)$ are of degrees i and j in D, $i + j = n$, the degree of $\delta(D)$.

The system (4, 5) is prepared for integration. We first integrate (5), a linear equation of degree j in y and t; its general solution gives y as a function of t containing j arbitrary constants. Substituting this value of y in (4), we have an equation of degree i in x and t; its general solution gives x as a function of t with i new arbitrary constants. Thus the general solution of the system (4, 5), and hence of (1, 2), comprises exactly $i + j = n$ arbitrary constants.

If i and j are the orders of the highest derivatives in (1) and (2), $\delta(D)$ will usually be of degree $i + j$. However, if the coefficients of the highest derivatives of x and y in (1) and (2) are a_1, b_1, a_2, b_2 and $\begin{vmatrix} a_1 & b_1 \\ a_2 & b_2 \end{vmatrix} = 0$, the degree of $\delta(D) < i + j$. The system is then called *degenerate*. This is the case in Example 6 where $\begin{vmatrix} 1 & 1 \\ 1 & 1 \end{vmatrix} = 0$. The most extreme case of degeneracy occurs when $\delta(D) = \text{const.} \neq 0$; then the solution contains *no* arbitrary constants (cf. Ex. 2). But if $\delta(D) \equiv 0$, the second row of $\delta(D)$ is some multiple k of the first and the equations become

$$f_1(D)x + f_2(D)y = \varphi_1(t)$$
$$kf_1(D)x + kf_2(D)y = \varphi_2(t).$$

If $\varphi_2(t) = k\varphi_1(t)$, the equations are *compatible* but the second is redundant. The first equation admits a solution for an arbitrary choice of $y(t)$ and its solution is *indeterminate*. If, however, $\varphi_2(t) \neq k\varphi_1(t)$, the equations are *incompatible* and have *no* solution.

We may also reduce the system (1, 2) to triangular form by removing y from one equation. See Example 1 where both reductions are performed.

We may write the system (1, 2) in matrix form:

(6) $$\begin{pmatrix} f_1(D) & g_1(D) \\ f_2(D) & g_2(D) \end{pmatrix} \begin{pmatrix} x \\ y \end{pmatrix} = \begin{pmatrix} \varphi_1(t) \\ \varphi_2(t) \end{pmatrix}$$

or
$$M(D)\mathbf{r} = \varphi(t)$$

where $M(D)$ is the 2×2 operator matrix and $\mathbf{r}$ and $\varphi(t)$ are 2×1 matrices or column vectors. To reduce the system (6) to triangular form we use row operations on the matrix $M(D)$. If row i is multiplied by $\lambda(D)$ and added to row j we describe the operation by the symbol

$$\lambda(D)(i) + (j).$$

Now the reduction of $M(D)$ to triangular form is accomplished by a series of operations T_1, T_2, $\ldots$, T_k of this kind. The resultant of all these operations is written

$$T = T_k T_{k-1} \cdots T_2 T_1.$$

If I is the 2×2 unit matrix,

$$TM = T(IM) = (TI)M$$

and the reduction of M to a triangular form may be made by premultiplying M by the matrix TI. Since each operation leaves the determinant unaltered, det $TM = $ det M.

The transforming matrix is useful when several systems (6) which differ only in their right-hand members must be solved. All such systems may be reduced to the triangular form by the same matrix.

It can be proved that a necessary and sufficient condition for the equivalence of two linear systems

$$M_1(D)r = 0, \qquad M_2(D)r = 0$$

is that

$$\det M_1(D) = C \det M_2(D)$$

where C is a constant.*

Example 1. The system

(i) $$D^2x + Dy = t$$
(ii) $$(D - 1)x + (D + 1)y = t^2$$

has the determinant

$$\begin{vmatrix} D^2 & D \\ D - 1 & D + 1 \end{vmatrix} = D(D^2 + 1)$$

of degree 3 in D. Therefore its general solution will contain *three* arbitrary constants.

The operation T_1: $-(1) + (2)$ gives the equivalent system

(i) $$D^2x + Dy = t$$
(iii) $$(-D^2 + D - 1)x + y = t^2 - t.$$

---

* Ince, ref. 29, p. 149.

The operation T_2: $-D(2) + (1)$ now gives the triangular system

(iv) $$(D^3 + D)x + 0 = -t + 1,$$

(iii) $$(-D^2 + D - 1)x + y = t^2 - t.$$

First solve (iv) for x:

(v) $$x = c_1 + c_2 \cos t + c_3 \sin t - \tfrac{1}{2}t^2 + t.$$

Using this value in (iii) gives

$$y = (1 - D + D^2)x + t^2 - t$$

or

(vi) $$y = c_1 - 2 - c_3 \cos t + c_2 \sin t + \tfrac{1}{2}t^2 + t.$$

Equations (v) and (vi) form the general solution.

The transforming matrix TI is

$$T_2 T_1 \begin{pmatrix} 1 & 0 \\ 0 & 1 \end{pmatrix} = T_2 \begin{pmatrix} 1 & 0 \\ -1 & 1 \end{pmatrix} = \begin{pmatrix} D+1 & -D \\ -1 & 1 \end{pmatrix};$$

as a check, we note that

$$\begin{pmatrix} D+1 & -D \\ -1 & 1 \end{pmatrix} \begin{pmatrix} D^2 & D \\ D-1 & D+1 \end{pmatrix} = \begin{pmatrix} D^3 + D & 0 \\ -D^2 + D - 1 & 1 \end{pmatrix},$$

$$\begin{pmatrix} D+1 & -D \\ -1 & 1 \end{pmatrix} \begin{pmatrix} t \\ t^2 \end{pmatrix} = \begin{pmatrix} -t+1 \\ t^2 - t \end{pmatrix}.$$

We may also reduce the system to triangular form by the operations

$$T_1: \ -(D+1)(2) + (1),$$
$$T_2: \ -(D-1)(1) + (2).$$

The transforming matrix TI is now

$$T_2 T_1 \begin{pmatrix} 1 & 0 \\ 0 & 1 \end{pmatrix} = T_2 \begin{pmatrix} 1 & -D-1 \\ 0 & 1 \end{pmatrix} = \begin{pmatrix} 1 & -D-1 \\ -D+1 & D^2 \end{pmatrix}$$

and yields the triangular system

$$\begin{pmatrix} 1 & -D^2 - D - 1 \\ 0 & D^3 + D \end{pmatrix} \begin{pmatrix} x \\ y \end{pmatrix} = \begin{pmatrix} -t - t^2 \\ 1 + t \end{pmatrix}.$$

Now we first find y, then x:

$$y = k_1 + k_2 \cos t + k_3 \sin t + \tfrac{1}{2}t^2 + t;$$
$$x = (1 + D + D^2)y - t - t^2$$
$$= k_1 + 2 + k_3 \cos t - k_2 \sin t - \tfrac{1}{2}t^2 + t.$$

This solution agrees with (v)–(vi) if

$$k_1 + 2 = c_1, \qquad k_3 = c_2, \qquad k_2 = -c_3.$$

The reader should carry out both solutions in full detail.

Example 2. The system

(i) $$(D + 5)x + (D + 4)y = 3t^2$$
(ii) $$(D + 2)x + (D + 1)y = 3t$$

has the operational determinant

$$\begin{vmatrix} D + 5 & D + 4 \\ D + 2 & D + 1 \end{vmatrix} = -3$$

of degree 0 in D. Therefore its general solution contains *no* arbitrary constants.

Apply T_1: $-(2) + (1)$; then T_2: $\frac{1}{3}(1)$:

$$x + \qquad y = t^2 - t,$$
$$(D + 2)x + (D + 1)y = 3t.$$

Apply T_3: $-(D + 1)(1) + (2)$:

$$x + y = \quad t^2 - t,$$
$$x + 0 = -t^2 + 2t + 1.$$

The unique solution is therefore

$$x = -t^2 + 2t + 1,$$
$$y = 2t^2 - 3t - 1.$$

The transforming matrix TI is

$$T_3 T_2 T_1 I = \frac{1}{3} \begin{pmatrix} 1 & -1 \\ -D - 1 & D + 4 \end{pmatrix}.$$

Example 3. The linear system

$$\begin{pmatrix} 4D - 3 & 2D \\ -D & 2D^2 - 4 \end{pmatrix} \begin{pmatrix} x \\ y \end{pmatrix} = \begin{pmatrix} 0 \\ 4t \end{pmatrix}$$

has the determinant

$$\begin{vmatrix} 4D - 3 & 2D \\ -D & 2D^2 - 4 \end{vmatrix} = 4(D - 1)^2(2D + 3)$$

and its general solution contains *three* arbitrary constants.
The operations

$$T_1: \quad -D(1) + (2)$$
$$T_2: \quad \frac{1}{2}(2)$$
$$T_3: \quad D(2) + (1)$$

reduce the system to the triangular form

$$\begin{pmatrix} -(D - L)^2(2D + 3) & 0 \\ -2D^2 + D & -2 \end{pmatrix} \begin{pmatrix} x \\ y \end{pmatrix} = \begin{pmatrix} 2 \\ 2t \end{pmatrix}.$$

This gives the general solution

$$x = (c_1 + c_2 t)e^t + c_3 e^{-3t/2} - \tfrac{2}{3},$$
$$y = -\tfrac{1}{2}(c_1 + 3c_2 + c_2 t)e^t - 3c_3 e^{-3t/2} - t.$$

The transforming matrix TI is

$$T_3 T_2 T_1 I = \begin{pmatrix} 1 - \tfrac{1}{2}D^2 & \tfrac{1}{2}D \\ -\tfrac{1}{2}D & \tfrac{1}{2} \end{pmatrix}.$$

Example 4. The system

(i) $\qquad\qquad (D^2 - 1)x + (D - 1)y = 1$
(ii) $\qquad\qquad (D + 1)x + (D^2 + 1)y = t$

has the operational determinant

$$\begin{vmatrix} D^2 - 1 & D - 1 \\ D + 1 & D^2 + 1 \end{vmatrix} = D^2(D^2 - 1).$$

The general solution will contain four arbitrary constants.

The operation $T: \ -(D - 1)(2) + (1)$ gives the triangular system

(iii) $\qquad\qquad -(D - 1)D^2 y = t,$
(ii) $\qquad\qquad (D + 1)x + (D^2 + 1)y = t.$

The general solution of (iii) is

(iv) $\qquad\qquad y = c_1 + c_2 t + c_3 e^t + \tfrac{1}{2}t^2 + \tfrac{1}{6}t^3.$

Substituting (iv) in (ii) gives the first-order equation for x:

$$(D + 1)x = t - y - D^2 y$$
$$= t - c_1 - c_2 t - c_3 e^t - \tfrac{1}{2}t^2 - \tfrac{1}{6}t^3$$
$$\qquad -1 - \qquad t - c_3 e^t,$$
$$(D + 1)x = -(c_1 + 1) - c_2 t - 2c_3 e^t - \tfrac{1}{2}t^2 - \tfrac{1}{6}t^3.$$

The complementary function is $c_4 e^{-t}$; and a particular integral is the sum of

$$\frac{1}{D + 1}(-2c_3 e^t) = -c_3 e^t,$$

and

$$-(1 - D + D^2 - D^3)\{(c_1 + 1) + c_2 t + \tfrac{1}{2}t^2 + \tfrac{1}{6}t^3\}$$
$$= -(c_1 + 1) - c_2 t - \tfrac{1}{2}t^2 - \tfrac{1}{6}t^3$$
$$\quad + c_2 \qquad\quad + \ t + \tfrac{1}{2}t^2$$
$$\quad - 1 \qquad\qquad - \ t$$
$$\quad + 1$$
$$= c_2 - c_1 - 1 - c_2 t - \tfrac{1}{6}t^3$$

Therefore the general solution consists of

(v) $\qquad x = (c_2 - c_1 - 1) - c_2 t - c_3 e^t + c_4 e^{-t} - \tfrac{1}{6}t^3:$

and (iv).

The transforming matrix TI is

$$T \begin{pmatrix} 1 & 0 \\ 0 & 1 \end{pmatrix} = \begin{pmatrix} 1 & -D + 1 \\ 0 & 1 \end{pmatrix}.$$

Alternative Procedure

Instead of reducing the system of equations to the triangular form, it is often more convenient first to eliminate one variable (say y) by treating the differential operators as algebraic quantities and then to solve the resulting differential equation in the other variable (say x). If the order of this equation is i, the expression for x thus obtained will contain i arbitrary constants. Now the total number of constants in the complete solution is known in advance, for it equals the degree n of the operational determinant $\delta(D)$. Hence an equation for y must be obtained from the given system which is exactly of order $j = n - i$. Integration of the latter will give an expression for y involving j constants.

It often happens that $i = n$ and hence $j = 0$; then the given equations must be so combined that y is given *algebraically* in terms of x, for further integrations would increase the number of constants above the allowable value n. The procedure is best explained by means of examples.

Example 5. Consider again Example 45.1,

(i) $$D^2x + \quad Dy \quad = t$$
(ii) $$(D - 1)x + (D + 1)y = t^2,$$

in which $\delta(D) = D^3 + D$. Eliminate y by "multiplying" (i) by $(D + 1)$, (ii) by $-D$, and adding. Then

$$[(D + 1)D^2 - D(D - 1)]x = 1 + t - 2t = 1 - t,$$
$$(D^3 + D)x = 1 - t.$$

As in Example 45.1, this gives

$$x = c_1 + c_2 \cos t + c_3 \sin t - \tfrac{1}{2}t^2 + t.$$

Since $\delta(D)$ is of degree 3, the complete solution can contain but 3 constants; and hence y must be obtainable from (i) and (ii) *without further integration*. This is easily done on eliminating Dy by subtracting (i) from (ii). We thus find

$$(D - 1 - D^2)x + y = t^2 - t.$$

This gives the value (vi) for y in Example 45.1.

Example 6. The system

(i) $$(D - 2)x + (D + 1)y = t$$
(ii) $$(D + 1)x + (D + 2)y = 1 + 2t$$

has the operational determinant

$$\begin{vmatrix} D - 2 & D + 1 \\ D + 1 & D + 2 \end{vmatrix} = (D^2 - 4) - (D^2 + 2D + 1) = -2D - 5.$$

Its complete solution, therefore, contains but one constant.
  Eliminate y by "multiplying" (i) by $(D + 2)$, (ii) by $-(D + 1)$, and adding.

Then

$$(-2D - 5)x = 1 + 2t - (2 + 1 + 2t),$$
$$(D + \tfrac{5}{2})x = 1;$$
$$x = (D + \tfrac{5}{2})^{-1} \cdot 1$$
$$= e^{-\frac{5}{2}t} D^{-1} e^{\frac{5}{2}t}$$
$$= e^{-\frac{5}{2}t}(\tfrac{2}{5} e^{\frac{5}{2}t} + c)$$

(iii)
$$x = ce^{-\frac{5}{2}t} + \tfrac{2}{5}.$$

Since our total of constants is already achieved, we must find y without further integration. Subtract (i) from (ii); then

$$3x + y = 1 + t,$$

and from (iii)

$$y = t - \tfrac{1}{5} - 3ce^{-\frac{5}{2}t}.$$

PROBLEMS

Reduce to triangular form and solve.

1. $Dx - y = t$
  $x - Dy = -t.$

2. $D^2x + (2D + 1)y = e^t$
  $Dx + 2y = t^2.$

3. $(D^2 - 3D)x - (D - 2)y = 3t$
  $(D - 3)x + Dy = t^2.$

4. $(D^2 + 1)x + (D^2 + D + 1)y = t^2 + t + 1$
  $Dx + (D + 1)y = t + 2.$

5. $(D - 1)x + (D + 1)y = t^2$
  $D^2x + Dy = t.$

6. $(D + 5)x + (D + 3)y = e^{-t}$
  $(D + 2)x + (D + 1)y = 3.$

7. $5Dx + (D^2 - 1)y = t$
  $(D^2 - 4)x - 2Dy = -2.$

8. $(D^2 + 1)x + (D + 1)y = t$
  $(D - 1)x + (D^2 - 1)y = 1.$

9. $(D^2 - D)x + (D + 2)y = 0$
  $D^2x + (D + 4)y = 0.$

10. $(2D^2 - D + 9)x - (D^2 + D + 3)y = 0$
  $(2D^2 + D + 7)x - (D^2 - D + 5)y = 0.$

11. $(2D + 1)x + (3D + 1)y = e^{-t}$
  $(D + 5)x + (D + 7)y = t.$

12. $(D^2 + D + 1)x + (2D^2 - D - 2)y = 8$
  $(D^2 + 2D + 3)x + (3D^2 + 3D + 2)y = 0.$

13. $(D^2 - 1)x + (D - 1)y = 1$

  $(D + 1)x + (D^2 + 1)y = t.$ Find x, then y (cf. Ex. 4).

14. Solve the initial value problem:

$$x' = x - y + 2t - 1, \qquad x(0) = 1,$$
$$y' = 2x - y + 3t + 1, \qquad y(0) = 0.$$

46. LINEAR SYSTEM OF THREE EQUATIONS

The system of three equations

(1) $$f_1(D)x + g_1(D)y + h_1(D)z = \varphi_1(t)$$

(2) $$f_2(D)x + g_2(D)y + h_2(D)z = \varphi_2(t)$$

(3) $$f_3(D)x + g_3(D)y + h_3(D)z = \varphi_3(t)$$

may be reduced to triangular form by the method of § 45. First one variable (say x) is removed from two of the equations; then, from one of these equations, a second variable (say y) may be removed. The system now assumes the triangular form

(4) $$u(D)x + p(D)y + q(D)z = \psi_1(t)$$

(5) $$v(D)y + r(D)z = \psi_2(t)$$

(6) $$w(D)z = \psi_3(t).$$

Since this reduction does not alter the determinant $\delta(D)$ of the system,

$$\delta(D) = u(D)v(D)w(D);$$

and if $u(D)$, $v(D)$, $w(D)$ are of degree i, j, k in D, $i + j + k = n$, the degree of $\delta(D)$.

The system (4, 5, 6) is prepared for integration. We first solve (6), a linear equation of order k, for z; then z is a function of t containing k arbitrary constants. Substitute this value of z in (5) and solve the resulting equation of order j for y; then y is a function of t containing j new arbitrary constants. Finally substitute the values of y and z in (4) and solve the resulting equation of order i for x; then x is a function of x with i new arbitrary constants. The general solution of the system will then contain exactly $i + j + k = n$ arbitrary constants.

In matrix form the system (1, 2, 3) becomes

(7) $$\begin{pmatrix} f_1(D) & g_1(D) & h_1(D) \\ f_2(D) & g_2(D) & h_2(D) \\ f_3(D) & g_3(D) & h_3(D) \end{pmatrix} \begin{pmatrix} x \\ y \\ z \end{pmatrix} = \begin{pmatrix} \varphi_1(t) \\ \varphi_2(t) \\ \varphi_3(t) \end{pmatrix}.$$

If this is reduced to the triangular form (4, 5, 6) by row operations $T_1, T_2, \ldots, T_k$ of the type $\lambda(D)(i) + (j)$, the entire reduction to triangular form may be accomplished by the transforming matrix

$$TI = I_k T_{k-1} \cdots T_2 T_1 I$$

where I is the 3×3 unit matrix. If the matrix equation (7) is pre-multiplied by TI, the matrix equivalent of the triangular form $(4, 5, 6)$ will be obtained. It is not necessary to find TI, but it does afford a check on the reduction.

If i, j, k are the orders of the highest derivatives in (1), (2) and (3), $\delta(D)$ will usually be of degree $i + j + k$. But if the determinant formed by the coefficients of the highest derivatives of x, y, z in the system (1, 2, 3) is zero, the degree of $\delta(D) < i + j + k$ and we have a *degenerate* system. If $\delta(D)$ reduces to a non-zero constant, the solution will contain *no* arbitrary constants; but when $\delta(D) \equiv 0$, there are two constants h, k such that row 3 of $\delta = h(\text{row } 1) + k(\text{row } 2)$. If $\varphi_3(t) = h\varphi_1(t) + k\varphi_2(t)$, the third equation is redundant and may be omitted; equations (1) and (2) then admit a solution for any choice of $z(t)$. If, however, $\varphi_3(t) \neq h\varphi_1(t) + k\varphi_2(t)$, the equations are *incompatible* and have *no* solution.

Example 1. The system

(i) $$D^2x + y - D^2z = t$$
(ii) $$-D^2x + D^2y + z = 1,$$
(iii) $$-(D^2 + 1)y + D^2z = t^2,$$

has the determinant

$$\begin{vmatrix} D^2 & 1 & -D^2 \\ -D^2 & D^2 & 1 \\ 0 & -(D^2 + 1) & D^2 \end{vmatrix} = \begin{vmatrix} D^2 & 1 & -D^2 \\ -D^2 & D^2 & 1 \\ 0 & 0 & 1 \end{vmatrix} = D^2(1 + D^2).$$

Hence there are four arbitrary constants in the general solution.

If we add (i) and (ii) to (iii), and then add (i) to (ii), we obtain an equivalent triangular system

(i) $$D^2x + y - D^2z = t,$$
(iv) $$(D^2 + 1)y + (1 - D^2)z = t + 1,$$
(v) $$z = t^2 + t + 1.$$

Equation (v) gives z; and from (iv)

$$(D^2 + 1)y = (D^2 - 1)(t^2 + t + 1) + t + 1 = 2 - t^2;$$

whence

(vi) $$y = C_1 \sin t + C_2 \cos t + 4 - t^2.$$

Now from (i)

$$D^2x = -y + D^2z + t = -C_1 \sin t - C_2 \cos t + t^2 + t - 2;$$

on integrating twice we obtain

(vii) $$x = C_1 \sin t + C_2 \cos t + C_3t + C_4 + \frac{t^4}{12} + \frac{t^3}{6} - t^2.$$

Equations (v), (vi), and (vii) form the general solution.

In this example the transforming matrix is obviously

$$TI = \begin{pmatrix} 1 & 0 & 0 \\ 1 & 1 & 0 \\ 1 & 1 & 1 \end{pmatrix}.$$

Example 2. The system

(i) $x + D y + D^2 z = t + 2,$
(ii) $D^2 x + y + D z = 2t + 1,$
(iii) $D x + D^2 y + z = t^2 + 1,$

has the determinant

$$\begin{vmatrix} 1 & D & D^2 \\ D^2 & 1 & D \\ D & D^2 & 1 \end{vmatrix} = \begin{vmatrix} 1 & D & D^2 \\ D^2 & 1 & D \\ 0 & 0 & 1 - D^3 \end{vmatrix} = (1 - D^3)^2.$$

The general solution will contain six arbitrary constants.

If we multiply (i) by D and subtract from (iii), then multiply (i) by D^2 and subtract from (ii), we obtain the triangular system

(i) $x + Dy + D^2 z = t + 2,$
(iv) $(1 - D^3)y + D(1 - D^3)z = 2t + 1,$
(v) $(1 - D^3)z = t^2.$

Since $1 - D^3 = 0$ has the roots $1, -\frac{1}{2} \pm i\frac{1}{2}\sqrt{3}$, the general solution of (v) is

(vi) $z = C_1 e^t - e^{-\frac{1}{2}t}\left(C_2 \cos \dfrac{\sqrt{3}}{2} t + C_3 \sin \dfrac{\sqrt{3}}{2} t \right) + t^2.$

In view of (v), equation (iv) may be written

$$(1 - D^3)y = 2t + 1 - Dt^2 = 1;$$

hence

(vii) $y = C_4 e^t - e^{-\frac{1}{2}t}\left(C_5 \cos \dfrac{\sqrt{3}}{2} t + C_6 \sin \dfrac{\sqrt{3}}{2} t \right) + 1.$

With these values of y and z, we may find x from (i):

(viii) $x = -Dy - D^2 z + t + 2.$

The transforming matrix is now

$$TI = \begin{pmatrix} 1 & 0 & 0 \\ -D^2 & 1 & 0 \\ -D & 0 & 1 \end{pmatrix}.$$

Example 3. The cyclic system

(i) $(D + 1)x - y - z = 0$
(ii) $-x + (D + 1)y - z = 0$
(iii) $-x - y + (D + 1)z = 0$

has the determinant $(D - 1)(D + 2)^2$; hence there are three arbitrary constants in the general solution. The operations

$$T_1: \quad (1) + (3) \quad \text{and} \quad T_2: \quad (2) + (3)$$

replace (iii) by

(iv) $$(D - 1)x + (D - 1)y + (D - 1)z = 0.$$

The operations

$$T_3: \quad -(1) + (2) \quad \text{and} \quad T_4: \quad (D - 1)(1) + (3)$$

reduce the system (i)—(ii)—(iv) to the triangular form

(i) $(D + 1)x - \qquad\qquad y - z = 0$

(v) $-(D + 2)x + (D + 2)y \qquad = 0$

(vi) $(D - 1)(D + 2)x \qquad\qquad = 0.$

From (vi),

$$x = c_1 e^t + c_2 e^{-2t}.$$

From (v), $(D + 2)(y - x) = 0$; hence

$$y - x = (D + 2)^{-1} 0 = e^{-2t} D^{-1} 0 = c_3 e^{-2t},$$
$$y = c_1 e^t + (c_2 + c_3)e^{-2t}.$$

Now from (i):

$$z = (D + 1)x - y.$$

Using the exponential shift,

$$(D + 1)x = 2c_1 e^t - c_2 e^{-2t};$$
$$z = c_1 e^t - (2c_2 + c_3)e^{-2t}.$$

The transforming matrix

$$TI = T_4 T_3 T_2 T_1 I = \begin{pmatrix} 1 & 0 & 0 \\ -1 & 1 & 0 \\ D & 1 & 1 \end{pmatrix}.$$

Example 4. Radioactive Disintegration. In the successive radioactive changes $A \to B \to C$, let x, y, z denote the number of atoms of A, B, C at time t; while the initial numbers at time $t = 0$ were x_0, 0, 0. The law of radioactive change gives rise to the system of differential equations

$$\frac{dx}{dt} = -ax, \qquad \frac{dy}{dt} = ax - by, \qquad \frac{dz}{dt} = by.$$

These may be arranged in the triangular form

(i) $(D + a)x \qquad\qquad\qquad = 0$

(ii) $-ax + (D + b)y \qquad\quad = 0$

(iii) $-by + Dz = 0.$

On integrating (i), we find

(iv) $x = x_0 e^{-at}.$

Put this value of x in (ii) and integrate the equation linear in y; then

$$y = \frac{ax_0}{b-a} e^{-at} + C_2 e^{-bt}, \qquad 0 = \frac{ax_0}{b-a} + C_2,$$

(v) $$y = \frac{ax_0}{b-a} (e^{-at} - e^{-bt}).$$

Hence from (iii)

$$z = \frac{abx_0}{b-a} \int_0^t (e^{-at} - e^{-bt})\, dt$$

$$= \frac{abx_0}{b-a} \left(\frac{1 - e^{-at}}{a} - \frac{1 - e^{-bt}}{b} \right),$$

(vi) $$z = x_0 \left(1 + \frac{ae^{-bt} - be^{-at}}{b-a} \right).$$

On adding (i), (ii), and (iii), we have

$$D(x + y + z) = 0, \qquad x + y + z = x_0,$$

expressing the conservation of mass. On adding (iv), (v), and (vi) we verify this relation.

PROBLEMS

1. In Examples 1, 2, and 3 show that the matrix TI reduces the system to triangular form.

2. $(D + 1)x + D^2 y + (D + 1)z = 0$
   $(D - 1)x + D\, y + (D - 1)z = 0$
   $x + y + Dz = 0$

Show that the operations

$$T_1: -D(3) + (2); \qquad T_2: -D^2(3) + (1); \qquad T_3: (-D^2 + D + 1)(2) + (1)$$

reduce the system to triangular form. What is the matrix $T_3 T_2 T_1 I$? Find z, x, y in turn.

Reduce to triangular form and solve.

3. $Dx = y, \qquad Dy = z, \qquad Dz = x.$

4. $-x + Dy + Dz = 0$
   $Dx - y + Dz = 0$
   $Dx + Dy - z = 0.$

5. $D^2 x + y - D^2 z = 0$
   $-D^2 x + D^2 y + z = 0$
   $-(D^2 + 1)\, y + D^2 z = 0.$

6. $(D + 1)y + (D + 1)z = 0$
   $(D - 2)x - 3Dy - 6z = 0$
   $2Dx - 2y + z = 0.$

7. $Dx - Dy + z = 1$
   $x + Dy - Dz = t$
   $(D + 1)x - Dz = -t^2.$

8. $Dx = y, \qquad Dy = z, \qquad Dz = w, \qquad Dw = x.$

47. FLUID FLOW IN THE PHASE PLANE

The differential equation

(1)
$$\frac{dy}{dx} = \frac{g(x, y)}{f(x, y)}$$

may be replaced by the *autonomous* system

(2)
$$\frac{dx}{dt} = f(x, y), \qquad \frac{dy}{dt} = g(x, y),$$

in which the functions f and g are independent of t. Every solution of (2) in which $dx/dt \neq 0$ (which rules out the lines $x = $ const.) is a parametric solution of (1); for

$$\frac{dy}{dx} = \frac{dy/dt}{dx/dt} = \frac{g(x, y)}{f(x, y)}.$$

If we interpret t as the time, dx/dt and dy/dt are the rectangular components of velocity; then equations (2) may be regarded as describing the *stationary* fluid flow in the xy or *phase-plane* in which the particle at the point (x, y) has the velocity

$$\mathbf{v} = \mathbf{i}f(x, y) + \mathbf{j}g(x, y) \qquad (\S\ 56).$$

The points where $\mathbf{v} = \mathbf{0}$ are called *equilibrium* or *critical points*; they satisfy the equations

(3)
$$f(x, y) = 0, \qquad g(x, y) = 0.$$

We shall suppose that in equations (2) the origin has been placed at an equilibrium point; then

(4)
$$f(0, 0) = 0, \qquad g(0, 0) = 0.$$

Since the function $g(x, y)/f(x, y)$ is not defined at $(0, 0)$, the origin is a *singular point* of equation (1).

We further suppose that in some region about the origin $f(x, y)$ and $g(x, y)$ may be expanded in convergent power series

$$f(x, y) = ax + by + \cdots, \qquad g(x, y) = cx + dy + \cdots,$$

where the dots signify terms of higher degree. We assume here that some terms of the first degree are present (in which dy is obviously a product). Thus close to the origin we may approximate equations (2) by the linear ("abridged") system

(5)
$$\frac{dx}{dt} = ax + by, \qquad \frac{dy}{dt} = cx + dy.$$

The integral curves of the equation

$$(6) \qquad \frac{dy}{dx} = \frac{cx + dy}{ax + by}$$

give the *stream lines* of the flow defined by (6). The stream lines have a definite sense, namely that of increasing t; they give the path and direction of the flow. The *direction* of a stream line (shown by an arrow) is determined by the *signs* of dx/dt and dy/dt.

If the signs of a, b, c, d are all changed, equation (6) is unaltered, but equations (5) become

$$(5)' \qquad \frac{dx}{dt} = -ax - by, \qquad \frac{dy}{dt} = -cx - dy.$$

If we put $t = -\tau$, these equations again assume the form (5); hence *the stream lines of the flow (5)' are the stream lines of the flow (5) reversed in sense.*

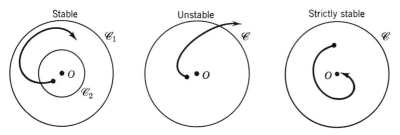

Fig. 47a Stable.   **Fig. 47b** Unstable.   **Fig. 47c** Strictly stable.

An equilibrium point O is said to be *stable* if, to every circle $\mathscr{C}_1$ about O there corresponds a second circle $\mathscr{C}_2$, such that all stream lines that start within $\mathscr{C}_2$ remain within $\mathscr{C}_1$ (Fig. 47a). If however there is no circle $\mathscr{C}_2$ with this property, the origin is said to be *unstable* (Fig. 47b).

If there is a circle $\mathscr{C}$ about a stable origin such that all stream lines that start within $\mathscr{C}$ tend to return to O, the origin is said to be *strictly or asymptotically stable* (Fig. 47c). For nonlinear equations strict stability is usually local. But if *all* stream lines or *trajectories* tend toward the origin, it is *strictly stable in the large*.* We shall also say that a point which is stable, but not strictly stable, is in *neutral equilibrium* or *metastable* (§41).

---

* We follow the definitions of Lasalle and Lefschetz, ref. 32.

Equations (5) may be written in the matrix form

(5)
$$\begin{pmatrix} \dot{x} \\ \dot{y} \end{pmatrix} = \begin{pmatrix} a & b \\ c & d \end{pmatrix} \begin{pmatrix} x \\ y \end{pmatrix}$$

where the dots signify time derivatives (Newton's notation). Such linear flows are completely specified by the matrix $\begin{pmatrix} a & b \\ c & d \end{pmatrix}$. The following examples give typical linear flow patterns near the origin, an equilibrium point, and illustrate stability and instability as defined above. For the linear equations (5) stability is *always* in the large.

Linear systems are characterized by the

Principle of Superposition.* *If* $\begin{pmatrix} x_1 \\ y_1 \end{pmatrix}$ *and* $\begin{pmatrix} x_2 \\ y_2 \end{pmatrix}$ *are any two solutions of* (5), *then for any two constants* c_1, c_2

$$\begin{pmatrix} x \\ y \end{pmatrix} = c_1 \begin{pmatrix} x_1 \\ y_1 \end{pmatrix} + c_2 \begin{pmatrix} x_2 \\ y_2 \end{pmatrix}$$

is also a solution.

The verification is immediate; for if $A = \begin{pmatrix} a & b \\ c & d \end{pmatrix}$,

$$\begin{pmatrix} \dot{x} \\ \dot{y} \end{pmatrix} = c_1 \begin{pmatrix} \dot{x}_1 \\ \dot{y}_1 \end{pmatrix} + c_2 \begin{pmatrix} \dot{x}_2 \\ \dot{y}_2 \end{pmatrix} = c_1 A \begin{pmatrix} x_1 \\ y_1 \end{pmatrix} + c_2 A \begin{pmatrix} x_2 \\ y_2 \end{pmatrix} = A \begin{pmatrix} x \\ y \end{pmatrix}.$$

---

* In order that the system (1) conform to the principle of superposition, the functions $f(x, y)$ and $g(x, y)$ must satisfy

(i)　　　　　　　　　　　$f(cx, cy) = cf(x, y),$

(ii)　　　　　　　$f(x_1 + x_2, y_1 + y_2) = f(x_1, y_1) + f(x_2, y_2),$

with similar equations for $g(x, y)$. Equation (i) states that $f(x, y)$ is homogeneous of degree one and hence, if differentiable, satisfies

$$f(x, y) = xf_x(x, y) + yf_y(x, y)$$

(*Advanced Calculus*, § 81). In particular, when $y = 0$,

$$f(x, 0) = xf_x(x, 0), \quad \text{hence} \quad f(x, 0) = ax$$

on integration since $f(0,0) = 0$ from (i). Similarly $f(0, y) = by$. Now from (ii)

$$f(x, y) = f(x + 0, 0 + y) = f(x, 0) + f(0, y) = ax + by.$$

In the same way $g(x, y) = cx + dy$. Thus the principle of superposition implies a linear system.

Equation (2) defines a vector field $\mathbf{v} = f(x, y)\mathbf{i} + g(x, y)\mathbf{j}$ at every point $P(x, y)$. If $\mathscr{C}$ is a simple closed circuit in this field that does not pass through a critical point, the vector $\mathbf{v}$, as P makes a counter-clock circuit, returns to its original position; hence $\mathbf{v}$ must sweep out an angle which is a multiple of 2π, say $2\pi m$, where m is an *integer*, positive, negative, or zero. The integer m is called the *index* of $\mathscr{C}$ relative to the field $\mathbf{v}$ or, if $\mathscr{C}$ encloses a single critical point, the index of the critical point.

If $\mathscr{C}$ is deformed continuously into another simple closed curve without crossing a critical point, the index of $\mathscr{C}$ varies continuously, and since it is an integer, the index must remain constant during the deformation.

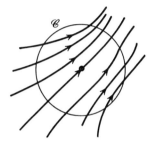

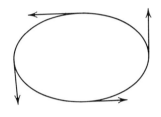

Fig. 47d   Regular point: Index = 0.   **Fig. 47e**   Closed trajectory: Index = 1.

Thus $\mathscr{C}$ may shrink into a small circle if no critical point is crossed; and if $\mathscr{C}$ encloses *no* critical points this circle and its index may be made arbitrarily small. Hence *the index of $\mathscr{C}$ about a regular point is zero* (Fig. 47d). On the other hand, if $\mathscr{C}$ is a closed *trajectory*, $\mathbf{v}$ is tangent to the trajectory and in a circuit sweeps out exactly 2π; thus *the index of a closed trajectory is* 1. Conclusion: *A closed trajectory surrounds at least one critical point* (Fig. 47e).

Reversing directions on all trajectories does not change the index; for the angles swept out by $\mathbf{v}$ and $-\mathbf{v}$ in a circuit are the same.

All types of critical points that a linear system (5) may have are called *elementary* and all of these are illustrated in the following examples. The system (1), however, may not have any linear terms and in this case critical points of greater complexity may arise. These are not discussed here.

Example 1. $\begin{pmatrix} Dx \\ Dy \end{pmatrix} = \begin{pmatrix} -1 & 0 \\ 0 & -2 \end{pmatrix} \begin{pmatrix} x \\ y \end{pmatrix},$ $(D = d/dt).$

$$(D + 1)x = 0, \qquad (D + 2)y = 0;$$

(i) $$x = c_1 e^{-t}, \qquad y = c_2 e^{-2t}.$$

The stream lines are parabolas $y = Kx^2$ tangent to the x-axis, and the axes are also solutions (c_1 or $c_2 = 0$). The origin is called a *node* (Latin, *nodus*, knot);

and since $x, y \to 0$ as $t \to \infty$, the node is strictly stable (Fig. 47*f*). The index of a node is 1. For the matrix $\begin{pmatrix} 1 & 0 \\ 0 & 2 \end{pmatrix}$ the stream lines

(ii)
$$x = c_1 e^t, \qquad y = c_2 e^{2t}$$

are the same parabolas; but since $x, y \to \infty$ as $t \to \infty$, the node is now unstable (Fig. 47*f* with arrows reversed). At the node all trajectories have a common tangent but different curvatures.

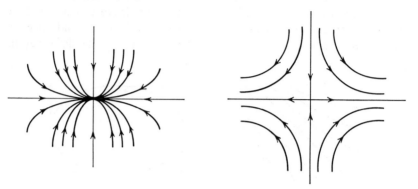

Fig. 47f Strictly stable node: Index = 1.   **Fig. 47g** Saddle point: Index = −1.

Example 2. $\begin{pmatrix} Dx \\ Dy \end{pmatrix} = \begin{pmatrix} 1 & 0 \\ 0 & -1 \end{pmatrix} \begin{pmatrix} x \\ y \end{pmatrix}$.

$$(D - 1)x = 0, \qquad (D + 1)y = 0;$$
(i)
$$x = c_1 e^t, \qquad y = c_2 e^{-t}.$$

The stream lines are equilateral hyperbolas $xy = K$ asymptotic to the axes, and the axes are also solutions. The origin is called a *saddle point*; for the curves suggest the contour lines about the high-low point of a saddle. Since $x \to \infty$ as $t \to \infty$, the point is unstable (Fig. 47*g*). The index of a saddle point is −1.

For the matrix $\begin{pmatrix} -1 & 0 \\ 0 & 1 \end{pmatrix}$ the stream lines

(ii)
$$x = c_1 e^{-t}, \qquad y = c_2 e^t$$

are the same hyperbolas. Since $y \to \infty$ as $t \to \infty$, the saddle point is still unstable (Fig. 47*g* with arrows reversed).

Example 3. $\begin{pmatrix} Dx \\ Dy \end{pmatrix} = \begin{pmatrix} 1 & 1 \\ 1 & 1 \end{pmatrix} \begin{pmatrix} x \\ y \end{pmatrix}$.

The system
$$(D - 1)x - y = 0, \qquad -x + (D - 1)y = 0$$

is equivalent to the triangular system
$$(D - 1)x - y = 0, \qquad D(D - 2)x = 0;$$
hence
(i)
$$x = c_1 e^{2t} + c_2, \qquad y = c_1 e^{2t} - c_2.$$

When $c_1 \neq 0$ we obtain the parallel stream lines

$$\frac{y + c_2}{x - c_2} = 1 \quad \text{or} \quad y = x + K.$$

When $c_1 = 0$, equations (i) yield the equilibrium line E, $x + y = 0$, all points of which are at rest. For points not on this line, $(x, y) \rightarrow (\infty, \infty)$ as $t \rightarrow \infty$ and the equilibrium at the origin is unstable (Fig. 47h). There is no index as every circuit about the origin crosses E at two critical points.

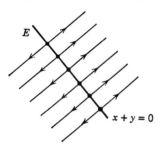

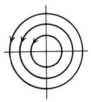

Fig. 47h Parallel lines cutting E: **Fig. 47i** Vortex or center: Index $= 1$.
unstable equilibrium.

For the matrix $\begin{pmatrix} -1 & -1 \\ -1 & -1 \end{pmatrix}$ the stream lines

(ii) $$x = c_1 e^{-2t} + c_2, \qquad y = c_1 e^{-2t} - c_2$$

are the same parallel lines and the line $x + y = 0$ is again in equilibrium. As $t \rightarrow \infty$, $(x, y) \rightarrow (c_2, -c_2)$, a point on the line $x + y = 0$. Thus a point near the origin will move on a trajectory toward the line $x + y = 0$ where it comes to rest. The origin is therefore in stable equilibrium (Fig. 47h with arrows reversed).

Example 4. $\begin{pmatrix} Dx \\ Dy \end{pmatrix} = \begin{pmatrix} 0 & -1 \\ 1 & 0 \end{pmatrix} \begin{pmatrix} x \\ y \end{pmatrix}.$

The system

$$Dx + y = 0, \qquad x - Dy = 0$$

is equivalent to the triangular system

$$Dx + y = 0, \qquad (D^2 + 1)x = 0;$$

hence

(i) $$x = c_1 \cos t + c_2 \sin t, \qquad y = c_1 \sin t - c_2 \cos t.$$

The stream lines are concentric circles $x^2 + y^2 = c_1^2 + c_2^2$ about the origin which is called a *vortex* or *center* (Fig. 47i). It is in neutral equilibrium; for a particle displaced from O to P will move in a circle of radius OP about O. The signs of Dx and Dy show that the motion is counterclockwise. To see this in another way, transform the system to polar coordinates: $x = r \cos \theta$, $y = r \sin \theta$; it then becomes $Dr = 0$, $D\theta = 1$, showing that the circular motion is counterclockwise, with unit speed. Since the trajectories are closed curves, the index of a vortex is 1.

For the matrix $\begin{pmatrix} 0 & 1 \\ -1 & 0 \end{pmatrix}$ the circular motion is clockwise.

Example 5. $\begin{pmatrix} Dx \\ Dy \end{pmatrix} = \begin{pmatrix} 1 & -1 \\ 1 & 1 \end{pmatrix}\begin{pmatrix} x \\ y \end{pmatrix}.$

The system
$$Dx = x - y, \qquad Dy = x + y$$
is simplified by transforming to polar coordinates as in Example 4; then
$$Dr = r, \qquad D\theta = 1,$$
(i)
$$r = c_1 e^t, \qquad \theta = t + c_2.$$

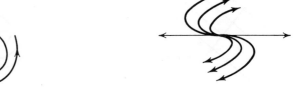

Fig. 47j   Unstable focus: Index = 1.   **Fig. 47k**   Unstable inflected node: Index = 1.

The stream lines are equiangular spirals
$$r = c_1 e^{\theta - c_2} = K e^\theta$$
cutting all rays from the pole at 45° (Fig. 47j). They wind counterclockwise away from the pole as $t \to \infty$. The pole is unstable and is called a *focus*. Its index is 1.

For the matrix $\begin{pmatrix} -1 & 1 \\ -1 & -1 \end{pmatrix}$ the stream lines

(ii)
$$r = c_1 e^{-t}, \qquad \theta = -t + c_2$$
are the same spirals winding in toward the pole as $t \to \infty$. The origin is now strictly stable (Fig. 47j with arrows reversed).

Example 6. $\begin{pmatrix} Dx \\ Dy \end{pmatrix} = \begin{pmatrix} 1 & 1 \\ 0 & 1 \end{pmatrix}\begin{pmatrix} x \\ y \end{pmatrix}.$

$$(D - 1)x - y = 0, \qquad (D - 1)y = 0;$$
(i)
$$x = (c_2 + c_1 t)e^t, \qquad y = c_1 e^t.$$
The stream lines are the curves
$$x = y(K + \log |y|)$$
along with the x-axis $y = 0$ ($c_1 = 0$) and are symmetric with respect to the origin. Since
$$\frac{dy}{dx} = \frac{1}{K + 1 + \log |y|} \to 0 \quad \text{as} \quad y \to 0 \text{ or } \infty,$$
they are tangent to the x-axis at the origin, cross it there, and tend toward its direction at infinity. As $t \to \infty$ both x and $y \to \infty$; hence the origin is an unstable *inflected node* (Fig. 47k). Unlike the node in Example 1, all curved

trajectories have a point of inflection at the origin. The index is still 1.

For the matrix $\begin{pmatrix} -1 & -1 \\ 0 & -1 \end{pmatrix}$ the stream lines

(ii) $x = y(c_2 - c_1 t)e^{-t}, \qquad y = c_1 e^{-t}$

are the same curves with arrows reversed and the node is strictly stable.

Example 7. $\begin{pmatrix} Dx \\ Dy \end{pmatrix} = \begin{pmatrix} 1 & 0 \\ 0 & 1 \end{pmatrix}\begin{pmatrix} x \\ y \end{pmatrix}$.

$$(D - 1)x = 0, \qquad (D - 1)y = 0;$$

(i) $x = c_1 e^t, \qquad y = c_2 e^t.$

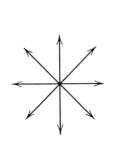

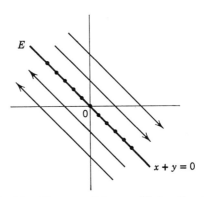

Fig. 47l Unstable star: Index = 1.   **Fig. 47m** Lines parallel to equilibrium line E.

The stream lines are the rays

$$y = Kx, \qquad x = 0$$

directed away from the origin. This type of node is called a *star*. It is unstable for x and $y \to \infty$ as $t \to \infty$ (Fig. 47l). Its index is 1.

For the matrix $\begin{pmatrix} -1 & 0 \\ 0 & -1 \end{pmatrix}$ the

(ii) $x = c_1 e^{-t}, \qquad y = c_2 e^{-t}$

are the same rays directed toward the origin. The origin is now stable (Fig. 47l with arrows reversed).

Example 8. $\begin{pmatrix} Dx \\ Dy \end{pmatrix} = \begin{pmatrix} 1 & 1 \\ -1 & -1 \end{pmatrix}\begin{pmatrix} x \\ y \end{pmatrix}$.

The system

$$(D - 1)x - y = 0, \qquad x + (D + 1)y = 0$$

is equivalent to the triangular system

$$(D - 1)x - y = 0, \qquad D^2 x = 0;$$

hence

(i) $x = c_1 + c_2 t, \qquad y = c_2 - c_1 - c_2 t.$

The stream lines are the parallel lines $x + y = c_2$; and the one E through the origin, $x + y = 0$, is in equilibrium. For points not on E, $x \rightarrow \pm\infty$ and $y \rightarrow \mp\infty$ as $t \rightarrow \infty$; the equilibrium at the origin is unstable (Fig. 47m). Note that $x \rightarrow \infty$ or $-\infty$ according as the intercepts (c_2) of the stream line are positive or negative. There is no index.

For the matrix $\begin{pmatrix} -1 & -1 \\ 1 & 1 \end{pmatrix}$ the stream lines in Fig. 47m have their arrows reversed and the origin is still unstable.

48. LINEAR FLOW

We shall now consider the stream line patterns of the autonomous linear system

(A) $$\frac{dx}{dt} = ax + by, \qquad \frac{dy}{dt} = cx + dy$$

in the neighborhood of the equilibrium point $(0, 0)$. With $D = d/dt$, we write this system in the form

(1) $$(a - D)x + by = 0, \qquad b \neq 0$$

(2) $$cx + (d - D)y = 0.$$

Here we assume $b \neq 0$ in order to give specific results. If $b = 0$ but $c \neq 0$, we make the changes in notation:

$$x \leftrightarrow y, \qquad a \leftrightarrow d, \qquad b \leftrightarrow c,$$

so that again $b \neq 0$. If $b = c = 0$, the system (1) $-$ (2) may be integrated at once; this simple case will be considered later.

The operations

$$T_1 : -b(2), \qquad T_2 = (d - D)(1) + (2)$$

give the triangular system

(1) $$(a - D)x + by = 0, \qquad b \neq 0,$$

(3) $$[(a - D)(d - D) - bc]x = 0.$$

The characteristic equation of (3) is

(4) $$\lambda^2 - (a + d)\lambda + (ad - bc) = 0;$$

or, in determinant form,

(4) $$\begin{vmatrix} a - \lambda & b \\ c & d - \lambda \end{vmatrix} = 0.$$

Its roots are the eigenvalues of the matrix $\begin{pmatrix} a & b \\ c & d \end{pmatrix}$ (§ 49) and their sum and product are given by

(5)(6) $\lambda_1 + \lambda_2 = a + d, \qquad \lambda_1\lambda_2 = ad - bc.$

The discriminant of (4) is

(7) $\Delta = (a + d)^2 - 4(ad - bc) = (\lambda_1 - \lambda_2)^2.$

Case I. $\Delta > 0$: λ_1, λ_2 *real and distinct.*

The solution of the system (3) − (1) is then

(8)
$$x = c_1 e^{\lambda_1 t} + c_2 e^{\lambda_2 t}$$
$$by = c_1(\lambda_1 - a)e^{\lambda_1 t} + c_2(\lambda_2 - a)e^{\lambda_2 t}.$$

We now write

(9)
$$u = (\lambda_2 - a)x - by = c_1(\lambda_2 - \lambda_1)e^{\lambda_1 t}$$
$$v = (\lambda_1 - a)x - by = c_2(\lambda_1 - \lambda_2)e^{\lambda_2 t}$$

For $c_1 = 0$, $c_2 = 0$, we see that the lines $u = 0$, $v = 0$ are included among the stream lines

(10) $v = Ku^n, \qquad n = \lambda_2/\lambda_1$

where the notation is chosen so that $\lambda_1 \neq 0$. There are three subcases: $ad - bc > 0, = 0, < 0$.

Case Ia. $\Delta > 0$, $ad - bc > 0$.

Since $\lambda_1\lambda_2 > 0$, λ_1 and λ_2 have the same sign and $n > 0$. The stream lines (10) are "general parabolas"; they pass through the origin and are there tangent to

$$v = 0 \quad \text{if} \quad n > 1, \qquad u = 0 \quad \text{if} \quad n < 1.$$

The origin, where all stream lines have a common tangent, is a *node*. It is strictly stable or unstable according as λ_1, λ_2 are negative or positive. (See Ex. 47.1.)

Case Ib. $\Delta > 0$, $ad - bc < 0$.

Since $\lambda_1\lambda_2 < 0$, λ_1 and λ_2 have opposite signs and $n < 0$. Writing $m = -n$, the stream lines

(11) $u^m v = K, \qquad m > 0,$

no longer pass through the origin but resemble hyperbolas asymptotic to the lines $u = 0$, $v = 0$, which are also part of the solution. The origin is a *saddle point* and unstable. (See Ex. 47.2.)

Case Ic. $\Delta > 0$, $ad - bc = 0$.

Now $\lambda_1 \lambda_2 = 0$, and since $\lambda_1 \neq \lambda_2$ we take $\lambda_1 \neq 0$, $\lambda_2 = 0$; then $n = 0$ and the stream lines (10) are the parallel lines $v = K$. All points of the line $u = 0$ ($ax + by = 0$) are at rest; for from (A), $dx/dt = 0$; and since $c/a = d/b$, $dy/dt = 0$ also. The equilibrium at the origin is unstable if $\lambda_1 > 0$; stable if $\lambda_1 < 0$. (See Ex. 47.3.)

Case II. $\Delta < 0$, λ_1, λ_2 *complex conjugate:*

$$\lambda_1 = \alpha + i\beta, \qquad \lambda_2 = \alpha - i\beta \qquad (\beta > 0).$$

Since a and b are real, equations (9) show that u and v are conjugate, say

$$u = re^{i\theta}, \qquad v = re^{-i\theta}.$$

Thus equations (9) become

(9)'
$$re^{i\theta} = c_1(\lambda_2 - \lambda_1)e^{\lambda_1 t},$$
$$re^{-i\theta} = c_2(\lambda_1 - \lambda_2)e^{\lambda_2 t}.$$

The second equation is the conjugate of the first; and if we write

$$c_1(\lambda_2 - \lambda_1) = Ce^{i\gamma} \qquad (C, \gamma \text{ real})$$

both may be replaced by

(9)''
$$re^{i\theta} = Ce^{i\gamma}e^{(\alpha+i\beta)t} = Ce^{\alpha t}e^{i(\gamma+\beta t)}.$$

Equating the lengths and angles of these complex numbers we have

(12)
$$r = Ce^{\alpha t}, \qquad \theta = \gamma + \beta t.$$

These are the polar parametric equations of the stream lines; and elimination of t gives their polar equation

(13)
$$r = K \exp\left(\frac{\alpha}{\beta}\theta\right).$$

There are now two subcases: $a + d \neq 0$, $a + d = 0$; and from (5)

$$a + d = \lambda_1 + \lambda_2 = 2\alpha.$$

Case IIa. $\Delta < 0$, $a + d = 2\alpha \neq 0$.

The curves (13) are spirals that wind asymptotically about the origin. Indeed, if we put $u = X + iY$, they are equiangular spirals in the XY-plane. Since X and Y are linear functions of x and y, the curves in the xy-plane are affine transforms of equiangular spirals. The origin is now a *focus*; it is strictly stable when $\alpha < 0$,* unstable when $\alpha > 0$. (See Ex. 47.5.)

---

* Since $\beta > 0$, $\alpha/\beta < 0$ in (13).

Case IIb. $\Delta < 0$, $a + d = 2\alpha = 0$.

The stream lines (13), $r = K$, are a family of concentric circles about the origin in the XY-plane. In the xy-plane they form a family of concentric ellipses. Their equation may be obtained directly from the equation

$$\frac{dy}{dx} = \frac{cx + dy}{ax + by} \qquad \text{when } d = -a.$$

This homogeneous equation

$$(cx - ay)\,dx - (ax + by)\,dy = 0$$

is also exact and admits two multipliers λ, μ (§ 19):

$$\lambda = 1, \qquad 1/\mu = x(cx - ay) - y(ax + by).$$

Its integral curves $\lambda/\mu = C$ (§ 10), or

(14) $$cx^2 - 2axy - by^2 = C,$$

are the affine transforms of concentric circles about the origin, namely, concentric ellipses.* The origin is a *vortex* and in stable equilibrium. (See Ex. 47.4.)

Case III. $\Delta = 0$, $\lambda_1 = \lambda_2 = \lambda$.

The solution of the system (3) − (1) is now

(15)
$$x = (c_1 + c_2 t)e^{\lambda t}$$
$$by = (\lambda - a)(c_1 + c_2 t)e^{\lambda t} + c_2 e^{\lambda t}.$$

When $b \neq 0$ there are two subcases: $ad - bc \neq 0$, $ad - bc = 0$.

Case IIIa. $\Delta = 0$, $ad - bc = \lambda^2 \neq 0$.

From (15)

$$v = (\lambda - a)x - by = -c_2 e^{\lambda t}, \qquad t = \frac{1}{\lambda} \log \frac{|v|}{|c_2|} \ ;$$

(16) $$x = v\left(K - \frac{1}{\lambda} \log |v|\right).$$

These curves and the one straight line $v = 0$ (for $c_2 = 0$) are the stream lines. All pass through the origin and are tangent there to the line $v = 0$.†

---

* Equation (7) also shows that (14) represents ellipses; for when $a + d = 0$, $\Delta = 4(a^2 + bc)$, and $\Delta < 0$ is the condition for ellipses.

     If $a + d = 0$ and $\Delta > 0$ we are in Case Ib; the curves (14) are then concentric hyperbolas and the origin is a saddle point.

† As $x \to 0$, $dx/dv \to \infty$ and $dv/dx \to 0$.

The origin is a strictly stable *node* if $\lambda < 0$, unstable if $\lambda > 0$. (See Ex. 47.6.)

Case IIIb. $\Delta = 0$, $ad - bc = \lambda^2 = 0$.

Equations (15), with $\lambda = 0$, become

(17)
$$x = c_1 + c_2 t,$$
$$by = c_2 - a(c_1 + c_2 t),$$

whence

(18)
$$ax + by = c_2.$$

These parallel lines are the stream lines. The one through the origin, $ax + by = 0$, is in equilibrium; for from (A), $dx/dt = 0$; and since $c/a = d/b$, $dy/dt = 0$ also. The origin is unstable. (See Ex. 47.8.)

Finally we must consider the case $b = c = 0$ ruled out thus far. The system (1) − (2) now becomes

(19)
$$(D - a)x = 0, \qquad (D - d)y = 0.$$

Then $\lambda_1 = a$, $\lambda_2 = d$, and

$$x = c_1 e^{\lambda_1 t}, \qquad y = c_2 e^{\lambda_2 t}.$$

Elimination of t gives the stream lines

(20)
$$y = Kx^n, \qquad n = \lambda_2/\lambda_1.$$

When $\lambda_1 \neq \lambda_2$ and $n > 0$, we are in Case Ia. The curves are "general parabolas" in the xy-plane and the origin is a *node*.

When $\lambda_1 \neq \lambda_2$ and $n < 0$, we are in Case Ib; putting $n = -m$, the curves $yx^m = K$ are hyperbola-like and asymptotic to the x and y axes. The origin is a *saddle point*.

When $\lambda_1 = \lambda_2$, $\Delta = 0$ and we are in Case III.

Case IIIc. $\Delta = 0$, $b = c = 0$, $\lambda \neq 0$.

Now $n = 1$ and the stream lines (20) become a family of straight lines through the origin

(21)
$$y = Kx.$$

Although all stream lines pass through the origin, they do not have a common tangent there as in Cases Ia and IIIa. We call this type of node a *star*. It is stable or unstable according as $\lambda < 0$ or $\lambda > 0$. (See Ex. 47.7.)

Case IIId. $\Delta = 0$, $b = c = 0$, $\lambda = 0$.

Now $a = d = 0$ also and equations (19) become

$$Dx = 0, \qquad Dy = 0.$$

Hence $x = c_1$, $y = c_2$ and all points are in equilibrium.

Table 48   Stability

$$\begin{pmatrix} Dx \\ Dy \end{pmatrix} = \begin{pmatrix} a & b \\ c & d \end{pmatrix} \begin{pmatrix} x \\ y \end{pmatrix}$$

Characteristic equation: $\begin{vmatrix} a - \lambda & b \\ c & d - \lambda \end{vmatrix} = 0$; roots λ_1, λ_2.

$$a + d = \lambda_1 + \lambda_2, \qquad ad - bc = \lambda_1\lambda_2,$$

$$\Delta = (a + d)^2 - 4(ad - bc) = (\lambda_1 - \lambda_2)^2.$$

Case I: $\Delta > 0, \lambda_1 \neq \lambda_2$ (*real*).
  (a) $\lambda_1\lambda_2 > 0$ Node $\lambda_1 > 0$ (un), $\lambda_1 < 0$ (ss)
  (b) $\lambda_1\lambda_2 < 0$ Saddle point (un)
  (c) $\lambda_1\lambda_2 = 0$, $\lambda_1 \neq 0$ Parallel lines, cutting equilibrium line
                                       $\lambda_1 > 0$ (un), $\lambda_1 < 0$ (ss)

Case II: $\Delta < 0, \lambda_1 = \alpha + i\beta, \lambda_2 = \alpha - i\beta$.
  (a) $\alpha \neq 0$ Focus $\alpha > 0$ (un), $\alpha < 0$ (ss)
  (b) $\alpha = 0$ Vortex (s)

Case III: $\Delta = 0, \lambda_1 = \lambda_2 = \lambda$.
  (a) $b^2 + c^2 \neq 0$, $\lambda \neq 0$ Inflected node $\lambda > 0$ (un), $\lambda < 0$ (ss)
  (b) $b^2 + c^2 \neq 0$, $\lambda = 0$ Parallel lines, one in equilibrium (un)
  (c) $b = c = 0$, $\lambda \neq 0$ Star $\lambda > 0$ (un), $\lambda < 0$ (ss)
  (d) $b = c = 0$, $\lambda = 0$ All points in equilibrium

The roots λ_1, λ_2 are the *eigenvalues* of the matrix $\begin{pmatrix} a & b \\ c & d \end{pmatrix}$. The origin is strictly stable (ss) when and only when the eigenvalues have negative real parts. The subcases in Cases II and III depend on the value of $a + d = 2\alpha$ and $a + d = 2\lambda$, respectively.

PROBLEMS

Find the stream lines and determine type and stability of the equilibrium point at $(0, 0)$ of equation

$$\begin{pmatrix} Dx \\ Dy \end{pmatrix} = \begin{pmatrix} a & b \\ c & d \end{pmatrix} \begin{pmatrix} x \\ y \end{pmatrix}$$

for the given matrix.

1. $\begin{pmatrix} 4 & -3 \\ 5 & -4 \end{pmatrix}$ 2. $\begin{pmatrix} 3 & -1 \\ 1 & 1 \end{pmatrix}$

3. $\begin{pmatrix} 2 & 0 \\ 2 & 1 \end{pmatrix}$ 4. $\begin{pmatrix} 1 & -2 \\ 2 & 1 \end{pmatrix}$

5. $\begin{pmatrix} 3 & 4 \\ 1 & 3 \end{pmatrix}$ 6. $\begin{pmatrix} 2 & 1 \\ -1 & 0 \end{pmatrix}$

7. $\begin{pmatrix} 7 & 3 \\ 4 & 6 \end{pmatrix}$ 8. $\begin{pmatrix} -3 & -2 \\ 2 & -3 \end{pmatrix}$

9. $\begin{pmatrix} 1 & -1 \\ -1 & 1 \end{pmatrix}$ 10. $\begin{pmatrix} 2 & 0 \\ 0 & 2 \end{pmatrix}$

49. EIGENVALUES OF A MATRIX

We shall consider square matrices A whose elements a_{ij} are real constants. If A is an $n \times n$ matrix, a number λ is said to be an *eigenvalue* of A if there is an $n \times 1$ non-zero column vector $\mathbf{e}$ such that

$$(1) \qquad\qquad A\mathbf{e} = \lambda\mathbf{e}.$$

Then $\mathbf{e}$ is an *eigenvector associated with* λ and we write $\mathbf{e} \sim \lambda$. If c is a non-zero arbitrary constant, $c\mathbf{e}$ is also an eigenvector associated with λ; but there may also be eigenvectors other than $c\mathbf{e}$ associated with λ.

The $n \times n$ *unit matrix*

$$I = \begin{pmatrix} 1 & 0 & \cdots & 0 \\ 0 & 1 & \cdots & 0 \\ \cdot & \cdot & \cdots & \cdot \\ 0 & 0 & \cdots & 1 \end{pmatrix}$$

has ones along the principal diagonal and zeros elsewhere. Its product with any $n \times m$ matrix B leaves it unchanged ($IB = B$) and this holds, in particular, for the $n \times 1$ vector $\mathbf{e}$. Then since $I\mathbf{e} = \mathbf{e}$, equation (1) may be written

$$(2) \qquad\qquad (A - \lambda I)\mathbf{e} = 0$$

where $\mathbf{0}$ is the $n \times 1$ zero vector $(0, 0, \ldots, 0)$. If $\mathbf{e} = (u_1, u_2, \ldots, u_n)$, the n linear homogeneous equations (2) will admit a non-zero solution $\mathbf{e}$

when and only when the determinant of their coefficients is zero:

(3) $\det(A - \lambda I) = 0$ or $$\begin{vmatrix} a_{11} - \lambda & a_{12} & \cdots & a_{1n} \\ a_{21} & a_{22} - \lambda & \cdots & a_{2n} \\ \cdot & \cdot & & \cdot \\ \cdot & \cdot & & \cdot \\ \cdot & \cdot & & \cdot \\ a_{n1} & a_{n2} & \cdots & a_{nn} - \lambda \end{vmatrix} = 0.$$

This *characteristic equation* of degree n has exactly n roots $\lambda_1, \lambda_2, \ldots, \lambda_n$ which may or may not be distinct; and since the coefficients of equations (3) are real, any complex roots will occur in conjugate pairs, $\alpha \pm i\beta$. The roots λ_i are the *eigenvalues* of the matrix A; for when $\lambda = \lambda_i$, equations (2) will admit at least one non-zero vector $\mathbf{e}_i$ as a solution. Then $\mathbf{e}_i$ is an eigenvector associated with λ_i ($\mathbf{e}_i \sim \lambda_i$).

The *transpose* of a matrix A is the matrix A^T whose rows are the columns of A taken in order: the element a_{ij} of row i, column j of A now lies in row j, column i of A^T. Thus the transpose of a column vector $\mathbf{a}$ is the row vector $\mathbf{a}^T$ with the same ordered components.

A matrix A is said to be *symmetric* if $a_{ij} = a_{ji}$; then $A = A^T$. If A is symmetric, we may readily verify that for any n-vectors $\mathbf{a}$, $\mathbf{b}$,

(4) $\mathbf{a}^T A \mathbf{b} = \mathbf{b}^T A \mathbf{a}.$

When $A = I$, the unit matrix, (4) becomes

(5) $\mathbf{a}^T \mathbf{b} = \mathbf{b}^T \mathbf{a} = a_1 b_1 + a_2 b_2 + \cdots + a_n b_n$

which is the scalar product $\mathbf{a} \cdot \mathbf{b}$ in Gibbs' notation. Two n-vectors $\mathbf{a}$, $\mathbf{b}$ are said to be *orthogonal* (Greek, right-angled) or perpendicular (Latin, *perpendiculum*, plumb line) when $\mathbf{a} \cdot \mathbf{b} = 0$.

Theorem 1. *A matrix and its transpose have exactly the same eigenvalues.*

PROOF. Since a determinant is not altered by transposition, their characteristic equations (3) are the same.

Theorem 2. *All eigenvalues of a real symmetric matrix are real; and eigenvectors associated with distinct eigenvalues are orthogonal.*

PROOF. Let the real symmetric matrix A have the eigenvalue $\lambda = \alpha + i\beta$ with an associated eigenvector $\mathbf{e} = \mathbf{a} + i\mathbf{b}$, $\mathbf{a}$ and $\mathbf{b}$ having real components. Then

$$A(\mathbf{a} + i\mathbf{b}) = (\alpha + i\beta)(\mathbf{a} + i\mathbf{b})$$

and on equating real and imaginary parts,

$$A\mathbf{a} = \alpha\mathbf{a} - \beta\mathbf{b}, \qquad A\mathbf{b} = \beta\mathbf{a} + \alpha\mathbf{b}.$$

From (4) we have

$$a^T(\beta a + \alpha b) = b^T(\alpha a - \beta b),$$

or since $a^T b = b^T a$,

$$\beta(a^T a + b^T b) = 0.$$

Now $a^T a + b^T b$ is a sum of squares and therefore non-negative; and since $e \neq 0$ we cannot have $a = b = 0$. Therefore $a^T a + b^T b > 0, \beta = 0$, and λ is real.

If λ_1 and λ_2 are distinct eigenvalues, $A e_1 = \lambda_1 e_1$, $A e_2 = \lambda_2 e_2$; hence

$$e_2{}^T A e_1 - e_1{}^T A e_2 = \lambda_1 e_2{}^T e_1 - \lambda_2 e_1{}^T e_2 = (\lambda_1 - \lambda_2) e_1 \cdot e_2$$

from (5). When A is symmetric, the left member is zero; hence the right member is zero and since λ_1, λ_2 are distinct, $\lambda_1 - \lambda_2 \neq 0$. Thus $e_1 \cdot e_2 = 0$ and e_1 and e_2 are orthogonal.

A set of vectors $a_1, a_2, \ldots, a_n$ is said to be *linearly independent* when any linear relation between them such as

$$c_1 a_1 + c_2 a_2 + \cdots + c_n a_n = 0 \quad \text{implies} \quad c_1 = c_2 = \cdots = c_n = 0.$$

In 2-space, linearly independent vectors are nonparallel, in 3-space, they are noncoplanar. We now have the important

Theorem 3. *The eigenvectors associated with a set of distinct eigenvalues are linearly independent.*

PROOF. Consider the case of three distinct eigenvalues $\lambda_1, \lambda_2, \lambda_3$ associated with e_1, e_2, e_3 and assume the linear relation

$$(6) \qquad\qquad v = c_1 e_1 + c_2 e_2 + c_3 e_3 = 0.$$

Then since $A e_i = \lambda_i e_i$, we have

$$(7) \qquad\qquad A v = \lambda_1 c_1 e_1 + \lambda_2 c_2 e_2 + \lambda_3 c_3 e_3 = 0,$$

$$(8) \qquad\qquad A^2 v = \lambda_1{}^2 c_1 e_1 + \lambda_2{}^2 c_2 e_2 + \lambda_3{}^2 c_3 e_3 = 0.$$

Now (6), (7), (8), regarded as a set of linear equations for $c_1 e_1, c_2 e_2, c_3 e_3$, have the Vandermonde determinant

$$\begin{vmatrix} 1 & 1 & 1 \\ \lambda_1 & \lambda_2 & \lambda_3 \\ \lambda_1{}^2 & \lambda_2{}^2 & \lambda_3{}^2 \end{vmatrix} = (\lambda_1 - \lambda_2)(\lambda_2 - \lambda_3)(\lambda_3 - \lambda_1) \neq 0$$

since each factor is not zero. Therefore the equations only admit the solution $c_1 e_1 = c_2 e_2 = c_3 e_3 = 0$; and since e_1, e_2, $e_3 \neq 0$, we must have $c_1 = c_2 = c_3 = 0$.

The proof for k distinct eigenvalues follows the same lines; for the k-rowed Vandermonde determinant in this case is a product of $\frac{1}{2}k(k-1)$ non-zero factors of the type $\lambda_i - \lambda_j$.

An eigenvector $e \sim \lambda$ is found from a set of linear equations

(9) $(A - \lambda I)e = 0$ whose $\det(A - \lambda I) = 0$.

The character of the solutions of such a system depends on the *rank* of the matrix $A - \lambda I$, defined as follows:

Definition. A rectangular matrix has the *rank* r if the biggest (in size) non-zero determinant formed from its square minors has r rows. Any $(r+1)$-rowed determinant formed from the matrix must therefore be zero.

A general method of solving any system of linear algebraic equations is given in Appendix 1; there also an efficient *rank test* may be found.

Example 1. $A = \begin{pmatrix} 0 & 1 \\ -3 & 4 \end{pmatrix}$. The characteristic equation of A

$$\begin{vmatrix} -\lambda & 1 \\ -3 & 4-\lambda \end{vmatrix} = \lambda^2 - 4\lambda + 3 = (\lambda - 1)(\lambda - 3) = 0$$

and its eigenvalues are $\lambda_1 = 1$, $\lambda_2 = 3$. For each λ_i we form equations (4) to obtain the associated eigenvectors $e_i = (u, v) \neq 0$. Thus for

$$\lambda_1 = 1, \qquad \begin{pmatrix} -1 & 1 \\ -3 & 3 \end{pmatrix}\begin{pmatrix} u \\ v \end{pmatrix} = \begin{pmatrix} 0 \\ 0 \end{pmatrix}, \qquad e_1 = (1, 1);$$

$$\lambda_2 = 3, \qquad \begin{pmatrix} -3 & 1 \\ -3 & 1 \end{pmatrix}\begin{pmatrix} u \\ v \end{pmatrix} = \begin{pmatrix} 0 \\ 0 \end{pmatrix}, \qquad e_2 = (1, 3).$$

Any non-zero multiples of e_1 and e_2 are also eigenvectors.

Example 2. $A = \begin{pmatrix} 1 & 1 & 0 \\ 1 & 0 & 1 \\ 0 & 1 & 1 \end{pmatrix}$. The characteristic equation (3) is

$$\begin{vmatrix} 1-\lambda & 1 & 0 \\ 1 & -\lambda & 1 \\ 0 & 1 & 1-\lambda \end{vmatrix} = -(\lambda - 1)(\lambda + 1)(\lambda - 2) = 0,$$

and the eigenvalues are $\lambda_1 = 1$, $\lambda_2 = -1$, $\lambda_3 = 2$. For each λ_i we form equations (4) and obtain a solution $e_i \neq 0$:

$$\lambda_1 = 1, \qquad \begin{pmatrix} 0 & 1 & 0 \\ 1 & -1 & 1 \\ 0 & 1 & 0 \end{pmatrix} \begin{pmatrix} u \\ v \\ w \end{pmatrix} = 0, \qquad e_1 = (1, 0, -1);$$

$$\lambda_2 = -1, \qquad \begin{pmatrix} 2 & 1 & 0 \\ 1 & -2 & 1 \\ 0 & 1 & 2 \end{pmatrix} \begin{pmatrix} u \\ v \\ w \end{pmatrix} = 0, \qquad e_2 = (1, -2, 1);$$

$$\lambda_3 = 2, \qquad \begin{pmatrix} -1 & 1 & 0 \\ 1 & -2 & 1 \\ 0 & 1 & -1 \end{pmatrix} \begin{pmatrix} u \\ v \\ w \end{pmatrix} = 0, \qquad e_3 = (1, 1, 1).$$

The eigenvector e_1, for example, is found from the determinants of rows 1 and 2 of $A - \lambda_1 I$ in the columns 23, 31, 12.

Note that A is symmetric and, in conformity with Theorem 2, the λ_i are real and the e_i mutually perpendicular.

Example 3. $A = \begin{pmatrix} -1 & 1 & 1 \\ 1 & -1 & 1 \\ 1 & 1 & -1 \end{pmatrix}$. The characteristic equation is

$$\begin{vmatrix} -1 - \lambda & 1 & 1 \\ 1 & -1 - \lambda & 1 \\ 1 & 1 & -1 - \lambda \end{vmatrix} = -(\lambda - 1)(\lambda + 2)^2 = 0,$$

and the eigenvalues are $\lambda_1 = 1$, $\lambda_2 = \lambda_3 = -2$. We find the eigenvectors from (4):

$$\lambda_1 = 1, \qquad \begin{pmatrix} -2 & 1 & 1 \\ 1 & -2 & 1 \\ 1 & 1 & -2 \end{pmatrix} \begin{pmatrix} u \\ v \\ w \end{pmatrix} = 0, \qquad e_1 = (1, 1, 1);$$

the matrix is of rank 2.

$$\lambda_2 = -2, \qquad \begin{pmatrix} 1 & 1 & 1 \\ 1 & 1 & 1 \\ 1 & 1 & 1 \end{pmatrix} \begin{pmatrix} u \\ v \\ w \end{pmatrix} = 0, \qquad e \perp e_1;$$

the matrix now is of rank 1.

For $\lambda_2 = -2$ there is but one equation

$$(1, 1, 1) \begin{pmatrix} u \\ v \\ w \end{pmatrix} = e_1 \cdot e_2 = 0.$$

Thus any vector e in the plane perpendicular to e_1 is an eigenvector $\sim \lambda_2$. For example, we may take

$$e_1 = (1, 1, 1), \qquad e_2 = (1, 1, -2), \qquad e_3 = (-1, 1, 0);$$

then e_1, e_2, e_3 are mutually perpendicular and linearly independent.

Example 4. $A = \begin{pmatrix} 1 & 1 & 2 \\ 0 & 1 & 3 \\ 0 & 0 & 2 \end{pmatrix}$. The characteristic equation is

$$\begin{vmatrix} 1 - \lambda & 1 & 2 \\ 0 & 1 - \lambda & 3 \\ 0 & 0 & 2 - \lambda \end{vmatrix} = (1 - \lambda)^2(2 - \lambda) = 0,$$

and the eigenvalues are $\lambda_1 = \lambda_2 = 1$, $\lambda_3 = 2$. We now have just *two* independent eigenvectors

$$\lambda_3 = 2, \qquad \begin{pmatrix} -1 & 1 & 2 \\ 0 & -1 & 3 \\ 0 & 0 & 0 \end{pmatrix}\begin{pmatrix} u \\ v \\ w \end{pmatrix} = \mathbf{0}, \qquad \mathbf{e}_3 = (5, 3, 1);$$

$$\lambda_1 = 1, \qquad \begin{pmatrix} 0 & 1 & 2 \\ 0 & 0 & 3 \\ 0 & 0 & 1 \end{pmatrix}\begin{pmatrix} u \\ v \\ w \end{pmatrix} = \mathbf{0}, \qquad \mathbf{e}_1 = (1, 0, 0).$$

In this event we define a *generalized* eigenvector $\mathbf{e}_1'$ by the equation

$$(9) \qquad\qquad (A - \lambda_1 I)\mathbf{e}_1' = \mathbf{e}_1.$$

For the given matrix this becomes

$$\begin{pmatrix} 0 & 1 & 2 \\ 0 & 0 & 3 \\ 0 & 0 & 1 \end{pmatrix}\begin{pmatrix} u \\ v \\ w \end{pmatrix} = \begin{pmatrix} 1 \\ 0 \\ 0 \end{pmatrix}, \qquad \mathbf{e}_1' = (0, 1, 0);$$

for the equations have the solution $(u, 1, 0)$, u arbitrary, and we may take $u = 0$. The vectors $\mathbf{e}_1, \mathbf{e}_1', \mathbf{e}_3$ are linearly independent; for if

$$c_1\mathbf{e}_1 + c_2\mathbf{e}_1' + c_3\mathbf{e}_3 = \mathbf{0},$$

multiply by $A - \lambda_1 I$ as a prefactor; then

$$c_2\mathbf{e}_1 + c_3(\lambda_3 - \lambda_1)\mathbf{e}_3 = \mathbf{0}$$

and since $\mathbf{e}_1$ and $\mathbf{e}_3$ are linearly independent, $c_2 = c_3 = 0$; hence $c_1\mathbf{e}_1 = \mathbf{0}$ and $c_1 = 0$.

Example 5. $A = \begin{pmatrix} 0 & 1 & 0 \\ 0 & 0 & 1 \\ 1 & -3 & 3 \end{pmatrix}$. The characteristic equation is

$$\begin{vmatrix} -\lambda & 1 & 0 \\ 0 & -\lambda & 1 \\ 1 & -3 & 3 - \lambda \end{vmatrix} = -(\lambda - 1)^3 = 0,$$

and now we have just *one* eigenvector:

$$\lambda_1 = 1, \qquad \begin{pmatrix} -1 & 1 & 0 \\ 0 & -1 & 1 \\ 1 & -3 & 2 \end{pmatrix}\begin{pmatrix} u \\ v \\ w \end{pmatrix} = \mathbf{0}, \qquad \mathbf{e}_1 = (1, 1, 1).$$

Now we define two generalized eigenvectors e_1', e_1'' by the equations

(10) $(A - \lambda_1 I)e_1' = e_1$ $(A - \lambda_1 I)e_1'' = e_1'.$

For the matrix given, the first becomes

$$\begin{pmatrix} -1 & 1 & 0 \\ 0 & -1 & 1 \\ 1 & -3 & 2 \end{pmatrix} \begin{pmatrix} u \\ v \\ w \end{pmatrix} = \begin{pmatrix} 1 \\ 1 \\ 1 \end{pmatrix}, \qquad e_1' = (0, 1, 2);$$

for the general solution is $(u, u + 1, u + 2)$, and with $u = 0$, $e_1' = (0, 1, 2)$.

We find next e_1'' from the equations

$$\begin{pmatrix} -1 & 1 & 0 \\ 0 & -1 & 1 \\ 1 & -3 & 2 \end{pmatrix} \begin{pmatrix} u \\ v \\ w \end{pmatrix} = \begin{pmatrix} 0 \\ 1 \\ 2 \end{pmatrix}, \qquad e_1'' = (0, 0, 1);$$

for their general solution is $(u, u, u + 1)$ and with $u = 0$, $e_1'' = (0, 0, 1)$.

The vectors e_1, e_1', e_1'' are linearly independent; for if

$$c_1 e_1 + c_2 e_1' + c_3 e_1'' = 0,$$

multiply twice by $A - \lambda I$ as a prefactor; then

$$c_2 e_1 + c_3 e_1' = 0, \qquad c_3 e_1 = 0,$$

whence $c_3 = 0$, $c_2 = 0$, $c_1 = 0$ in turn.

Example 6. Jordan normal form. Denote three linearly independent eigenvectors of A, *proper or generalized*, by e_1, e_2, e_3 and their reciprocal set by e^1, e^2, e^3. By definition (*Advanced Calculus*, § 110)

(11) $e_i \cdot e^j = \begin{cases} 1 & i = j \\ 0 & i \neq j \end{cases}.$

Then if the matrix E has e_1, e_2, e_3 as *columns*, its inverse E^{-1} has e^1, e^2, e^3 as *rows*; for

$$E^{-1}E = \begin{pmatrix} e^1 \\ e^2 \\ e^3 \end{pmatrix} (e_1 \mid e_2 \mid e_3) = \begin{pmatrix} 1 & 0 & 0 \\ 0 & 1 & 0 \\ 0 & 0 & 1 \end{pmatrix} = I.$$

The Jordan normal form of A is then

(12) $J_1 = \begin{pmatrix} \lambda_1 & 0 & 0 \\ 0 & \lambda_2 & 0 \\ 0 & 0 & \lambda_3 \end{pmatrix}$, $J_2 = \begin{pmatrix} \lambda_1 & 1 & 0 \\ 0 & \lambda_1 & 0 \\ 0 & 0 & \lambda_3 \end{pmatrix}$, $J_3 = \begin{pmatrix} \lambda_1 & 1 & 0 \\ 0 & \lambda_1 & 1 \\ 0 & 0 & \lambda_1 \end{pmatrix}$,

according as all eigenvectors are proper (even if roots are multiple), $\lambda_1 = \lambda_2$ and $e_2 = e_1'$ is generalized, $\lambda_1 = \lambda_2 = \lambda_3$ and $e_2 = e_1'$, $e_3 = e_1''$ are generalized. The row-column rule of matrix multiplication now shows that the above Jordan forms are given by

(13) $J = E^{-1}AE.$

if we take account of (11) and the equations

(14) $A\mathbf{e} = \lambda\mathbf{e}, \qquad A\mathbf{e}' = \lambda\mathbf{e}' + \mathbf{e}, \qquad A\mathbf{e}'' = \lambda\mathbf{e}'' + \mathbf{e}',$

which define proper and generalized eigenvectors.

Thus in Example 5 we have $\lambda_1 = \lambda_2 = \lambda_3 = 1$ with the eigenvectors

$$\mathbf{e}_1 = (1, 1, 1), \qquad \mathbf{e}_2 = \mathbf{e}_1' = (0, 1, 2), \qquad \mathbf{e}_3 = \mathbf{e}_1'' = (0, 0, 1);$$

then

$$\mathbf{e}^1 = (1, 0, 0), \qquad \mathbf{e}^2 = (-1, 1, 0), \qquad \mathbf{e}^3 = (1, -2, 1);$$

$$E = \begin{pmatrix} 1 & 0 & 0 \\ 1 & 1 & 0 \\ 1 & 2 & 1 \end{pmatrix}, \quad E^{-1} = \begin{pmatrix} 1 & 0 & 0 \\ -1 & 1 & 0 \\ 1 & -2 & 1 \end{pmatrix}, \quad A = \begin{pmatrix} 0 & 1 & 0 \\ 0 & 0 & 1 \\ 1 & -3 & -3 \end{pmatrix}$$

$$AE = \begin{pmatrix} 1 & 1 & 0 \\ 1 & 2 & 1 \\ 1 & 3 & 3 \end{pmatrix}, \quad J = E^{-1}AE = \begin{pmatrix} 1 & 1 & 0 \\ 0 & 1 & 1 \\ 0 & 0 & 1 \end{pmatrix}.$$

PROBLEMS

Find the eigenvalues and associated eigenvectors of the following matrices:

1. $\begin{pmatrix} -2 & 1 \\ -1 & -4 \end{pmatrix}$

2. $\begin{pmatrix} 6 & 2 \\ 6 & -7 \end{pmatrix}$

3. $\begin{pmatrix} 2 & 1 \\ -3 & 2 \end{pmatrix}$

4. $\begin{pmatrix} 1 & -1 \\ 1 & 1 \end{pmatrix}$

5. $\begin{pmatrix} 0 & -1 & 0 \\ -1 & -1 & 1 \\ 0 & 1 & 0 \end{pmatrix}$

6. $\begin{pmatrix} 8 & -8 & -2 \\ 4 & -3 & -2 \\ 3 & -4 & 1 \end{pmatrix}$

7. $\begin{pmatrix} 7 & 4 & -4 \\ 4 & -8 & -1 \\ -4 & -1 & -8 \end{pmatrix}$

8. $\begin{pmatrix} 2 & -2 & 3 \\ 1 & 1 & 1 \\ 1 & 3 & -1 \end{pmatrix}$

9. $\begin{pmatrix} 6 & 1 & 1 \\ 1 & 6 & 1 \\ 3 & 3 & 6 \end{pmatrix}$

10. $\begin{pmatrix} 2 & 1 & 2 \\ -1 & 0 & -2 \\ 1 & 1 & 0 \end{pmatrix}$

11. $\begin{pmatrix} 0 & 1 & 0 \\ 0 & 0 & 1 \\ 2 & -5 & 4 \end{pmatrix}$

12. $\begin{pmatrix} 0 & 1 & 0 \\ 0 & 0 & 1 \\ 4 & -8 & 5 \end{pmatrix}$

13. $\begin{pmatrix} 0 & 1 & 1 \\ 1 & 0 & 1 \\ 1 & 1 & 0 \end{pmatrix}$

14. $\begin{pmatrix} -1 & 1 & 0 \\ 0 & -1 & 4 \\ 1 & 0 & -4 \end{pmatrix}$

15. The matrix $C = \begin{pmatrix} 0 & 1 & 0 \\ 0 & 0 & 1 \\ -c & -b & -a \end{pmatrix}$ is called the *companion matrix* of the polynomial

$$f(\lambda) = \lambda^3 + a\lambda^2 + b\lambda + c.$$

Show that the characteristic equation of C is

$$\det (C - \lambda I) = -f(\lambda) = 0$$

and that the equation $f(\lambda) = 0$ can be written

$$C\begin{pmatrix} 1 \\ \lambda \\ \lambda^2 \end{pmatrix} = \lambda \begin{pmatrix} 1 \\ \lambda \\ \lambda^2 \end{pmatrix}.$$

If $f(\lambda) = 0$ has the roots $\lambda_1, \lambda_2, \lambda_3$, show that $\lambda_1, \lambda_2, \lambda_3$ are the eigenvalues of C and that the eigenvector $\sim \lambda_i$ is

$$\mathbf{e}_i = (1, \lambda_i, \lambda_i^2).$$

16. If the equation $f(\lambda) = 0$ of Problem 15 has a double root λ_1, show that λ_1 has the associated eigenvectors

$$\mathbf{e}_1 = (1, \lambda_1, \lambda_1^2), \qquad \mathbf{e}_1' = (0, 1, 2\lambda_1).$$

17. If the equation $f(\lambda) = 0$ of Problem 15 has the triple root λ_1, show that λ_1 has the associated eigenvectors

$$\mathbf{e}_1 = (1, \lambda_1, \lambda_1^2), \qquad \mathbf{e}_1' = (0, 1, 2\lambda_1), \qquad \mathbf{e}_1'' = (0, 0, 1).$$

18. Construct a matrix with 1, 2, 3 as eigenvalues and find the associated eigenvectors (Prob. 15).

19. Construct a matrix with the eigenvalues 1, i, $-i$ and find the associated eigenvectors (Prob. 15).

20. If a matrix A has the eigenvalues $\lambda_i \sim \mathbf{e}_i$, show that A^2 has the eigenvalues $\lambda_i^2 \sim \mathbf{e}_i$.

21. If a matrix A is nonsingular (det $A \neq 0$), show that
(a) no eigenvalue is zero,
(b) if A has the eigenvalues $\lambda_i \sim \mathbf{e}_i$, show that A^{-1} has the eigenvalues $\lambda_i^{-1} \sim \mathbf{e}_i$.

22. In Example 1, reduce A to the diagonal form $\begin{pmatrix} 1 & 0 \\ 0 & 3 \end{pmatrix}$.

23. In Example 2, reduce A to the Jordan form J_1.
24. In Example 3, reduce A to the Jordan form J_1.
25. In Example 4, reduce A to the Jordan form J_2.
26. Construct a 3×3 matrix A whose eigenvalues α, β, γ are associated with the respective eigenvectors $(0, 1, 1)$, $(1, 0, 1)$, $(1, 1, 0)$.

27. Construct a 3×3 matrix A whose eigenvalues all equal 1 and which has a proper eigenvector $\mathbf{e}_1 = (1, -1, 0)$ and two generalized eigenvectors $\mathbf{e}_1' = (0, 1, 1)$, $\mathbf{e}_1'' = (1, 0, 2)$. $[E^{-1}AE = J_3.]$

28. Construct a 4×4 matrix A whose eigenvalues are $\lambda_1 = \lambda_2 = \lambda_3 = 1$, $\lambda_4 = 2$ with the associated eigenvectors $\mathbf{e}_1 = (2, 0, -1, 1)$, $\mathbf{e}_2 = \mathbf{e}_1' = (-1, 1, 1, 1)$, $\mathbf{e}_3 = (1, 1, 1, 1)$, $\mathbf{e}_4 = (2, 0, 1, 0)$.

50. LINEAR AUTONOMOUS SYSTEMS

The system of linear equations

$$\frac{dx}{dt} = a_{11}x + a_{12}y + a_{13}z$$

$$\frac{dy}{dt} = a_{21}x + a_{22}y + a_{23}z$$

$$\frac{dz}{dt} = a_{31}x + a_{32}y + a_{33}z$$

is said to be *autonomous* since t (usually the time) does not occur explicitly. If we put the column vector $(x, y, z) = \mathbf{r}$ and the matrix $(a_{ij}) = A$, the system becomes

(1)
$$\frac{d\mathbf{r}}{dt} = A\mathbf{r}.$$

We shall show that the general solution of (1) may be written down at once when the eigenvalues and three linearly independent eigenvectors, proper or generalized, are known.

   To find solutions of (1), write it in the form

(1)′
$$(D - \lambda)\mathbf{r} = (A - \lambda I)\mathbf{r}, \qquad D = d/dt.$$

If λ is an eigenvalue of A, namely a root of the cubic equation

(2)
$$\det (A - \lambda I) = 0,$$

and $\mathbf{e}$ a proper associated eigenvector, then

(3)
$$\mathbf{r} = e^{\lambda t}\mathbf{e}$$

is a solution of (1)′; for

(4)
$$(A - \lambda I)\mathbf{r} = e^{\lambda t}(A\mathbf{e} - \lambda\mathbf{e}) = 0,$$
$$(D - \lambda)\mathbf{r} = e^{\lambda t}D\mathbf{e} = 0$$

on using the exponential shift (36.1).

   Case I. A has three noncoplanar eigenvectors $\mathbf{e}_1$, $\mathbf{e}_2$, $\mathbf{e}_3$.

   1. Eigenvalues λ_1, λ_2, λ_3 distinct.
   The eigenvectors are then noncoplanar (Theorem 49.3) and from (3) we have the independent solutions

(5)
$$\mathbf{r}_1 = e^{\lambda_1 t}\mathbf{e}_1, \qquad \mathbf{r}_2 = e^{\lambda_2 t}\mathbf{e}_2, \qquad \mathbf{r}_3 = e^{\lambda_3 t}\mathbf{e}_3.$$

When multiplied by arbitrary constants and added, they yield the general solution of (1)

$$(6) \qquad\qquad \mathbf{r} = c_1\mathbf{r}_1 + c_2\mathbf{r}_2 + c_3\mathbf{r}_3.$$

Note that any eigenvector $\mathbf{e}$ may be replaced by any constant multiple $c\mathbf{e}$.

2. Two distinct eigenvalues, $\lambda_1 = \lambda_2 \neq \lambda_3$, and rank $(A - \lambda_1 I) = 1$.

Then all 2-rowed determinants of $A - \lambda_1 I$ are zero, and rows 2 and 3 are multiples of row 1. If $\mathbf{a}$ is the vector in row 1 we may choose $\mathbf{e}_1$ and $\mathbf{e}_2$ perpendicular to $\mathbf{a}$; then $\mathbf{e}_1$, $\mathbf{e}_2$, $\mathbf{e}_3$ are noncoplanar (Ex. 49.3), and we again have the solution (6).

3. All eigenvalues equal, $\lambda_1 = \lambda_2 = \lambda_3$, and rank $(A - \lambda_1 I) = 0$.

Then all elements of $A - \lambda_1 I$ are zero and we may choose any three noncoplanar vectors as $\mathbf{e}_1$, $\mathbf{e}_2$, $\mathbf{e}_3$. The solution is again given by (6).

Case II. A does not have three noncoplanar eigenvectors.

1. Two distinct eigenvalues, $\lambda_1 = \lambda_2 \neq \lambda_3$, and rank $(A - \lambda I) = 2$.

There is now but a single eigenvector $\mathbf{e}_1$ associated with the double root λ_1. To get a second eigenvector we define the generalized eigenvector $\mathbf{e}_1'$ by

$$(7) \qquad\qquad (A - \lambda_1 I)\mathbf{e}_1' = \mathbf{e}_1. \qquad\qquad \text{(Ex. 49.4)}$$

Corresponding to $\lambda_1 = \lambda_2$ and λ_3 we now have the independent solutions

$$(8) \qquad \mathbf{r}_1 = e^{\lambda_1 t}\mathbf{e}_1, \qquad \mathbf{r}_2 = e^{\lambda_1 t}(t\mathbf{e}_1 + \mathbf{e}_1'), \qquad \mathbf{r}_3 = e^{\lambda_3 t}\mathbf{e}_3.$$

Equations (4) show that $\mathbf{r}_1$ and $\mathbf{r}_3$ are solutions; as for $\mathbf{r}_2$

$$(A - \lambda_1 I)\mathbf{r}_2 = e^{\lambda_1 t}(A - \lambda_1 I)\mathbf{e}_1' = e^{\lambda_1 t}\mathbf{e}_1 \qquad \text{from (7)},$$
$$(D - \lambda_1 I)\mathbf{r}_2 = e^{\lambda_1 t} D(t\mathbf{e}_1 + \mathbf{e}_1') = e^{\lambda_1 t}\mathbf{e}_1$$

on using the exponential shift (36.1). From (8) we can now form the general solution (6).

2. All eigenvalues equal, $\lambda_1 = \lambda_2 = \lambda_3$, and rank $(A - \lambda I) = 2$.

There is now but a single eigenvector associated with the triple root λ_1. We now define two generalized eigenvectors, the first $\mathbf{e}_1'$ by (7), the second $\mathbf{e}_1''$ by

$$(9) \qquad\qquad (A - \lambda_1 I)\mathbf{e}_1'' = \mathbf{e}_1'.$$

Then $\mathbf{e}_1$, $\mathbf{e}_1'$, $\mathbf{e}_1''$ can be chosen linearly independent and we have the particular solutions

$$(10) \quad \mathbf{r}_1 = e^{\lambda_1 t}\mathbf{e}_1, \qquad \mathbf{r}_2 = e^{\lambda_1 t}(t\mathbf{e}_1 + \mathbf{e}_1'), \qquad \mathbf{r}_3 = e^{\lambda_1 t}(\tfrac{1}{2}t^2\mathbf{e}_1 + t\mathbf{e}_1' + \mathbf{e}_1'')$$

Our previous work shows that $\mathbf{r}_1$ and $\mathbf{r}_2$ are solutions; as for $\mathbf{r}_3$,

$$(A - \lambda_1 I)\mathbf{r}_3 = e^{\lambda_1 t}(A - \lambda_1 I)(t\mathbf{e}_1' + \mathbf{e}_1'') = e^{\lambda_1 t}(t\mathbf{e}_1 + \mathbf{e}_1'),$$

from (7) and (9), and

$$(D - \lambda_1)\mathbf{r}_3 = e^{\lambda_1 t}D(\tfrac{1}{2}t^2\mathbf{e}_1 + t\mathbf{e}_1' + \mathbf{e}_1'') = e^{\lambda_1 t}(t\mathbf{e}_1 + \mathbf{e}_1')$$

on using the exponential shift (36.1). From (10) we can now form the general solution (6).

A linear equation of the third order with constant coefficients

(11) $\qquad (D^3 + aD^2 + bD + c)x = 0, \qquad D = \dfrac{d}{dt},$

may be replaced by the system

$$
\begin{aligned}
Dx &= & y & \\
Dy &= & & z \\
Dz &= & -cx - by - az
\end{aligned}
$$

(11)′

whose matrix

(12) $\qquad A = \begin{pmatrix} 0 & 1 & 0 \\ 0 & 0 & 1 \\ -c & -b & -a \end{pmatrix}$

is the *companion matrix* of the characteristic equation of (11):

(13) $\qquad \lambda^3 + a\lambda^2 + b\lambda + c = -\det(A - \lambda I) = 0.$

The roots of (13) are the eigenvalues λ_i of (11) or (11)′ and if they are distinct, the associated eigenvectors are

(14) $\qquad \mathbf{e}_i = (1, \lambda_i, \lambda_i^2), \qquad i = 1, 2, 3.$

Stability

Equation (1) is said to be strictly stable if all of its solutions are transients, that is, tend to zero as $t \to \infty$. Evidently, this will be the case if each member of the solution basis $\mathbf{r}_1, \mathbf{r}_2, \mathbf{r}_3$ is a transient. Since each basis vector contains $e^{\lambda_i t}$ as a factor, equation (1) will be strictly stable when and only when all eigenvalues of the matrix A have negative real parts (cf. § 42). In all four of the following examples the equation is unstable; but in Example 1 and Example 2 the particular solutions corresponding to negative eigenvalues are strictly stable.

Example 1. $A = \begin{pmatrix} 1 & 1 & 0 \\ 1 & 0 & 1 \\ 0 & 1 & 1 \end{pmatrix}$. From Example 49.2, $\lambda_1 = 1$, $\lambda_2 = -1$, $\lambda_3 = 2$;

$\qquad \mathbf{e}_1 = (1, 0, -1), \qquad \mathbf{e}_2 = (1, -2, 1), \qquad \mathbf{e}_3 = (1, 1, 1).$

The equations $d\mathbf{r}/dt = A\mathbf{r}$ have the general solution

$$\mathbf{r} = c_1 e^t \mathbf{e}_1 + c_2 e^{-t} \mathbf{e}_2 + c_3 e^{2t} \mathbf{e}_3.$$

from which x, y, z can be written down.

Example 2. $A = \begin{pmatrix} -1 & 1 & 1 \\ 1 & -1 & 1 \\ 1 & 1 & -1 \end{pmatrix}$. From Example 49.3, $\lambda_1 = 1, \lambda_2 = \lambda_3 = -2$;

$$\mathbf{e}_1 = (1, 1, 1), \qquad \mathbf{e}_2 = (1, 1, -2), \qquad \mathbf{e}_3 = (1, -1, 0).$$

The equations $d\mathbf{r}/dt = A\mathbf{r}$ have the general solution

$$\mathbf{r} = c_1 e^t \mathbf{e}_1 + e^{-2t}(c_2 \mathbf{e}_2 + c_3 \mathbf{e}_3).$$

Example 3. $A = \begin{pmatrix} 1 & 1 & 2 \\ 0 & 1 & 3 \\ 0 & 0 & 2 \end{pmatrix}$. From Example 49.4, $\lambda_1 = \lambda_2 = 1, \lambda_3 = 2$;

$$\mathbf{e}_1 = (1, 0, 0), \qquad \mathbf{e}_1' = (0, 1, 0), \qquad \mathbf{e}_3 = (5, 3, 1).$$

The equations $d\mathbf{r}/dt = A\mathbf{r}$ have the general solution

$$\mathbf{r} = c_1 e^t \mathbf{e}_1 + c_2 e^t (t\mathbf{e}_1 + \mathbf{e}_1') + c_3 e^{2t} \mathbf{e}_3.$$

Example 4. $A = \begin{pmatrix} 0 & 1 & 0 \\ 0 & 0 & 1 \\ 1 & -3 & 3 \end{pmatrix}$. From Example 49.5, $\lambda_1 = \lambda_2 = \lambda_3 = 1$;

$$\mathbf{e}_1 = (1, 1, 1), \qquad \mathbf{e}_1' = (0, 1, 2), \qquad \mathbf{e}_1'' = (0, 0, 1).$$

The equations $d\mathbf{r}/dt = A\mathbf{r}$ have the general solution

$$\mathbf{r} = e^t \{ c_1 \mathbf{e}_1 + c_2 (t\mathbf{e}_1 + \mathbf{e}_1') + c_3 (\tfrac{1}{2} t^2 \mathbf{e}_1 + t\mathbf{e}_1' + \mathbf{e}_1'') \}.$$

PROBLEMS

1–14. Find the general solution of the equation $d\mathbf{r}/dt = A\mathbf{r}$ with the matrix A given in Problems 1 to 14 of § 49.

15. Prove that the eigenvectors of the companion matrix A in (12) are given by (14).

16. Show that equation (1), with the matrix A given in Problem 49.14, is not strictly stable but all of its solutions are bounded.

17. If the elements of a matrix $X(t)$ are functions of t, dX/dt is defined as the matrix whose elements are the derivatives of the elements of $X(t)$.

If $d\mathbf{r}/dt = A\mathbf{r}$ has linearly independent solutions $\mathbf{r}_1, \mathbf{r}_2, \mathbf{r}_3$, let X denote the matrix $(\mathbf{r}_1 \mid \mathbf{r}_2 \mid \mathbf{r}_3)$ whose columns are $\mathbf{r}_1, \mathbf{r}_2, \mathbf{r}_3$. Since $\det X \neq 0$, X has an inverse $Y = X^{-1}$. Show that

$$\text{(a) } dX/dt = AX; \qquad \text{(b) } dY/dt = -YA.$$

18. Discuss the solution of the linear system $d\mathbf{r}/dt = A\mathbf{r}$ when A is a 2×2 matrix of real constants following the methods of this article.

51. STABILITY TEST OF LIAPUNOV

An important contribution to the theory of stability was made by the Russian mathematician Liapunov.[*] Before explaining his methods, some definitions are needed. Let $\mathbf{x}$ and $\mathbf{x}^T = (x_1, x_2, \ldots, x_n)$ denote $n \times 1$ and $1 \times n$ vectors and $C = (c_{ij})$ a symmetric $n \times n$ matrix of real constants. Then

$$\mathbf{x}^T C \mathbf{x} = c_{11}x_1^2 + 2c_{12}x_1x_2 + 2c_{13}x_1x_3 + \cdots + c_{nn}x_n^2$$

is a *quadratic form* in n variables. Such a form will have in general $\frac{1}{2}n(n + 1)$ terms; thus when $n = 2$,

$$\mathbf{x}^T C \mathbf{x} = c_{11}x_1^2 + 2c_{12}x_1x_2 + c_{22}x_2^2.$$

When $\mathbf{x} = 0$, $\mathbf{x}^T C \mathbf{x} = 0$; and if the form does not change sign for all $\mathbf{x} \neq 0$, it is called *positive* or *negative definite* according as its sign is positive or negative. We shall also apply these terms to the *matrix C* of the quadratic form.

We state without proof two well-known criteria for definite quadratic forms:[†]

Theorem 1. *The form* $\mathbf{x}^T C \mathbf{x}$ *is positive definite if, and only if, the n leading principal minors of* $\det C$,

$$c_{11}, \quad \begin{vmatrix} c_{11} & c_{12} \\ c_{21} & c_{22} \end{vmatrix}, \quad \begin{vmatrix} c_{11} & c_{12} & c_{13} \\ c_{21} & c_{22} & c_{23} \\ c_{31} & c_{32} & c_{33} \end{vmatrix}, \quad \ldots, \quad \det c_{ij}$$

are all positive. It is negative definite if, and only if, $c_{11} < 0$ *and the following minors in this sequence alternate in sign.*

The second part of the theorem is a consequence of the first part; for if the form $\mathbf{x}^T C \mathbf{x}$ is negative definite, the form $-\mathbf{x}^T C \mathbf{x}$ is positive definite and a minor of $-C$ of order k is $(-1)^k$ times the corresponding minor of C.

We now state the fundamental

Theorem 2 (Liapunov). *If the* $n \times n$ *matrix A of the linear system*

(1)
$$\frac{d\mathbf{x}}{dt} = A\mathbf{x}$$

---

[*] A. M. Liapunov, *Problème général de la stabilité du mouvement*, Annals of Mathematics Study, No. 17, Princeton University Press, 1949.
[†] F. R. Gantmacher, ref. 6, vol. 1, pp. 304–308.

has all eigenvalues with negative real parts, then to every negative definite form $\mathbf{x}^T W \mathbf{x}$ *there corresponds a unique positive definite form* $\mathbf{x}^T V \mathbf{x}$ *which, by virtue of* (1), *satisfies*

$$(2) \qquad \frac{d}{dt}(\mathbf{x}^T V \mathbf{x}) = \mathbf{x}^T W \mathbf{x}.$$

Conversely, if for every negative definite form $\mathbf{x}^T W \mathbf{x}$ *there exists a positive definite form* $\mathbf{x}^T V \mathbf{x}$ *which satisfies* (2) *by virtue of* (1), *then all eigenvalues of* V *have negative real parts.*

For the proof see Gantmacher, ref. 6, vol. 2, pp. 187–188.

If we perform the differentiation in (2) (writing $\dot{\mathbf{x}}$ for dx/dt),

$$\dot{\mathbf{x}}^T V \mathbf{x} + \mathbf{x}^T V \dot{\mathbf{x}} = \mathbf{x}^T W \mathbf{x},$$

or since $\dot{\mathbf{x}} = A\mathbf{x}$ and $\dot{\mathbf{x}}^T = \mathbf{x}^T A^T$,

$$(3) \qquad \mathbf{x}^T(A^T V + VA - W)\mathbf{x} = 0.$$

Since V and W are symmetric, the matrix $A^T V + VA - W$ is also symmetric. Thus (3) is a quadratic form whose value is zero for every $\mathbf{x}$; and we therefore conclude that its matrix is zero:

$$(4) \qquad A^T V + VA = W.*$$

We may choose for W the matrix of any negative definite form in n variables. The simplest choice is $W = -I$ for

$$-\mathbf{x}^T I \mathbf{x} = -x_1{}^2 - x_2{}^2 - \cdots - x_n{}^2;$$

then (4) yields

Theorem 3. *All the eigenvalues of the matrix A will have negative real parts when, and only when, the matrix equation*

$$(5) \qquad A^T V + VA = -I$$

has a unique positive definite solution V. Equation (1) *is then strictly stable.*

If V satisfies (5), the transpose of both members yields

$$V^T A + A^T V^T = -I,$$

so that V^T is also a solution; and, since the solution is unique, $V^T = V$, that is, V is symmetric. Equation (5) is equivalent to n^2 scalar equations, but since the ij and ji elements of $A^T V + VA$ are the same, these reduce to $\frac{1}{2}n(n + 1)$ equations, precisely the number of distinct elements in the

---

* The symmetry of the matrix is essential in drawing this conclusion. If Q is an anti-symmetric matrix ($Q^T = -Q$), $\mathbf{x}^T Q \mathbf{x} = 0$ for every $\mathbf{x}$; for $\mathbf{x}^T Q \mathbf{x}$ yields $-\mathbf{x}^T Q \mathbf{x}$ on transposition and since $\mathbf{x}^T Q \mathbf{x}$ is a scalar, $\mathbf{x}^T Q \mathbf{x} = -\mathbf{x}^T Q \mathbf{x}$ and $\mathbf{x}^T Q \mathbf{x} = 0$.

symmetric matrix V. It can be shown that (5) has a unique solution V when A has no zero eigenvalue and no two eigenvalues whose sum is zero.

This theorem gives a test for the strict stability of all solutions of the linear system (1). It also gives a test for the strict stability of a nonlinear system having (1) as its linear approximation, provided the solutions are restricted to a sufficiently small neighborhood of the origin. This important result is proved in the next article.

In practical problems, however, it is important to know the *extent* of strict stability. In a strictly stable linear system a solution trajectory will *always* tend to the origin no matter where is starts; it is strictly stable *in the large*. But in nonlinear systems this is not the case. The criterion in Theorem 3 may tell us that the system is strictly stable in *some* region about the origin but gives no indication of its size—and this may be of paramount importance in practice. This defect may be remedied in part by the use of *Liapunov functions* which we now proceed to define and study.

Example 1. Consider the equations

(6)
$$\begin{pmatrix} \dot{x} \\ \dot{y} \end{pmatrix} = A \begin{pmatrix} x \\ y \end{pmatrix}, \qquad A = \begin{pmatrix} a & b \\ c & d \end{pmatrix},$$

studied in § 48. Let the symmetric matrix

$$V = \begin{pmatrix} \alpha & \beta \\ \beta & \gamma \end{pmatrix};$$

then the matrix equation (5),

$$\begin{pmatrix} a & c \\ b & d \end{pmatrix} \begin{pmatrix} \alpha & \beta \\ \beta & \gamma \end{pmatrix} + \begin{pmatrix} \alpha & \beta \\ \beta & \gamma \end{pmatrix} \begin{pmatrix} a & b \\ c & d \end{pmatrix} = \begin{pmatrix} -1 & 0 \\ 0 & -1 \end{pmatrix}$$

is equivalent to the three scalar equations

$$\begin{aligned} a\alpha + c\beta &= -\tfrac{1}{2} \\ b\alpha + (a+d)\beta + c\gamma &= 0 \\ b\beta + d\gamma &= -\tfrac{1}{2} \end{aligned}$$

whose determinant

$$D = \begin{vmatrix} a & c & 0 \\ b & a+c & c \\ 0 & b & d \end{vmatrix} = (a+d)\delta, \qquad \delta = \begin{vmatrix} a & b \\ c & d \end{vmatrix}.$$

If $D \neq 0$, we obtain the unique solution

$$\alpha = -\frac{\delta + c^2 + d^2}{2D}, \qquad \beta = \frac{ac + bd}{2D}, \qquad \gamma = -\frac{\delta + a^2 + b^2}{2D}.$$

The summary of § 48 shows that when $D \neq 0$ the eigenvalues of A are not zero ($\delta \neq 0$) and not of opposite sign ($a + d \neq 0$). Thus neutral equilibrium, which requires a zero or two opposed pure imaginary eigenvalues, is ruled out when $D \neq 0$. When $D \neq 0$, the solutions are strictly stable when V is positive definite ($a > 0$, $\alpha\gamma - \beta^2 > 0$); otherwise they are unstable.

If $A = \begin{pmatrix} -2 & 1 \\ 4 & -3 \end{pmatrix}$, the solutions are strictly stable; for

$a + d = -5$, $\delta = 2$, $D = -10$; $\alpha = \frac{27}{20}$, $\beta = \frac{11}{20}$, $\gamma = \frac{7}{20}$; $\alpha\gamma - \beta^2 > 0$.

If $A = \begin{pmatrix} 1 & -1 \\ -2 & 0 \end{pmatrix}$, the solutions are unstable; for

$a + d = 1$, $\delta = -2$, $D = -2$; $\alpha = \frac{1}{2}$, $\beta = \frac{1}{2}$, $\gamma = 0$; $\alpha\gamma - \beta^2 < 0$.

52. LIAPUNOV FUNCTIONS

The system

$$(1) \qquad \frac{dx}{dt} = f(x, y), \qquad \frac{dy}{dt} = g(x, y)$$

has a critical point at (a, b) if

$$f(a, b) = 0, \qquad g(a, b) = 0.$$

Then the translation of axes

$$x = X + a, \qquad y = Y + b$$

will convert (1) into another linear system which has a critical point at the origin.

Let us therefore regard (1) as a system with a critical point at the origin: $f(0, 0) = 0$, $g(0, 0) = 0$. Then if

$$f_x(0, 0) = a, \quad f_y(0, 0) = b, \quad g_x(0, 0) = c, \quad g_y(0, 0) = d$$

and $f(x, y)$ and $g(x, y)$ have continuous partial derivatives of the second order, the mean-value theorem for functions of two variables* shows that

$$(2) \quad f(x, y) = ax + by + \varphi(x, y), \qquad g(x, y) = cx + dy + \psi(x, y)$$

where both φ and ψ are $O(x^2 + y^2)$, that is, satisfy

$$(3) \quad |\varphi|, |\psi| < M(x^2 + y^2) \quad \text{for} \quad M > 0 \quad \text{and sufficiently small } |x| + |y|.$$

In any case we assume that condition (3) is fulfilled and write

$$(1) \qquad \frac{dx}{dt} = ax + by + \varphi(x, y), \qquad \frac{dy}{dt} = cx + dy + \psi(x, y)$$

and speak of

$$(4) \qquad \frac{dx}{dt} = ax + by, \qquad \frac{dy}{dt} = cx + dy$$

---

* *Advanced Calculus*, § 90.

as the *linear approximation* of (1). System (1) may be regarded as system (4) *perturbed* by the functions φ and ψ. The stability of (4) *in the large* has been completely treated in § 48. We shall show that the nonlinear system (1) is strictly stable in some neighborhood of the origin when its linear approximation (4) is strictly stable.

The solutions of (1) may be tested for local stability in an open region $\mathscr{R}$ about the origin if we can find a *Liapunov function* $V(x, y)$ for the system, namely

(a) $V(x, y)$ and its partial derivatives are continuous in $\mathscr{R}$;

(b) $V(x, y)$ is positive definite in $\mathscr{R}$: $V(x, y) > 0$ except $V(0, 0) = 0$;

(c) $\dot{V}(x, y)$ is negative definite in $\mathscr{R}$: $\dot{V}(x, y) < 0$ except $\dot{V}(0, 0) = 0$.

Here $\dot{V}(x, y)$ denotes the total derivatives dV/dt deduced from equations (1):

$$\dot{V}(x, y) = \frac{\partial V}{\partial x}\frac{dx}{dt} + \frac{\partial V}{\partial y}\frac{dy}{dt} = V_x f(x, y) + V_y g(x, y).$$

From (a) the function $V(x, y)$ has an isolated minimum at the origin. Thus the surface $z = V(x, y)$ resembles a reversed cup whose plane sections projected on the xy-plane are ovals $V(x, y) = k$. These ovals grow in size as k increases from zero and each oval encloses all others of smaller k. If, for example, $V(x, y)$ is the positive definite form

$$(x, y)\begin{pmatrix} \alpha & \beta \\ \beta & \gamma \end{pmatrix}\begin{pmatrix} x \\ y \end{pmatrix} = \alpha x^2 + 2\beta xy + \gamma y^2,$$

the ovals are a family of concentric ellipses for $\alpha > 0$ and $\alpha\gamma - \beta^2 > 0$.

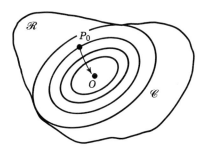

Fig. 52a   Strict stability.

Theorem 1 (Strict Stability). *Let equations* (1) *have a critical point at the origin and admit a Liapunov function in an open region $\mathscr{R}$ about it. Then if the oval $\mathscr{C}$, $V(x, y) = k$, does not cross the boundary of $\mathscr{R}$, all solution trajectories that start at points $P_0(x_0, y_0)$ within $\mathscr{C}$ will tend to the origin as $t \to \infty$.*

PROOF. Since P_0 lies within the oval $\mathscr{C}$, the oval $\mathscr{C}_0$,

$$V(x, y) = V(x_0, y_0) = k_0 < k,$$

lies within $\mathscr{C}$. Since $dV/dt < 0$, V is decreasing at P_0 and the trajectory will cross $\mathscr{C}_0$ to its interior. There the trajectory will encounter other ovals and cross all toward their interior as V continues to decrease until it finally reaches the origin where $V(0, 0) = 0$.

If $V(x, y)$ fulfills conditions (a) and (b) but (c) is replaced by

(d) $$\frac{dV}{dt} = \dot{V}(x, y) \leqq 0 \quad \text{in} \quad \mathscr{R},$$

we call $V(x, y)$ a *weak* Liapunov function for equation (1). We now have

Theorem 2 (Neutral Stability). *If all conditions of Theorem 1 are fulfilled except that $V(x, y)$ is a weak Liapunov function, all solution trajectories that start within the oval $\mathscr{C}$ will remain inside.*

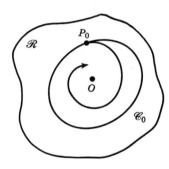

Fig. 52b Neutral stability.

PROOF. Let the trajectory start at P_0 on the oval $\mathscr{C}_0$. If $\dot{V}(x_0, y_0) < 0$, the trajectory will cross $\mathscr{C}_0$ to its interior. If $\dot{V}(x_0, y_0) = 0$, the trajectory will be tangent to $\mathscr{C}_0$ at P_0 and will either continue along $\mathscr{C}_0$ (in which case $\mathscr{C}_0$ itself is a solution curve) or emerge in the interior of $\mathscr{C}_0$. It cannot cross $\mathscr{C}_0$ to higher values of k since $V(x, y)$ never increases along a trajectory. Thus all trajectories that start within $\mathscr{C}$ can never reach $\mathscr{C}$; that is, they are bounded.

The oval $\mathscr{C}$ determines the *extent* of stability; it should be chosen as large as possible, say tangent to the boundary of $\mathscr{R}$ as in Figure 52a.

Theorem 3 (Instability). *Let equations (1) have a critical point at the origin and admit a function $U(x, y)$ in an open region $\mathscr{R}$ about the origin such that*
(a') *$U(x, y)$ is bounded and with its partial derivatives is continuous in $\mathscr{R}$;*
(b') *$U(0, 0) = 0$ and $U(x, y)$ assumes positive values in every neighborhood of the origin;*
(c') *$\dot{U}(x, y)$ is positive definite in $\mathscr{R}$: $\dot{U}(x, y) > 0$ except $\dot{U}(0, 0) = 0$. Then in every neighborhood of the origin there are points P_0 from which issue trajectories that attain the boundary of $\mathscr{R}$.*

PROOF. In any neighborhood of the origin, however small, there are points P_0 where $U(x_0, y_0) > 0$. Along a trajectory that starts at P_0, $U(x, y)$ can only increase and therefore is bounded away from the origin where

$U(0, 0) = 0$. Therefore along the trajectory

$$U(x, y) > U(x_0, y_0) = U_0.$$

Moreover, since

$$\dot{U}(x, y) = U_x f(x, y) + U_y g(x, y)$$

is positive definite, $\dot{U}$ has a definite lower bound m on the trajectory so that $\dot{U} - m \geq 0$ and hence

$$U - U_0 - mt \geq 0 \quad \text{or} \quad U > mt.$$

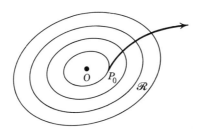

Fig. 52c   Instability.

Thus no matter how small m is, U will eventually exceed its bound in the region $\mathcal{R}$ and cross its boundary; that is, the origin is an unstable critical point. In Figure 52c the ovals about the origin are the level curves for the positive definite function $U(x, y)$.

We now use Theorem 1 to prove the important

Theorem 4.   *A critical point at the origin for the nonlinear system*

$$\text{(1)} \qquad \begin{pmatrix} \dot{x} \\ \dot{y} \end{pmatrix} = A \begin{pmatrix} x \\ y \end{pmatrix} + \begin{pmatrix} \varphi(x, y) \\ \psi(x, y) \end{pmatrix}, \qquad A = \begin{pmatrix} a & b \\ c & d \end{pmatrix},$$

in which

$$\text{(3)} \qquad |\varphi|, |\psi| = O(x^2 + y^2)$$

will be strictly stable if its linear approximation is strictly stable.

PROOF.   If the linear system

$$\text{(4)} \qquad \begin{pmatrix} \dot{x} \\ \dot{y} \end{pmatrix} = A \begin{pmatrix} x \\ y \end{pmatrix} \quad \text{or} \quad (\dot{x}, \dot{y}) = (x, y)A^{\mathsf{T}}$$

is strictly stable, the eigenvalues of A will have negative real parts and hence, from Theorem 51.3, the matrix equation

$$\text{(5)} \qquad A^{\mathsf{T}}V + VA = -I$$

will have a positive definite symmetric matrix V as its unique solution.

Then the positive definite quadratic form

(6)
$$(x, y)V\begin{pmatrix} x \\ y \end{pmatrix}$$

is a Liapunov function for the system (1). To prove this we must show that its total t-derivative

(7)
$$(\dot{x}, \dot{y})V\begin{pmatrix} x \\ y \end{pmatrix} + (x, y)V\begin{pmatrix} \dot{x} \\ \dot{y} \end{pmatrix} < 0$$

in some open region about the origin. Using equations (1), the left member becomes

$$(x, y)A^{\mathsf{T}}V\begin{pmatrix} x \\ y \end{pmatrix} + (x, y)VA\begin{pmatrix} x \\ y \end{pmatrix} + (\varphi, \psi)V\begin{pmatrix} x \\ y \end{pmatrix} + (x, y)V\begin{pmatrix} \varphi \\ \psi \end{pmatrix}.$$

The first two terms reduce to $-(x^2 + y^2)$ by virtue of (5). Since V is symmetric, the other terms reduce to $2(\varphi, \psi)V\begin{pmatrix} x \\ y \end{pmatrix}$. Now if all elements of V are less than K in absolute value,

$$2\left| (\varphi, \psi)V\begin{pmatrix} x \\ y \end{pmatrix} \right| < 2K(|\varphi| + |\psi|)(|x| + |y|)*$$

$$< 2KM(x^2 + y^2)(|x| + |y|)$$

$$< x^2 + y^2$$

in the open square $\mathscr{R}$: $|x| + |y| < 1/2KM$. Thus (7) is established, (6) is a Liapunov function for the system (1) in $\mathscr{R}$ and, by Theorem 1, we can find a region of strict stability about the origin.

Example 1. The linear system

$$dx/dt = y, \qquad dy/dt = x$$

has a saddle point at the origin. The trajectories are equilateral hyperbolas $x^2 - y^2 = C$ including their asymptotes ($C = 0$):

$$x - y = 0: \qquad x = ae^t, \qquad y = ae^t;$$

$$x + y = 0: \qquad x = be^{-t}, \qquad y = -be^{-t}.$$

---

* This is obvious when $(\varphi, \psi)V\begin{pmatrix} x \\ y \end{pmatrix}$ is expanded.

The general pattern of the trajectories (equilateral hyperbolas and their asymptotes) is suggested by Figure 52d.

Let us now examine the effect of adding the simple nonlinear term xy in each equation:

$$dx/dt = y(1 + x), \qquad dy/dt = x(1 + y).$$

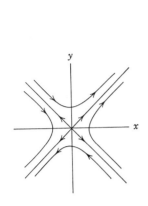

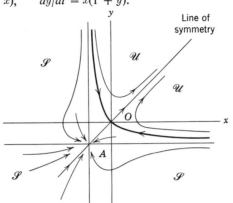

Fig. 52d
$\begin{cases} \dot{x} = y \\ \dot{y} = x \end{cases}$ in phase plane.

Fig. 52e
$\begin{cases} \dot{x} = y + xy \\ \dot{y} = x + xy \end{cases}$ in phase plane.

We have now two critical points, $O(0, 0)$ and $A(-1, -1)$. The origin is still a saddle point and unstable. If we take (cf. Theorem 3)

$$U = xy, \qquad \dot{U} = x^2(1 + y) + y^2(1 + x),$$

$U > 0$ when $xy > 0$ and $\dot{U}$ is positive definite when $x, y > -1$. Theorem 3 now affirms that all paths that start in the first or third quadrants of the open circle $x^2 + y^2 < 1$ will attain its boundary (Fig. 52e). The trajectories now satisfy the equation

$$\frac{y \, dy}{1 + y} - \frac{x \, dx}{1 + x} = 0;$$

and, on integration,

$$y - \log (1 + y) - x + \log (1 + x) = C.$$

The left member is divisible by $y - x$ and may be written

$$(y - x)f(x, y) = C.$$

When $C = 0$, this equation gives the asymptotic curves

$$y - x = 0, \qquad f(x, y) = 0,$$

which divide the trajectories into four sets as shown in Figure 52e.

Along the straight asymptote $y - x = 0$,

$$\frac{dx}{dt} = x(1 + x), \qquad \frac{dy}{dt} = y(1 + y).$$

If $x = x_0$ when $t = 0$, we find, on integration,

$$\log \frac{x}{x + 1} = t + \log \frac{x_0}{x_0 + 1}, \qquad x = \frac{x_0}{(x_0 + 1)e^{-t} - x_0}.$$

When $x_0 > 0$ $(\dot{x} > 0)$; $\quad x \to \infty \quad$ as $\quad t \to \log \dfrac{x_0 + 1}{x_0}$;

$-1 < x_0 < 0$ $(\dot{x} < 0)$: $\quad x \to -1 \quad$ as $\quad t \to \infty$;

$\qquad x_0 < -1 (\dot{x} > 0)$: $\quad x \to -1 \quad$ as $\quad t \to \infty$;

and y behaves in the same way.

A point on the curvilinear asymptote $f(x, y) = 0$ always tends toward the origin. This asymptote, drawn heavy in Fig. 52e, divides the plane into two parts $\mathscr{S}$ and $\mathscr{U}$. The point $A(-1, -1)$ is now a stable node; $\mathscr{S}$ and $\mathscr{U}$ are the regions of stability and instability. Figure 52e (adapted from Cunningham)* shows the general situation. The introduction of the stable node A through the term xy has thus wrought a radical change of pattern.

PROBLEMS

Find the critical points of the following systems and determine their character.
1. $dx/dt = y^2 - x, \qquad dy/dt = x^2 - 8y.$
2. $dx/dt = 2x - y, \qquad dy/dt = 2 - xy.$
3. $dx/dt = y, \qquad dy/dt = -6x - y - 3x^2.$
4. $dx/dt = x^2 + y^2 - 5, \qquad dy/dt = x^2 - y^2 - 3.$
5. $dx/dt = x - y, \qquad dy/dt = 2x^2 + y^2 - 3.$
6. Show that the equations

$$dx/dt = x(y - b), \qquad dy/dt = y(x - a)$$

have a region of strict stability within the ellipse $x^2/a^2 + y^2/b^2 = 1$.

53. PERIODIC SOLUTIONS AND LIMIT CYCLES

The differential equation

(1) $$\ddot{x} = g(x, \dot{x}),$$

in which $\dot{x}$ and $\ddot{x}$ denote time derivatives (Newton's notation), is said to be *autonomous* when the time t does not occur explicitly. It may be replaced by the system of two first-order equations

(2) $$\dot{x} = y, \qquad \dot{y} = g(x, y)$$

---

* W. J. Cunningham, *The Concept of Stability*, American Scientist, Dec. 1963, p. 434, Fig. 3. The stability of the node $(0, 0)$ for the equations

$$\frac{dx}{dt} = x(y - 2), \qquad \frac{dy}{dt} = y(x - 1)$$

is discussed with the aid of the Liapunov function $x^2 + y^2$.

in the xy or *phase-plane*. These equations are included in the more general autonomous system

(3) $$\dot{x} = f(x, y), \qquad \dot{y} = g(x, y).$$

The linear case

$$\dot{x} = ax + by, \qquad \dot{y} = cx + dy$$

was fully treated in §§ 47 and 48 with graphs of the stream lines in all typical cases.

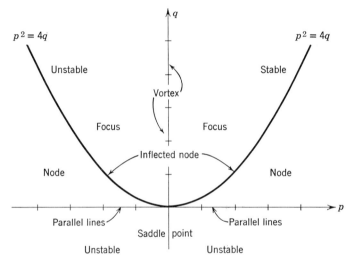

Fig. 53a   Stability chart for $\ddot{x} + p\dot{x} + qx = 0$.

When equation (1) is linear with constant coefficients,

(4) $$\ddot{x} + p\dot{x} + qx = 0$$

the corresponding first-order system is

(5) $$\dot{x} = y, \qquad \dot{y} = -qx - py.$$

The stability table of § 48 now applies to the matrix $\begin{pmatrix} 0 & 1 \\ -q & -p \end{pmatrix}$ in which

$$a + d = -p, \qquad ad - bc = q, \qquad \Delta = p^2 - 4q.$$

The stability conditions are shown graphically in Figure 53a. The parabola $p^2 - 4q = 0$ of Case III separates the region below of Case I ($p^2 - 4q > 0$) from the region above of Case II ($p^2 - 4q < 0$). *All cases of strict stability ($p, q > 0$) lie inside the first quadrant.*

When $f(x, y)$ or $g(x, y)$ are nonlinear, exact solutions are rarely feasible or, if known, are complicated implicit functions. Then an analysis of the trajectories in the xy-plane may yield important information as to stability, periodicity, and behavior at infinity. The method of isoclines (§ 4) is often useful in suggesting the general shape of the trajectories, and the direction of flow is given by

(6) $$\mathbf{v} = \mathbf{i} f(x, y) + \mathbf{j} g(x, y).$$

Suppose now that

(7) $$x = \varphi(t), \qquad y = \psi(t)$$

are parametric equations of a *closed* trajectory of equation (3) which satisfies the initial conditions

(8) $$x_0 = \varphi(0), \qquad y_0 = \psi(0).$$

Since the curve is *closed*, after a time lapse τ we shall again have

(9) $$x_0 = \varphi(\tau), \qquad y_0 = \psi(\tau).$$

In view of this,

(10) $$x = \varphi(t + \tau), \qquad y = \psi(t + \tau)$$

is also a solution of the initial value problem (3)–(8). Now when $f(x, y)$ and $g(x, y)$ are continuous and satisfy a Lipschitz condition (cf. § 156), the solution of problem (3)–(8) is *unique* and in this case the solutions (7) and (10) are the same, so that

(11) $$\varphi(t + \tau) = \varphi(t), \qquad \psi(t + \tau) = \psi(t).$$

Thus a closed trajectory, free from equilibrium points, corresponds to a periodic solution—an oscillation having a fixed period τ.

It is possible to have a closed curve consisting entirely of equilibrium points; this is illustrated in Example 1. A more important phenomenon that characterizes some nonlinear equations is the existence of a *limit cycle*, an isolated closed curve in the phase plane. When the limit cycle is stable, all solutions in its vicinity tend toward the cycle as $t \to \infty$; thus both exterior and interior solutions spiral around the limit cycle and wind into it asymptotically. *A stable limit cycle is an isolated, closed, asymptotic solution.* Such a limit cycle is shown in Example 2. The general problem of finding a limit cycle is one of the most difficult in nonlinear analysis.

If the system (3) admits a closed trajectory $\mathscr{C}$, its index must be 1 (§ 47). For example, the closed trajectories about a vortex have the index 1. But a closed trajectory is also possible about a focus (as in Ex. 5) or a node but not about a saddle point (index -1) if this is the only critical point enclosed. A closed trajectory may enclose several critical points if the *sum* of their indices is 1; for we may apply the

Index Theorem. *If a closed trajectory does not pass through any critical points but encloses a finite number, its index is the sum of the "enclosed" indices.*

When $\mathscr{C}$ encloses two critical points P_1, P_2 of indices m_1, m_2, draw an arc AB that divides $\mathscr{C}$ into two closed curves $\mathscr{C}_1$, $\mathscr{C}_2$ having AB in common (Fig. 53b), so that $\mathscr{C}_1$ encloses P_1 and $\mathscr{C}_2$ en-closes P_2. Then the sum of the angular changes of the field vector

$$\mathbf{v} = \mathbf{i} f(x, y) + \mathbf{j} g(x, y)$$

in making a positive circuit of $\mathscr{C}_1$ and $\mathscr{C}_2$ is precisely the angular change of $\mathbf{v}$ over $\mathscr{C}$, for the changes over AB and BA cancel as they are traversed in opposite directions; thus

$$2\pi m = 2\pi(m_1 + m_2) \quad \text{or} \quad m = m_1 + m_2.$$

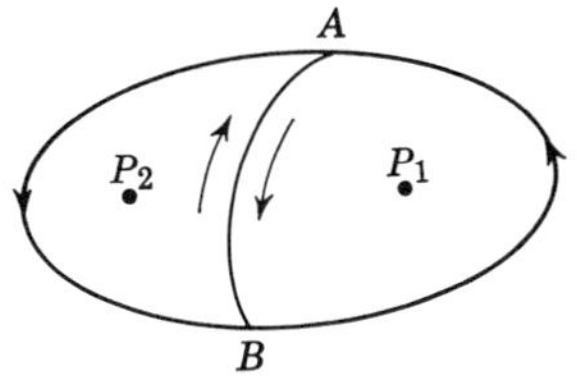

Fig. 53b Trajectory about critical points P_1, P_2.

The theorem for n enclosed critical points now follows by mathematical induction.

*Example 1. **Closed Equilibrium Curve.*** Every point on the circle $\mathscr{C}$, $x^2 + y^2 = 1$, is in equilibrium for the equations

(i) $\dot{x} = (x - y)(1 - x^2 - y^2), \qquad \dot{y} = (x + y)(1 - x^2 - y^2)$

and there is also an isolated equilibrium point $(0, 0)$. In the linear approximation

$$\dot{x} = x - y, \qquad \dot{y} = x + y,$$

the origin is an unstable focus (Ex. 47.5), and this is also true for the nonlinear system; for if we take $U(x, y) = x^2 + y^2$,

$$\dot{U}(x, y) = 2(1 - x^2 - y^2)(x^2 + y^2)$$

is positive definite within $\mathscr{C}$ and Theorem 52.3 shows that every trajectory that starts from a point (x_0, y_0) inside $\mathscr{C}$ $(0 < x_0^2 + y_0^2 < 1)$ will end on $\mathscr{C}$. Outside of $\mathscr{C}$, $\dot{U}(x, y) < 0$ and every trajectory that starts from a point (x_0, y_0) outside of $\mathscr{C}$ $(x_0^2 + y_0^2 > 1)$ will also end on $\mathscr{C}$.

A change to polar coordinates

$$x = r \cos \theta, \qquad y = r \sin \theta$$

reduces system (1) to

(ii) $\dot{r} = r(1 - r^2), \qquad \dot{\theta} = 1 - r^2.$

The trajectories satisfy

$$\frac{dr}{d\theta} = \frac{\dot{r}}{\dot{\theta}} = r$$

and are the equiangular spirals $r = Ce^\theta$, cutting all radial lines at an angle $\pi/4$.

Inside of $\mathscr{C}$ $(r < 1)$ $\dot{r}$ and $\dot{\theta}$ are positive and all trajectories spiral outward to meet and end on $\mathscr{C}$. Outside of $\mathscr{C}$ $(r > 1)$ $\dot{r}$ and $\dot{\theta}$ are negative and all trajectories spiral inward until they meet and end on $\mathscr{C}$ (Fig. 53c). All trajectories meet $\mathscr{C}$ at an angle $\pi/4$ for their polar slope

$$\tan \varphi = r \frac{d\theta}{dr} = \frac{r\dot{\theta}}{\dot{r}} = 1,$$

Fig. 53c Closed equilibrium curve.

where φ is the angle at which a radial line cuts a trajectory.

From (ii) we see that when $r < 1$, $\dot{r} > 0$ and when $r > 1$, $\dot{r} < 0$; thus inner and outer trajectories reach and *end* at $r = 1$ where $\dot{r} = \dot{\theta} = 0$.

Example 2. **Limit Cycle.** The equations

(i) $\dot{x} = x - y - x(x^2 + y^2), \qquad \dot{y} = x + y - y(x^2 + y^2)$

have their only equilibrium point at $(0, 0)$; for if

$$x - y = x(x^2 + y^2), \qquad x + y = y(x^2 + y^2),$$

$$x(x - y) + y(x + y) = (x^2 + y^2)^2$$

and hence $x^2 + y^2 = 0$. The origin is an unstable focus for the linear approximation (Ex. 47.5) and also for the nonlinear system; for if $U(x, y) = x^2 + y^2$, we find that

$$\dot{U}(x, y) = 2(x^2 + y^2)(1 - x^2 - y^2)$$

is positive definite within the circle $\mathscr{C}$, $x^2 + y^2 = 1$, and Theorem 52.3 assures us that $(0, 0)$ is unstable. All trajectories inside of the circle $\mathscr{C}$ ultimately reach $\mathscr{C}$. Outside of $\mathscr{C}$ $\dot{U}(x, y) < 0$ and all trajectories outside of $\mathscr{C}$ also tend toward $\mathscr{C}$. Moreover $\mathscr{C}$ is a solution curve of (i); for when $x^2 + y^2 = 1$, equations (i) become

$$\dot{x} = -y, \qquad \dot{y} = x \quad \text{and} \quad x\dot{x} + y\dot{y} = 0.$$

All this becomes more obvious on changing to polar coordinates. Then the system (i) becomes

(ii) $\dot{r} = r(1 - r^2), \qquad \dot{\theta} = 1$

and the trajectories are given by

$$r^2 = \frac{1}{1 + Ae^{-2t}}, \qquad \theta = t + \theta_0,$$

and $A = r_0^{-2} - 1$. Irrespective of the initial values, $r \to 1$ as $t \to \infty$; trajectories on both sides of $\mathscr{C}$ spiral into $\mathscr{C}$ asymptotically and $\mathscr{C}$ $(r = 1)$ itself is a periodic solution of (ii) traversed completely at unit speed every 2π seconds.

Note that the polar slope

$$\tan \varphi = r \frac{d\theta}{dr} = \frac{r\dot\theta}{\dot r} = \frac{1}{1 - r^2} \to \infty$$

as $r \to 1$, so that the trajectories spiral *tangentially* into the limit cycle $r = 1$ (Fig. 53d). In Example 1 the spirals met the circle $\mathscr{C}$ at an angle $\pi/4$.

This problem was set up to give the limit cycle $r = 1$; for when $r < 1$, $\dot r > 0$ and when $r > 1$, $\dot r < 0$. When $r = 1$, the circle is traversed with unit angular speed.

Example 3. Periodic Solutions. The equation

(i) $$\ddot x - 4\dot x + x^3 = 0$$

is equivalent to the system

(ii) $$\dot x = y, \qquad \dot y = 4x - x^3$$

which has three equilibrium points $(0, 0)$, $(\pm 2, 0)$.

For the linear approximation of matrix $\begin{pmatrix} 0 & 1 \\ 4 & 0 \end{pmatrix}$, we have

$$a + d = 0, \qquad ad - bc = -4, \qquad \Delta = 16,$$

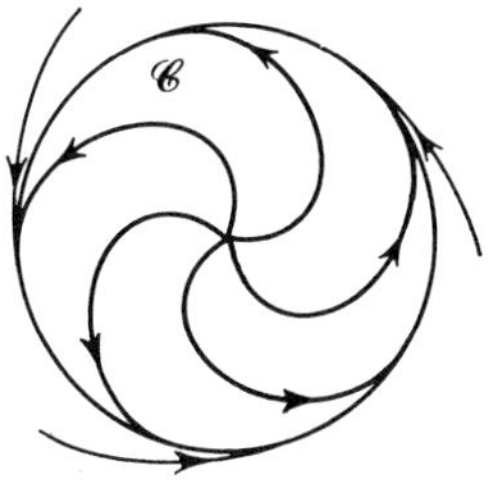

Fig. 53d   Limit cycle.

and Table 48 (p. 187) shows a saddle point at $(0, 0)$.

To find the character of $(2, 0)$, translate axes: $x = X + 2$, $y = Y$; then

$$\dot X = Y, \qquad \dot Y = -8X - 6X^2 - X^3$$

and in the matrix $\begin{pmatrix} 0 & 1 \\ -8 & 0 \end{pmatrix}$,

$$a + d = 0, \qquad ad - bc = 8, \qquad \Delta = -24,$$

and Table 48 suggests a vortex at $(2, 0)$. The same matrix applies to $(-2, 0)$ which is also a vortex.

The equation

$$y\dot y = 4x\dot x - x^3 \dot x$$

yields on integration the equations of the stream lines

$$y^2 = 4x^2 - \tfrac{1}{2}x^4 + C,$$

or on putting $C = \tfrac{1}{2}(K^2 - 16)$,

$$y^2 = \tfrac{1}{2}[K^2 - (x^2 - 4)^2] = \tfrac{1}{2}(K + 4 - x^2)(K - 4 + x^2).$$

When $K = 0$, we obtain the isolated points $(\pm 2, 0)$; for $0 < K < 4$, we have a series of loops about these points. When $K = 4$,

(iii) $$y^2 = \tfrac{1}{2}(8 - x^2)x^2$$

and the loops join to form a continuous curve like a lemniscate whose tangents at the origin have the slope $\lim (y/x) = \pm 2$. Each loop is a *separatrix*; together they separate the periodic solutions about each vortex $(0 < K < 4)$ from the periodic solutions around both vortices $(K > 4)$. The separatrices are *not* periodic solutions, for the motion comes to rest at $(0, 0)$ where $\dot{x} = \dot{y} = 0$ (Fig. 53*e*).

Consider the periodic solution for $K = 5$:

(iv) $$y^2 = \tfrac{1}{2}(9 - x^2)(x^2 + 1).$$

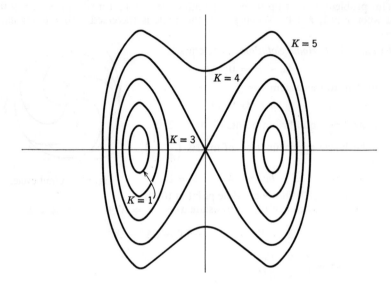

Fig. 53e   Periodic trajectories: $2y^2 = (K + 4 - x^2)(K - 4 + x^2)$.

When $y = \dot{x} = 0$, we obtain the extreme values ± 3 of x; the vibration is therefore symmetrical with an amplitude of 3. Replacing y by dx/dt, solving for dt and integrating between $x = 0$ and $x = 3$, we obtain the quarter period

$$\frac{1}{4}\tau = \sqrt{2}\int_0^3 \frac{dx}{\sqrt{9 - x^2}\sqrt{x^2 + 1}} = \sqrt{2}\int_0^{\pi/2} \frac{d\theta}{\sqrt{9\cos^2\theta + 1}}$$

on making the substitution $x = 3\cos\theta$. Hence,

$$\frac{1}{4}\tau = \sqrt{2}\int_0^{\pi/2} \frac{d\theta}{\sqrt{10 - 9\sin^2\theta}} = \frac{1}{\sqrt{5}}\int_0^{\pi/2} \frac{d\theta}{\sqrt{1 - 0.9\sin^2\theta}}.$$

The integral is a complete elliptic integral with $k = \sqrt{0.9} = 0.9468$, $\sin^{-1} k = 71°14'$; its value is roughly 2.56 (Standard Mathematical Tables, ref. 4, p. 279) and hence $\tau = 4(2.56/\sqrt{5}) = 4.48$ seconds.

We note that the closed curve (iv) encloses a saddle point $(0, 0)$ and two vortices $(\pm 2, 0)$ and that the sum of their indices $-1 + 1 + 1 = 1$, in accordance with the index theorem (p. 213).

Example 4. Liénard's Equation. In 1928 the French physicist Pierre Liénard showed that the equation

(i) $$\ddot{x} + f(x)\dot{x} + g(x) = 0$$

has a unique stable limit cycle under the following conditions:
  (a) $f(x)$ is even, $g(x)$ odd, both continuous for all x, and $f(0) < 0$;
  (b) $xg(x) > 0$ for $x \neq 0$;
  (c) for every interval $|x| < K$ there is an L such that

$$|g(x_1) - g(x_2)| < L\,|x_1 - x_2|\quad \text{(Lipschitz condition)};$$

  (d) $F(x) = \displaystyle\int_0^x f(x)\,dx \uparrow \infty$ as $x \uparrow \infty$;
  (e) $F(x)$ has a single positive zero at $x = a$ and is monotone increasing for $x \geqq a$.
  For the proof see Lefshetz, ref. 33, p. 208, also ref. 25, p. 402, Prob. 5.
  With $F(x)$ as defined in (c), Liénard's equation is equivalent to

(ii) $$\dot{x} = y - F(x), \qquad \dot{y} = -g(x);$$

for

$$\ddot{x} = \dot{y} - F'(x)\dot{x} = -g(x) - f(x)\dot{x}.$$

When $y = \dot{x} + F(x)$, the xy-plane is called the *Liénard plane*; except when $f(x) = 0$ it differs from the *phase plane*, in which $y = \dot{x}$.
  Liénard's equation may be regarded as the equation of motion of a unit mass subjected to the restoring force $g(x)$ and the damping force $-f(x)\dot{x}$. The work done by the damper is

(iii) $$W = -\int_0^x f(x)\dot{x}\,dx \quad \text{and} \quad \frac{dW}{dx} = -f(x)\,\dot{x}.$$

Since $f(0) < 0$ by condition (a), $dW/dx > 0$ when the mass passes through $x = 0$ with positive velocity $\dot{x}$, and the damper adds energy to the system until $f(x) = 0$. With $\dot{x}$ and $f(x)$ positive, the damper removes energy from the system until $\dot{x} = 0$; after that point, with $\dot{x} < 0$ and $f(x) > 0$, energy is again added to the system until $f(x) = 0$, and so forth (Fig. 53f). If the total of such energy changes in a cycle is zero, we have the possibility of a self-sustaining periodic motion—a limit cycle.[*]
  If we put $\dot{x} = v$ in (iii), the total work of damping over a cycle is

$$W = -\oint f(x)v\,dx = -vF(x)\Big|_{\text{cycle}} + \oint F(x)\,dv$$

on integrating by parts. The integrated part is zero for its value is the same at the start and end of a cycle. Now from (ii), $dv = dy - f(x)\,dx$ and hence

$$W = \oint F(x)\,dv = \oint F(x)\,dy$$

---

[*] C. A. Ludeke, A Physical Interpretation of the Criterion for the Existence of a Limit Cycle, *Am. J. Phys.*, Vol. 13, no. 11, 1964.

for the integral $\oint F(x)f(x)\,dx$ vanishes over a cycle. Thus for a limit cycle we must have

(iv) $$\oint F(x)\,dy = 0.$$

This condition holds in the phase plane ($y = \dot{x}$) or in the Liénard plane ($y = \dot{x} + F(x)$).

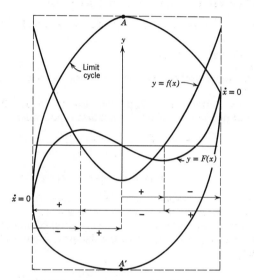

Fig. 53f Energy changes in a limit cycle.

When x, y in equations (ii) are replaced by $-x$, $-y$, the equations are still satisfied since $F(x)$ and $g(x)$ are odd functions. Hence if $x = \varphi(t)$, $y = \psi(t)$ is a solution, so is $x = -\varphi(t), y = -\psi(t)$. Thus if Γ is a trajectory, its symmetric image in the origin is also a trajectory Γ'. When Γ and Γ' coincide we have a limit cycle, a closed trajectory symmetric with respect to the origin.

The trajectories are the integral curves of the equation

(v) $$\frac{dy}{dx} = -\frac{g(x)}{y - F(x)}.$$

Since $g(0) = 0$, all have a horizontal tangent where they cut the y-axis ($x = 0$) and a vertical tangent where they cut the curve $y = F(x)$ which is also symmetric about the origin. A limit cycle will cut the y-axis at points A, A' equidistant from the origin; and it can be shown that any trajectory with this property is the limit cycle. The problem of its stability can also be treated geometrically.

Example 5. The van der Pol Equation.

(ii) $\ddot{x} + \mu(x^2 - 1)\dot{x} + x = 0,$ $\mu \neq 0$

arose in the study of oscillatory vacuum tube circuits.* It is a Liénard equation in which

$$f(x) = \mu(x^2 - 1), \qquad F(x) = \mu(\tfrac{1}{3}x^3 - x), \qquad g(x) = x.$$

The stability of its solutions depends on the sign of μ.

Case 1. $\mu < 0$.

The phase plane equations

(ii) $\dot{x} = y,$ $\dot{y} = -x - \mu(x^2 - 1)y$

have a single critical point $(0, 0)$. When $x^2 < 1$, $V(x, y) = x^2 + y^2$ is a Liapunov function; for

$$\dot{V}(x, y) = 2(x\dot{x} + y\dot{y}) = -2\mu(x^2 - 1)y^2 < 0.$$

Theorem 52.1 now shows that the interior of the circle $x^2 + y^2 = 1$ is a region of strict stability; any trajectory that starts at a point within the circle tends toward the origin. The linear part of equations (ii) has the matrix $\begin{pmatrix} 0 & 1 \\ -1 & \mu \end{pmatrix}$ for which $\lambda_1 + \lambda_2 = \mu$, $\lambda_1\lambda_2 = 1$, $\Delta = \mu^2 - 4$ in the notation of Table 48. This suggests that the origin is a stable node, inflected node, or a focus, according as $\mu < -2$, $\mu = -2$, $-2 < \mu < 0$; its strict stability is assured, but its exact character may depend on the nonlinear term $-\mu x^2 y$.

Case 2. $\mu > 0$.

Now $f(0) = -\mu < 0$ and all conditions (a) to (e) of Example 4 are fulfilled; hence the equation has a unique stable limit cycle. The origin is now unstable. Indeed, *the trajectories for any positive μ are the same as those for $-\mu$ reversed in sense*; for changing t to $-t$ merely reverses the sign of μ in (i). All trajectories inside the limit cycle tend to merge with it as $t \to \infty$. The discussion in Case 1 shows that the limit cycle encloses the circle $x^2 + y^2 = 1$ in the phase plane.

Trajectories in the phase plane are constructed by the method of isoclines (§ 4). Figures 53g, h, i pertain to $\mu = 0.1, 1, 10$ and are taken from van der Pol's paper cited above. The short dashes on the isoclines show the corresponding inclinations. The limit cycles are the heavy closed curves and exhibit $y = \dot{x}$ as a function of x. The x-t curves in Figure 53j are obtained by approximate integration of $dx/dt = y$; thus if $\bar{y}$ is the average value of y in the interval Δx, $\Delta t \simeq \Delta x/\bar{y}$ and points on the x-t curve are found step by step.

When $\mu = 0.1$, the limit cycle is nearly circular and is attained after a series of sinusoidal oscillations whose amplitude gradually increases to the limiting value 2. When $\mu = 1$, the steady oscillation is reached more rapidly and shows a definite departure from sinusoidal form. Finally, when, $\mu = 10$, the steady state is reached in a single period and the wave is radically altered in shape to produce a very jerky motion. In a cycle, x decreases slowly from 2 to 1, then suddenly drops to -2, increases slowly to -1, and suddenly jumps back to 2.

---

* B. van der Pol, On "Relaxation Oscillations," *Phil. Mag.*, ser. 7, vol. 2, pp. 978–992, (1926). Figures 1, 2, 3 showing limit cycles for $\mu = 0.1, 1, 10$, and figure 4 are reproduced by permission of the *Philosophical Magazine*.

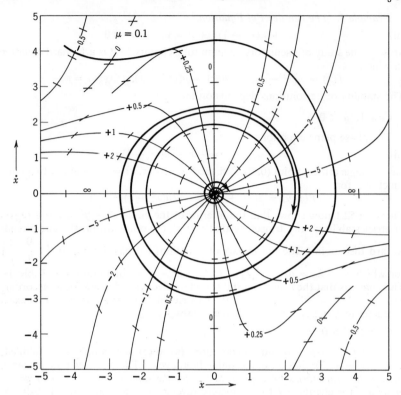

Fig. 53g Trajectories and limit cycle for the van der Pol equation with $\mu = 0.1$.

This remarkable periodic self-sustained motion is due to the changes in the energy cycle as explained in Example 4.

The criterion of Example 4

(iii)
$$\oint F(x)\, dy = \mu \oint (\tfrac{1}{3}x^3 - x)\, dy = 0$$

may be applied to find the approximate amplitude of the limit cycle. If we assume a nearly sinusoidal wave, say

$$x = a \sin t, \qquad y = \dot{x} = a \cos t,$$

we find, on substitution in (iii), that $a = 2$, in surprisingly good agreement with the actual value.

In the Liénard plane, equation (i) becomes

(iv)
$$\dot{x} = y - \mu(\tfrac{1}{3}x^3 - x), \qquad \dot{y} = -x.$$

If $\mu < 0$, $V(x, y) = \tfrac{1}{2}(x^2 + y^2)$ is a Liapunov function; for

$$\dot{V}(x, y) \; x[y - \mu(\tfrac{1}{3}x^3 - x)] \; -yx = \mu x^2(1 - \tfrac{1}{3}x^2) < 0 \quad \text{when} \quad x^2 < 3;$$

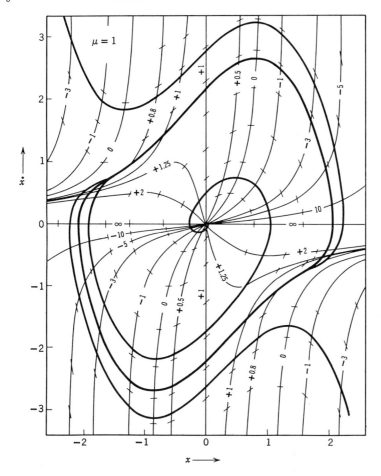

Fig. 53h   Trajectories and limit cycle for the van der Pol equation with $\mu = 1$.

hence all paths within the circle $x^2 + y^2 = 3$ tend toward the origin. For the corresponding positive $|\mu|$, all such paths are reversed in sense, cross the circle and eventually merge with the limit cycle. *For all positive values of μ, the limit cycle of the van der Pol equation in the Liénard plane encloses the circle $x^2 + y^2 = 3$.*
   The trajectories of equations (iv) in the Liénard plane satisfy

$$\frac{dy}{dx} = -\frac{x}{y - \mu(\frac{1}{3}x^3 - x)}$$

and may be constructed by a method due to Liénard. Draw the cubic curve

(v) $y = \mu(\frac{1}{3}x^3 - x)$

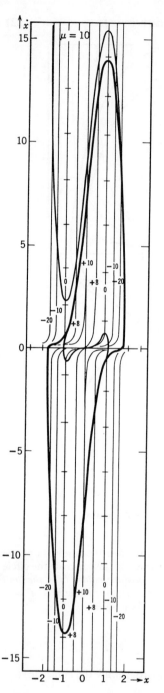

Figure 53*j* shows that the time from $x = 2$ to $x = 1$ is about a half period ($\frac{1}{2}\tau$) and that $\dot{x}$ is nearly constant, and hence $\ddot{x} \simeq 0$ in this interval. With $\ddot{x} = 0$, the van der Pol equation becomes

$$\mu(x^2 - 1)\dot{x} + x = 0.$$

Integral curves of this equation are shown dotted in Figure 53*j*. To obtain the approximate period, we have

$$\tau = 2\mu \int_2^1 \left(\frac{1}{x} - x\right) dx = \mu\left(\frac{3}{2} - \log 2\right) = 1.614\mu.$$

This rough estimate gives only the first term of a more accurate formula due to Dorodnicyn[*] and Urabe[†]

$$\tau = 1.6137\mu + \frac{7.014}{\mu^{1/3}} - \frac{1}{3}\frac{\log \mu}{\mu} - \frac{1.2092}{\mu}$$
$$+ O(\mu^{-4/3}).$$

For $\mu = 10$, this gives $\tau = 19.184$ sec, which more nearly agrees with Figure 53*j*, which shows $\tau \simeq 20$ sec. The papers cited also contain accurate formulas for the amplitude a; for $\mu = 10$, $a = 2.014$. The amplitude, however, varies but slightly with μ and remains in the neighborhood of 2, attaining a maximum of 2.0235 when $\mu = 3.2651$.

[*] Dorodnicyn, A. A., *Asymptotic Solutions of van der Pol's Equation*, Am. Math. Soc. Translation No. 88, corrected.
[†] Urabe, M., *Periodic Solutions of van der Pol's Equation with damping coefficient $\lambda = 0 \sim 10$*, IRE Transactions in Circuit Theory, vol. 7, pp. 382–386, 1960.

Fig. 53i Trajectories and limit cycle for the van der Pol equation with $\mu = 10$.

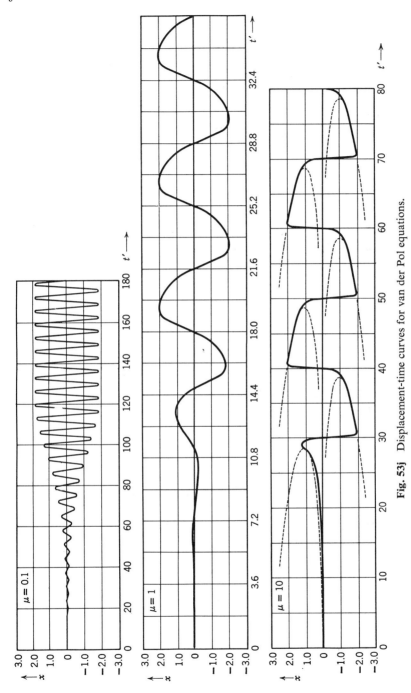

Fig. 53j   Displacement-time curves for van der Pol equations.

which is symmetrical about the origin, with intercepts $\pm\sqrt{3}$ and extremes of $\mp 2\mu/3$ at $x = \pm 1$ (Fig. 53k).

Through a point P of the trajectory draw a vertical to cut the curve (v) at Q, a horizontal through Q to cut the y-axis at R. Then RP is normal to the trajectory; for

$$-\frac{dx}{dy} = \frac{y - \mu(\tfrac{1}{3}x^3 - x)}{x} = \frac{QP}{RQ},$$

and its sense is given by $dy/dt = -x$; thus y decreases when $x > 0$, increases when $x < 0$.

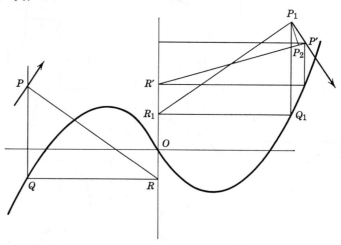

Fig. 53k   Liénard construction.

This *Liénard construction* reveals that a trajectory in the Liénard plane

(a) cuts the y-axis horizontally,
(b) cuts the curve (v) vertically,
(c) cuts the lines $x = \pm\sqrt{3}$ normal to OP.

To sketch a trajectory, the following orderly procedure may be used to advance from a point P_1 to P_2 (Fig. 53k). Advance a short distance d along the tangent at P_1 to P', find the normal $R'P'$ by the Liénard construction, and drop a perpendicular on it from P_1 to get an approximate P_2. Proceed from P_2 to P_3 in the same way keeping d constant. A small d promotes accuracy, but naturally increases the labor.

PROBLEMS

1. Find the critical points and determine their nature for the following equations:
(a) $\ddot{x} + 3\dot{x} + 2x + x^2 = 0$;
(b) $\ddot{x} + 2\dot{x} + 2x + 2x^2 = 0$;
(c) $\ddot{x} + \dot{x} + 6x + 3x^2 = 0$.

2. Find a limit cycle for the equations

$$\dot{x} = -x - y + \frac{x}{\sqrt{x^2 + y^2}}, \qquad \dot{y} = x - y + \frac{y}{\sqrt{x^2 + y^2}}.$$

Find the polar equation of the trajectories and show that they spiral tangentially into the limit cycle as $t \to \infty$.

3. Use the Liénard construction to draw the trajectory of the van der Pol equation when $\mu = 1$, starting at the point $(2, 0)$.

4. Devise a Liénard construction for the trajectories of the equation $\ddot{x} + \varphi(\dot{x}) + x = 0$ when written in the form

$$\dot{x} = y, \qquad \dot{y} = -x - \varphi(y).$$

[The guide curve is $x = -\varphi(y)$.]

5. Apply the Liénard construction of Problem 4 to the equation

$$\ddot{x} + |\dot{x}|\, \dot{x} + x = 0$$

to obtain the trajectory through the point $x = \frac{3}{8}$, $y = 0$. The guide curve consists of the parabolic arcs $x = -|y|\, y$. Use a scale of one inch $= \frac{1}{8}$. Proceed from point to point, using $d = \frac{1}{2}$ inch (cf. Ex. 4).

6. Apply the Liénard construction of Problem 4 to the equation

$$\ddot{x} + 0.2\, \mathrm{sgn}\, \dot{x} + 4x = 0$$

when written in the form

$$\dot{x} = 2y, \qquad \dot{y} = -2x - 0.1\, \mathrm{sgn}\, y.$$

Obtain the *precise* trajectory through $x = 0.225$, $y = 0$ and show that it consists of two semicircles ending at the point $x = 0.025$, $y = 0$. The guide curve is now $x = -0.05\, \mathrm{sgn}\, y$. and consists of two vertical lines ending at the x-axis.

7. Show that the system

$$\dot{r} = r(r^2 - 1), \qquad \dot{\theta} = 1$$

has an unstable limit cycle $r = 1$; and the system

$$\dot{r} = r(r^2 - 1)^2, \qquad \dot{\theta} = 1$$

has a limit cycle which is stable internally, unstable externally.

8. In Example 4, let $\mathscr{R}$ be an open region about the origin in which

$$g(x)F(x) > 0, \qquad \int_0^x g(x)\, dx > 0, \qquad x \neq 0.$$

Show that

$$V(x, y) = \tfrac{1}{2}y^2 + \int_0^x g(x)\, dx$$

is a Liapunov function in $\mathscr{R}$ and that the origin is strictly stable. Note that $g(x)F(x) > 0$ violates condition (a) for a stable limit cycle.

9. Construct the trajectory of the van der Pol equation in the Liénard plane which passes through $(2, 0)$ by the method of Example 5 when $\mu = 0.1$ and $\mu = 10$. Show that the respective limit cycles are nearly circular and nearly rectangular.

10. In a closed sea there are two species of fish, A which feeds on plants and B which subsists by eating A. If A or B alone were present, their numbers would increase or decrease, respectively, according to exponential laws of growth and decay (§ 11):

$$\dot{x} = ax, \qquad \dot{y} = -by, \qquad a, b > 0.$$

Volterra assumed in his *Mathematical Theory of the Struggle for Existence** that these equations become

$$\dot{x} = ax - cxy, \qquad \dot{y} = -by + dxy, \qquad c, d > 0.$$

(i) Show that the origin is a saddle point.

(ii) Translate the axes, $x = X + b/d$, $y = Y + a/c$, and show that the point $(b/d, a/c)$ is a stable vortex.

(iii) When X and Y are both small, show that the trajectories are nearly ellipses $X^2 + ab\,Y^2 = $ const.

(iv) The trajectories have the equations

$$dx + cy - b \log x - a \log y = \text{const.}$$

11. *Bendixon's Negative Theorem.* In the equations

$$\dot{x} = P(x, y), \qquad \dot{y} = Q(x, y),$$

let P, Q, P_x, Q_y be continuous in the open region $\mathscr{R}$ bounded by a simple closed curve. Then if $P_x + Q_y$ has a fixed sign in $\mathscr{R}$, the equations can have no limit cycle $\mathscr{C}$ in $\mathscr{R}$.

[Apply Green's theorem to the cycle $\mathscr{C}$:

$$\oint_{\mathscr{C}} P\,dy - Q\,dx = \iint (P_x + Q_y)\,dx\,dy.$$

Note that if $\mathbf{f} = P\mathbf{i} + Q\mathbf{j}$, div $\mathbf{f} = P_x + Q_y$ and the circuit integral is the normal flux of $\mathbf{f}$ through $\mathscr{C}$. Cf. *Advanced Calculus*, § 160.]

12. Apply Bendixon's theorem to show that the van der Pol equation can have no limit cycle within the circle $x^2 + y^2 = 1$ in the phase plane.

---

* Volterra, V., *Théorie mathématique de la lutte pour la vie*, Gauthier-Villars, Paris, 1931.

CHAPTER 6

Applications

54. CATENARY

The ideal curve assumed by a heavy uniform flexible string hanging freely from two points of support is called a *catenary*. To find its equation draw the y-axis through the lowest point A of the string and choose the origin O at a distance y_0 below A (Fig. 54a). We shall choose y_0 to simplify the equation as much as possible.

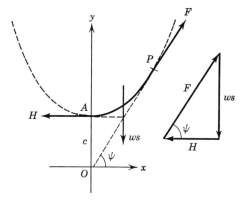

Fig. 54a Equilibrium of forces on a catenary.

Consider the portion AP of the string; if the string weighs w lb/ft, and the arc $AP = s$ ft, the weight of AP is $W = ws$ lb. A string is called *flexible* when the tension at any point is tangent to its curve; then the part AP, considered as a free body, is in equilibrium under three forces (Fig. 54a): its weight W, the horizontal tension H at A, the tension F at P making an angle ψ with the horizontal. The laws of statics now require that the vectors representing W, H, and F form a closed triangle and that their lines of action meet in a point. Then from the force triangle

(1)   (2) $F \sin \psi = W = ws, \quad F \cos \psi = H = wc;$

here $c = H/w$ is called the *parameter* of the catenary and has the dimensions of length. A horizontal line at a distance c below the vertex A is the *directrix* of the catenary. We shall take the directrix as the x-axis ($y_0 = c$). On dividing equation (1) by (2) we have $\tan \psi = s/c$ or

(3) $$s = c \tan \psi.$$

This is the *intrinsic equation* of the catenary for it is entirely independent of coordinates. From it we obtain the differential equation

(4) $$\frac{dy}{dx} = \frac{s}{c}, \qquad \frac{d^2y}{dx^2} = \frac{1}{c}\frac{ds}{dx} = \frac{1}{c}\sqrt{1 + \left(\frac{dy}{dx}\right)^2}.$$

Since both x and y are missing, (4) may be integrated by the methods of the next article. We prefer, however, a different approach which shows how the intrinsic equation of a curve may be used to deduce its Cartesian equation.

Recalling that

$$\frac{dx}{ds} = \cos \psi, \qquad \frac{dy}{ds} = \sin \psi^*,$$

we have from (3)

$$\frac{dx}{d\psi} = \frac{dx}{ds}\frac{ds}{d\psi} = \cos \psi \cdot c \sec^2 \psi = c \sec \psi,$$

$$\frac{dy}{d\psi} = \frac{dy}{ds}\frac{ds}{d\psi} = \sin \psi \cdot c \sec^2 \psi = c \tan \psi \sec \psi.$$

On integrating these equations from $\psi = 0$ to ψ, and taking account of the initial conditions

$$x = 0, \qquad y = c \qquad \text{when} \quad \psi = 0,$$

we have

(5) $$x = c \log (\sec \psi + \tan \psi),$$

(6) $$y = c \sec \psi.$$

We now eliminate ψ from these parametric equations to obtain the Cartesian equation. From (5) we have

$$\sec \psi + \tan \psi = e^{x/a},$$

and since $\sec^2 \psi - \tan^2 \psi = 1$, also

$$\sec \psi - \tan \psi = e^{-x/c}.$$

---

* *Advanced Calculus*, p. 218 (2).

On adding and subtracting these equations, we find

(7) $$\sec \psi = \cosh \frac{x}{c},$$

(8) $$\tan \psi = \sinh \frac{x}{c}.$$

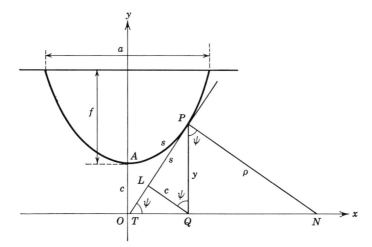

Fig. 54b Catenary.

The Cartesian equation of the catenary,

(9) $$y = c \cosh \frac{x}{c},$$

now follows from (6) and (7); and from (3) and (8) we have also the arc length measured from the vertex,

(10) $$s = c \sinh \frac{x}{c}.$$

Since $\cosh^2 u - \sinh^2 u = 1$, these equations also show that

(11) $$y^2 = s^2 + c^2.$$

If we drop a perpendicular QL on the tangent to the catenary at P (Fig. 54b), this equation states the Pythagorean Theorem for the triangle PQL. For from (6) and (3)

$$QL = y \cos \psi = c, \qquad PL = c \tan \psi = s.$$

A string stretched along the arc $AP = s$, when unwrapped, becomes the segment $PL = s$; hence the locus of L is the *involute* of the catenary. This curve is normal to PL and tangent to LQ; and since LQ has the constant length c, the involute is a *tractrix;* for the tractrix is defined as a plane curve whose tangent between the curve and a fixed line (here the x-axis) has a constant length c. From Figure 54c we see that the differential equation of the tractrix is

(12)
$$\left(\frac{dy}{dx}\right)^2 = \tan^2 \theta = \frac{y^2}{c^2 - y^2}$$

where x, y are the coordinates of L.

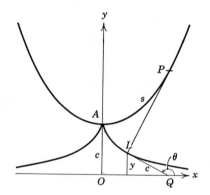

Fig. 54c   Tractrix: arc AP unwinds into PL.

The radius of curvature of the catenary is found from (3) and (6):

(13)
$$\rho = \frac{ds}{d\psi} = c \sec^2 \psi = y \sec \psi = PN.$$

The parameter c of the catenary is equal to its radius of curvature at the vertex ($\psi = 0$); hence the flatter the catenary, the larger its parameter.

The slope $m = y'(x)$ at any point x of a catenary determines its parameter c; for from (9)

$$m = \sinh \frac{x}{c} = \frac{1}{2}(e^{x/c} - e^{-x/c}),$$

$$e^{2x/c} - 2me^{x/c} - 1 = 0,$$

and on solving this quadratic for $e^{x/c}$ we find

(14)
$$\frac{x}{c} = \log(m + \sqrt{m^2 + 1}).$$

Finally, from (2) and (6) we find the tension F at the point P:

(15) $$F = wc \sec \psi = wy.$$

Thus the tension varies as the height varies above the directrix. This agrees with $H = wc$.

PROBLEMS

1. Find the Cartesian equation of the tractrix from (12).

2. Find the sag of a cable 150 feet long over a span of 100 feet.

3. A cable of length l and sag f has supports on the same level; show that its horizontal span is

$$a = \left(\frac{l^2}{4f} - f\right) \log \frac{l + 2f}{l - 2f}.$$

4. A cable of length l has supports on the same level where its inclination to the horizontal is ψ; show that its sag $f = \frac{1}{2}l \tan \frac{1}{2}\psi$.

55. SECOND-ORDER EQUATIONS WITH ONE VARIABLE ABSENT

The general equation of the second order

(1) $$F(x, y, y', y'') = 0$$

may often be integrated by first-order methods when x or y do not appear explicitly.

1. If y is absent, equation (1), solved for y'', may be written

(2) $$y'' = f(x, y').$$

Putting

(3) $$y' = p, \qquad y'' = \frac{dp}{dx}$$

converts (2) into an equation of the first order in p and x:

$$\frac{dp}{dx} = f(x, p).$$

If it can be solved, express the solution in the form

$$p = \frac{dy}{dx} = \varphi(x, c_1)$$

where c_1 is an arbitrary constant. A direct integration now gives the general solution of (2):

$$y = \int \varphi(x, c_1) \, dx + c_2.$$

Example 1. $xy'' + (x - 1)y' = x^2$. The substitution (3) gives the equation

$$\frac{dp}{dx} + \left(1 - \frac{1}{x}\right)p = x$$

linear in p. This admits the multiplier

$$\mu = \exp(x - \log x) = e^x/x;$$

hence

$$\frac{d}{dx}\left(\frac{pe^x}{x}\right) = e^x, \qquad \frac{pe^x}{x} = e^x + c_1,$$

$$p = x + c_1 x e^{-x}.$$

Putting $p = dy/dx$ and integrating gives the general solution

$$y = \tfrac{1}{2}x^2 - c_1(x + 1)e^{-x} + c_2.$$

2. If x is absent, equation (1) may be written

(4) $$y'' = f(y, y').$$

We now put

(5) $$y' = p, \qquad y'' = \frac{dp}{dx} = \frac{dp}{dy}\frac{dy}{dx} = p\frac{dp}{dy};$$

then (4) becomes

$$p\frac{dp}{dy} = f\left(y, p\frac{dp}{dy}\right),$$

a first-order equation in p and y. If it can be solved, express the solution in the form

$$p = \frac{dy}{dx} = \varphi(y, c_1)$$

where c_1 is an arbitrary constant. An integration now gives the general solution of (2):

$$x = \int \frac{dy}{\varphi(y, c_1)} + c_2.$$

Example 2. $y'' + 2yy' = 0$.   The substitution of (4) gives the equation $p \, dp/dy + 2py = 0$; hence either

$$p = 0 \quad \text{or} \quad \frac{dp}{dy} + 2y = 0.$$

The first gives $y = c_1$. The second may be integrated at once:

$$p = k - y^2.$$

Further integration depends on the sign of k.
  If $k > 0$, put $k = c_1^2$; then

$$dx = \frac{dy}{c_1^2 - y^2},$$

$$x = \frac{1}{c_1} \tanh^{-1} \frac{y}{c_1} + c_2,$$

$$y = c_1 \tanh c_1(x - c_2).$$

If $k < 0$, put $k = -c_1^2$; then

$$dx = -\frac{dy}{c_1^2 + y^2},$$

$$x = -\frac{1}{c_1} \tan^{-1} \frac{y}{c_1} + c_2,$$

$$y = -c_1 \tan c_1(x - c_2).$$

The initial conditions determine which solution is applicable.

PROBLEMS

1. Solve Example 1 if $y = 0$, $y' = 0$ when $x = -1$.
2. Solve Example 2 under the initial conditions:
(a) $y' = 0$, $y = 0$ when $x = 0$;   (b) $y' = 1$, $y = 0$ when $x = 0$;
(c) $y' = -1$, $y = 0$ when $x = 0$;   (d) $y' = -1$, $y = 0$ when $x = 0$.
3. Solve $y'' + xy'^2 = 0$ under the conditions:
(a) $y(0) = 1$, $y'(0) = 0$;   (b) $y(0) = 0$, $y'(0) = 2$;
(c) $y(0) = 0$, $y'(0) = -2$;   (d) $y(1) = 0$, $y'(1) = 2$.
4. Solve the differential equation of the catenary (54.4):

$$y'' = \frac{1}{c} \sqrt{1 + (y')^2}$$

(a) by method 1; (b) by method 2.
  5. $y'' = (1 + y'^2)^{3/2}$.
Show that the answer can be written down without computation.
  6. $yy'' + y'^2 - y' = 0$.
  7. $2y'' = e^y$; $y' = 1$, $y = 0$ when $x = 0$.
  8. $2y'' = e^y$; $y' = -1$, $y = 0$ when $x = 0$.
  9. $2y'' = 3y^2$; $y(0) = 1$, $y'(0) = -1$.

56. DYNAMICS OF A PARTICLE

Let $\mathbf{r} = \overrightarrow{OP}$ be the position vector of a moving particle P relative to some reference frame containing the origin O of rectangular axes (Fig. 56a). If the path of P has the equation $\mathbf{r} = \mathbf{r}(t)$ in terms of the time t as parameter, the *velocity* $\mathbf{v}$ and the *acceleration* $\mathbf{a}$ of P relative to this frame are vectors defined as the time derivatives

$$\mathbf{v} = \frac{d\mathbf{r}}{dt}, \qquad \mathbf{a} = \frac{d\mathbf{v}}{dt} = \frac{d^2\mathbf{r}}{dt^2}.$$

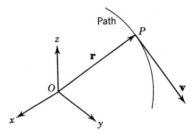

Fig. 56a Velocity vector.

If P has the rectangular coordinates x, y, z in this reference frame, its position vector

$$\overrightarrow{OP} = \mathbf{r} = x(t)\mathbf{i} + y(t)\mathbf{j} + z(t)\mathbf{k}$$

and its velocity and acceleration are given by

$$\mathbf{v} = x'\mathbf{i} + y'\mathbf{j} + z'\mathbf{k}, \qquad \mathbf{a} = x''\mathbf{i} + y''\mathbf{j} + z''\mathbf{k}$$

where the primes denote time derivatives. For motion in the xy-plane, $z = 0$; for motion along the x-axis, $y = z = 0$.

In a dynamical problem a body is called a *particle* when the matter composing it is regarded as concentrated in a single point. Thus the motion of the earth around the sun may be determined quite accurately by treating earth and sun as particles. But a billiard ball, whose motion may involve rolling, sliding, and spinning certainly cannot be regarded as a particle. In brief, to know when a body can be treated as a particle depends on the nature of the problem and the degree of accuracy to be attained.

When the bodies involved may be treated as particles, their motion in response to forces acting on them may be determined from three basic principles.

I. FORCE AND ACCELERATION. *A free particle acted on by a force* **f** *acquires an acceleration* **a** *in the direction of that force; that is*

(1) $$\mathbf{f} = m\mathbf{a}$$

where m is a scalar constant, the mass of the particle, whose value in a given system of units depends entirely on the nature of the body designated as a particle.

II. VECTOR ADDITION OF FORCES. *A system of forces acting simultaneously on a particle may be replaced by a single force on the particle equal to their vector sum.*

III. ACTION AND REACTION. *The interaction between two particles, whether in direct contact or at a distance from each other, may be represented by two forces of equal magnitude and opposite direction acting along their joining line.*

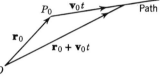

Equation (1) is the *fundamental equation of dynamics*. It is Newton's *second law of motion*. Newton's *first law of motion* is a consequence of equation (1) and is known as the

Fig. 56b Rectilinear motion.

LAW OF INERTIA. *A particle will continue in its state of rest or of uniform motion in a straight line unless acted on by an unbalanced force.**

PROOF. When no force is acting on the particle, or when the forces acting have zero sum, $\mathbf{f} = \mathbf{0}$ in (1); thus

(2) $$\mathbf{a} = \frac{d\mathbf{v}}{dt} = \mathbf{0}.$$

If the initial conditions are

$$\mathbf{v} = \mathbf{v}_0, \qquad \mathbf{r} = \mathbf{r}_0 \quad \text{when} \quad t = 0,$$

integration of (2) gives $\mathbf{v} = \mathbf{v}_0$ or

$$\frac{d\mathbf{r}}{dt} = \mathbf{v}_0.$$

Integrating again, we have

(3) $$\mathbf{r} = \mathbf{r}_0 + \mathbf{v}_0 t.$$

If $\mathbf{r}_0 = \overrightarrow{OP_0}$, this is the vector equation of a *ray* ($t \geqq 0$) issuing from P_0 in the direction of v_0 (Fig. 56b). If $\mathbf{v}_0 = \mathbf{0}$, $\mathbf{r} = \mathbf{r}_0$ and the body will remain at rest; otherwise it will move along the ray (3) with the constant velocity $\mathbf{v}_0$.

---

* Galileo was the first to realize the truth of this law.

In the cgs system the units of mass, length, and time are regarded as fundamental and their dimensions are denoted by M, L, T. The names and dimensions of important derived units are given in the following table.*

Table 56 cgs Units

Quantity	Symbol	Dimensions	Unit
Mass	m	M	gram
Length	l	L	centimeter
Time	t	T	second
Velocity	v	LT^{-1}	cm/sec
Acceleration	a	LT^{-2}	cm/sec^2
Momentum	mv	MLT^{-1}	gram cm/sec
Force	f, F	MLT^{-2}	dyne
Work	W	ML^2T^{-2}	joule
Kinetic energy	$\frac{1}{2}mv^2$	ML^2T^{-2}	joule
Power	P	ML^2T^{-3}	watt

A table of dimensions may be used to check any rational formula of geometry or physics; for

(i) all additive terms must have the same dimensions;

(ii) the arguments of all nonalgebraic functions (as the sine, exponential, logarithm) must be dimensionless.†

We shall denote the dimensions of a quantity q by Maxwell's symbol $[q]$. Thus $[\frac{1}{2}mv^2] = ML^2T^{-2}$. If q is dimensionless (a pure number), $[q] = 1$.

In civil and mechanical engineering the foot-pound-second (fps) system of units is often employed in the United States and Britain. In this system the *pound*, the fundamental unit of *force*, is the weight (or earth-pull) on the standard pound body in a locality where the falling acceleration $g_0 = 32.1740$ ft/sec^2. Mass is then a derived quantity; and a force of one pound, acting on a body of unit mass, will produce an acceleration of 1 ft/sec^2. Thus the mass of the standard pound body at the standard locality is $1/g_0$ units; for $(1/g_0)g_0 = 1$. The name "slug" has been coined for this unit; it is, however, rarely used. It suffices to remember that a body which weighs W pounds where the falling acceleration is g has the mass $m = W/g$;

---

* For the mks (meter-kilogram-second) system of units, with the addition of the coulomb for electrical theory, see the author's *Vector Analysis*, § 77, with a table of dimensions on p. 267.

† For a proof of the fundamental theorem in this connection see L. Brand, "The Pi Theorem of Dimensional Analysis," *Archive for Rational Mechanics and Analysis*, vol. 1, no. 1, 1957, pp. 35–45.

although W and g vary from place to place, their *ratio*, the mass of the body remains constant. The derived units are now ft/sec (velocity), ft/sec² (acceleration), and ft lb (work and energy). For reference we note that

$$1 \text{ mile} = 5280 \text{ ft}, \qquad 1 \text{ mi/hr} = 88 \text{ ft/sec},$$
$$1 \text{ ton} = 2000 \text{ lb}, \qquad 1 \text{ horsepower} = 550 \text{ ft-lb/sec}.$$

Example. If a constant force acts on a particle its acceleration $\mathbf{a} = \mathbf{f}/m$ is also constant. If the initial conditions are

$$\mathbf{r} = \mathbf{r}_0, \qquad \mathbf{v} = \mathbf{v}_0 \quad \text{when} \quad t = 0,$$

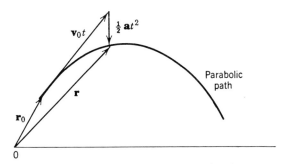

Fig. 56c   Motion under constant acceleration.

we may find its position vector $\mathbf{r}$ and its velocity $\mathbf{v}$ at any time t by integrating the equation $dv/dt = \mathbf{a}$ twice; thus

(i) $$\mathbf{v} = \mathbf{v}_0 + \mathbf{a}t, \qquad \mathbf{r} = \mathbf{r}_0 + \mathbf{v}_0 t + \tfrac{1}{2}\mathbf{a}t^2.$$

Its path is the result of adding to $\mathbf{r}_0$ the displacements $\mathbf{v}_0 t$, due to a motion of constant velocity $\mathbf{v}_0$, and $\tfrac{1}{2}\mathbf{a}t^2$, due to the acceleration. It is easily shown to be a parabola with axis parallel to $\mathbf{a}$ (Fig. 56c).

To find the path of a projectile under gravity when air resistance is neglected, we choose the x-axis horizontal and the y-axis vertically upward (Fig. 56d).

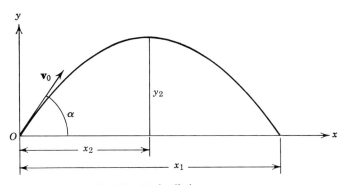

Fig. 56d   Projectile in a vacuum.

Then the acceleration $\mathbf{a} = -\mathbf{j}g$ is substantially constant and g is approximately 32 ft/sec². Then if the body is projected from the origin at an angle α with the x-axis,

$$\mathbf{r} = 0, \qquad \mathbf{v} = v_0 \,(\mathbf{i} \cos \alpha + \mathbf{j} \sin \alpha).$$

Taking components of $\mathbf{r}$ given in (i), we have the parametric equations of the path

$$x = (v_0 \cos \alpha)t, \qquad y = (v_0 \sin \alpha)t - \tfrac{1}{2}gt^2.$$

Since $y = 0$ at the time

$$t_1 = \frac{2v_0}{g} \sin \alpha, \qquad x_1 = \frac{v_0{}^2}{g} \sin 2\alpha$$

is the horizontal range. The range has its maximum value $v_0{}^2/g$ when $\alpha = \pi/4$. The body will reach its highest point y_2 when $dy/dt = 0$; then

$$t_2 = \frac{v_0}{g} \sin \alpha = \tfrac{1}{2}t_1, \qquad x_2 = \frac{v_0{}^2}{g} \cos \alpha \sin \alpha = \tfrac{1}{2}x_1, \qquad y_2 = \frac{v_0{}^2}{2g} \sin^2 \alpha.$$

When the body is shot straight up ($\alpha = \pi/2$), $t_2 = v_0/g$, $y_2 = v_0{}^2/2g$.

PROBLEMS

1. A particle has the constant acceleration $\mathbf{a}$. If its velocity is $\mathbf{v}_1$ and $\mathbf{v}_2$ at the times t_1 and t_2, find $\mathbf{a}$.

2. A particle P moves in an ellipse

$$x = a \cos nt, \qquad y = b \sin nt.$$

Show that its acceleration $\mathbf{a} = -n^2\mathbf{r}$, where $\mathbf{r} = \overrightarrow{OP}$ issues from the center of the ellipse.

Show that this *elliptic harmonic motion* is the projection of uniform motion along the circle $r = a$ with the constant angular speed n on the ellipse. Find the period T.

3. Find the acceleration of a particle P which moves along the hyperbola

$$x = a \cosh nt, \qquad y = b \sinh nt.$$

4. In Prob. 2 and 3 show that the sectorial area swept out by OP in time t is

$$S = \tfrac{1}{2}\int_0^t (x\dot{y} - y\dot{x})\, dt = \tfrac{1}{2}ab\, nt$$

and hence the sectorial speed dS/dt is constant.

57. EQUATIONS OF MOTION

The central problem of particle dynamics is the solution of the second-order differential equation

(1) $$m \frac{d^2\mathbf{r}}{dt^2} = \mathbf{f}$$

subject to the initial conditions

(2) $\mathbf{r} = \mathbf{r}_0,\quad \mathbf{v} = \mathbf{v}_0,\quad$ when $\quad t = 0.$

In some problems we can solve this vector equation directly. But in general equation (1) is replaced by one, two, or three scalar equations according as the motion is in a straight line, a plane, or in 3-space. For this purpose we resolve both acceleration and force into components and equate like components in equation (1).

For motion along a straight line, we take this line as x-axis and choose origin and positive direction (i) at pleasure. If $\mathbf{f} = f\mathbf{i}$, the equation of motion is

(3) $$m\frac{d^2x}{dt^2} = f.$$

If this equation is linear in x it may be integrated directly. If f is a function of t or of x, it may be written as a first-order equation

(4) $$m\frac{dv}{dt} = f(t),$$

(5) $$mv\frac{dv}{dx} = f(x),$$

where $v = dx/dt$ is a signed scalar, the "velocity". The actual velocity is, of course, the vector $v\mathbf{i}$ and $|v|$ is the speed. After finding v from (4) or (5), we finally find x by integrating $dx/dt = v$.

For motion in the xy-plane under the force $\mathbf{f} = f_1\mathbf{i} + f_2\mathbf{j}$, the equations of motion are

(6) $$m\frac{d^2x}{dt^2} = f_1,\quad m\frac{d^2y}{dt^2} = f_2.$$

If plane-polar coordinates r, θ are used, let

(7) $$\mathbf{R} = \mathbf{i}\cos\theta + \mathbf{j}\sin\theta$$

be a unit radial vector making an angle of θ radians with the initial line. Recalling that the derivatives of $\cos\theta$ and $\sin\theta$ are $\cos(\theta + \frac{1}{2}\pi)$ and $\sin(\theta + \frac{1}{2}\pi)$, we have

(8) $$\frac{d\mathbf{R}}{d\theta} = \mathbf{R}(\theta + \pi) = \mathbf{P},\quad \frac{d\mathbf{P}}{d\theta} = \mathbf{R}(\theta + \pi) = -\mathbf{R},$$

where $\mathbf{P}$ is a unit radial vector 90° ahead of $\mathbf{R}$. Similarly $-\mathbf{R}$ is 90° ahead of $\mathbf{P}$. Thus the time derivatives of $\mathbf{R}$ and $\mathbf{P}$ are

(9) $$\frac{d\mathbf{R}}{dt} = \frac{d\mathbf{R}}{d\theta}\frac{d\theta}{dt} = \mathbf{P}\frac{d\theta}{dt},\quad \frac{d\mathbf{P}}{dt} = \frac{d\mathbf{P}}{d\theta}\frac{d\theta}{dt} = -\mathbf{R}\frac{d\theta}{dt}.$$

Using these results we now find on differentiating $\mathbf{r} = r\mathbf{R}$ by the usual rule for a product,

(10)
$$\mathbf{v} = \frac{dr}{dt}\mathbf{R} + r\frac{d\theta}{dt}\mathbf{P}.$$

The coefficients of $\mathbf{R}$ and $\mathbf{P}$ are the radial and transverse components of velocity.

The five terms that result on differentiating $\mathbf{v}$ with respect to t, namely

$$\frac{d^2r}{dt^2}\mathbf{R} + \frac{dr}{dt}\frac{d\theta}{dt}\mathbf{P} + \frac{dr}{dt}\frac{d\theta}{dt}\mathbf{P} + r\frac{d^2\theta}{dt^2}\mathbf{P} - r\left(\frac{d\theta}{dt}\right)^2\mathbf{R}$$

may be grouped so that

(11)
$$\mathbf{a} = \left\{\frac{d^2r}{dt^2} - r\left(\frac{d\theta}{dt}\right)^2\right\}\mathbf{R} + \left\{2\frac{dr}{dt}\frac{d\theta}{dt} + r\frac{d^2\theta}{dt^2}\right\}\mathbf{P}.$$

The coefficients of $\mathbf{R}$ and $\mathbf{P}$ in (11) are the radial and transverse components of acceleration. If the force $\mathbf{f} = f_1\mathbf{R} + f_2\mathbf{P}$, the equations of motion are

(12)
$$m\left\{\frac{d^2r}{dt^2} - r\left(\frac{d\theta}{dt}\right)^2\right\} = f_1, \qquad m\left\{2\frac{dr}{dt}\frac{d\theta}{dt} + r\frac{d^2\theta}{dt^2}\right\} = f_2.$$

When the transverse component $f_2 = 0$, the second equation shows that

$$\frac{d}{dt}\left(r^2\frac{d\theta}{dt}\right) = 0, \qquad r^2\frac{d\theta}{dt} = \text{const.}$$

Since $\frac{1}{2}r^2\dot\theta$ is the sectorial speed of the particle (cf. § 63), this result is known as the

Law of Areas. *Whenever the force on a particle P is purely radial, its position vector $\overrightarrow{OP}$ sweeps out area at a constant rate.*

Example 1. Falling Body: Air Resistance Neglected. Take the origin at the starting point and the x-axis directed downward. If the body falls from rest, the initial conditions are

$$x = 0, \qquad v = 0 \quad \text{when} \quad t = 0.$$

If g is the local value of the falling acceleration, the force exerted by the earth on a body of mass m (its *weight*) is mg. Hence the equation of motion is $ma = mg$ or simply

(i)
$$a = g.$$

With $a = dv/dt$ we have

(ii)
$$\frac{dv}{dt} = g, \qquad v = gt;$$

(iii)
$$\frac{dx}{dt} = gt, \qquad x = \tfrac{1}{2}gt^2.$$

All constants of integration are zero.

With $a = v \, dv/dx$,

(iv) $$v \frac{dv}{dx} = g, \qquad v^2 = 2gx.$$

We may also deduce (iii) from (i) and (ii):

$$v^2 = g^2 t^2 = g^2 \cdot \frac{2x}{g} = 2gx.$$

Note that both terms in these equations have the same dimensions.

The resistance of the air is a function $R(v)$ of the speed. Experiment shows that $R(v)$ increases indefinitely with v. For very low speeds R is proportional to v, whereas for higher speeds, say up to 800 ft/sec, R is proportional to v^2. Beyond this R/v^2 increases sharply with v, particularly in the neighborhood of the speed of sound (about 1100 ft/sec). For still higher values of v, R/v^2 rises to a maximum and then decreases. No simple function $R(v)$ applies to all speeds.

Example 2. Falling Body: Air Resistance Varies as v. Choose the origin and x-axis as in Example 1. If the body falls from rest,

$$x = 0, \qquad v = 0 \quad \text{when} \quad t = 0.$$

Let the air resistance be mkv; then the equation of motion, after dividing out m, is

$$a = g - kv.$$

When v increases to the value V for which $g - kV = 0$, the acceleration is zero and the velocity will remain constant. Therefore $V = g/k$ is called the *terminal velocity*. Putting $k = g/V$, the equation of motion becomes

(i) $$a = g\left(1 - \frac{v}{V}\right).$$

To find v in terms of t, put $a = dv/dt$ and integrate the separable equation. We have

$$\log\left(1 - \frac{v}{V}\right) = -\frac{gt}{V}$$

and hence

(ii) $$v = V(1 - e^{-gt/V}).$$

As $t \to \infty$, $v \to V$; thus theoretically, the terminal velocity is attained only after infinite time. Practically, the body attains the velocity V after a relatively short time since $e^{-gt/V} \to 0$ very rapidly.

To find x in terms of t, put $v = dx/dt$ in (ii) and integrate:

$$x = V \int_0^t (1 - e^{-gt/V}) \, dt,$$

(iii) $$x = Vt + \frac{V^2}{g}(e^{-gt/V} - 1).$$

To find x in terms of v, put $a = v\,dv/dx$ in (i); then

$$\frac{v\,dv}{1 - \dfrac{v}{V}} = g\,dx \quad \text{and} \quad \int_0^v \left(\frac{1}{1 - \dfrac{v}{V}} - 1 \right) dv = \frac{g}{V} \int_0^x dx.$$

On integration we find

(iv)
$$-V \log \left(1 - \frac{v}{V} \right) - v = \frac{g}{V} x.$$

The first term is positive since the logarithm is negative. We may also obtain (iv) by eliminating t between (ii) and (iii).

In these equations note that the arguments of exp and log are dimensionless and that the terms in each equation have the same dimensions.

Example 3. *Falling Body: Air Resistance Varies as v^2*. Choose the origin and x-axis as in Example 1. If the body falls from rest,

$$x = 0, \quad v = 0 \quad \text{when} \quad t = 0.$$

Let the air resistance be mkv^2; then the equation of motion, after dividing out m, is

$$a = g - kv^2.$$

When v increases to the value V for which $g - kV^2 = 0$, the acceleration is zero and the velocity will remain constant. The *terminal velocity* in this case is $V = \sqrt{g/k}$. Putting $k = g/V^2$, the equation of motion becomes

(i)
$$a = g \left(1 - \frac{v^2}{V^2} \right).$$

To find v in terms of t, put $a = dv/dt$ and integrate the separable equation. We have

$$\int_0^v \frac{dv/V}{1 - \dfrac{v^2}{V^2}} = \frac{g}{V} \int_0^t dt,$$

and hence

$$\tanh^{-1} \frac{v}{V} = \frac{gt}{V} \qquad \text{(Table 5)},$$

(ii)
$$v = V \tanh \frac{gt}{V}.$$

As $t \to \infty$, $v \to V$ since $\tanh \infty = 1$.

To find x in terms of t, put $v = dx/dt$ in (ii) and integrate:

$$x = \frac{V^2}{g} \int_0^t \frac{\sinh gt/V}{\cosh gt/V} \frac{g\,dt}{V},$$

(iii)
$$x = \frac{V^2}{g} \log \cosh \frac{gt}{V}.$$

To find x in terms of v, put $a = v \, dv/dx$ in (i) and integrate:

$$\int_0^v \frac{-2v \, dv/V^2}{1 - v^2/V^2} = -\frac{2g}{V^2} \int_0^x dx$$

$$\log \left(1 - \frac{v^2}{V^2} \right) = -\frac{2gx}{V^2},$$

(iv) $$x = -\frac{V^2}{2g} \log \left(1 - \frac{v^2}{V^2} \right).$$

We may also obtain (iv) by eliminating t between (ii) and (iii).

In these equations note that the arguments of tanh, log cosh, and log are dimensionless and that the terms in each have the same dimensions.

PROBLEMS

(Take $g = 32$ ft/sec².)

1. A raindrop has a terminal velocity of 25 ft/sec. If the air resistance varies as v, show that the drop, starting from rest, will attain a velocity of 20 ft/sec in about 1.25 seconds.

2. A body falling in air will attain a terminal velocity of 320 ft/sec. If the air resistance varies as v^2, and the body is projected vertically upward with this velocity, how high will it rise? How high would it rise in the absence of resistance?

3. A body falls from rest in a medium whose resistance varies as v. The resistance is one-tenth of the weight when $v = 8$ ft/sec. Find (a) the terminal velocity, (b) the speed and distance fallen after 5 seconds.

4. The air resistance is an increasing function $R(v)$ of v. Two bodies of weight W_1, W_2 falling in air under gravity have the terminal velocities V_1, V_2. If $W_1 > W_2$, show that $V_1 > V_2$.

5. A man rowing in still water ships his oars when his speed is v_0. Find his subsequent motion if the water resistance varies as v. [Here $ma = -mkv$; find v and x as functions of t.]

6. A vessel going forward at full speed V has its engines reversed. How long and how far will it move forward if the resistance of the water varies as v^2?

[If F is the constant propelling force, the forward equation of motion is $ma = F - kv^2$, and $0 = F - kV^2$. When the engines are reversed, $ma = -F - kv^2$.]

7. A body is projected straight upward with the initial velocity v_0. If the resistance of the air is mkv^2, how high will it go? Show that it will return to the point of projection with the velocity

$$v_1 = -v_0 \sqrt{g/(g + kv_0^2)}.$$

8. In Problem 7 show that the body attains its greatest height in the time

$$t = \frac{1}{\sqrt{kg}} \tan^{-1} \sqrt{\frac{k}{g}} .$$

Does this result check dimensionally?

9. A uniform chain of length $2L$ hangs over a smooth peg. At time t the two parts on either side of the peg are of length $L + x$, $L - x$. Determine the motion if $x = a$, $v = 0$ when $t = 0$. With what speed V will the chain leave the peg?

10. If the chain in Problem 9 originally hangs in equilibrium and is slightly disturbed from rest, with what speed V will it leave the peg?

11. A uniform chain of length L lies partly on a smooth table perpendicular to its edge and partly hanging over. At time t the hanging portion is of length x. Determine the motion if $x = a$, $v = 0$ when $t = 0$ and the height of the table exceeds L. With what speed V will the chain leave the table?

12. Deduce the radial and transverse components of $\mathbf{v}$ and $\mathbf{a}$ given in (10) and (11) by differentiating the complex position vector $z = re^{i\theta}$ twice with respect to t. Note that

$$\mathbf{R} = e^{i\theta}, \quad \frac{d\mathbf{R}}{d\theta} = ie^{i\theta} = \mathbf{P}.$$

13. When the only force acting is constant sliding friction, $x'' = -k \text{ sgn } x'$, where the *signum function* sgn is 1, 0, -1 according as its argument is positive, zero, or negative. Show that the trajectories in the phase plane are half

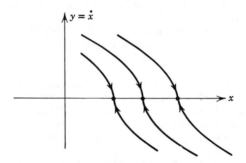

Fig. 57 Trajectories for sliding friction in phase plane.

parabolas that end on the x-axis, and determine their sense. (Fig. 57). [In the phase-plane, $x' = y$, $y' = -k \text{ sgn } y$; $yy' = -k(\text{sgn } y)x'$, $\frac{1}{2}y^2 = C - k(\text{sgn } y)x$.]

14. In Problem 13 show that the body comes to rest when $x - x_0 = (\text{sgn } v_0)v_0^2/2k$.

58. SIMPLE HARMONIC MOTION

A particle P of mass m moving along a straight line is attracted to a point O of the line with a force $\mathbf{F} = -k\mathbf{r}$ proportional to the distance OP. Choose O as origin, the line as x-axis; then its position, velocity, and acceleration are

$$\mathbf{r} = x\mathbf{i}, \quad \mathbf{v} = \frac{dx}{dt}\mathbf{i}, \quad \mathbf{a} = \frac{d^2x}{dt^2}\mathbf{i}.$$

If the particle moves in a medium which resists the motion with a force $h\mathbf{v}$ proportional to $\mathbf{v}$, its equation of motion is

$$m\mathbf{a} = -k\mathbf{r} - h\mathbf{v}, \qquad k, h > 0.$$

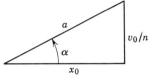

Fig. 58a   Amplitude of shm.

Divide the equation by m and write the *positive* constants $k/m = n^2$, $h/m = 2b$; then

$$D^2\mathbf{r} + 2b\,D\mathbf{r} + n^2\mathbf{r} = 0$$

where $D = d/dt$. Since $\mathbf{r} = x\mathbf{i}$, this is equivalent to the scalar equation

(1) $$(D^2 + 2bD + n^2)x = 0.$$

We first consider the motion when the resistance, or *damping*, is negligible; then $b = 0$ and (1) becomes

(2) $$(D^2 + n^2)x = 0.$$

We shall solve this equation subject to the initial conditions

$$x = x_0, \qquad v = v_0 \quad \text{when} \quad t = 0.$$

The roots of the characteristic equation are $\pm ni$, and from (38.3)

$$x = c_1 \cos nt + c_2 \sin nt.$$

The initial conditions give $c_1 = x_0$, $c_2 = v_0/n$; hence

(3) $$x = x_0 \cos nt + \frac{v_0}{n} \sin nt.$$

If we construct a right triangle with legs equal to x_0 and v_0/n (Fig. 58a), its hypotenuse

(4) $$a = \sqrt{x_0{}^2 + (v_0/n)^2}; \quad \text{and} \quad x_0 = a \cos \alpha, \qquad v_0/n = a \sin \alpha.$$

On substituting these values in (3) we have

(5) $$x = a \cos(nt - \alpha).$$

Since x varies between the limits $\pm a$, a is called the *amplitude* of the *simple harmonic motion* (shm). If $x = x_1$ when $t = t_1$, x will again equal x_1 when t_1 is increased by any integral multiple of $2\pi/n$; hence the *period* of the motion is

(6) $$\tau = \frac{2\pi}{n} \text{ sec}; \quad \text{and} \quad \nu = \frac{n}{2\pi}$$

is the *frequency*—the number of complete (to and fro) oscillations per second.

A very clear picture of shm may be obtained by drawing a circle of radius a about O as center (Fig. 58b) and constructing the angle $AOQ = \theta = nt - \alpha$. Then if P is the projection of Q on a horizontal diameter (x-axis),

$$x = OP = a \cos \theta.$$

Moreover, since $d\theta/dt = n$ radians per second, the angular speed of the radius OQ is the constant n. We therefore have the accurate and graphic description of shm:

Simple harmonic motion is the projection of uniform circular motion on a diameter.

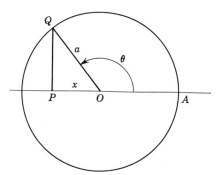

Fig. 58b Shm as projection of uniform circular motion.

In a complete revolution OQ sweeps out 2π radians; hence we again see that a complete revolution of Q, or a complete oscillation of P, occurs every $2\pi/n$ seconds.

Let us now consider equation (2) in the phase plane:

$$x' = y, \qquad y' = -n^2 x.$$

Then

$$yy' + n^2 xx' = 0$$

and on integration

$$\tfrac{1}{2}y^2 + \tfrac{1}{2}n^2 x^2 = E.$$

If the mass $m = 1$, $y^2/2$ is the kinetic energy, $n^2 x/2$ is the potential energy, and the constant E is the total energy. The trajectory in the phase plane is the ellipse represented by this equation. Since its semiaxes are $a = \sqrt{2E}$, $b = \sqrt{2E}/n$, its area is $\pi ab = 2\pi E/n$. As time increases the ellipse is traversed clockwise (why?) and a sector is given by*

$$S = \frac{1}{2} \int_0^t (yx' - xy')\, dt = \int_0^t (y^2 + n^2 x^2)\, dt = Et$$

---

* This follows from the line integral for the area of a sector (*Advanced Calculus*, § 154) taken *negative* for a clockwise circuit.

so that $dS/dt = E$ is the sectorial speed. Hence the period

$$\tau = \frac{2\pi E/n}{E} = \frac{2\pi}{n}.$$

In this phase-plane analysis we found the period *without solving the differential equation*.

Example 1. Linear Springs. Let a body of weight W be suspended from a vertical spring (Fig. 58c). When it hangs in equilibrium, it will stretch the spring an amount ε, so that the tension developed is just equal to W. According to Hooke's law the tension of the spring produced by an elongation or contraction ε (within the elastic limit) is proportional to ε, say $k\varepsilon$. The constant k is called the *spring constant*; and since the equilibrium tension is W, $W = k\varepsilon$. Now let the body be drawn down a further distance r and released. When the elongation is $\varepsilon + x$ the spring tension is $k(\varepsilon + x)$. Here x is measured from the equilibrium position and the positive direction is downward. The body is now subject to the downward force $W = k\varepsilon$, and the upward spring tension $k(\varepsilon + x)$; its equation of motion is therefore

$$\frac{W}{g} x'' = k\varepsilon - k(\varepsilon + x) = -kx;$$

or since $k = W/\varepsilon$,

(i) $$x'' + \frac{g}{\varepsilon} x = 0.$$

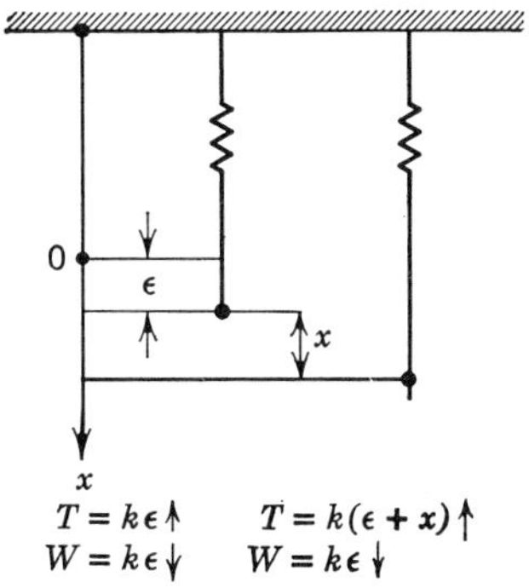

Fig. 58c Vibration of a spring.

This is the characteristic equation of a shm for which $n^2 = g/\varepsilon$ and the period

(ii) $$\tau = 2\pi \sqrt{\varepsilon/g}.$$

Note that ε/g has the dimensions $L/LT^{-2} = T^2$ so that τ has the dimensions of time. Since the initial conditions are

$$x = r, \qquad v = 0 \quad \text{when} \quad t = 0,$$

the vibrations have the amplitude r.

Problem. A 4-pound weight stretches a spring 1.5 inches. If it is pulled down 2 inches more and released from rest, describe the motion.

Using the foot and pound as units, Hooke's law gives

$$4 = k\frac{1.5}{12} = \frac{k}{8}, \qquad k = 32 \text{ lb/ft}.$$

Taking $g = 32$ ft/sec², the equation of motion is

$$\tfrac{4}{32}x'' = -32x \quad \text{or} \quad x'' + 256x = 0.$$

Thus $n^2 = 256$, $n = 16$ and the period $\tau = 2\pi/16 = 0.39$ seconds. With $\varepsilon = \tfrac{1}{8}$ ft, this agrees with formula (ii). The solution of the differential equation which satisfies $x_0 = \tfrac{1}{6}$ ft, $v_0 = 0$, is

$$x = \tfrac{1}{6} \cos 16t;$$

the amplitude of the vibration is $\tfrac{1}{6}$ ft.

Example 2. Floating Body. Consider a body of weight W floating in equilibrium on a liquid of weight w per unit volume. By the principle of Archimedes, it experiences an upward force equal to the weight of liquid displaced; and since the body is in equilibrium, this upward force is exactly equal to W. Now let the body be given a slight downward displacement x. If the section-area A of the body at the liquid surface is nearly constant for small displacements, the additional weight of liquid displaced is nearly wAx, and the total upward thrust on the body will be $W + wAx$. If the positive direction of x is downward, the equation of motion of the body is

$$\frac{W}{g} x'' = W - (W + wAx) \quad \text{or} \quad x'' + \frac{wAg}{W} x = 0.$$

This corresponds to a shm for which

$$n^2 = \frac{wAg}{W} = \frac{Ag}{V}.$$

where V is the volume of liquid displaced at equilibrium. Hence the body will vibrate up and down with the period

$$\tau = \frac{2\pi}{n} = 2\pi \sqrt{\frac{V}{Ag}}.$$

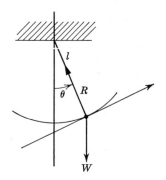

Fig. 58d Simple pendulum.

Note that the right-hand member has the dimensions of time.

Thus for a hydrometer which displaces 40 cm³ and whose stem is 1.2 cm in diameter, $V = 40$ cm³, $A = \pi(0.6)^2 = 0.36\pi$ cm², $g = 981$ cm/sec²; hence if disturbed from equilibrium, it will oscillate with the period

$$\tau = 2\pi \sqrt{\frac{40}{0.36\pi \times 981}} = 1.42 \text{ sec.}$$

Example 3. Simple Pendulum. Consider an ideal pendulum consisting of a weightless string (or rod) of length l supported at one end and attached to a particle of weight W at the other (Fig. 58d). If the pendulum is displaced a small angle β from the vertical and then released, it will swing in a vertical plane. In any position of the pendulum, the forces acting on the particle are its weight $\mathbf{W}$ and the tension $\mathbf{R}$ of the string. The vector equation of motion is $m\mathbf{a} = \mathbf{R} + \mathbf{W}$. The tangential and normal components of acceleration are from (57.11), with $r = l$, $dr/dt = 0$:

$$l\frac{d^2\theta}{dt^2} \quad \text{in the direction of increasing } \theta,$$

$$l\left(\frac{d\theta}{dt}\right)^2 \quad \text{directed radially toward the support.}$$

Hence on taking tangential and normal components of the equation of motion,

we have

$$\frac{W}{g} l \frac{d^2\theta}{dt^2} = -W \sin \theta, \qquad \frac{W}{g} l \left(\frac{d\theta}{dt}\right)^2 = R - W \cos \theta$$

or

(1)(2) $\qquad \dfrac{d^2\theta}{dt^2} + \dfrac{g}{l} \sin \theta = 0, \qquad R = W \left[\dfrac{l}{g} \left(\dfrac{d\theta}{dt}\right)^2 + \cos \theta \right].$

For small oscillations, say $\theta \leqq 5°$, $\sin \theta$ may be replaced by θ (radians) and we have approximately

$$\frac{d^2\theta}{dt^2} + \frac{g}{l} \theta = 0, \qquad \theta = \beta, \frac{d\theta}{dt} = 0 \quad \text{when} \quad t = 0.$$

This is the equation for a shm with x replaced by θ and $n^2 = g/l$. The period of the pendulum, the time of a complete oscillation to and fro, is therefore

(3) $\qquad\qquad\qquad \tau_0 = 2\pi \sqrt{\dfrac{l}{g}} \qquad$ approximately.

The exact value of τ for any angle of swing β may be obtained as follows. Let $\omega = d\theta/dt$, multiply (1) by 2ω and integrate; then

$$2\omega \frac{d\omega}{dt} + \frac{2g}{l} \sin \theta \frac{d\theta}{dt} = 0$$

(4) $\qquad\qquad\qquad \omega^2 - \dfrac{2g}{l} \cos \theta = 0 - \dfrac{2g}{l} \cos \beta$

since $\omega = 0$ when $\theta = \beta$. Hence

$$\left(\frac{d\theta}{dt}\right)^2 = \frac{2g}{l} (\cos \theta - \cos \beta) = \frac{4g}{l} (\sin^2 \tfrac{1}{2}\beta - \sin^2 \tfrac{1}{2}\theta),$$

$$\frac{dt}{d\theta} = \tfrac{1}{2} \sqrt{\frac{l}{g}} (\sin^2 \tfrac{1}{2}\beta - \sin^2 \tfrac{1}{2}\theta)^{-1/2}.$$

As θ increases from 0 to β, t increases by $\tau/4$ (one fourth of the period); hence

(5) $\qquad\qquad\qquad \tau = 2 \sqrt{\dfrac{l}{g}} \displaystyle\int_0^\beta \dfrac{d\theta}{\sqrt{\sin^2 \tfrac{1}{2}\beta - \sin^2 \tfrac{1}{2}\theta}}.$

This integral may be reduced to a complete elliptic integral of the first kind* by the substitution

$$\sin \tfrac{1}{2}\theta = \sin \tfrac{1}{2}\beta \sin \varphi;$$

---

* Defined as

$$K(k) = \int_0^{\pi/2} \frac{d\varphi}{\sqrt{1 - k^2 \sin^2 \varphi}}.$$

See ref. 4 for table of values.

and since

$$\frac{d\theta}{\sqrt{\sin^2 \frac{1}{2}\beta - \sin^2 \frac{1}{2}\theta}} = \frac{\dfrac{2 \sin \frac{1}{2}\beta \cos \varphi}{\cos \frac{1}{2}\theta} d\varphi}{\sin \frac{1}{2}\beta \cos \varphi} = \frac{2d\varphi}{\cos \frac{1}{2}\theta},$$

(6) $$\tau = 4\sqrt{\frac{l}{g}} \int_0^{\pi/2} \frac{d\varphi}{\sqrt{1 - \sin^2 \frac{1}{2}\beta \sin^2 \varphi}} = 4\sqrt{\frac{l}{g}} K(\sin \frac{1}{2}\beta).$$

As $\beta \to 0$, $K(\sin \frac{1}{2}\beta) \to \frac{1}{2}\pi$ and we again obtain the approximate period τ_0 for small oscillations. For example, if $\beta = 30°$, $K(\sin 15°) = 1.5981*$ and the period $\tau = 6.3924 \sqrt{l/g}$ whereas (3) gives $\tau_0 = 6.2832 \sqrt{l/g}$. However, when $\beta \le 7°$, $(\tau - \tau_0)/\tau < 0.001$.

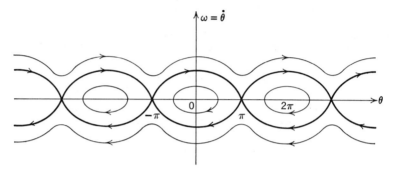

Fig. 58e   Simple pendulum in the phase plane.

The tension in the string may be found from equation (2). Since

$$\omega^2 = \frac{2g}{l} (\cos \theta - \cos \beta)$$

from (4), we have

(7) $$R = W \left(\frac{l}{g} \omega^2 + \cos \theta \right) = W (3 \cos \theta - 2 \cos \beta).$$

Phase-plane analysis. Equation (1) is replaced by

(8) $$\frac{d\theta}{dt} = \omega, \qquad \frac{d\omega}{dt} = -\frac{g}{l} \sin \theta.$$

These disclose infinitely many critical points on the θ-axis: $\theta = 0$, $\pm\pi$, $\pm 2\pi, \ldots$. Even multiples of π correspond to vortices; odd multiples to saddle points—the unstable inverted pendulum (Fig. 58e). To obtain the trajectories we assume that $\omega = \omega_0$ when $\theta = 0$; then on integrating

$$\omega \frac{d\omega}{dt} = -\frac{g}{l} \sin \theta \frac{d\theta}{dt},$$

---

* Ref. 4, p. 279; ref. 13, p. 133.

we have

$$\omega^2 - \omega_0{}^2 = \frac{2g}{l} (\cos\theta - 1) = -\frac{4g}{l} \sin^2 \frac{\theta}{2}$$

or

(9) $$\omega^2 + \Omega^2 \sin^2 \frac{\theta}{2} = \omega_0{}^2$$

where $\Omega = 2\sqrt{g/l}$ is the *critical value* of ω. We can now characterize the three types of curves in the phase plane.

1. $|\omega_0| < \Omega$. The angle θ attains its greatest value $\Theta = 2 \sin^{-1} (\omega_0/\Omega) < \pi$ when $\omega = 0$ and the pendulum swings between the limiting angles $\pm\Theta$. The closed trajectories are symmetrical about both axes and are traversed clockwise.

2. $|\omega_0| > \Omega$. The open waves above and below represent complete counterclock and clockwise revolutions of the pendulum.

3. $|\omega_0| = \Omega$. The open and closed trajectories are separated by the heavy-lined *separatrices*. Thus the upper arc from $-\pi$ to π represents a complete counterclock revolution from the unstable vertical position; it requires infinite time since the integral $K(\frac{1}{2}\pi)$ in (6) diverges. The equations of the separatrices are given by (9) when $\omega_0{}^2 = \Omega^2$, namely

$$\omega^2 = \omega_0{}^2 \left(1 - \sin^2 \frac{\theta}{2}\right) \quad \text{or} \quad \omega = \pm\omega_0 \cos \frac{\theta}{2}.$$

Example 4. Nonlinear Springs. The initial value problem

$$x'' + n^2 x = 0, \quad x(0) = a, \quad x'(0) = 0,$$

represents a linear oscillator of unit mass and amplitude a. The corresponding oscillations, $x = a \cos nt$, have the period $\tau = 2\pi/n$ which is independent of the amplitude.

If the unit mass is subjected to the restoring force

$$f(x) = -n^2 x - bx^3,$$

the equation of motion

(1) $$x'' + n^2 x + bx^3 = 0$$

is known as *Duffing's equation*. The nonlinear term bx^3 is small for small oscillations if $|b|$ is small. We shall show that the period τ now depends on the amplitude a, which as before depends on the initial conditions $x(0) = a$, $x'(0) = 0$.

In the phase-plane equation (1) becomes

(2) $$x' = y, \quad y' = -n^2 x - bx^3.$$

The energy equation is

(3) $$yy' = -(n^2 x + bx^3)x'$$

and gives on integration

(4) $$\tfrac{1}{2}y^2 + \tfrac{1}{2}n^2 x^2 + \tfrac{1}{4}bx^4 = E,$$

where E is the constant total energy made up of the kinetic energy $\tfrac{1}{2}y^2$ and the potential energy

(5) $$W(x) = \tfrac{1}{2}n^2 x^2 + \tfrac{1}{4}bx^4.$$

There are now two nonlinear cases, $b > 0$ and $b < 0$, called *hard* and *soft* springs, respectively.

1. *Hard spring.* $(b > 0)$. The origin is the only critical point of the system (2). Then the left member of (4),

$$V(x, y) = \tfrac{1}{2}y^2 + \tfrac{1}{2}n^2x^2 + \tfrac{1}{4}bx^4$$

is a weak Liapunov function; for $V(x, y) > 0$ except $V(0, 0) = 0$, and from (3)

$$\frac{dV}{dt} = yy' + (n^2x + bx^3)x' \equiv 0.$$

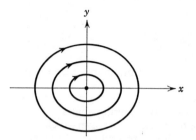

Fig. 58f Hard spring ($b > 0$).

Theorem 52.2 now assures us that the origin is in neutral equilibrium. The trajectories in the phase plane are the ovals (4) symmetric about the origin (Fig. 58f). The linear approximation

$$\begin{pmatrix} x' \\ y' \end{pmatrix} = \begin{pmatrix} 0 & 1 \\ -n^2 & 0 \end{pmatrix} \begin{pmatrix} x \\ y \end{pmatrix}$$

shows that the origin is a *vortex* and that the ovals are traversed clockwise. See the Stability Table 48, $\Delta < 0$, $\alpha = 0$; also Example 47.4. The pattern in Figure 58f is valid in the large.

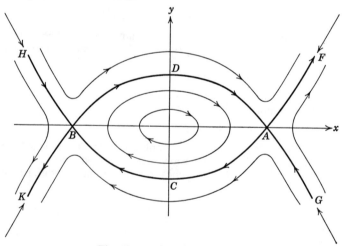

Fig. 58g Soft spring ($b < 0$).

2. *Soft spring.* $(b < 0)$. Equations (2) now have three critical points: $(0, 0)$ and $(0, \pm x_1)$ where $x_1 = \sqrt{-n^2/b}$. The origin is still a vortex surrounded by closed trajectories—but not in the large for $A(x_1, 0)$ and $B(-x_1, 0)$ which are now saddle points (Fig. 58g). For if we shift the origin to A, putting $x = X + x_1$, $y = Y$, we obtain the system

$$X' = Y, \qquad Y' = -n^2(X + x_1) - b(X + x_1)^3$$

whose linear approximation is

$$X' = Y, \qquad Y' = -(n^2 + 3bx_1^2)X = 2n^2 X$$

or

$$\begin{pmatrix} X' \\ Y' \end{pmatrix} = \begin{pmatrix} 0 & 1 \\ 2n^2 & 0 \end{pmatrix} \begin{pmatrix} X \\ Y \end{pmatrix}$$

so that (Table 48)

$$ad - bc = -2n^2 < 0, \qquad \Delta = 8n^2 > 0.$$

The trajectories are suggested in Figure 58g. Each of the six paths ACB, BDA, AF, AG, BH, BK is called a *separatrix*. The loop $ACBDA$ is not a limit cycle, for the paths ACB and BDA *terminate* at B and A respectively.

3. Dependence of period on amplitude. At the limits of an oscillation the speed $y = x' = 0$; the two real roots $\pm a$ of equation (4) then give the amplitude a. The energy there is entirely potential, namely $E = W(a)$; hence from (4) and (5)

$$(6) \qquad y^2 = \left(\frac{dx}{dt}\right)^2 = 2[W(a) - W(x)] = (a^2 - x^2)[n^2 + \tfrac{1}{2}b(a^2 + x^2)].$$

Since the spring is symmetric, the period of the spring

$$\tau = 4 \int_0^a \frac{dx}{(a^2 - x^2)^{1/2}[n^2 + \tfrac{1}{2}b(a^2 + x^2)]^{1/2}}$$

or, on making the change of variable $x = a \cos \theta$,

$$(7) \qquad \tau = 4 \int_0^{\pi/2} \frac{d\theta}{[n^2 + \tfrac{1}{2}ba^2(1 + \cos^2 \theta)]^{1/2}}.$$

When $b > 0$, an increase of a increases the denominator and decreases τ. *The period of a hard spring decreases as the amplitude increases.*

When $b < 0$, an increase of a decreases the denominator and increases τ; the integral will remain proper if the force does not vanish at a, that is, $n^2 + ba^2 > 0$; for when $x = a$, $\theta = \pi/2$ and the radical in the denominator of (7) remains positive. *The period of a soft spring increases as the amplitude increases.*

If we put $\cos^2 \theta = 1 - \sin^2 \theta$ in (7) we find that

$$(8) \qquad \tau = 4 \int_0^{\pi/2} \frac{d\theta}{(n^2 + ba^2 - \tfrac{1}{2}ba^2 \sin^2 \theta)^{1/2}} = \frac{4}{\sqrt{n^2 + ba^2}} \int_0^{\pi/2} \frac{d\theta}{\sqrt{1 - k^2 \sin^2 \theta}}$$

where

$$(9) \qquad k = \sqrt{\frac{\tfrac{1}{2}ba^2}{n^2 + ba^2}} = \sin \varphi$$

determines φ. The period is therefore

$$(10) \qquad \tau = \frac{4}{\sqrt{n^2 + ba^2}} K(\sin \varphi);$$

$K(\sin \varphi)$ is a complete elliptic integral of the first kind which may be obtained from a table when φ is computed from (9). (See ref. 4 or 13.)

If $b = -n^2/6$, equation (1)

$$x'' + n^2(x - \tfrac{1}{6}x^3) = 0 \quad \text{approximates} \quad x'' + n^2 \sin x = 0$$

which is the equation of a simple pendulum when $x = \theta$, $n^2 = g/l$. The simple pendulum may therefore be classed as a soft spring.

PROBLEMS

(Take $g = 32$ ft/sec².)

1. The springs of a truck deflect 1.5 inches under the weight of the body and load. What is the period of vibration?

2. A cylinder floats vertically on the water with 2 feet submerged. If it is given a slight downward displacement, find the period of its vibrations.

3. A 1-pound weight, suspended from a helical spring, originally 2 feet long, has a period of 1 second when set in vibration. How long is the spring when the weight hangs in equilibrium.

4. If the spring in Problem 3 supports a 2-pound weight, what is the period of vibration?

5. A particle weighing w pounds on a smooth horizontal plane, is attached to two elastic strings, alike in all respects, whose ends are fastened to two pegs d feet apart. Each string has a natural length of l foot and will support the particle when stretched ε inches. If the particle is displaced toward one of the pegs, find the period of the vibrations if $d > 2l$ and the strings are never slack.

6. If the strings in Problem 5 are fastened to two pegs vertically above one another, set up the equation of motion with the origin midway between the pegs. Find the general integral, the equilibrium position, and the period of vibrations.

7. The mercury column in a U-tube is 12 inches long measured along an axial line. Find its period when set in vibration.

8. When the pendulum of Example 3 just swings into the upper vertical, so that $\beta = \pi$, show that equation (4) may be integrated to give

$$t = \sqrt{\frac{g}{l}} \log \tan \frac{1}{4}(\theta + \pi).$$

What time is required to swing from θ to 0 to $\theta = \pi$?

9. Obtain the approximate formula for the period of a simple pendulum

$$\tau = 2\pi \sqrt{\frac{l}{g}} \left(1 + \frac{1}{4}\sin^2 \frac{1}{2}\beta\right)$$

by replacing the radical in (6) by its binomial expansion. Find τ when $\beta = 30°$ and compare with τ_0 and its exact value.

10. A particle of mass $m = 5$ grams is attached to the mid-point of a wire stretched to a tension $T = 200,000$ dynes between two pegs on a smooth table at a distance $d = 100$ centimeters apart. If the particle is given a small lateral

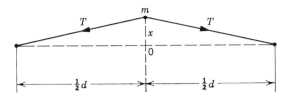

Fig. 58h   Vibrating particle.

displacement x ($\ll d$), find the period of its vibrations if slight changes in the tension T are neglected. (Fig. 58h). [Show that the equation of motion is approximately $mx'' + 4Tx/d = 0$.]

11. The bob of a simple pendulum 2 feet long is moving 8 ft/sec as it passes its lowest point. To what angle with the downward vertical will it rise? [Use equation (4).]

12. Show that the trajectories of

$$x'' - 4x + x^3 = 0$$

in the phase plane are the curves $y^2 - 4x^2 + \frac{1}{2}x^4 = C$ which have a saddle point at $(0, 0)$ and vortices at $(\pm 2, 0)$. Sketch the curves.

13. Plot the phase-plane trajectory for $x'' + 2x^3 = 0$, $x(0) = a$, $x'(0) = 0$, and compute the period.

14. Show that the separatrices for the soft spring ($b < 0$) are the parabolas $y = \pm \sqrt{-b/2}\,(x^2 - a^2)$.

59. DAMPED HARMONIC MOTION

We return now to the problem of § 58 when the resistance of the medium is taken into account; the equation of motion is then

$$(1) \qquad\qquad (D^2 + 2bD + n^2)x = 0. \qquad\qquad (58.1)$$

The characteristic equation

$$r^2 + 2br + n^2 = 0$$

has the roots $-b \pm \sqrt{b^2 - n^2}$; and there are three cases to consider (§ 38).

Case 1. $b > n$.

Writing $q = \sqrt{b^2 - n^2}$, the roots $-b \pm q$ are real and distinct and the general solution

$$x = e^{-bt}(c_1 \cosh qt + c_2 \sinh qt).$$

Both $\cosh qt$ and $\sinh qt$ contain e^{qt} but since $q < b$, $e^{-(b-q)t} \to 0$ as $t \to \infty$. Hence the particle approaches the origin as $t \to \infty$. But it may cross the origin just *once* before this ultimate approach. To find when this happens we determine c_1 and c_2 from the initial conditions

(2)
$$x = x_0, \qquad v = v_0 \quad \text{when} \quad t = 0.$$

An easy calculation shows that

$$c_1 = x_0, \qquad c_2 = \frac{v_0 + bx_0}{q},$$

and hence

(3)
$$x = e^{-bt}\left\{x_0 \cosh qt + \frac{v_0 - bx_0}{q} \sinh qt\right\}.$$

Thus $x = 0$ when

$$\tanh qt = \frac{-qx_0}{v_0 + bx_0} = \frac{q}{-(v_0/x_0) - b}.$$

Since $-1 < \tanh qt < 1$, this equation is satisfied by a single positive value of t only when

$$-\frac{v_0}{x_0} - b > q > 0.$$

The motion is said to be *overdamped*.

Case 2. $b = n$.

The double root $-b$ now leads to the solution

$$x = e^{-bt}(c_1 + c_2 t);$$

and from the initial conditions (2) we find

(4)
$$x = e^{-bt}\{x_0 + (v_0 + bx_0)t\}.$$

Since $te^{-bt} \to 0$ as $t \to \infty$ (why?) the particle ultimately approaches the origin; but as in Case 1 it may cross the origin just *once* at the time

$$t = \frac{1}{-(v_0/x_0) - b}$$

provided $-(v_0/x_0) - b > 0$. The motion is said to be *critically damped*.

Case 3. $b < n$.

Writing $q = \sqrt{n^2 - b^2}$, the roots $-b \pm qi$ are now complex and the solution of (1) is

$$x = e^{-bt}(c_1 \cos qt + c_2 \sin qt).$$

The constants c_1 and c_2 have the same values as in Case 1 and hence

(5)
$$x = e^{-bt}\left\{x_0 \cos qt + \frac{v_0 + bx_0}{q} \sin qt\right\}$$

in complete analogy with (3). Now $x = 0$ when

$$\tan qt = \frac{-qx_0}{v_0 + bx_0}.$$

This equation always has an infinite number of positive solutions; and if t_0 is the smallest, all others are given by

$$t = t_0 + k\frac{\pi}{q}, \qquad k = 1, 2, 3, \ldots.$$

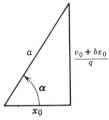

Two passages across O *in the same direction* always occur at equal intervals $2\pi/q$. Thus the motion is periodic with period $2\pi/q$; and since $q < n$, the period is greater than the period $2\pi/n$ of the corresponding undamped shm. The damping slows down the motion but still leaves it periodic.

Fig. 59a

If we construct a right triangle with legs equal to x_0 and $(v_0 + bx_0)/q$ (Fig. 59a), its hypotenuse

$$a = \sqrt{x_0^2 + \left(\frac{v_0 + bx_0}{q}\right)^2}; \quad \text{and} \quad x_0 = a\cos\alpha, \quad \frac{v_0 + bx_0}{q} = a\sin\alpha.$$

With these values (5) becomes

(6) $$x = ae^{-bt}\cos(qt - \alpha)$$

From (6) we may obtain a clear idea of the nature of damped harmonic motion by regarding x as the x-component of a vector $\overrightarrow{OQ}$ of variable length $r = ae^{-bt}$ which forms an angle $\theta = qt + \alpha$ with the x-axis (Fig. 59b). As t increases, the length of $\overrightarrow{OQ}$ diminishes while it turns about O with the constant angular speed $d\theta/dt = q$. The curve described by Q is an equiangular spiral whose equation in polar coordinates is

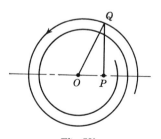

$$r = ae^{-b(\theta+\alpha)/q} = a'e^{-b\theta/q}, \qquad a' = ae^{-b\alpha/q}.$$

When $b = 0$, the spiral becomes the circle $r = a$ in the analogous Figure 58b for shm.

The motion is now said to be *underdamped*. Its exact character is given in the statement:

Fig. 59b

Underdamped harmonic motion is the projection of uniform angular motion along an equiangular spiral on a line through its pole.

  Example. Harmonic Oscillator with Coulomb Damping.

(7) $$x'' = -n^2x - k \operatorname{sgn} x'.$$

The damping $-k \operatorname{sgn} x'$ is of constant magnitude and always opposes the motion; hence its sign is the opposite of x'.

  With the initial conditions

(8.0) $$x = x_0, \qquad x' = 0, \qquad t = 0,$$

the motion will begin if the restoring force exceeds the friction: $n^2x_0 > k$. Then $x'' < 0$, $x' < 0$ and (7) becomes

(7.0) $$x'' + n^2x = k.$$

The solution of (7.0) under conditions (8.0) is

(9.0) $$x = \left(x_0 - \frac{k}{n^2}\right) \cos nt + \frac{k}{n^2}$$

and applies until $t = \pi/n$; then x equals

(8.1) $$x_1 = \frac{2k}{n^2} - x_0, \qquad x_1' = 0, \qquad t_1 = \frac{\pi}{n}.$$

  The motion will reverse and satisfy

(7.1) $$x'' + n^2x = -k$$

if at time t_1

$$x_1'' = -k - n^2x_1 > 0 \quad \text{or} \quad n^2x_0 > 3k.$$

The solution of (7.1) under conditions (8.1) is

(9.1) $$x = \left(x_0 - \frac{3k}{n^2}\right) \cos nt - \frac{k}{n^2}$$

and applies until $t = 2\pi/n$; then x equals

(8.2) $$x_2 = x_0 - \frac{4k}{n^2}, \qquad x_2' = 0, \qquad t_2 = \frac{2\pi}{n}.$$

  The motion will reverse again and satisfy (7.0) if at time t_2

$$x_2'' = k - n^2x_2 < 0 \quad \text{or} \quad n^2x_0 > 5k.$$

The solution of (7.0) under conditions (8.2) is

(9.2) $$x = \left(x_0 - \frac{5k}{n^2}\right) \cos nt + \frac{k}{n^2}$$

and applies until $t = 3\pi/n$; then x equals

(8.3) $$x_3 = \frac{6k}{n^2} - x_0, \qquad x_3' = 0, \qquad t_3 = \frac{3\pi}{n}.$$

The motion will reverse and satisfy (7.1) if at time t_3

$$x_3'' = -k - n^2 x_3 > 0 \quad \text{or} \quad n^2 x_0 > 7k.$$

These oscillations of half-period π/n continue until $n^2 x_0$ fails to exceed an odd multiple of k; then they abruptly end. If $(2N - 1)k < n^2 x_0 < (2N + 1)k$, there will be exactly N half oscillations in the time $N\pi/n$. before the motion stops. See Problem 53.6 for the phase-plane analysis.

PROBLEMS

1. When $v_0 = 0$ in Case 3 ($b < n$), show that

$$x = \frac{n x_0}{q} \cos (qt - \alpha), \qquad \alpha = \tan^{-1} \frac{b}{q}.$$

2. If three consecutive vibrations of the needle of a damped galvanometer give the readings a, b, c on its scale, show that the equilibrium reading is $(ac - b^2)/(a + c - 2b)$.
[If e is the equilibrium reading, $a - e$, $b - e$, $c - e$ are in geometric progression.]

3. An undamped body vibrates 30 times per minute. When its motion is damped the amplitude is reduced one-half in 10 seconds. Find the damping constant b and the period of the damped vibration.

4. A 16 pound weight stretches a spring 3.84 inches. If the weight is pulled down 1 inch below its equilibrium position and released, find the period and amplitude of the motion.

5. Solve the equation

$$x'' + 0.2 \operatorname{sgn} x' + 4x = 0$$

when $x = 0.225$, $x' = 0$ when $t = 0$. Draw the x-t graph for the complete motion.

6. If $n^2 = 10$, $k = 0.02$ and $x_0 = 5$, how many half oscillations will be made before rest and in what time?

60.   FORCED VIBRATIONS

Suppose that a particle of mass m is subject to the attraction $-k\mathbf{r}$, the resistance $-h\mathbf{v}$, and an external force $\mathbf{f}$ per unit of mass along the line of motion. The equation of motion is then

$$m\mathbf{a} = -k\mathbf{r} - h\mathbf{v} + m\mathbf{f}.$$

Putting $\mathbf{r} = x\mathbf{i}$, $\mathbf{f} = f(t)\mathbf{i}$, this is equivalent to the scalar equation

(1) $$(D^2 + 2bD + n^2)x = f(t),$$

where $2b = h/m$, $n^2 = k/m$ as in § 58. The general solution of the reduced equation

(2) $$(D^2 + 2bD + n^2)x = 0$$

has been given in § 59 in all cases; denote it by $u(t)$. Then if $x_1(t)$ is any particular solution of (1), the general solution of (1) is

$$(3) \qquad x(t) = u(t) + x_1(t).$$

The complementary function $u(t)$ contains the arbitrary constants; these are determined from the initial conditions.

When $b < n$ we have (§ 59, Case 3)

$$(4) \qquad u(t) = e^{-bt}(c_1 \cos qt + c_2 \sin qt), \qquad q = \sqrt{n^2 - b^2}.$$

These damped vibrations of period $2\pi/q$ will be modified by the particular solution x_1 appropriate to the disturbing force $f(t)$.

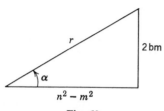

$n^2 - m^2$

Fig. 60

If $f(t)$ is a constant f, the particular solution $x_1 = f/n^2$ and the resulting motion

$$(5) \qquad x(t) = u(t) + \frac{f}{n^2}$$

is simply a damped oscillation of period $2\pi/q$ about the point $x_1 = f/n^2$ instead of about the origin.

The most important case, however, arises when the disturbing force is periodic, say $f(t) = a \cos mt$. To find a particular solution in this case we replace $a \cos mt$ by ae^{imt} and take the real part of the corresponding particular solution as in § 41; thus

$$(6) \qquad x_1 = \text{Re} \, \frac{ae^{imt}}{n^2 - m^2 + 2bmi}.$$

Form a right triangle with legs $n^2 - m^2$ and $2bm$ (Fig. 60). Then if the hypotenuse is

$$r = \sqrt{(n^2 - m^2)^2 + 4b^2m^2},$$
$$n^2 - m^2 + 2bmi = r(\cos\alpha + i\sin\alpha) = re^{i\alpha}.$$

The particular solution x_1 is now the real part of $(a/r)e^{i(mt-\alpha)}$, that is

$$(7) \qquad x_1 = \frac{a}{r} \cos(mt - \alpha).$$

The general solution

$$(8) \qquad x = u(t) + \frac{a}{r} \cos(mt - \alpha),$$

where $u(t)$ is given by (4). As $t \to \infty$, the factor e^{-bt} makes $u(t) \to 0$. Thus $u(t)$ is a *transient* and the motion ultimately becomes the forced vibration x_1 given by (7). This has the same period $2\pi/m$ as the disturbing force $f(t)$ but lags behind it in phase by the angle α. From Figure 60 we see that $\sin \alpha \geq 0$ but

$$\cos \alpha \gtreqless 0 \quad \text{according as} \quad n \gtreqless m.$$

Thus α can always be chosen in the interval from 0 to π and

$$\alpha \lesseqgtr \frac{\pi}{2} \quad \text{according as} \quad \frac{\text{free}}{\text{period}} \lessgtr \frac{\text{impressed}}{\text{period}} \; .$$

With feeble damping (b small), $\sin \alpha = 0$ and

$$\alpha \simeq \frac{0}{\pi} \quad \text{according as} \quad \frac{\text{free}}{\text{period}} \lessgtr \frac{\text{impressed}}{\text{period}} \; .$$

With given values of n and b, the amplitude a/r of the forced vibration is a function of m which attains its maximum value when r is a minimum; then

$$m^2 = n^2 - 2b^2, \qquad \text{Min } r = 2b\sqrt{n^2 - b^2},$$

$$\text{Max amplitude of } x_1 = \frac{a}{2b\sqrt{n^2 - b^2}} \; .$$

When $b \ll n$ (feeble damping), the value of m which gives this maximum amplitude is close to n. The impressed period $2\pi/m$ is then close to the free period $2\pi/n$, and the amplitude of x_1 may become very large due to the small number b in the denominator. In this event the displacement x may become so large that the restoring force is no longer proportional to x and the basic equation (1) ceases to apply.

This phenomenon, called *resonance*, can occur in any vibratory system acted on by an external force whose period nearly coincides with one of the natural periods of the system. Thus an automobile traveling over a washboard road may receive a series of jolts having nearly the same period as its springs and be thereby set in violent vibration. This can be remedied by widening the gap between the two periods—by going faster or slower.

The term *resonance*, as its derivation suggests, was originally used to describe the striking cases that occur in the propagation of sound waves. The electrical analog of resonance, also of great importance, is considered in the following article.

In an undamped system ($b = 0$), acted on by the force $f = a \cos mt$ (per unit mass), the equation of motion is

$$(9) \qquad (D^2 + n^2)x = a \cos mt.$$

We now have

$$u = c_1 \cos nt + c_2 \sin nt,$$

$$x_1 = \frac{a}{n^2 - m^2} \cos mt,$$

if $n \neq m$; and the general solution

$$x = c_1 \cos nt + c_2 \sin nt + \frac{a}{n^2 - m^2} \cos mt.$$

If the initial conditions are

$$(10) \qquad\qquad x = 0, \quad \frac{dx}{dt} = 0 \quad \text{when} \quad t = 0,$$

we find $c_1 = a/(m^2 - n^2)$, $c_2 = 0$; hence

$$x = \frac{a}{n^2 - m^2}(\cos mt - \cos nt),$$

or using the formula for the difference of cosines,

$$(11) \qquad\qquad x = \frac{2a}{n^2 - m^2} \sin \frac{n - m}{2} t \sin \frac{n + m}{2} t.$$

We may regard this as a wave

$$x = A(t) \sin \frac{n + m}{2} t$$

whose variable amplitude

$$A(t) = \frac{2a}{n^2 - m^2} \sin \frac{n - m}{2} t$$

has a longer period, $4\pi/(n - m)$, than the rapidly varying sine wave $\sin \dfrac{n + m}{2} t$ of period $4\pi/(n + m)$. For example, if $n = 10$, $m = 8$ and $a = 36$,

$$x = 2 \sin t \sin 9t.$$

Such a wave is said to be *amplitude modulated*.

When the free and impressed periods agree ($n = m$) equation (9) has the solution

$$(12) \qquad\qquad x = c_1 \cos nt + c_2 \sin nt + \frac{a}{2n} t \sin nt.$$

With the same initial conditions (10), $c_1 = c_2 = 0$ and

$$(13) \qquad\qquad x = \frac{a}{2n} t \sin nt.$$

The variable amplitude $A(t) = at/2n$ now increases without limit, or at least as long as the equation of motion (9) remains valid. Graphically, the wave $A(t) \sin nt$ varies between the lines $x = \pm at/2n$ which delimit its maximum amplitudes.

Example. A body B hanging in equilibrium from a light helical spring stretches it 1.5 inches beyond its natural length. If the upper end A of the spring is then given a vertical shm of amplitude 3 inches and of period $\frac{1}{2}$ second, find the amplitude of the motion of the body B at the lower end when it has reached its steady state.

Use the foot and pound as units. Then from Example 58.1, the free period

$$\frac{2\pi}{n} = 2\pi\sqrt{\varepsilon/g} = 2\pi\frac{1.5}{12 \times 32} = \frac{2\pi}{16}, \qquad n = 16.$$

When the free vibration has been damped out, the forced vibration will have the period

$$\frac{2\pi}{m} = \frac{1}{2}; \quad \text{hence} \quad m = 4\pi.$$

Let y denote the displacement of A taken positive when downward. Then if $y = 0$ when $t = 0$ and A is displaced upward at the start,

$$y = -\tfrac{1}{4}\sin 4\pi t,$$

and the disturbing force per unit mass is

$$f = 1 \cdot \frac{d^2y}{dt^2} = 4\pi^2 \sin 4\pi t.$$

With $n^2 = 256$, B's equation of motion is

$$(D^2 + 2bD + 256)x = 4\pi^2 \sin 4\pi t$$

where x is the displacement of B from its original position. After the free vibration has been damped, the residual forced vibration is approximately (if $b = 0$)

$$x_1 = \frac{4\pi^2}{256 - 16\pi^2} \sin 4\pi t.$$

It has the amplitude

$$\frac{4\pi^2}{256 - 16\pi^2} = 0.4025 \text{ ft} = 4.83 \text{ in.}$$

and is in phase with the force f and hence opposed in phase to y; in other words, the body is lowest when the upper end of the spring is highest.

PROBLEMS

1. A 32-pound body hangs in equilibrium from a spring whose constant is 9 lb/ft. A force $f = 6 \sin 3t$ is then applied to the body. If the damping is negligible, determine the motion if $x = 0$, $v = 0$ when $t = 0$.
Show that v is in phase with f.

2. The equation of motion of a forced vibration is

$$(D^2 + n^2)x = 4 \sin^3 \omega t.$$

For what values of ω does resonance occur?

3. The disturbing force $f(t)$ in a forced vibration $(D^2 + n^2)x = f(t)$ has the period $p : f(t + p) = f(t)$. If $f(t)$ is expanded in a Fourier series

$$f(t) = \sum_{k=0}^{\infty} \left(a_k \cos \frac{2\pi k}{p} t + b_k \sin \frac{2\pi k}{p} t \right),$$

show that resonance occurs when

$$p = \frac{2\pi k}{n}, \qquad k = 1, 2, 3, \dots .$$

4. Show that when the free and impressed periods of a damped system coincide, the velocity of the forced vibration is in phase with the disturbing force.

5. A pendulum of length l, hanging at rest, is acted on by a constant force f per unit mass. Show that its motion is given by

$$\theta = \frac{2f}{g} \sin^2 \sqrt{\frac{g}{l}} t$$

where θ is the angle measured from the downward vertical.

6. A plumb-bob hangs vertically from the roof of a railway coach running at constant speed. When the brakes are applied it swings through an angle of $3°$. If the retardation is uniform, show that it equals $\pi g/120$. (See Prob. 2.)

61. THE SERIES *RLC* CIRCUIT

Consider an electric circuit containing a resistance of *R ohms*, and inductance of *L henries*, and a capacitance of *C farads*. A current of *I amperes* is sustained by an electromotive force of *E volts* supplied by a battery or a generator. The units italicized are the "practical" electrical units. According to Kirchhoff's second law the sum of the voltage drops in the direction in which the current flows is zero. These drops are

$$RI \quad \text{volts across the resistor}$$

$$L \frac{dI}{dt} \quad \text{volts across the inductor,}$$

$$\frac{Q}{C} \quad \text{volts across the capacitor,}$$

where Q is the charge in *coulombs* on the capacitor. We shall assume that R, L, C are positive constants and that E, I, Q are functions of the time t. Since the "drop" across the generator is $-E$, the differential equation of this *LRC* circuit is

$$(1) \qquad\qquad L \frac{dI}{dt} + RI + \frac{Q}{C} = E.$$

Since the current $I = dQ/dt$, we obtain the second-order equation for Q:

(2) $$\left(LD^2 + RD + \frac{1}{C}\right)Q = E.$$

The initial conditions specify Q and dQ/dt (I) at zero time:

$$Q(0) = Q_0, \qquad I(0) = I_0.$$

The roots of the characteristic equation

(3) $$L\lambda^2 + R\lambda + \frac{1}{C} = 0$$

are

(4) $$\lambda_1, \lambda_2 = -\frac{R}{2L} \pm \sqrt{\frac{R^2}{4L^2} - \frac{1}{LC}}.$$

These determine the solution of the reduced equation, and as in § 59 there are three cases to consider according as λ_1, λ_2 are real and distinct, equal, or complex conjugates. In each case the factor $\exp(-Rt/2L) \to 0$ so strongly as $t \to \infty$ that the entire solution of the reduced equation also vanishes. In other words, the solution of the reduced equation is a *transient* which we denote by Q_t.

The solution of the complete equation (2) now has the form $Q = Q_t + Q_s$, where Q_s, the *steady-state* solution, is that particular solution of (2) which is free from transient terms. From Q we can now find the current:

$$I = \frac{dQ}{dt} = \frac{dQ_t}{dt} + \frac{dQ_s}{dt} = I_t + I_s.$$

We shall see that the steady current I_s may be found without finding the roots of the characteristic equation (3).

The most important case arises when the roots λ_1, λ_2 are complex conjugates. In damped harmonic motion this case led to periodic vibrations; in this analogous electrical problem we have periodic electrical oscillations of the current I.

If E is constant, say the voltage supplied by a battery, $Q_s = CE$, and

$$Q = Q_t + CE, \qquad I = \frac{dQ_t}{dt},$$

and the oscillatory current dies rapidly away.

If a sinusoidal voltage is supplied by an alternating current generator,

$$E = E_0 \sin \omega t,$$

where the *period* of the emf is $2\pi/\omega$, the *frequency* $\omega/2\pi$.* To find Q_s we

---

* ω is often called the *circular frequency*.

replace $\sin \omega t$ by $e^{i\omega t}$, find the particular solution from (41.5), and take its imaginary part; then $I_s = dQ_s/dt$. Thus we find

$$Q_s = \operatorname{Im} \frac{E_0 e^{i\omega t}}{\omega Ri + \dfrac{1}{C} - \omega^2 L}$$

$$I_s = \operatorname{Im} \frac{E_0 i\omega e^{i\omega t}}{\omega Ri + \dfrac{1}{C} - \omega^2 L}$$

or

(4) $$I_s = \operatorname{Im} \frac{E_0 e^{i\omega t}}{R + \left(\omega L - \dfrac{1}{\omega C}\right) i}.$$

We now construct a right triangle with legs equal to R and $\omega L - (1/\omega C)$; its hypotenuse (Fig. 61)

(5) $$Z = \sqrt{R^2 + \left(\omega L - \frac{1}{\omega C}\right)^2}$$

is called the *impedance* of the circuit and the angle α the *phase angle*. We now have

$$R = Z \cos \alpha, \qquad \omega L - \frac{1}{\omega C} = Z \sin \alpha,$$

$$R + \left(\omega L - \frac{1}{\omega C}\right) i = Z(\cos \alpha + i \sin \alpha) = Ze^{i\alpha}.$$

The fraction in (4) now assumes the simple form $(E_0/Z)e^{i(\omega t - \alpha)}$; and on taking its imaginary part,

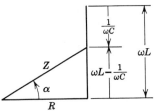

Fig. 61 Impedance in series *RLC* circuit.

(6) $$I_s = \frac{E_0}{Z} \sin (\omega t - \alpha).$$

Thus according as $\alpha > 0$ or $\alpha < 0$, the alternating current *lags behind* or *leads* the electromotive force $E_0 \sin \omega t$. The maximum current I_{max} is $E_0/Z = E_{max}/Z$; thus for the maxima of I and E we have the relation

(7) $$E_{max} = ZI_{max}$$

which is analogous to Ohm's law, with the impedance Z playing the role of the resistance R.

When $\omega L = 1/\omega C$ or $\omega = 1/\sqrt{LC}$, $Z = R$, $\alpha = 0$ and the current is in phase with the emf; then $I = ER$ at every instant. When R is small this may give rise to a heavy current, and we have a case of electrical *resonance*. Notice that when $R = 0$ the free oscillations in the circuit have, from (4), the period $2\pi\sqrt{LC}$ and this is precisely the period $2\pi/\omega$ of the impressed emf when $\alpha = 0$.

When the current is steady, the average power generated in one cycle is

$$P = \frac{E_0 I_0}{2\pi} \int_0^{2\pi} \sin \theta \sin (\theta - \alpha) \, d\theta = \tfrac{1}{2} E_0 I_0 \cos \alpha;$$

here $\theta = \omega t$ and $I_0 = E_0/Z$ is the maximum current. Since $\sin^2 \theta + \cos^2 \theta = 1$, the mean values of $\sin^2 \theta$ and $\cos^2 \theta$ over one cycle are one-half; hence the mean values of $E^2 = E_0^2 \sin^2 \theta$ and $I^2 = I_0^2 \sin^2 (\theta - \alpha)$ over one cycle are $\tfrac{1}{2} E_0^2$ and $\tfrac{1}{2} I_0^2$. The square roots of these mean squares, $E_0/\sqrt{2}$ and $I_0/\sqrt{2}$, are the so-called *effective* values; they are actually the volts and amperes registered on an alternating voltmeter or ammeter. Thus the average power is

$$P = E_{\text{eff}} I_{\text{eff}} \cos \alpha.$$

For this reason $\cos \alpha$ is called the *power factor;* and P attains its maximum value when $\alpha = 0$.

PROBLEM

1. Solve equation (2) when $E = 0$ and its characteristic roots are real $(-\alpha \pm \beta)$; complex $(-\alpha \pm i\beta)$.

62. LINEAR VECTOR EQUATIONS

A differential equation which is linear in the position vector $\mathbf{r} = \overrightarrow{OP}$

$$(a D^2 + b D + c)\mathbf{r} = \mathbf{0}, \qquad D = \frac{d}{dt},$$

may be solved in the same way as the corresponding scalar equation of § 38 provided the arbitrary constants are *vectors*. The characteristic equation is the same, and we have the same three cases depending on the nature of its roots. The independent solutions are now $\mathbf{c}_1 u(t)$, $\mathbf{c}_2 v(t)$, where $\mathbf{c}_1$, $\mathbf{c}_2$ are arbitrary vector constants, and

$$\mathbf{r} = \mathbf{c}_1 u(t) + \mathbf{c}_2 v(t)$$

is the general solution. When x is replaced by t (which is now the independent variable), the solutions u, v of § 38 give the following results.

Case 1. $b^2 - 4ac > 0$. Roots $\alpha \pm \beta$ real and distinct.

(1) $r = e^{\alpha t}(\mathbf{c}_1 \cosh \beta t + \mathbf{c}_2 \sinh \beta t).$

Case 2. $b^2 - 4ac = 0$. Double root $\alpha = -b/2a$.

(2) $r = e^{\alpha t}(c_1 + c_2 t)$.

Case 3. $b^2 - 4ac < 0$. Complex roots $\alpha \pm i\beta$.

(3) $r = e^{\alpha t}(\mathbf{c}_1 \cos \beta t + \mathbf{c}_2 \sin \beta t)$.

In all cases $\mathbf{c}_1$ and $\mathbf{c}_2$ are determined by the initial conditions

(4) $\mathbf{r} = \mathbf{r}_0$, $\mathbf{v} = \mathbf{v}_0$ when $t = 0$.

If $\mathbf{r}_0$ and $\mathbf{v}_0$ are not parallel vectors, the motion takes place in their plane; if $\mathbf{r}_0$ and $\mathbf{v}_0$ are parallel, the motion is in their line.

Example. Elliptic Harmonic Motion. A particle P of mass m is attracted to a fixed point O by a force proportional to $\overrightarrow{OP} = \mathbf{r}$. The equation of motion is $m\mathbf{a} = -k\mathbf{r}$ $(k > 0)$, or on writing $k/m = n^2$,

(i) $(D^2 + n^2)\mathbf{r} = \mathbf{0}$.

Since the roots of the characteristic equation are $\pm ni$, the general solution is

$$\mathbf{r} = \mathbf{c}_1 \cos nt + \mathbf{c}_2 \sin nt.$$

The initial conditions (4) give $\mathbf{c}_1 = \mathbf{r}_0$, $\mathbf{c}_2 = \mathbf{v}_0/n$; hence

(i) $\mathbf{r} = \mathbf{r}_0 \cos nt + \dfrac{\mathbf{v}_0}{n} \sin nt$.

Referred to oblique axes through O parallel to $\mathbf{r}_0$ and $\mathbf{v}_0$, the parametric equations of the path are

(ii) $x = r_0 \cos nt$, $y = \dfrac{v_0}{n} \sin nt$.

These represent an ellipse whose equation in oblique coordinates is

(iii) $\dfrac{x^2}{r_0^2} + \dfrac{y^2}{(v_0/n)^2} = 1$.

The particle makes a complete circuit in the time given by $nt = 2\pi$; thus the *period p* of the motion is $p = 2\pi/n$.

When $t = 0$, $\mathbf{r} = \mathbf{r}_0$ and when $t = \pi/2n$, $\mathbf{r} = \mathbf{v}_0/n$; and since $\mathbf{v}_0$ is tangent to the ellipse when $\mathbf{r} = \mathbf{r}_0$, $\mathbf{r}_0$ and $\mathbf{v}_0/n$ are *conjugate* radial vectors of the ellipse.

When $\mathbf{v}_0 \parallel \mathbf{r}_0$, write $\mathbf{r} = x\mathbf{i}$, $\mathbf{v} = v\mathbf{i}$; then (i) becomes equation (58.3) for simple harmonic motion.

PROBLEMS

1. A particle P of mass m is repelled from a fixed point O by a force proportional to $\overrightarrow{OP} = \mathbf{r}$. Show that the equation of motion may be written

$$(D^2 - n^2)\mathbf{r} = \mathbf{0}$$

and that the vector equation of the path is

$$\mathbf{r} = \mathbf{r}_0 \cosh nt + \dfrac{\mathbf{v}_0}{n} \sinh nt.$$

As t varies from $-\infty$ to $+\infty$, show that the direction of $\mathbf{r}$ varies from $\mathbf{r}_0 - \mathbf{v}_0/n$ to $\mathbf{r}_0 + \mathbf{v}_0/n$; and that the path is a hyperbola whose asymptotes have these directions.

[tanh $(\pm\infty) = \pm 1$.]

2. A particle of mass m falls in a vacuum under gravity. Show that the equation of motion $D^2\mathbf{r} = \mathbf{g}$ has the solution

$$\mathbf{r} = \mathbf{r}_0 + \mathbf{v}_0 t + \tfrac{1}{2}\mathbf{g}t^2,$$

under the initial conditions (4).

3. A particle P of mass m is attracted to a fixed point O by a force proportional to $\overrightarrow{OP} = \mathbf{r}$ and resisted by a force proportional to $\mathbf{v}$. Show that the equation of motion may be written

$$\frac{d^2\mathbf{r}}{dt} + 2b\frac{d\mathbf{r}}{dt} + n^2\mathbf{r} = 0$$

where b and n are real constants, and that

$$\mathbf{r} \times \mathbf{v} = \mathbf{C}e^{-2bt}, \qquad \mathbf{C} \text{ const.,}$$

and deduce therefrom that the orbit is a *plane* curve. If $\gamma = \sqrt{|n^2 - b^2|}$,

$$\mathbf{r} = e^{-bt}(\mathbf{A}\cosh\gamma t + \mathbf{B}\sinh\gamma t) \qquad \text{when} \quad n < b,$$
$$\mathbf{r} = e^{-bt}(\mathbf{A} + \mathbf{B}t) \qquad \text{when} \quad n = b,$$
$$\mathbf{r} = e^{-bt}(\mathbf{A}\cos\gamma t + \mathbf{B}\sin\gamma t) \qquad \text{when} \quad n > b;$$

the initial conditions $\mathbf{r} = \mathbf{r}_0$, $\mathbf{v} = \mathbf{v}_0$ when $t = 0$ determine the vector constants $\mathbf{A}$, $\mathbf{B}$.

4. A particle P of mass m falls under gravity in a medium whose resistance to the motion is proportional to $\mathbf{v}$. Show that the equation of motion may be written

$$\frac{d^2\mathbf{r}}{dt^2} + k\frac{d\mathbf{r}}{dt} = \mathbf{g}$$

and that its solution under the initial conditions (4) is

$$\mathbf{r} = \mathbf{r}_0 + \mathbf{V}t - \frac{\mathbf{V} - \mathbf{v}_0}{k}(1 - e^{-kt})$$

where $\mathbf{V} = \mathbf{g}/k$ is the terminal velocity.

5. The motion of an electron in a constant magnetic field satisfies the equation

$$\ddot{\mathbf{r}} = \mathbf{c} \times \dot{\mathbf{r}}$$

where $\mathbf{c}$ is a constant vector and the dots denote time derivatives. Show that

(a) the speed $v = |\dot{\mathbf{r}}|$ is constant,
(b) $\mathbf{c} \cdot \dot{\mathbf{r}} = vc\cos\alpha$ is constant,
(c) $|\dot{\mathbf{r}} \times \ddot{\mathbf{r}}| = cv^2\sin\alpha$,
(d) $\dot{\mathbf{r}} \cdot \ddot{\mathbf{r}} \times \dddot{\mathbf{r}} = c^3v^3\sin^2\alpha\cos\alpha$,
(e) the curvature and torsion

$$\kappa = \frac{|\dot{\mathbf{r}} \times \ddot{\mathbf{r}}|}{|\dot{\mathbf{r}}|^3} = \frac{c\sin\alpha}{v}, \qquad \tau = \frac{\dot{\mathbf{r}} \cdot \ddot{\mathbf{r}} \times \dddot{\mathbf{r}}}{|\dot{\mathbf{r}} \times \ddot{\mathbf{r}}|^2} = \frac{c\cos\alpha}{v}$$

are constant and therefore the path is a circular helix. (*Advanced Calculus*, § 104.)

63. MOTION OF A PLANET

Consider the motion of a planet P about the sun O. We regard the sun and planet as particles of mass M and m concentrated at their centers. If the density of a star or planet is a function of the distance from its center, this assumption is strictly correct; for two such spheres attract each other with the same forces as two particles at their centers having the respective masses.

Now Newton's Law of Universal Gravitation asserts that two particles of masses m and M attract each other with twin forces that act along their joining line; these forces have opposite directions but the same magnitude $\gamma mM/r^2$, where r is the distance between the particles and γ is the *constant of gravitation*. Two particles of one gram mass one centimeter apart thus attract each other with a force of γ dynes. The Cavendish experiment shows that $\gamma = 6.670 \times 10^{-8}$ in the cgs system.* Now the vector force exerted by the sun on the planet is

$$\mathbf{F} = -\frac{\gamma mM}{r^2}\mathbf{R} = m\mathbf{a}$$

by Newton's second law of motion. On equating radial and transverse components in this vector equation, we have from (57.12)

(1)
$$\frac{d^2\mathbf{r}}{dt^2} - r\left(\frac{d\theta}{dt}\right)^2 = -\frac{\gamma M}{r^2},$$

(2)
$$2\frac{dr}{dt}\frac{d\theta}{dt} + r\frac{d^2\theta}{dt^2} = \frac{1}{r}\frac{d}{dt}\left(r^2\frac{d\theta}{dt}\right) = 0.$$

From (2) we have

(3)
$$r^2\frac{d\theta}{dt} = h, \qquad \text{a constant.}$$

This result has a simple meaning; for the sectorial area swept out by OP measured from any line $\theta = \alpha$ is

$$S = \frac{1}{2}\int_\alpha^\theta r^2\,d\theta;$$

and the rate at which OP sweeps out area is

$$\frac{dS}{dt} = \frac{dS}{d\theta}\frac{d\theta}{dt} = \frac{1}{2}r^2\frac{d\theta}{dt} = \frac{1}{2}h.$$

---

* Since force has the dimensions MLT^{-2} (mass times acceleration), γ has the dimensions $(MLT^{-2})L^2M^{-2}$ or $M^{-1}L^3T^{-2}$. This formula shows how to compute γ in any other system of units.

Hence the line OP sweeps out area at the constant rate $\frac{1}{2}h$. This is Kepler's second law:

> *The radial vector from sun to planet sweeps out equal areas in equal times.*
> On putting $d\theta/dt = h/r^2$ in (1), this equation becomes

(4)
$$\frac{d^2r}{dt^2} - \frac{h^2}{r^3} = -\frac{\gamma M}{r^2}.$$

With the aid of (3) we now convert (4) into an equation connecting r and θ. Thus

$$\frac{dr}{dt} = \frac{dr}{d\theta}\frac{d\theta}{dt} = \frac{h}{r^2}\frac{dr}{d\theta} = -h\frac{du}{d\theta}$$

where $u = 1/r$. Moreover,

$$\frac{d^2r}{dt^2} = \frac{d}{d\theta}\left(-h\frac{du}{d\theta}\right)\frac{d\theta}{dt} = -h\frac{d^2u}{d\theta^2}\cdot hu^2,$$

so that (4) becomes

$$-h^2u^2\frac{d^2u}{d\theta^2} - h^2u^3 = -\gamma Mu^2$$

or

(5)
$$\frac{d^2u}{d\theta^2} + u = \frac{\gamma M}{h^2}.$$

The general solution of this linear equation in u is

(6)
$$u = \frac{1}{r} = A\cos\theta + B\sin\theta + \frac{\gamma M}{h^2};$$

for $A\cos\theta + B\sin\theta$ is the general solution of $u'' + u = 0$ and $\gamma M/h^2$ is obviously a particular integral of (5).

Let us now take the initial line $\theta = 0$ through the planet's perihelion—the point on the orbit where r has its least value; then

$$r = r_0, \qquad \frac{dr}{d\theta} = 0 \quad \text{when } \theta = 0.$$

Equation (6) will satisfy these conditions if

$$\frac{1}{r_0} = A + \frac{\gamma M}{h^2}, \qquad 0 = B;$$

with these values (6) becomes

$$\frac{1}{r} = \left(\frac{1}{r_0} - \frac{\gamma M}{h^2}\right)\cos\theta + \frac{\gamma M}{h^2} = \frac{\gamma M}{h^2}(1 + E\cos\theta)$$

on writing

$$(7) \qquad E = \dfrac{\dfrac{1}{r_0} - \dfrac{\gamma M}{h^2}}{\dfrac{\gamma M}{h^2}} = \dfrac{h^2}{\gamma M r_0} - 1.$$

The polar equation of the orbit is therefore

$$(8) \qquad r = \frac{h^2/\gamma M}{1 + E \cos \theta}.$$

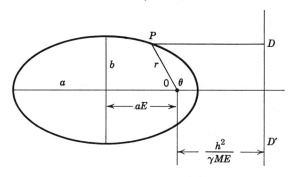

Fig. 63a   Elliptical orbit of a planet.

If we write this equation as

$$\frac{r}{(h^2/\gamma ME) - r \cos \theta} = E \quad \text{or} \quad \frac{OP}{PD} = E \qquad (\cos \theta < 0 \text{ in Fig. 63}a),$$

we see that the orbit is a conic section of eccentricity E with focus at O and directrix DD' at a distance $h^2/\gamma ME$ from the focus (Fig. 63a); for the ratio OP/PD has always the constant value E. The only *closed* orbit is an ellipse $(0 \leqq E < 1)$. We have thus deduced Kepler's first law:

The planets move in ellipses with the sun at one focus.

Let the elliptic orbit have the semiaxes a and $b = a\sqrt{1 - E^2}$. Then a focus and its corresponding directrix are at distances aE and a/E from the center, and the perihelion distance $r_0 = a - aE$. From (7) we now have

$$(9) \qquad h^2 = \gamma M r_0 (1 + E) = \gamma M a(1 - E^2).*$$

---

* This equation also follows from

$$\frac{a}{E} - aE = \frac{h^2}{\gamma ME},$$

giving the distance between focus and directrix.

Since the area of the orbital ellipse is

$$\pi ab = \pi a^2 \sqrt{1 - E^2}$$

and the sectorial speed, from (9), is

$$\tfrac{1}{2}h = \tfrac{1}{2}\sqrt{\gamma M a (1 - E^2)},$$

the period of the planet is

$$T = \frac{\pi ab}{\tfrac{1}{2}h} = 2\pi \sqrt{\frac{a^3}{\gamma M}}.$$

Therefore for any planet of the solar system the ratio

(10) $$\frac{T^2}{a^3} = \frac{4\pi^2}{\gamma M}$$

is the same. Thus we have proved Kepler's third law:

The squares of the periods of the planets are proportional to the cubes of their mean distances from the sun.

The major semiaxis a is called the *mean distance*; for it is the mean of the perihelion and aphelion distances of the planet from the focus. But the mean distance of the planet for all positions from $\theta = 0$ to $\theta = \pi$ is actually

$$\frac{1}{\pi}\int_0^\pi r\, d\theta = \frac{h^2}{\gamma M}\frac{1}{\pi}\int_0^\pi \frac{d\theta}{1 + E\cos\theta} = \frac{h^2}{\gamma M \sqrt{1 - E^2}} = a\sqrt{1 - E^2} = b,$$

as we see from (9).

Although (4) cannot be integrated in terms of the elementary functions to give r as a function of t, a first integral is readily obtained; for if we multiply (4) by dr/dt and integrate each term, we find

(11) $$\frac{1}{2}\left(\frac{dr}{dt}\right)^2 + \frac{1}{2}\frac{h^2}{r^2} = \frac{\gamma M}{r} + C.$$

Since dr/dt and $h/r = r\, d\theta/dt$ are the radial and transverse components of velocity, the left member of (11) becomes $v^2/2$. On multiplying (11) by m we now have

(12) $$\frac{1}{2}mv^2 - \frac{\gamma Mm}{r} = C;$$

here the first term is the kinetic energy of the planet, the second its potential energy in the field of the sun; and the equation states that the total energy is conserved.

If r_0, v_0 denote the values of r and v at perihelion, we have from (12)

(13)
$$v^2 - \frac{2\gamma M}{r} = v_0{}^2 - \frac{2\gamma M}{r_0}.$$

But $r_0 = a(1 - E)$, $v_0 = r_0\left(\dfrac{d\theta}{dt}\right)_0 = h/r_0$; hence, with the value of h^2 from (9),

$$v_0{}^2 - \frac{2\gamma M}{r_0} = \frac{h^2}{r_0{}^2} - \frac{2\gamma M}{r_0}$$

$$= \frac{\gamma M a(1 - E^2)}{a^2(1 - E)^2} - \frac{2\gamma M}{a(1 - E)}$$

$$= \frac{\gamma M}{a}\left(\frac{1 + E - 2}{1 - E}\right) = -\frac{\gamma M}{a}.$$

With this value (13) becomes

(14)
$$v^2 = \gamma M\left(\frac{2}{r} - \frac{1}{a}\right).$$

Thus the semimajor axis of a planet's orbit is determined by a pair of corresponding values of r and v.

In Einstein's general theory of relativity the differential equation of a planet's orbit is

(15)
$$\frac{d^2u}{d\theta^2} + u = \frac{\gamma M}{h^2} + 3\frac{\gamma M}{c^2}u^2,$$

where c is the velocity of light, 30,000,000,000 cm/sec. This differs from the Newtonian equation (5) in the last term only, a very small addition owing to c^2 in the denominator. This is really a mathematical miracle, for Einstein makes no use of Newtonian mechanics or the inverse square law. The planets move along the shortest possible paths (geodesic lines) in a space-time curved by the presence of the sun. Their orbits are essentially ellipses whose axes revolve very slowly in the plane of motion. In the case of Mercury, the planet nearest the sun, this *motion of the perihelion* is measurable, a trifling 43 seconds of arc per century. The theoretical amount, computed from a resonance effect due to the extra term, is in substantial agreement with this figure.

In the sun-planet problem the sun was regarded as fixed; but since the planet exerts the force $\dfrac{\gamma mM}{r^2}$ **R** on the sun by the law of action and reaction (§ 56), this is not strictly true. But if we choose an origin at the center of mass of sun and planet, this origin O will remain at rest if originally at rest.*

---

* See L. Brand, *Vector Analysis*, Wiley (1957), p. 175

Now the equations of motion of planet and sun, referred to their center mass O, are

$$m\frac{d^2\mathbf{p}}{dt^2} = -\frac{\gamma Mm}{r^2}\mathbf{R}, \qquad \mathbf{p} = \overrightarrow{OP},$$

$$M\frac{d^2\mathbf{s}}{dt^2} = +\frac{\gamma Mm}{r^2}\mathbf{R}, \qquad \mathbf{s} = \overrightarrow{OS},$$

where $\mathbf{r} = \overrightarrow{SP} = \mathbf{p} - \mathbf{s}$ and r is the distance SP (Fig. 63b). Canceling m and M respectively and subtracting these equations we have

(16) $$\frac{d^2\mathbf{r}}{dt^2} = -\frac{\gamma(M + m)}{r^2}\mathbf{R}$$

as the planet's equation of motion referred to O. This equation has the same form as our previous vector equation with $M + m$ in place of M.

Fig. 63b Sun and planet.

The orbit of P relative to the sun S is therefore an ellipse in which SP sweeps out equal areas in equal times. But in place of (10) we now have

(17) $$\frac{T^2}{a^3} = \frac{4\pi^2}{\gamma(M + m)}.$$

Hence T^2/a^3 is not strictly the same for all planets, as Kepler's third law asserts. But since the mass of the sun is more than 1,000 times that of Jupiter, the greatest planet, $M + m$ in (17) may be replaced by M without serious error. The third law is therefore very nearly true.

Equation (17) also applies to a planet of mass M and its satellites if we neglect all gravitational forces exerted by bodies external to this system. Thus if m, a, T refer to an artificial satellite of the earth (mass M) and m_0, a_0, T_0 refer to the moon, we have from (17)

$$\frac{T^2(M + m)}{a^3} = \frac{T_0^2(M + m_0)}{a_0^3}.$$

Since we may neglect m in $M + m$,

(18) $$\frac{T}{T_0} = \left(\frac{a}{a_0}\right)^{3/2}\left(1 + \frac{m_0}{M}\right)^{1/2} \qquad \text{where} \quad m_0/M = 1/80.$$

If an artificial satellite is projected into its orbit with the speed v at a distance r from the center of the earth, we may compute the major semi-axis a of its orbit from (14) and its period from (18).

Example. Halley's Comet. It has a period of about 76 years; this was correctly computed by Edmund Halley in 1682. At perihelion its distance from the sun is $r_0 = 0.58$ of an astronomical unit (the mean distance of the earth from the sun). Find its distance at aphelion and the eccentricity of its orbit.

With astronomical units and years as units of length and time, Kepler's third law, applied to the comet and the earth, gives

$$\frac{T^2}{a^3} = \frac{1^2}{1^3} = 1, \qquad a = T^{2/3} = 76^{2/3} = 17.94 \text{ astronomical units}$$

for the comet. Its aphelion distance is therefore

$$r_1 = 2 \times 17.94 - 0.58 = 35.30 \text{ astronomical units.}$$

Halley's Comet therefore travels beyond the orbit of Neptune ($a = 30.07$) but not as far as Pluto ($a = 39.46$) and passes closer to the sun than Venus ($a = 0.723$), but farther than Mercury ($a = 0.387$).

The eccentricity of its orbit may be found from the equation $r_0 = a(1 - E)$; hence

$$E = 1 - \frac{r_0}{a} = 1 - \frac{0.58}{17.94} = 0.968.$$

The next appearance of Halley's Comet will be in 1986—it will be the thirtieth recorded passage about the sun. Its last visit was a magnificent sight.

PROBLEMS

1. When a body is projected into the sun's field with a purely radial velocity, show that $\theta = \text{const.}$, $v = dr/dt$; and if $r = r_0$, $v = v_0$ when $t = 0$,

$$v^2 - v_0^2 = 2\gamma M \left(\frac{1}{r} - \frac{1}{r_0} \right).$$

Prove that the body will leave the solar system if $v_0 \geqq \sqrt{2\gamma M/r_0}$.

2. If $v_0 = 0$ in Problem 1, show that the body will fall into the sun (radius R) in the time

$$t = \frac{1}{\sqrt{2\gamma M}} \int_{u_0}^{1/R} \frac{du}{u^2(u - u_0)}, \qquad u = \frac{1}{r}.$$

3. If in Problem 1, $0 < v_0 < \sqrt{2\gamma M/r_0}$, what is the greatest value of r the body will attain?

4. If the orbit of a planet is a circle of radius a, show that its angular speed has the constant value $\sqrt{\gamma M/a^3}$.

5. A body of mass m moving in the field of the sun has the vector equation of motion

$$m \frac{d\mathbf{v}}{dt} = - \frac{\gamma mM}{r^2} \mathbf{R}.$$

By multiplying this equation by $\mathbf{v}$ (the *scalar* product) and integrating with respect to t, deduce the energy equation (12). If $v = 0$ when $r = \infty$, show that the body will acquire the speed

(16) $$v_c = \sqrt{\frac{2\gamma M}{r}} \quad \text{(the } critical \; speed\text{)}$$

at a distance r from the sun.

6. From equation (8) show that the mean distance of the planet from the sun is

(17) $$a = \frac{h^2/\gamma M}{1 - E^2}$$

7. From equations (14), (16), and (17) show that

(18) $$1 - E^2 = \frac{h^2}{\gamma^2 M^2}(v_c^2 - v^2).$$

Hence prove that a body launched in the field of the sun with the speed v will have an elliptic $(E < 1)$, parabolic $(E = 1)$, or hyperbolic orbit $(E > 1)$ according as $v < v_c$, $v = v_c$ or $v > v_c$, provided $h \neq 0$.

8. Prove that the mean density of the earth (radius R, mass M) is

$$\rho = \frac{3g}{4\pi\gamma R} = 5.512 \text{ gm/cm}^3.$$

if $R = 6.371 \times 10^8$ cm, $g = 981$ cm/sec^2, $\gamma = 6.670 \times 10^{-8}$.

[The force of attraction on a mass m at the earth's surface is mg and also $\gamma m M/R^2$.]

9. A body is projected radially upward from the earth (mass M, radius R). If air resistance is neglected, show that

(a) $$\frac{dr}{dt} = -\frac{\gamma M}{r^2} = -\frac{g R^2}{r^2};$$

(b) it will escape from the earth's attraction if its initial speed $v_0 = \sqrt{2gR} \simeq 7$ miles per second ($R \simeq 3960$ miles).

64. VARIABLE MASS

If we integrate the equation of motion of a particle, $m \, d\mathbf{v}/dt = \mathbf{f}$, between $t = t_1(\mathbf{v} = \mathbf{v}_1)$ and $t = t_2(\mathbf{v} = \mathbf{v}_2)$, we obtain

(1) $$m\mathbf{v}_2 - m\mathbf{v}_1 = \int_{t_1}^{t_2} \mathbf{f} \, dt.$$

The left member is change in momentum in the interval $\Delta t = t_2 - t_1$. The time integral of the force over this interval is called the *impulse* of the force $\mathbf{f}$. Thus equation (1) states the

Principle of Impulse and Momentum. The change in the momentum of a particle in any time interval is equal to the impulse of the resultant force in this interval.

For a system of particles this principle is still valid: the change in momentum of the system is equal to the sum of the impulses of all the *external* forces acting on the system, for the impulses of the *internal* forces cancel in pairs by the principle of action and reaction (§ 56). Even in systems of variable mass this principle may be applied over a short interval Δt to set up the equation of motion. The external forces may be regarded as constant over a very small interval; but we must be sure that all are included.

While the velocity of a body of mass m changes from $\mathbf{v}$ to $\mathbf{v} + \Delta\mathbf{v}$, let it gain the mass Δm. Let the velocity of Δm change from $\mathbf{v} + \mathbf{u}$ to $\mathbf{v} + \Delta\mathbf{v}$ in the interval Δt. Then if the external forces $\mathbf{f}_1$, $\mathbf{f}_2$ act on m and Δm, and the twin forces $\mathbf{f}'$, $-\mathbf{f}'$ represent the internal action on Δm and the reaction on m, the momentum-impulse equations are

$$m\,\Delta\mathbf{v} = (\mathbf{f}_1 - \mathbf{f}')\,\Delta t,$$

$$\Delta m(\mathbf{v} + \Delta\mathbf{v} - \mathbf{v} - \mathbf{u}) = (\mathbf{f}_2 + \mathbf{f}')\,\Delta t.$$

On dividing these equations by Δt and passing to the limit $\Delta t \to 0$, we have

(1)
$$m\frac{d\mathbf{v}}{dt} = \mathbf{f}_1 - \mathbf{f}',$$

(2)
$$-u\frac{dm}{dt} = \mathbf{f}_2 + \mathbf{f}'.$$

Hence on addition we obtain the basic equation

(3)
$$m\frac{d\mathbf{v}}{dt} - \mathbf{u}\frac{dm}{dt} = \mathbf{f}_1 + \mathbf{f}_2.$$

Here $\mathbf{u}$ is the velocity of Δm relative to the body at the instant of joining it; and if Δm is at rest relative to the body $\mathbf{u} + \mathbf{v} = 0$, $\mathbf{u} = -\mathbf{v}$ and (3) becomes

(4)
$$\frac{d}{dt}(m\mathbf{v}) = \mathbf{f}_1 + \mathbf{f}_2.$$

When the body is losing mass (as in a rocket), $\Delta m < 0$. Then if the velocity of m changes from $\mathbf{v}$ to $\mathbf{v} + \Delta\mathbf{v}$ while that of $(-\Delta m)$ changes from $\mathbf{v}$ to $\mathbf{v} + \mathbf{u}$ in Δt seconds, the momentum-impulse equations become

$$m\,\Delta\mathbf{v} = (\mathbf{f}_1 - \mathbf{f}')\,\Delta t,$$

$$(-\Delta m)(\mathbf{v} + \mathbf{u} - \mathbf{v}) = (\mathbf{f}_2 + \mathbf{f}')\,\Delta t.$$

Dividing by Δt and passing to the limit $\Delta t \to 0$ again gives equations (1) and (2).

Thus equation (3) holds in both cases; when $\Delta m > 0$, **u** is its velocity relative to the body just before joining it; and when $\Delta m < 0$, **u** is its velocity relative to the body just after leaving it.

In the case of a rocket whose initial mass is $M + m_0$, where m_0 is the mass of fuel, and which loses mass (gases formed by combustion) at the rate of a grams per second, the mass after t seconds is

$$m = M + m_0 - at \text{ grams.}$$

If the gas is expelled with the velocity $u = -b$ cm/sec relative to the rocket, equation (3) becomes

$$(5) \qquad (M + m_0 - at) \frac{dv}{dt} - ab = f, \qquad 0 \leqq t \leqq \frac{m_0}{a}.$$

The fuel is exhausted after $t_1 = m_0/a$ seconds and after this $m = M$.

If the kinetic energy developed by burning one gram of fuel is a constant k, we have $k = \frac{1}{2}b^2$, $b = \sqrt{2k}$.

Example 1. A rocket is propelled by burning a grams of fuel per second and the exhaust gases have a constant velocity $u = -b$ cm/sec relative to the rocket. In the absence of any external force its motion is given by (5) with $f = 0$. If $v = 0$ when $t = 0$, its velocity after t seconds is

$$v = ab \int_0^t \frac{dt}{M + m_0 - at} = -b \log \frac{M + m_0 - at}{M + m_0}, \qquad 0 \leqq t \leqq \frac{m_0}{a}.$$

Putting $v = dx/dt$, we obtain the distance traveled in t seconds:

$$x = -b \int_0^t \log \frac{M + m_0 - at}{M + m_0} \, dt, \qquad 0 \leqq t \leqq \frac{m_0}{a}.$$

With the new variable of integration

$$y = \frac{M + m_0 - at}{M + m_0}, \qquad dt = -\frac{M + m_0}{a} \, dy,$$

$$x = \frac{b(M + m_0)}{a} \int_1^y \log y \, dy = \frac{b(M + m_0)}{a} \left[y \, (\log y - 1) \right]_1^y$$

$$= \frac{b}{a} \left[(M + m_0 - at) \log \frac{M + m_0 - at}{M + m_0} - M - m_0 + at + M + m_0 \right],$$

or finally,

$$x = bt + \frac{b}{a}(M + m_0 - at) \log \frac{M + m_0 - at}{M + m_0}.$$

When the fuel is exhausted $t = t_1 = m_0/a$, and

$$v_1 = -b \log \frac{M}{M + m_0}, \qquad x_1 = b \frac{m_0}{a} + \frac{b}{a} M \log \frac{M}{M + m_0}.$$

Example 2. A fine uniform chain is collected in a heap on a horizontal table, and to one end is attached a fine string which passes over a smooth pulley vertically above the chain and carries a weight equal to the weight of a length a of the chain. Prove that the length of the chain raised before the weight comes to rest is $a\sqrt{3}$, and find the length suspended when the weight next comes to rest.*

1. Let x be the height of the chain, of linear density ρ, at the time t from the start (Fig. 64). Neglecting the string, the mass in motion is $m = \rho(a + x)$, the external force is $f = g\rho(a - x)$; and since the added mass is at rest, its velocity relative to m is $0 - v = -v$. With $u = -v$, equation (3) becomes

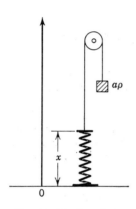

Fig. 64 Moving chain.

$$\rho(a + x)\frac{dv}{dt} + \rho v\frac{dx}{dt} = g\rho(a - x)$$

or since $dv/dt = v\,dv/dx$,

(i) $\qquad (a + x)\,v\dfrac{dv}{dx} + v^2 = g(a - x).$

This equation is linear in v^2,

$$\frac{dv^2}{dx} + \frac{2}{a + x}v^2 = \frac{2g(a - x)}{a + x},$$

and has the multiplier $(a + x)^2$; hence

(ii) $\qquad \dfrac{d}{dx}[(a + x)^2 v^2] = 2g(a^2 - x^2),$

$$(a + x)^2 v^2 = 2g\left((a^2 x - \frac{x^3}{3}\right)$$

on integrating from $x = 0$ ($v = 0$) to x. Thus v will again be zero when $x = a\sqrt{3}$.

In this upward motion the force that lifts the element $\Delta m = \rho v\Delta t$ of the chain is the *internal* force f' given by

$$f'\Delta t = \Delta m(v - 0) = \rho v^2\Delta t, \qquad f' = \rho v^2,$$

and is exerted by the chain in motion on the part at rest.

2. When the chain reaches its highest point $x = a\sqrt{3}$, it is acted on by the downward force $\rho g a(1 - \sqrt{3})$. As the chain falls, the element $\Delta m = \rho v\Delta t$ is stopped at the table by the *external* force $f_2 = \rho v^2$ exerted by the *table* and this is exactly balanced by the internal force $f' = -\rho v^2$ exerted on Δm by the chain in motion. Thus in the downward motion of the chain ρv^2 must be added to the right member of the equation of motion; hence v^2 must be added to the right member of equation (i). The differential equation for the downward motion is therefore

(iii) $\qquad (a + x)v\dfrac{dv}{dx} = g(a - x).$

---

* Satterly, J. Some Experiments in Dynamics, *Am. J. Phys.*, **18**, no. 7, 1950. The solution on page 415 of part 2 of this problem is erroneous.

On integrating

$$v \, dv = g \frac{a - x}{a + x} \, dx = g \left(\frac{2a}{a + x} - 1 \right) dx$$

from $x = a\sqrt{3}, \, v = 0$ to $x, \, v$ we have

$$\tfrac{1}{2} v^2 = 2ga \log \frac{a + x}{a(1 + \sqrt{3})} - g(x - a\sqrt{3}).$$

Writing $x = \lambda a$ we see that v will again be zero when λ satisfies the equation

$$2 \log \frac{1 + \lambda}{1 + \sqrt{3}} = \lambda - \sqrt{3} \quad \text{or} \quad \lambda = 0.413.$$

PROBLEMS

1. If the rocket in Example 1 is shot directly upward from rest and is subject to gravity, find the velocity and distance traveled when the fuel is exhausted. [Put $f = mg$ in (5).]

2. A spherical raindrop falls under gravity and grows at a rate proportional to its surface area. If the initial radius of the drop is negligible ($r_0 \simeq 0$), prove that its falling acceleration is $g/4$.

[If the moisture added to the drop is at rest, $u = -v$. The mass of the drop is $m = \tfrac{4}{3} \pi r^3 \rho$ where ρ is the density of water; if $dm/dt = k \, 4\pi r^2$, show that $r = r_0 + (kt/\rho)$.]

3. If $r_0 \neq 0$ in Problem 2, show that the acceleration, velocity, and distance traversed by the drop are

$$a = \frac{g}{4} \left(1 + 3 \frac{r_0^4}{r^4} \right), \qquad v = \frac{\rho g}{4k} \left(r - \frac{r_0^4}{r^3} \right), \qquad x = \frac{g}{8} \frac{\rho^2}{k^2} \cdot \frac{(r^2 - r_0^2)^2}{r^2},$$

where $r = r_0 + (kt/\rho)$. Give dimensional check.

4. A spherical raindrop falls under gravity by sweeping up the moisture in a fog through which it passes. If the fog has a uniform aqueous density δ and the initial radius r_0 of the drop is negligible, prove that the drop will fall with the acceleration $g/7$.

$$\left[u = -v; \ m = \tfrac{4}{3} \pi r^3 \rho, \qquad \frac{dm}{dt} = \pi r^2 \delta v. \right]$$

5. A chain L feet long lies on a smooth table h feet high with one end touch-

ing the floor. Show that the other end will slide off with the velocity $\sqrt{\dfrac{g}{h} (L^2 - h^2)}$ ft/sec.

[After t seconds let x feet of chain remain on the table; then if the chain weighs w lb/ft, $m = (h + x)w/g$, $f = hw$ and since $u = -v$, we may apply (4).]

CHAPTER 7

$$\pounds\{f(t)\} = \int_0^\infty e^{-st} f(t)\, dt$$

Laplace Transform

65. LAPLACE TRANSFORM

Let $f(t)$ be a function defined when $t \geq 0$; then the *Laplace transform* of $f(t)$ is the function

(1)
$$F(s) = \int_0^\infty e^{-st} f(t)\, dt$$

for all values of s for which the improper integral converges. The Laplace transform of functions denoted by lower case letters are written with the corresponding capitals; thus the transforms of $g(t)$, $y(t)$ are written $G(s)$, $Y(s)$.

In (1), e^{-st} is the *kernel* of the transformation and s, the *transform variable*, may be real or complex. Although we shall limit s to real values, it may be shown that when s is complex and the integral exists when $\operatorname{Re} s > \alpha$, then $F(s)$ is an *analytic* function defined over the complex half-plane $\operatorname{Re} s > \alpha$. Indeed the inverse transformation, which expresses $f(t)$ in terms of $F(s)$, is an integral in the complex plane.

We may regard $F(s)$ as produced by an operation $\pounds$ performed on $f(t)$ and write

$$F(s) = \pounds\{f(t)\}.$$

Then (1) shows that $\pounds$ is a *linear operator*: If a and b are constants,

(2)
$$\pounds\{af(t) + bg(t)\} = a\pounds\{f(t)\} + b\pounds\{g(t)\}.$$

As examples of Laplace transforms,

(3)
$$\pounds\{1\} = \int_0^\infty e^{-st}\, dt = \frac{e^{-st}}{s}\Big|_0^\infty = \frac{1}{s}, \qquad s > 0.$$

(4)
$$\pounds\{e^{at}\} = \int_0^\infty e^{-(s-a)t}\, dt = \frac{e^{-(s-a)t}}{-(s-a)}\Big|_0^\infty = \frac{1}{s-a}, \qquad s > a.$$

282

The transforms of

$$\cosh bt = \frac{1}{2}(e^{bt} + e^{-bt}), \qquad \sinh bt = \frac{1}{2}(e^{bt} - e^{-bt})$$

now follow from (2) and (4):

(5) $\qquad \pounds\{\cosh bt\} = \frac{1}{2}\left(\frac{1}{s-b} + \frac{1}{s+b}\right) = \frac{s}{s^2 - b^2}, \qquad s > b;$

(6) $\qquad \pounds\{\sinh bt\} = \frac{1}{2}\left(\frac{1}{s-b} - \frac{1}{s+b}\right) = \frac{b}{s^2 - b^2}, \qquad s > b.$

A direct calculation from the integrals

$$\int e^{-st} \cos bt\, dt = e^{-st}\left(\frac{-s\cos bt - b\sin bt}{s^2 + b^2}\right),$$

$$\int e^{-st} \sin bt\, dt = e^{-st}\left(\frac{-s\sin bt + b\cos bt}{s^2 + b^2}\right)$$

shows that

(7) $\qquad\qquad \pounds\{\cos bt\} = \frac{s}{s^2 + b^2}, \qquad s > 0,$

(8) $\qquad\qquad \pounds\{\sin bt\} = \frac{b}{s^2 + b^2}, \qquad s > 0.$

Since

$$e^{ibt} = \cos bt + i\sin bt,$$

we now have from (2)

(9) $\qquad\qquad \pounds\{e^{ibt}\} = \frac{s + ib}{s^2 + b^2} = \frac{1}{s - ib}, \qquad s > 0,$

which extends (4) to imaginary exponents.

A simple way to recall formulas (7) and (8) is to take real and imaginary parts of (9).

We next prove two general theorems on Laplace transforms.

Theorem 1. *The transform*

$$\pounds\{f(t)\} = F(s), \qquad s > \sigma,$$

implies that

(10) $\qquad\qquad \pounds\{e^{-at}f(t)\} = F(s + a), \qquad s > \sigma - a.$

PROOF. From the definition of $F(s)$ in (1) we have

$$\pounds\{e^{-at}f(t)\} = \int_0^\infty e^{-(s+a)t}f(t)\, dt = F(s + a), \qquad s > \sigma - a.$$

As special cases of (10) we have from (7) and (8):

(11) $$\pounds\{e^{-at}\cos bt\} = \frac{s+a}{(s+a)^2+b^2}, \qquad s > -a;$$

(12) $$\pounds\{e^{-at}\sin bt\} = \frac{b}{(s+a)^2+b^2}, \qquad s > -a.$$

We can now extend (4) to complex exponents; for from (9)

(13) $$\pounds\{e^{(a+ib)t}\} = \frac{1}{s-a-ib}, \qquad s > a.$$

Theorem 2. *If $a > 0$, the transform*

$$\pounds\{f(t)\} = F(s), \qquad s > \sigma,$$

implies that

(14) $$\pounds\{f(at)\} = \frac{1}{a} F\left(\frac{s}{a}\right), \qquad s > a\sigma.$$

PROOF. Putting $at = \tau$, we have

$$\pounds\{f(at)\} = \int_0^\infty e^{-st}f(at)\,dt = \frac{1}{a}\int_0^\infty e^{-\frac{s}{a}\tau}f(\tau)\,d\tau$$

which is (14). The integral converges when $s/a > \sigma$.

The next theorem gives sufficient conditions that $f(t)$ possess a Laplace transform. We first define our terms.

Definition 1. A function $f(t)$ is said to be *piecewise continuous* when $t \geqq 0$ if it is continuous in any finite interval $0 \leqq t \leqq b$, except for a finite number of *finite* jumps.

Definition 2. A function $f(t)$ is said to be of *exponential order* α if there are positive constants M and b such that

(15) $$|f(t)| \leqq Me^{\alpha t} \quad \text{when} \quad t \geqq b.$$

Definition 3. Functions $f(t)$ which are piecewise continuous when $t \geqq 0$ and of exponential order α, are said to belong to the class $\mathscr{T}(\alpha)$—or simply class $\mathscr{T}$ if α is not specified.

Theorem 3. *A function $f(t)$ of class $\mathscr{T}(\alpha)$ will have a Laplace transform $F(s)$ when $s > \alpha$.*

PROOF. The integral in (1) may be written

$$F(s) = \int_0^b e^{-st}f(t)\,dt + \int_b^\infty e^{-st}f(t)\,dt.$$

The first integral exists since $e^{-st}f(t)$ is piecewise continuous; and from (15)

$$e^{-st}|f(t)| \leqq Me^{-(s-\alpha)t}, \qquad t \geqq b,$$

so that the second integral converges absolutely when $s > \alpha$.

In the first integral $|f(t)| < M_1$ since $f(t)$ is piecewise continuous; hence when $s > \alpha$,

$$|F(s)| \leqq \left| M_1 \int_0^b e^{-st} \, dt \right| + \left| M \int_b^\infty e^{-(s-\alpha)t} \, dt \right|$$

$$= \frac{M_1}{s}(1 - e^{-sb}) + \frac{M}{s - \alpha} e^{-(s-\alpha)b} \leqq \frac{M_1}{s - \alpha} + \frac{M}{s - \alpha}.$$

Consequently, we may state

Theorem 4. *When $f(t)$ is of class $\mathcal{T}(\alpha)$*

(16) $$\lim_{s \to \infty} F(s) = 0$$

and $sF(s)$ is bounded as s becomes infinite.

The absolute values of the functions 1, $\sin bt$, $\cos bt$, e^{ibt} do not exceed $e^0 = 1$; hence all of them are of exponential order 0. Moreover, if α is any positive constant, *however small*, t^n is of exponential order α; for

$$e^{\alpha t} = \sum_{n=0}^{\infty} \frac{\alpha^n t^n}{n!} > \frac{\alpha^n t^n}{n!}, \qquad t^n < \frac{n!}{\alpha^n} e^{\alpha t}.$$

If $f(t)$ and $g(t)$ belong to the classes $\mathcal{T}(\alpha)$ and $\mathcal{T}(\beta)$, $f(t)g(t)$ belongs to the class $\mathcal{T}(\alpha + \beta)$. To prove this we need only multiply the inequalities (15) for the functions. In particular if $f(t)$ belongs to the class $\mathcal{T}(\alpha)$, $t^n f(t)$ belongs to the class $\mathcal{T}(\alpha + \varepsilon)$, where ε is arbitrarily small.

If $f(t)$ belongs to the class $\mathcal{T}(\alpha)$ we may differentiate the equation of transformation (1) with respect to s under the integral sign* to obtain

$$F'(s) = -\int_0^\infty e^{-st} tf(t) \, dt, \qquad s > \alpha.$$

Since $tf(t)$, $t^2 f(t)$, ... are all of class $\mathcal{T}(\alpha + \varepsilon)$ we may differentiate n times to obtain

$$D^n F(s) = (-1)^n \int_0^\infty e^{-st} t^n f(t) \, dt, \qquad s > \alpha.$$

From these equations we have

---

* *Advanced Calculus*, p. 435.

Theorem 5. *If $f(t)$ belongs to class $\mathcal{T}(\alpha)$,*

(17) $$\mathcal{L}\{tf(t)\} = -F'(s), \qquad s > \alpha;$$

(18) $$\mathcal{L}\{t^n f(t)\} = (-1)^n D^n F(s), \qquad s > \alpha,$$

for $n = 1, 2, 3, \ldots$.

In particular, when $f(t) = 1$, $F(s) = s^{-1}$; and

(19) $$\mathcal{L}\{t\} = \frac{1}{s^2}, \qquad s > 0;$$

(20) $$\mathcal{L}\{t^n\} = \frac{n!}{s^{n+1}}, \qquad s > 0, n = 1, 2, 3, \ldots .$$

In the next article we shall obtain $\mathcal{L}\{t^n\}$ for any real exponent $n > -1$.

If $f(t)$ belongs to class $\mathcal{T}(\alpha)$ and we formally integrate the equation of transformation (1) from s to ∞ under the integral sign, we obtain

$$\int_s^\infty F(s)\, ds = \int_0^\infty f(t)\, dt \int_s^\infty e^{-st}\, ds = \int_0^\infty e^{-st} \frac{f(t)}{t}\, dt, \qquad s > \alpha.$$

This operation is valid when $\lim f(t)/t$ exists as $t \to 0+$. The content of the last equation is stated in

Theorem 6. *If $f(t)$ belongs to the class $\mathcal{T}(\alpha)$ and $\lim f(t)/t$ exists as $t \to 0+$,*

(21) $$\mathcal{L}\left\{\frac{f(t)}{t}\right\} = \int_s^\infty F(s)\, ds, \qquad s > \alpha.$$

We may apply this formula to

$$f(t) = \sin bt, \qquad F(s) = \frac{b}{s^2 + b^2}$$

since $\sin bt$ is of class $\mathcal{T}(0)$ and $t^{-1} \sin bt \to b$ as $t \to 0$; and since

$$\int_s^\infty \frac{b}{s^2 + b^2}\, ds = \frac{\pi}{2} - \tan^{-1}\frac{s}{b} = \cot^{-1}\frac{s}{b},$$

(22) $$\mathcal{L}\left\{\frac{\sin bt}{t}\right\} = \cot^{-1}\frac{s}{b}, \qquad s > 0.$$

Example 1. The function $1/t$ is not piecewise continuous because it becomes infinite at $t = 0$. $\mathcal{L}\{1/t\}$ does not exist; for

$$\int_\varepsilon^b \frac{e^{-st}}{t}\, dt > e^{-sb} \int_\varepsilon^b \frac{dt}{t} = e^{-sb} \log\frac{b}{\varepsilon}$$

which becomes infinite as $\varepsilon \to 0$.

Example 2. The function e^{t^2} is not of exponential order for

$$e^{-\alpha t} e^{t^2} = \exp\left(-\tfrac{1}{4}\alpha^2\right) \exp\left(t - \tfrac{1}{2}\alpha\right)^2 \to \infty \quad \text{as} \quad t \to \infty.$$

Moreover $£\{e^{t^2}\}$ does not exist; for

$$\int_0^b e^{-st}e^{t^2}\,dt = e^{-s^2/4}\int_0^b e^{(t-s/2)^2}\,dt > e^{-s^2/4}\int_0^b dt = be^{-s^2/4}$$

which becomes infinite as $b \to \infty$.

PROBLEMS

Deduce the following transforms:

1. $£\left\{\dfrac{e^{at} - e^{bt}}{a - b}\right\} = \dfrac{1}{(s - a)(s - b)}$.

2. $£\left\{\dfrac{ae^{at} - be^{bt}}{a - b}\right\} = \dfrac{s}{(s - a)(s - b)}$.

3. $£\left\{\dfrac{1 - \cos bt}{b^2}\right\} = \dfrac{1}{s(s^2 + b^2)}$.

4. $£\{\cos^2 bt\} = \dfrac{s^2 + 2b^2}{s(s^2 + 4b^2)}$.

5. $£\{\sin^2 bt\} = \dfrac{2b^2}{s(s^2 + 4b^2)}$.

6. $£\{\cos (bt + c)\} = \dfrac{s \cos c - b \sin c}{s^2 + b^2}$.

Test the special cases: $b = 0$; $c = 0$; $c = \pi/2$.

7. $£\{\sin (bt + c)\} = \dfrac{b \cos c + s \sin c}{s^2 + b^2}$.

8. $£\{\sin bt \sinh bt\} = \dfrac{2b^2 s}{s^4 + 4b^4}$.

9. Prove that

$$£\{t^n e^{at}\} = \frac{n!}{(s - a)^{n+1}}, \qquad n = 1, 2, 3, \ldots,$$

(a) by applying Theorem 1 to $f(t) = t^n$;
(b) by applying Theorem 5 to $f(t) = e^{at}$.

10. Use Theorem 5 to obtain the transforms 11 and 12 in the table of § 67.

11. Find $£\{t \cosh bt\}$ and $£\{t \sinh bt\}$.

12. Deduce $£\{t^{n+1}\}$ from $£\{t^n\}$.

13. $£\left\{\dfrac{1 - \cos bt}{t}\right\} = \dfrac{1}{2}\log\dfrac{s^2 + b^2}{s^2}$, $\qquad s > 0$.

14. $£\left\{\dfrac{1 - \cosh bt}{t}\right\} = \dfrac{1}{2}\log\dfrac{s^2 - b^2}{s^2}$, $\qquad s > b$.

15. $£\left\{\dfrac{e^{-at} - e^{-bt}}{t}\right\} = \log\dfrac{s + b}{s + a}$, $\qquad s > -a, -b$.

16. Verify that $\lim\limits_{s \to \infty} F(s) = 0$ in the foregoing problems.

66. GAMMA FUNCTION

The Laplace transform of t^n is

$$\pounds\{t^n\} = \int_0^\infty e^{-st} t^n \, dt = \int_0^\infty e^{-\tau} \left(\frac{\tau}{s}\right)^n \frac{d\tau}{s} = \frac{1}{s^{n+1}} \int_0^\infty e^{-\tau} \tau^n \, d\tau$$

on changing the variable of integration from t to $\tau = st$ $(s > 0)$. With Euler's definition of the *gamma function**,

$$(1) \qquad\qquad \Gamma(x) = \int_0^\infty e^{-t} t^{x-1} \, dt, \qquad x > 0,$$

we have

$$(2) \qquad\qquad \pounds\{t^n\} = \frac{\Gamma(n + 1)}{s^{n+1}}, \qquad s > 0, n > -1.$$

Also from § 65, Theorem 1,

$$(3) \qquad\qquad \pounds\{t^n e^{at}\} = \frac{\Gamma(n + 1)}{(s - a)^{n+1}}, \qquad s > a, n > -1.$$

The gamma function satisfies the functional equation

$$(4) \qquad\qquad \Gamma(x + 1) = x\Gamma(x), \qquad x > 0.$$

PROOF. Let $0 < a < b$ and integrate $\int_a^b e^{-t} t^{x-1} \, dt$ by parts, putting

$$u = e^{-t} \qquad\qquad dv = t^{x-1}$$

$$du = -e^{-t} \, dt \qquad\qquad v = \frac{t^x}{x};$$

then

$$\int_a^b e^{-t} t^{x-1} \, d = \frac{t^x}{x} e^{-t} \Big|_a^b + \frac{1}{x} \int_a^b e^{-t} t^x \, dt.$$

As $a \to 0$ and $b \to \infty$, the integrated part vanishes at both limits $(a^x e^{-a} \to 0,\ b^x e^{-b} \to 0)$, and the integrals approach $\Gamma(x)$ and $\frac{1}{x}\Gamma(x + 1)$ respectively.

By direct calculation,

$$(5) \qquad\qquad \Gamma(1) = \int_0^\infty e^{-t} \, dt = 1.$$

---

* *Advanced Calculus*, § 91. Of course any letter may be used for the variable of integration.

Using (4) we now find successively

$$\Gamma(2) = 1, \qquad \Gamma(3) = 2, \qquad \Gamma(4) = 3!,$$

and in general when n is a positive integer,

(6) $$\Gamma(n + 1) = n!, \qquad n = 1, 2, 3, \ldots .$$

From (2) we now have

(7) $$\pounds\{t\} = \frac{\Gamma(2)}{s^2} = \frac{1}{s^2}.$$

The functional equation (4) will give $\Gamma(n + \tfrac{1}{2})$ as soon as

$$\Gamma(\tfrac{1}{2}) = \int_0^\infty e^{-t} t^{-\frac{1}{2}} \, dt = 2 \int_0^\infty e^{-u^2} \, du, \qquad (t = u^2)$$

is known; and since $\displaystyle\int_0^\infty e^{-u^2} \, du = \tfrac{1}{2}\sqrt{\pi},$ *

(8) $$\Gamma(\tfrac{1}{2}) = \sqrt{\pi}.$$

From (2) we now have

(9) $$\pounds\{t^{-\frac{1}{2}}\} = \frac{\Gamma(\tfrac{1}{2})}{\sqrt{s}} = \sqrt{\frac{\pi}{s}},$$

(10) $$\pounds\{t^{\frac{1}{2}}\} = \frac{\Gamma(\tfrac{3}{2})}{\sqrt{s^3}} = \frac{1}{2}\sqrt{\frac{\pi}{s^3}}$$

Equation (1) only defines $\Gamma(x)$ for $x > 0$. As $x \to 0$, $\Gamma(x) \to \infty$. We now extend the definition of $\Gamma(x)$ to negative nonintegral values of x by means of the functional equation (4). Thus we *define*

(11) $$\Gamma(x) = \frac{\Gamma(x + 1)}{x}, \qquad -1 < x < 0,$$

$$\Gamma(x) = \frac{\Gamma(x + 2)}{x(x + 1)}, \qquad -2 < x < -1,$$

and, in general,

(12) $$\Gamma(x) = \frac{\Gamma(x + n)}{x(x + 1) \cdots (x + n - 1)}, \qquad -n < x < -n + 1.$$

Note that $\Gamma(x + n)$ in the interval $-n < x < -n + 1$ passes through the values of $\Gamma(x)$ in the interval $0 < x < 1$. In fact, $\Gamma(x)$ may be extended by the sole use of (11); this is first used to get $\Gamma(x)$ in $(-1, 0)$; then these values being known, (11) may be used to get $\Gamma(x)$ in $(-2, -1)$, and so on.

---

* *Advanced Calculus*, p. 365.

Thus it is evident that the extended gamma function still satisfies the functional equation (4).

Since $\Gamma(x) > 0$ in $(0, 1)$, (11) shows that $\Gamma(x) < 0$ in $(-1, 0)$, $\Gamma(x) > 0$ in $(-2, -1)$, changing sign each time we move a unit distance to the left (Fig. 66). $\Gamma(-n) = \pm\infty$ for $n = 0, 1, 2, \ldots$, the sign depending on the direction in which $-n$ is approached.

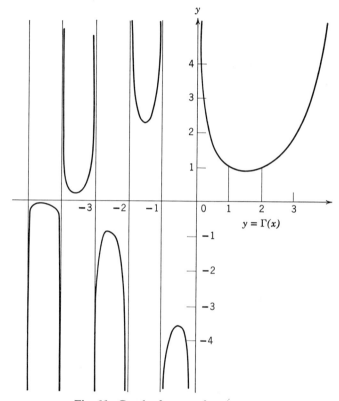

Fig. 66 Graph of gamma function.

The gamma function is not completely determined by the functional equation (4) and the value $\Gamma(1) = 1$. In this connection we have the

Theorem. *If $f(x)$ is defined for $x > 0$ and (a) $f(x) > 0$, (b) $f(1) = 1$, (c) $f(x + 1) = xf(x)$, (d) $\log f(x)$ is convex downward, then $f(x) = \Gamma(x)$, the Euler gamma function.**

---

* See P. G. Davis, Leonhard Euler's Integral, *Am. Math. Monthly*, vol. 66, no. 10, 1959, for an historical account of the gamma function. E. Artin's, *Einführung in die Theorie der Gammafunktion*, Leipzig, 1931, is a classic. This beautiful monograph has been revised and translated into English: *The Gamma Function*, Holt, Rinehart and Winston, New York, 1964.

We give without proof the important *reflection formula* of Euler,

(13) $$\Gamma(x)\Gamma(1 - x) = \frac{\pi}{\sin \pi x} \, ;$$

and the *duplication formula* of Legendre

(14) $$\Gamma(2x) = \frac{2^{2x-1}}{\pi} \Gamma(x)\Gamma(x + \tfrac{1}{2}).$$

When x is large, $\Gamma(x)$ is given approximately by *Stirling's formula*:

(15) $$\Gamma(x) \sim x^x e^{-x}\sqrt{2\pi/x}.$$

If $\Gamma'(x)$ denotes the derivative of $\Gamma(x)$,

(16) $$-\Gamma'(1) = \gamma = 0.57721\ 56649 \cdots ,$$

a number known as *Euler's constant*. It is defined as

$$\gamma = \lim_{n \to \infty} \left(1 + \frac{1}{2} + \frac{1}{3} + \cdots + \frac{1}{n} - \log n \right)$$

(cf. *Advanced Calculus*, p. 310). The irrationality of γ has not yet been proved. The value of γ to ten places is computed in Example 175.2.

Euler also defined the *beta function* $B(x, y)$ as

(17) $$B(x, y) = \int_0^1 t^{x-1}(1 - t)^{y-1}\, dt, \qquad x, y > 0.$$

The beta and gamma functions are connected by the fundamental relation

(18) $$B(x, y) = \frac{\Gamma(x)\Gamma(y)}{\Gamma(x + y)}, \qquad x, y > 0.*$$

A noteworthy property of the gamma function is that it satisfies no algebraic differential equation $F(y, y', \ldots, y^{(n)}, x) = 0$ where F is a polynomial in all of its variables. This was first proved by Otto Hölder in 1886.

PROBLEMS

1. $\pounds\, \{t^{n-\frac{1}{2}}\} = \dfrac{1 \cdot 3 \cdot 5 \ldots (2n - 1)}{2^n s^n} \sqrt{\dfrac{\pi}{s}}, \qquad n = 1, 2, \ldots .$

2. $\pounds\, \{te^{at}\} = \dfrac{1}{(s - a)^2}.$

3. $\pounds\, \{t^n e^{at}\} = \dfrac{\Gamma(n + 1)}{(s - a)^{n+1}}.$

---

* *Advanced Calculus*, § 193. See also C. S. Ogilvy, *The Beta Function*, Am. Math. Monthly vol. 58, no. 7, 1951.

4. Use (4) to show that if $f(x) = \Gamma(x)\,\Gamma(1 - x)$, then $f(x + 2) = f(x)$. Verify from (13).

5. Use (4) to show that $\Gamma(x)/\Gamma(2x) \to 2$ as $x \to 0+$. Verify from (14).

6. Show that $\Gamma\left(n + \dfrac{1}{2}\right) = \dfrac{(2n)!}{4^n n!}\,\sqrt{\pi}$.

7. Show that there are 158 digits in 100!. [Find $\log \Gamma(101)$ from (15).]

8. From $\pounds\{te^{ibt}\}$ show that

$$\pounds\{t \cos bt\} = \frac{s^2 - b^2}{(s^2 + b^2)^2}, \qquad s > 0,$$

$$\pounds\{t \sin bt\} = \frac{2bs}{(s^2 + b^2)^2}, \qquad s > 0.$$

67. TRANSFORM PAIRS

We can now construct a short table of transforms based on the transforms of e^{at} and t^n:

$$\pounds\{e^{at}\} = \frac{1}{s - a}\ (s > a), \qquad \pounds\{t^n\} = \frac{\Gamma(n + 1)}{s^{n+1}}, \qquad s > 0,\ n > -1.$$

Note that

$$\pounds(1) = \frac{1}{s}$$

follows from the first when $a = 0$ and from the second when $n = 0$. From (66.3)

$$\pounds\{te^{ibt}\} = \frac{1}{(s - ib)^2} = \frac{(s + ib)^2}{(s^2 + b^2)^2}, \qquad s > 0;$$

and on equating real and imaginary parts we obtain the entries 11 and 12 of the following table. Entries 13 and 14 now follow from (8) and (11).

Table A gives $F(s)$ when $f(t)$ is known. In order to use the table in reverse, to get $f(t)$ when $F(s)$ is known, we make use of

Lerch's Theorem. *If the functions $f(t)$ and $g(t)$ have the same Laplace transform, they can differ at most by an additive null function $n(t)$; that is,*

$$f(t) = g(t) + n(t) \quad \text{where} \quad \int_0^x n(t)\,dt = 0 \qquad \text{for all } x > 0.$$

For the proof see D. V. Widder, ref. 19, p. 63.

In particular, if two *continuous* functions for $t \geqq 0$ have the same Laplace transform they are identical; for the only continuous null function is everywhere zero. This follows from

$$\frac{d}{dx} \int_0^x n(t)\, dt = n(x) = 0 \qquad \text{wherever } n(x) \text{ is continuous.}^*$$

In other words, the integral equation

(1)
$$F(s) = \int_0^\infty e^{-st} f(t)\, dt$$

has but one continuous solution $f(t)$. Thus we may use the following table of transform pairs as a set of one-to-one correspondences: $f(t) \sim F(s)$

Table A, with some additional entries, is also placed at the end of the book, along with Tables B and C. A number of operational results, from § 65 and later articles, are collected in Table B for easy reference. Table C deals with the transforms of certain periodic functions.

Equation (1) yields a useful dimensional test for Laplace transforms: If dim $t = T$ and dim $s = T^{-1}$ (so that dim $e^{-st} = 0$),

$$\dim F(s) = T \dim f(t),$$

provided the arguments of transcendental functions in $f(t)$ have zero dimension.

Thus in (9), dim $a = \dim b = T^{-1}$, and dim $F(s) = T$.

Not every function of s has an inverse transform. For one thing, if $f(t)$ is of class $\mathcal{T}$,

(2)
$$\lim_{s \to \infty} \mathfrak{L}\{f(t)\} = 0.^\dagger$$

Thus a rational function, $F(s) = P(s)/Q(s)$, will have an inverse transform $f(t)$ only when the degree of the polynomial $P(s)$ is less than that of $Q(s)$. Then $f(t)$ can be found by resolving $P(s)/Q(s)$ into partial fractions with linear or quadratic denominators. If $Q(s)$ has a simple linear factor $s - a$, the corresponding fraction is

(3)
$$\frac{A}{s - a}; \qquad A = \lim_{s \to a} \frac{(s - a)P(s)}{Q(s)} = \frac{P(a)}{Q'(a)}.$$

For a double linear factor $(s - a)^2$ the corresponding fractions are

(4)
$$\frac{A_1}{s - a} + \frac{A_2}{(s - a)^2}; \qquad A_2 = \lim_{s \to a} \frac{(s - a)^2 P(s)}{Q(s)} = \frac{2P(a)}{Q''(a)},$$

---

* *Advanced Calculus*, p. 261, Theorem 2.
† *Advanced Calculus*, p. 427, Theorem.

Table A   Laplace Transforms: Special Functions

	$f(t)$ $(t \geqq 0)$	$F(s)$ $(s > \sigma)$	σ
1	1	$\dfrac{1}{s}$	0
2	e^{at}	$\dfrac{1}{s - a}$	a
3	t^n	$\dfrac{\Gamma(n + 1)}{s^{n+1}}$	0
	t, t^2	$\dfrac{1}{s^2}, \quad \dfrac{2}{s^3}$	
4	$t^n e^{at}$	$\dfrac{\Gamma(n+1)}{(s - a)^{n+1}}$	a
	$te^{at}, \quad t^2 e^{at}$	$\dfrac{1}{(s - a)^2}, \quad \dfrac{2}{(s - a)^3}$	
5	$\cosh bt$	$\dfrac{s}{s^2 - b^2}$	$|b|$
6	$\sinh bt$	$\dfrac{b}{s^2 - b^2}$	$|b|$
7	$\cos bt$	$\dfrac{s}{s^2 + b^2}$	0
8	$\sin bt$	$\dfrac{b}{s^2 + b^2}$	0
9	$e^{-at} \cos bt$	$\dfrac{s + a}{(s + a)^2 + b^2}$	$-a$
10	$e^{-at} \sin bt$	$\dfrac{b}{(s + a)^2 + b^2}$	$-a$
11	$t \cos bt$	$\dfrac{s^2 - b^2}{(s^2 + b^2)^2}$	0
12	$t \sin bt$	$\dfrac{2bs}{(s^2 + b^2)^2}$	0
13	$\dfrac{1}{2b} \sin bt - \dfrac{t}{2} \cos bt$	$\dfrac{b^2}{(s^2 + b^2)^2}$	0
14	$\dfrac{1}{2b} \sin bt + \dfrac{t}{2} \cos bt$	$\dfrac{s^2}{(s^2 + b^2)^2}$	0
15	$h(t - a) \quad a \geqq 0$	$\dfrac{e^{-as}}{s} \quad$ (§71)	
16	$\delta(t - a) \quad a \geqq 0$	$e^{-as} \quad$ (§73)	

but A_1 must be otherwise determined. Single and double quadratic factors $s^2 + as + b$ correspond to

$$\frac{As + B}{s^2 + as + b} \quad \text{and} \quad \frac{A_1 s + B_1}{s^2 + as + b} + \frac{A_2 s + B_2}{(s^2 + as + b)^2}.$$

There are rules to find the unknown constants, but they are easily forgotten. The following general procedure is *always* applicable.

Express P/Q as a sum of appropriate partial fractions, multiply this equation by Q to clear of fractions, and equate the coefficients of like powers of s on both sides of the resulting *identity*. There will always be just as many linear equations as there are unknown constants. To reduce the number of unknowns, the rules (3) and (4) given above may be used to find the constants over the *highest* powers of the linear factors.

Example 1. $F(s) = 1/s(s + 1)^2$.

$$\frac{1}{s(s + 1)^2} = \frac{A}{s} + \frac{B}{s + 1} + \frac{C}{(s + 1)^2};$$

$$1 = A(s + 1)^2 + Bs(s + 1) + Cs$$
$$= (A + B)s^2 + (2A + B + C)s + A;$$
$$A + B = 0, \quad 2A + B + C = 0, \quad A = 1;$$

hence $A = 1$, $B = -1$, $C = -1$. Thus

$$F(s) = \frac{1}{s} - \frac{1}{s + 1} - \frac{1}{(s + 1)^2},$$

$$f(t) = 1 - e^{-t} - te^{-t}.$$

Example 2. $F(s) = s/(s + 1)^2(s^2 + 1)$.

$$\frac{s}{(s + 1)^2(s^2 + 1)} = \frac{A}{s + 1} + \frac{B}{(s + 1)^2} + \frac{Cs + D}{s^2 + 1};$$

$$s = A(s + 1)(s^2 + 1) + B(s^2 + 1) + (Cs + D)(s + 1)^2$$
$$= (A + C)s^3 + (A + B + 2C + D)s^2 + (A + C + 2D)s + (A + B + D);$$
$$A + C = 0, \quad A + B + 2C + D = 0, \quad A + C + 2D = 1,$$
$$A + B + D = 0.$$

We find in turn, $C = 0$, $A = 0$, $D = \frac{1}{2}$, $B = -\frac{1}{2}$. Thus

$$F(s) = \frac{-\frac{1}{2}}{(s + 1)^2} + \frac{\frac{1}{2}}{s^2 + 1},$$

$$f(t) = -\tfrac{1}{2}te^{-t} + \tfrac{1}{2}\sin t.$$

Example 3. $F(s) = s/(s^3 + 1)$.

$$\frac{s}{s^3 + 1} = \frac{A}{s + 1} + \frac{Bs + C}{s^2 - s + 1};$$

$$s = A(s^2 - s + 1) + (Bs + C)(s + 1)$$
$$= (A + B)s^2 + (B + C - A)s + A + C;$$
$$A + B = 0, \quad B + C - A = 1, \quad A + C = 0.$$

Since $B = C = -A$, $-3A = 1$; $\quad A = -\frac{1}{3}$, $\quad B = C = \frac{1}{3}$. Hence

$$F(s) = \frac{1}{3} \frac{s+1}{s^2 - s + 1} - \frac{1}{3} \frac{1}{s+1}$$

$$= \frac{1}{3} \frac{s - \frac{1}{2} + \frac{3}{2}}{(s - \frac{1}{2})^2 + \frac{3}{4}} - \frac{1}{3} \frac{1}{s+1},$$

$$f(t) = e^{t/2}\left(\frac{1}{3}\cos\frac{\sqrt{3}}{2}t + \frac{1}{\sqrt{3}}\sin\frac{\sqrt{3}}{2}t\right) - \frac{1}{3}e^{-t}.$$

PROBLEMS

Given $F(s)$, find its mate $f(t)$.

1. $s^2/(s + 2)^2$

2. $1/(s^3 + 1)$

3. $s/(s^2 + a^2)(s^2 + b^2)$

4. $1/(s + 1)(s^2 + 2s + 2)$

5. $\dfrac{cs + d}{(s + a)^2 + b^2}$

6. $\dfrac{cs + d}{(s + a)^2 - b^2}$

7. $\dfrac{s + 2}{(s^2 + 1)(s^2 + 4)}$

8. $\dfrac{2s + 2}{(s^2 + 2s + 2)^2}$

68. TRANSFORMS OF DERIVATIVES AND INTEGRALS

The use of the Laplace transform in solving differential equations rests on the important

Theorem 1. *Under the conditions*
  (i) *$f(t)$ is continuous when $t \geq 0$,*
 (ii) *$f'(t)$ is piecewise continuous when $t \geq 0$,*
(iii) *$f(t)$ is of exponential order α,*
$f'(x)$ has the transform

(1) $$\mathcal{L}\{f'(t)\} = s\mathcal{L}\{f(t)\} - f(0), \qquad s > \alpha.$$

PROOF. Conditions (i) and (ii) justify the integration by parts*

$$\int_0^b e^{-st}f'(t)\, dt = e^{-st}f(t)\Big|_0^b + s\int_0^b e^{-st}f(t)\, dt.$$

From (iii), $|f(b)| \leq Me^{\alpha b}$ for all sufficiently large values of b; hence as $b \to \infty$

$$e^{-sb}|f(b)| \leq Me^{-(s-\alpha)b} \to 0 \quad \text{when} \quad s > \alpha.$$

---

* *Advanced Calculus*, § 122.

Thus when $b \to \infty$, the equation above becomes

$$\int_0^\infty e^{-st} f'(t)\, dt = 0 - f(0) + s\int_0^\infty e^{-st} f(t)\, dt.$$

This is formula (1).

Theorem 2. *Under the conditions*
 (i) *$f'(t)$ is continuous when $t \geqq 0$,*
 (ii) *$f''(t)$ is piecewise continuous when $t \geqq 0$,*
 (iii) *$f(t)$ and $f'(t)$ are of exponential order α,*
$f''(x)$ has the transform

(2) $\pounds\{f''(t)\} = s^2\pounds\{f(t)\} - sf(0) - f'(0), \qquad s > \alpha.$

PROOF. The existence of $f'(t)$ at a point implies the continuity of $f(t)$ there. Two applications of Theorem 1 now show that when $s > \alpha$,

$$f''(t) = s\pounds\{f'(t)\} - f'(0)$$
$$= s[s\pounds\{f(t)\} - f(0)] - f'(0).$$

Theorem 3. *Under the conditions*
 (i) *$f(t)$ is piecewise continuous when $t \geqq 0$,*
 (ii) *$f(t)$ is of exponential order α,*
$\int_0^t f(t)\, dt$ *has the transform*

(3) $\pounds\left\{\int_0^t f(x)\, dx\right\} = \dfrac{1}{s}\pounds\{f(t)\}, \qquad s > \alpha.$

PROOF. The function $g(t) = \int_0^t f(x)\, dx$ is continuous.* Moreover $g'(t) = f(t)$ except at those points where $f(t)$ is discontinuous;† hence $g'(t)$ is piecewise continuous from (i). We may take $\alpha > 0$ in (ii); for if $\alpha \leqq 0$, (ii) holds *a fortiori* when $\alpha > 0$. Hence from (ii)

$$|g(t)| \leqq \int_0^t |f(x)|\, dx \leqq M\int_0^t e^{\alpha x}\, dx = \frac{M}{\alpha}(e^{\alpha t} - 1) < \frac{M}{\alpha}e^{\alpha t},$$

so that $g(t)$ is also of exponential order α. Thus we may apply Theorem 1 to $g(t)$:

$$\pounds\{g'(t)\} = s\pounds\{g(t)\} - g(0), \qquad s > \alpha.$$

Since $g(0) = 0$, this gives (3).

---

* *Advanced Calculus*, § 119, Theorem 1.
† *Advanced Calculus*, § 119, Theorem 2.

If $f(t)$ is of class $\mathcal{T}$ and has the transform $F(s)$,

(4) $$\lim_{s \to \infty} F(s) = 0.$$ (67.2).

Therefore, if $f'(t)$ is of class $\mathcal{T}$ and has the transform (1),

(5) $$\lim_{s \to \infty} sF(s) = f(0).$$

Under appropriate conditions we have from (1)

$$\mathcal{L}\{f'''(t)\} = s\mathcal{L}\{f''(t)\} - f''(0)$$

or, on making use of (2),

(6) $$\mathcal{L}\{f'''(t)\} = s^3\mathcal{L}\{f(t)\} - s^2f(0) - sf'(0) - f''(0).$$

The corresponding general formula

(7) $$\mathcal{L}\{f^{(n)}(t)\} = s^n F(s) - s^{n-1}f(0) - s^{n-2}f'(0) - \cdots - f^{(n-1)}(0)$$

is readily derived.

Example. The *error function* erf(t) and the *co-error function* erfc(t) are defined as

(8) $$\operatorname{erf}(t) = \frac{2}{\sqrt{\pi}} \int_0^t e^{-x^2}\, dx, \qquad \operatorname{erfc}(t) = 1 - \operatorname{erf} t.$$

Note that erf$(0) = 0$,   erf$(\infty) = 1.$*
We shall find $\mathcal{L}\{\operatorname{erf} \sqrt{t}\}$. If we put $u = x^2$,

$$\operatorname{erf} \sqrt{t} = \frac{2}{\sqrt{\pi}} \int_0^{\sqrt{t}} e^{-x^2}\, dx = \frac{1}{\sqrt{\pi}} \int_0^t u^{-\frac{1}{2}}e^{-u}\, du;$$

hence from (3)

$$\mathcal{L}\{\operatorname{erf} \sqrt{t}\} = \frac{1}{\sqrt{\pi}} \frac{1}{s}\, \mathcal{L}\{t^{-\frac{1}{2}}e^{-t}\}.$$

Now $$\mathcal{L}\{t^{-\frac{1}{2}}\} = \sqrt{\pi}/\sqrt{s}$$ (66.9)

$$\mathcal{L}\{t^{-\frac{1}{2}}e^{-t}\} = \sqrt{\pi}/\sqrt{s+1}$$ (65.10)

and hence from (3),

(9) $$\mathcal{L}\{\operatorname{erf} \sqrt{t}\} = \frac{1}{s\sqrt{s+1}}.$$

Using (65.14) we find that if $a > 0$,

(10) $$\mathcal{L}\{\operatorname{erf} a\sqrt{t}\} = \frac{a}{s\sqrt{s+a^2}}.$$

---

* *Advanced Calculus*, p. 315. Table for erf(t) in ref. 13, p. 128–132.

PROBLEMS

1. Verify equation (1) when $f(t) = t^n$ and $\cos bt$.

2. Verify equations (4) and (5) in the table of § 67.

3. If $f''(t)$ is of class $\mathcal{T}$ and has the transform (2), prove that

$$\lim_{s \to \infty} s^2 F(s) = A \quad \text{implies} \quad f(0) = 0 \quad \text{and} \quad f'(0) = A.$$

Verify on entries 11 and 14 of Table A.

4. Verify equation (6) when $f(t) = e^{at}$ and $\cos bt$.

5. Prove that

$$\pounds\left\{\int_a^t f(x) \, dx\right\} = \frac{1}{s}\left[\pounds\{f(t)\} - \int_0^a f(x) \, dx\right].$$

6. The *sine-integral* function is defined by

$$Si(t) = \int_0^t \frac{\sin x}{x} \, dx.$$

Prove that

$$\pounds\{Si(t)\} = \frac{1}{s} \cot^{-1} s, \qquad s > 0. \qquad [\text{Cf. (65.21).}]$$

7. The *cosine-integral* function is defined by

$$Ci(t) = -\int_t^\infty \frac{\cos u}{u} \, du = -\int_1^\infty \frac{\cos tv}{v} \, dv \qquad (u = tv).$$

Show by transforming under the integral sign that

$$\pounds\{Ci(t)\} = -\int_1^\infty \frac{1}{v}\frac{s}{s^2 + v^2} \, dv = -\frac{1}{2s}\log(s^2 + 1).$$

8. The *exponential-integral* function is defined by

$$Ei(t) = \int_{-\infty}^t \frac{e^u}{u} \, du \quad \text{when} \quad t < 0.$$

When $t > 0$ we have, on putting $u = -vt$,

$$-Ei(-t) = -\int_{-\infty}^{-t} \frac{e^u}{u} \, du = \int_1^\infty \frac{e^{-vt}}{v} \, dv.$$

Show that

$$\pounds\{-Ei(-t)\} = \int_1^\infty \frac{dv}{v(s + v)} = \frac{\log(s + 1)}{s}.$$

9. Find the transforms of $Si(at)$, $Ci(at)$, $-Ei(-at)$ and verify dimensions when $\dim a = T^{-1}$.

69. SOLUTION OF LINEAR DIFFERENTIAL EQUATIONS WITH CONSTANT COEFFICIENTS

We can now solve an equation such as

(1) $$y'' + ay' + by = f(t)$$

with prescribed initial values of $y(0)$ and $y'(0)$ by transforming the derivatives according to the formulas of § 68. Thus if $Y(s)$, $F(s)$ denote the transforms of $y(t)$ and $f(t)$, equation (1) becomes

$$s^2 Y - sy(0) - y'(0) + a\{sY - y(0)\} + bY = F(s),$$

and hence

$$Y(s) = \frac{F(s) + sy(0) + y'(0) + ay(0)}{s^2 + as + b}$$

Then $y(t) = \pounds^{-1}\{Y(s)\}$ is the solution of (1) which fulfills the given initial conditions. We need not be too concerned over the validity of this process, for $y(t)$ may be checked as a solution of (1) which has the given values $y(0)$ and $y'(0)$. The simple check on initial conditions should *always* be made to catch errors, but of course this alone is not a guarantee of correctness. Note that the equation itself gives $y''(0)$ when $y'(0)$ and $y(0)$ are known.

Example 1. $y'' + y = 2 \sin t$; $y(0) = 1$, $y'(0) = 3$. The transformed equation is

$$(s^2 Y - s - 3) + Y = \frac{2}{s^2 + 1} ;$$

whence

$$Y = \frac{s}{s^2 + 1} + \frac{3}{s^2 + 1} + \frac{2}{(s^2 + 1)^2} .$$

The table (nos. 7, 8, 13) now gives the inverse transform

$$y = \cos t + 3 \sin t + (\sin t - t \cos t) + (1 - t) \cos t + 4 \sin t.$$

Example 2. $y'' - 3y' + 2y = t$; $y(0) = 1$, $y'(0) = 2$. The transformed equation is

$$(s^2 Y - s - 2) - 3(sY - 1) + 2Y = \frac{1}{s^2} .$$

Solving for Y and resolving into partial fractions:

$$Y = \frac{s^3 - s^2 + 1}{s^2(s - 1)(s - 2)} = \frac{\frac{1}{2}}{s^2} + \frac{\frac{3}{4}}{s} - \frac{1}{s - 1} + \frac{\frac{5}{4}}{s - 2} .$$

The table (nos. 3, 1, 2) gives the inverse transform

$$y = \tfrac{1}{2}t + \tfrac{3}{4} - e^t + \tfrac{5}{4}e^{2t}.$$

Example 3. Find x and y as functions of t:

$$2x' + x + y'' = e^t, \qquad x(0) = 1,$$
$$2x + y' = 0, \qquad y(0) = 2, \, y'(0) = -2.$$

The transformed equations are

$$2(sX - 1) + X + (s^2 Y - 2s + 2) = \frac{1}{s - 1}$$

$$2X + (sY - 2) = 0$$

or

$$(2s + 1)X + s^2 Y = \frac{1}{s - 1} + 2s$$

$$2X + sY = 2.$$

Solving for X and Y,

$$X = \frac{1}{s - 1}, \qquad Y = \frac{2s - 4}{s(s - 1)} = \frac{4}{s} - \frac{2}{s - 1};$$

and from the table (nos. 1, 2)

$$x = e^t, \qquad y = 4 - 2e^t.$$

Example 4. $y' + 2y + \displaystyle\int_0^t y \, dt = \sin t, \qquad y(0) = 1.$

Using Theorem 3 to transform the integral, we have

$$(sY - 1) + 2Y + \frac{Y}{s} = \frac{1}{s^2 + 1},$$

$$\left(s + 2 + \frac{1}{s}\right) Y = \frac{s^2 + 2}{s^2 + 1},$$

$$Y = \frac{s(s^2 + 2)}{(s + 1)^2(s^2 + 1)} = \frac{A}{s + 1} + \frac{B}{(s + 1)^2} + \frac{Cs + D}{s^2 + 1}.$$

From this identity in s we obtain the equations

$$A + C = 1, \qquad A + B + 2C + D = 0, \qquad A + 2D + C = 0,$$
$$A + B + D = 0,$$

whence $D = \tfrac{1}{2}$, $C = 0$, $A = 1$, $B = -\tfrac{3}{2}$. Thus

$$Y = \frac{1}{s + 1} - \frac{\tfrac{3}{2}}{(s + 1)^2} + \frac{\tfrac{1}{2}}{s^2 + 1},$$

and from the table (nos. 2, 4, 8)

$$y = e^{-t} - \tfrac{3}{2}te^{-t} + \tfrac{1}{2}\sin t.$$

The reader should check this answer. The equation itself gives $y'(0) = -2$, and this is easily verified.

PROBLEMS

Solve the following differential equations:

1. $y' = 5 - 2y$; $y(0) = 2$.
2. $y'' + a^2 y = \cos ax$; $y(0) = y'(0) = 0$.
3. $y'' - 3y' + 2y = e^t$; $y(0) = 1$, $y'(0) = -1$.
4. $y'' + y = 2t$; $y(0) = 1$, $y'(0) = 0$.
5. $y'' - y' - 6y = 2$; $y(0) = 1$, $y'(0) = 0$.
6. $y''' + y = 1$; $y(0) = y'(0) = y''(0) = 0$.
7. $y^{\mathrm{iv}} + 2y'' + y = 0$; $y(0) = 0$, $y'(0) = 1$, $y''(0) = 2$, $y'''(0) = -3$.
8. $y''' + y^{\mathrm{iv}} = \cos t$; $y(0) = y'(0) = y''(0) = 0$, $y'''(0) = 2$.
9. $x' + y = t$, $x + y' = 1$; $x(0) = 1$, $y(0) = -1$.
10. $x'' - y = t$, $x(0) = x'(0) = 0$,
    $y'' - x = 1$; $y(0) = y'(0) = 0$.
11. $x' + 2y = 0$, $x(0) = 2$, $x'(0) = -2$,
    $x'' + 2y' + y = e^t$; $y(0) = 1$.
12. $x' + 3x + 2\int_0^t x \, dt = \sin t$; $[x'(0) = ?]$.
13. $x'' + 2y' + y = e^t$, $x(0) = -2$;
    $x' + 2y = t^2$;   Find $x'(0)$ and $y(0)$ from equations.
14. $x' + y' + y = t$,   Show that $x(0) + y(0) = -1$.
    $x'' + y'' + y' + x + y = t^2$. $x'(0) + y'(0) + y(0) = 0$.
15. $Ri + \dfrac{1}{C}\int_0^t i \, dt = E$, $\left[i(0) = \dfrac{E}{R} \right]$.
16. Solve Problem 40.17.

70. CONVOLUTION

Two sequences $\{a_n\}$, $\{b_n\}$, where $n = 0, 1, 2, \ldots$, correspond to the functions

$$\alpha(t) = \sum_{n=0}^{\infty} a_n t^n, \qquad \beta(t) = \sum_{n=0}^{\infty} b_n t^n$$

over their common interval of convergence. If one of these power series converges absolutely in this interval, the *Cauchy sequence*

$$(1)' \qquad c_n = a_0 b_n + a_1 b_{n-1} + \cdots + a_n b_0 = \sum_{k=0}^{n} a_k b_{n-k}$$

corresponds to the function $\gamma(t) = \alpha(t)\beta(t)$.†

The sequence $\{c_n\}$ is called the *convolution* of the sequences $\{a_n\}$ and $\{b_n\}$ and is denoted by $\{a_n * b_n\}$. The "product" $a_n * b_n$ is obviously

---

† *Advanced Calculus*, p. 71, Mertens' Theorem.

commutative and also associative and distributive:

(2)′ $$a_n * b_n = b_n * a_n,$$

(3)′ $$a_n * (b_n * c_n) = (a_n * b_n) * c_n,$$

(4)′ $$a_n * (b_n + c_n) = a_n * b_n + a_n * c_n.$$

We shall now consider the integral analogs of these results. Instead of sequences (functions of the integral argument $0, 1, 2, \ldots$), we take functions of the continuous argument t over the interval $0 \leq t < \infty$. The *convolution* of the functions $a(t)$ and $b(t)$ is defined as the function

(1) $$a(t) * b(t) = \int_0^t a(x)b(t - x)\, dx.$$

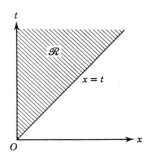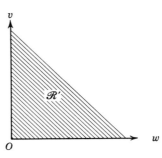

Fig. 70

This "product" is also commutative; for if we put $t - x = y$, $dx = -dy$,

(2) $$a(t) * b(t) = \int_0^t b(y)a(t - y)\, dy = b(t) * a(t).$$

This convolution is obviously distributive. It may be proved directly that it is also associative, but it follows more readily from the

Convolution Theorem 1. *If the functions $f(t)$ and $g(t)$ belong to class $\mathscr{T}(\alpha)$ and have the transforms $F(s)$ and $G(s)$, their convolution $f(t) * g(t)$ has the transform $F(s)G(s)$:*

(3) $$\mathcal{L}\{f(t) * g(t)\} = F(s)G(s), \qquad s > \alpha.$$

PROOF. The transform of $f * g$ is

(4) $$\int_0^\infty e^{-st} \int_0^t f(x)g(t - x)\, dx\, dt = \iint_{\mathscr{R}} e^{-st} f(x)g(t - x)\, dx\, dt$$

where the double integral is taken over the region $\mathscr{R}$ between the ray $x = t$ and the positive t-axis (Fig. 70). When the variables are changed from x, t to u, v through the equations $x = u, t = u + v$, the Jacobian

$$\frac{\partial(x, t)}{\partial(u, v)} = \begin{vmatrix} x_u & x_v \\ t_u & t_v \end{vmatrix} = \begin{vmatrix} 1 & 0 \\ 1 & 1 \end{vmatrix} = 1,$$

and the region $\mathcal{R}$ is mapped on the first quadrant $\mathcal{R}'$ of the uv-plane. Therefore the double integral in (4) becomes†

$$\iint_{\mathcal{R}'} e^{-s(u+v)} f(u)g(v) \, du \, dv = \int_0^\infty e^{-su} f(u) \, du \cdot \int_0^\infty e^{-sv} g(v) \, dv.$$

Since the right-hand member is $F(s)G(s)$, the theorem is established.

Corollary. *The convolution "product" is associative.*‡

This follows from Lerch's theorem; for

$$\mathcal{L}\{f * (g * h)\} = F(GH) = (FG)H = \mathcal{L}\{(f * g) * h\}.$$

Example. In the convolution integral

$$t^m * t^n = \int_0^t x^m (t - x)^n \, dx, \qquad m, n > -1,$$

make the change of variable $x = ty$; then

$$t^m * t^n = \int_0^1 t^m y^m \cdot t^n (1 - y)^n \cdot t \, dy = t^{m+n+1} B(m + 1, n + 1)$$

where

$$B(m + 1, n + 1) = \frac{\Gamma(m + 1)\Gamma(n + 1)}{\Gamma(m + n + 2)}, \qquad m, n > -1.$$

is Euler's *beta function*.§ Therefore

(5) $$t^m * t^n = \frac{\Gamma(m + 1)\Gamma(n + 1)}{\Gamma(m + n + 2)} t^{m+n+1}, \qquad m, n > -1.$$

The convolution theorem now states that

$$\mathcal{L}\{t^m * t^n\} = \mathcal{L}\{t^m\}\mathcal{L}\{t^n\} = \frac{\Gamma(m + 1)\Gamma(n + 1)}{s^{m+n+2}}.$$

But according to no. 3 of Table A this is precisely the transform of the function given in (5). The exponents m and n are any real numbers greater than -1.

The convolution theorem is of great help in finding inverse transforms.

---

† *Advanced Calculus*, p. 364, equation (162.2).
‡ We assume here that the functions are of exponential order; but the theorem is true when the functions are merely piecewise continuous in any finite interval $0 \leqq t \leqq T$. The proof is given in § 136.
§ *Advanced Calculus*, §§ 192, 193.

Thus if $F(s) = G(s)H(s)$ and the inverse transforms $g(t)$, $h(t)$ are known,

(6) $$\mathcal{L}^{-1}\{F(s)\} = \mathcal{L}^{-1}\{G(s)H(s)\} = g(t) * h(t).$$

For example,

$$\mathcal{L}^{-1}\left\{\frac{s}{(s^2 + 1)^2}\right\} = \mathcal{L}^{-1}\left\{\frac{1}{s^2 + 1} \cdot \frac{s}{s^2 + 1}\right\} = \sin t * \cos t$$

$$= \int_0^t \sin x \cos (t - x) \, dx = \tfrac{1}{2} t \sin t$$

in agreement with no. 13 of the table.

If $\mathcal{L}^{-1}\{F(s)\} = f(t)$ is known,

(7) $$\mathcal{L}^{-1}\left\{\frac{1}{s} F(s)\right\} = 1 * f(t) = \int_0^t f(x) \, dx.$$

We may also use convolution to prove (cf. Theorem 39.1).

Theorem 2. *If $v(t)$ is the solution of the system*

(8) $$av'' + bv' + c = 0, \qquad v(0) = 0, \qquad v'(0) = \frac{1}{a},$$

then the system

(9) $$ay'' + by' + cy = f(t), \qquad y(0) = 0, \qquad y'(0) = 0,$$

has the solution $f(t) * v(t)$.

PROOF. The transform of equation (8) with $v(0) = 0$, $v'(0) = 1/a$ is

$$as^2 V - 1 + bsV + cV = 0,$$

$$V(s) = \frac{1}{as^2 + bs + c}.$$

The transform of equation (9) with $y(0) = 0$, $y'(0) = 0$ is

$$as^2 Y + bsY + cY = F(s),$$

$$Y(s) = \frac{F(s)}{as^2 + bs + c} = F(s)V(s);$$

hence

$$y(t) = f(t) * v(t).$$

Integral equations of the Volterra type with a *difference kernel* $k(t - x)$ such as

(10) $$y(t) = g(t) + \int_0^t k(t - x)y(x) \, dx$$

are readily solved for the unknown function $y(t)$ by use of the convolution theorem. The transform of (10) is

$$Y(s) = G(s) + K(s) Y(s)$$

from which $Y(s)$ may be found.

Integral equations of this type are solved by the Mikusiński operational calculus in § 145.

Example. $y(t) = \cos t + \int_0^t e^{-(t-x)} y(x)\, dx = \cos t + e^{-t} * y$ has the transform

$$Y(s) = \frac{s}{s^2 + 1} + \frac{1}{s + 1}\, Y.$$

Hence

$$Y(s) = \frac{s + 1}{s^2 + 1}, \qquad y = \cos t + \sin t.$$

PROBLEMS

Verify the following convolutions:

1. $1 * 1 = t$.

2. $e^{at} * e^{bt} = \dfrac{e^{at} - e^{bt}}{a - b}$, $\qquad a \neq b$; $\qquad e^{at} * e^{at} = t e^{at}$.

3. $\cos at * \cos bt = \dfrac{a \sin at - b \sin bt}{a^2 - b^2}$, $\qquad a \neq b$.

4. $\cos at * \cos at = \dfrac{1}{2a} (\sin at + at \cos at)$.

5. $\sin at * \sin bt = \dfrac{a \sin bt - b \sin at}{a^2 - b^2}$, $\qquad a \neq b$.

6. $\sin at * \sin at = \dfrac{1}{2a} (\sin at - at \cos at)$.

7. $t * \sin t = t - \sin t$.

8. $t^{-\frac{1}{2}} * t^{-\frac{1}{2}} = \pi$.

9. $y' + ay = f(t)$, $\qquad y(0) = 0$.
Prove: $y = e^{-at} * f(t)$.

10. $y'' + n^2 y = f(t)$, $\qquad y(0) = y'(0) = 0$.

Prove: $y = \dfrac{1}{n} f(t) * \sin nt$.

11. $y'' + n^2 y = f(t)$, $\qquad y(0) = a$, $\quad y'(0) = b$,

Prove: $y = \dfrac{1}{n} f(t) * \sin nt + a \cos nt + \dfrac{b}{n} \sin nt$.

Solve the following integral equations for $y(t)$:

12. $y(t) = 1 + 8t + \int_0^t (6t - 6x + 5) \, y(x) \, dx.$

13. $y(t) = \sinh t + e^{-t} \int_0^t e^x y(x) \, dx.$

14. $f(t) = \int_0^t (t - u)^{-k} y'(u) \, du, \qquad 0 < k < 1.$ (Abel's integral equation.)

Show that $y(t) = \dfrac{\sin k\pi}{\pi} \int_0^t f(u)(t - u)^{k-1} \, du + y(0).$

71. HEAVISIDE'S UNIT FUNCTION

The simple and important discontinuous function defined by

$$(1) \qquad\qquad h(t) = \begin{cases} 0 & t < 0 \\ 1 & t \geq 0 \end{cases}$$

is called *Heaviside's unit function.** When $t \geq 0$, $h(t)$ is the same as the *unit function*

Fig. 71a   Unit function: $\{1\}$. Heaviside unit function: $h(t)$.

$$(2) \qquad\qquad \{1\} = 1 \quad \text{for all real } t;$$

thus $h(t) = \{1\}$ when $t \geq 0$ (Fig. 71a). In accordance with (1)

$$(3) \qquad\qquad h(t - a) = \begin{cases} 0 & t < a \\ 1 & t \geq a \end{cases}.$$

The Laplace transform of $h(t - a)$,

$$(4) \qquad \pounds\{h(t - a)\} = \int_a^\infty e^{-st} \, dt = \frac{e^{-as}}{s}, \qquad s > 0.$$

---

* The notations $H(t)$ and $u(t)$ are also in current use.

If the graph of $y = f(t)$ is shifted a units to the right (Fig. 71*b*), its equation referred to the same axes is $y = f(x - a)$. If the part of this graph to the left of $x = a$ is cut off and discarded, the remainder (Fig. 71*c*) represents the function

$$h(t - a)f(t - a) = \begin{cases} 0 & t < a, \\ f(t - a) & t \geq a. \end{cases}$$

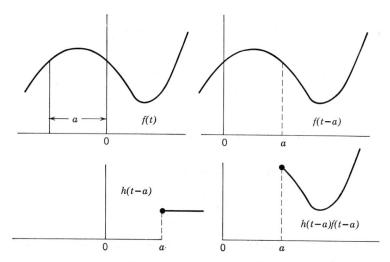

Fig. 71b, c Shift and cut-off.

Theorem 1. *If* $\pounds\{f(t)\} = F(s)$,

(5) $$\pounds\{h(t - a)f(t - a)\} = e^{-as}F(s).$$

PROOF. The transform of $h(t - a)f(t - a)$ is

$$\int_a^\infty e^{-st}f(t - a)\, dt = \int_0^\infty e^{-s(a+\tau)}f(\tau)\, d\tau = e^{-as}\int_0^\infty e^{-s\tau}f(\tau)\, d\tau$$

on putting $t = \tau + a$, $dt = d\tau$.

When $f(t) = 1$, $F(s) = 1/s$, and (5) becomes (4).

If $f(t)$ is a polynomial of degree n, the transform of $h(t - a)f(t)$ may be obtained by replacing $f(t)$ by its finite Taylor expansion in powers of $t - a$,

$$f(t) = \sum_{k=0}^n \frac{f^{(k)}(a)}{k!} (t - a)^k,$$

and applying formula (5) to each term:

(6) $$\pounds\{h(t - a)f(t)\} = e^{-as}\sum_{k=0}^n \frac{f^{(k)}(a)}{s^{k+1}}.$$

Note that the factorials cancel.

The portion of $f(t)$ lying in the interval $a \leq t < b$ is given by

(7)
$$f(t)[h(t-a) - h(t-b)] = \begin{cases} 0 & t < a \\ f(t) & a \leq t < b \\ 0 & t \geq b; \end{cases}$$

for the function in brackets equals 0, 1, 0 in the three intervals.
The function $f(t)$ is said to be periodic of period p if

$$f(t+p) = f(t) \quad \text{for all } t.$$

An *element* of this function is given by

$$g(t) = f(t)h(t) - f(t-p)h(t-p) = \begin{cases} f(t) & 0 \leq t < p \\ 0 & t \geq p. \end{cases}$$

The Laplace transform of this equation

$$G(s) = F(s) - e^{-ps}F(s)$$

yields the transform of $f(t)$, namely

(8)
$$F(s) = \frac{G(s)}{1 - e^{-ps}}, \qquad G(s) = \int_0^p e^{-st}f(t)\,dt.$$

Example 1. Find $\pounds\{h(t-1)(3 - 7t + 6t^2 - t^3)\}$.
With $f(t) = 3 - 7t + 6t^2 - t^3$ we find

$$f(1) = 1, \qquad f'(1) = 2, \qquad f''(1) = 6, \qquad f'''(1) = -6;$$

$$\pounds\{h(t-1)f(t)\} = e^{-s}\left[\frac{1}{s} + \frac{2}{s^2} + \frac{6}{s^3} - \frac{6}{s^4}\right].$$

Example 2. **The Square Wave** $f_1(t)$. A square wave of unit amplitude and period $2a$ is shown in Figure 71d. An element of this wave is

$$g(t) = h(t) - 2h(t-a) + h(t-2a)$$

and the complete wave

$$f_1(t) = h(t) - 2h(t-a) + h(t-2a) +$$
$$h(t-2a) - 2h(t-3a) + h(t-4a) + \cdots$$
$$= h(t) + 2\sum_{j=1}^{\infty} (-1)^j h(t-ja).$$

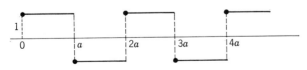

Square wave: $f_1(t)$

Fig. 71d

Its transform is therefore

(9)
$$F_1(s) = \frac{1}{s}\left[1 + 2\sum_{j=1}^{\infty}(-1)^j e^{-jas}\right].$$

We may also use formula (8) with

$$G(s) = \frac{1}{s}(1 - 2e^{-as} + e^{-2as}) = \frac{(1 - e^{-as})^2}{s};$$

then

(9)′
$$F_1(s) = \frac{1}{s}\frac{(1 - e^{-as})^2}{1 - e^{-2as}} = \frac{1}{s}\frac{1 - e^{-as}}{1 + e^{-as}} = \frac{1}{s}\tanh\frac{as}{2}.$$

Formula (9)′ also follows from formula (9) by summing the geometric series.

Example 3. Rectified Triangular Wave $f_2(t)$. This wave (Fig. 71e) is said to be rectified because the negative portions of a triangular wave have been reversed.

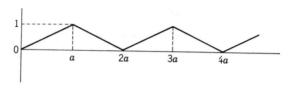

Rectified triangular wave: $f_2(t)$

Fig. 71e

The rectified wave of amplitude 1 and period $2a$ has the slope $f_2'(t) = \pm 1/a$ according as $f_2(t)$ is increasing or decreasing; thus

$$f_2'(t) = \frac{1}{a}f_1(t)$$

where $f_1(t)$ is the square wave of Example 1. Since $f_2(0) = 0$, we have on integration

$$f_2(t) = \frac{1}{a}\int_0^t f_1(\tau)\,d\tau;$$

the transform $F_2(s)$ is therefore given by formula II of Table B:

(10)
$$F_2(s) = \frac{1}{a}\frac{F_1(s)}{s} = \frac{1}{as^2}\left[1 + 2\sum_{j=0}^{\infty}(-1)^j e^{-jas}\right] = \frac{1}{as^2}\tanh\frac{as}{2}$$

where $F_1(s)$ is given by (9).

Example 4. In the differential equation

$$y'' + y = h(t - \pi) - h(t - 2\pi), \qquad y(0) = y'(0) = 0,$$

the right member is 1 when $\pi \leq t < 2\pi$ and zero elsewhere (Fig. 71f). Its transform is

$$s^2 Y + Y = \frac{1}{s}(e^{-\pi s} - e^{-2\pi s})$$

and

$$Y = \frac{e^{-\pi s} - e^{-2\pi s}}{s(s^2 + 1)}.$$

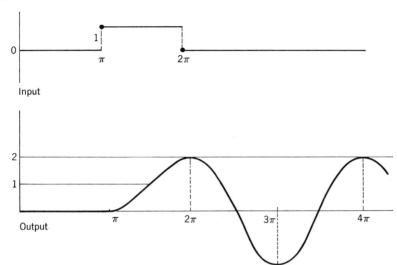

Input

Output

Fig. 71f

Since $\quad \mathcal{L}^{-1}\left\{\dfrac{1}{s(s^2+1)}\right\} = \mathcal{L}^{-1}\left\{\dfrac{1}{s} - \dfrac{s}{s^2+1}\right\} = 1 - \cos t,$

formula VII of Table B gives

$$y = [1 - \cos(t - \pi)]h(t - \pi) - [1 - \cos(t - 2\pi)]h(t - 2\pi)$$
$$= (1 + \cos t)h(t - \pi) - (1 - \cos t)h(t - 2\pi).$$

The solution is therefore the function

$$y(t) = \begin{cases} 0, & 0 \leqq t < \pi \\ 1 + \cos t, & \pi \leqq t < 2\pi \\ 2 \cos t, & 2\pi \leqq t \end{cases}$$

which is continuous and has a continuous derivative. Except at $t = \pi$ and 2π, where y'' is not defined, $y(t)$ satisfies the differential equation and the initial conditions.

If the equation is solved without transforming, it must be done piecewise over the three intervals, using each partial solution to get the initial conditions for the one following.

Example 5. The integro-differential equation with discontinuous input, namely, 1 for $1 \leqq t < 2$, 0 elsewhere:

(i) $\qquad y' + 3y + 2\displaystyle\int_0^t y(\tau)\, d\tau = h(t - 1) - h(t - 2), \qquad y(0) = 1,$

has the transform

$$sY - 1 + 3Y + \frac{2}{s}Y = \frac{1}{s}(e^{-s} - e^{-2s});$$

hence

$$Y = \frac{1}{(s+1)(s+2)}(s + e^{-s} - e^{-2s}).$$

Now

$$\mathcal{L}^{-1}\left\{\frac{s}{(s+1)(s+2)}\right\} = \mathcal{L}^{-1}\left\{\frac{2}{s+2} - \frac{1}{s+1}\right\} = 2e^{-2t} - e^{-t} = g(t),$$

$$\mathcal{L}^{-1}\left\{\frac{1}{(s+1)(s+2)}\right\} = \mathcal{L}^{-1}\left\{\frac{1}{s+1} - \frac{1}{s+2}\right\} = e^{-t} - e^{-2t} = f(t).$$

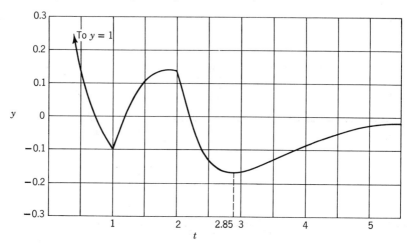

Fig. 71g

Using formula VII of Table B we now have

$$y(t) = g(t) + f(t-1)h(t-1) - f(t-2)h(t-2),$$

or, in detail,

(ii)
$$y(t) = \begin{cases} g(t), & 0 \le t < 1 \\ g(t) + f(t-1), & 1 \le t < 2 \\ g(t) + f(t-1) - f(t-2), & 2 \le t < \infty. \end{cases}$$

Since $g(0) = 1$, the initial condition $y(0) = 1$ is satisfied and $g'(0) = -3$ implies $y'(0) = -3$ given by the equation. Moreover since $f(0) = 0$, $y(t)$ is continuous at $t = 1$ and $t = 2$ where the input is discontinuous. But since

$$f'(t) = 2e^{-2t} - e^{-t}, \qquad f'(0) = 1,$$

$y'(t)$ has jumps of 1 and -1 at these points, precisely the same jumps as the input. This is, of course, no coincidence; for since $y(t)$ and the integral in (i) are continuous, the jumps of $y(t)$ must be the same as those of the input.

From the solution (ii) we have the table of values

t	0	0.5	1.0	1.5	2.0	2.5	3.0	4.0	5.0
y	1	0.129	−0.098	0.116	0.134	−0.135	−0.161	−0.087	−0.037

Moreover $y = 0$ when $t = 0.69$ and 1.15; and $y(t)$ has a cusp minimum at $t = 1$, a cusp maximum at $t = 2$, points where the slope changes sign. Then $y(t)$ decreases to a smooth minimum at $t = 2.85$ after which it increases asymptotically to zero (Fig. 71g).

PROBLEMS

1. Show that the graph of Figure 71h represents a function $g(t)$ for which

$g'(t) = h(t) - 2h(t - a) + 2h(t - 3a) - h(t - 4a),$

$g(t) = th(t) - 2(t - a)h(t - a) + 2(t - 3a)h(t - 3a) - (t - 4a)h(t - 4a),$

$G(s) = \dfrac{1}{s^2}(1 - 2e^{-as} + 2e^{-3as} - e^{-4as}).$

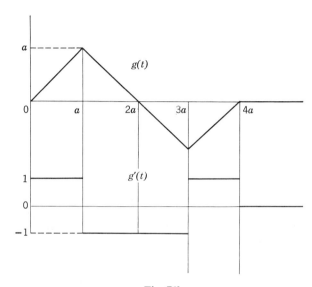

Fig. 71h

2. Show that the graph of Figure 71i represents a function $f(t)$ for which

$f'(t) = h(t) - h(t - a) - h(t - 2a) + h(t - 3a),$

$f(t) = th(t) - (t - a)h(t - a) - (t - 2a)h(t - 2a) + (t - 3a)h(t - 3a),$

$F(s) = \dfrac{1}{s^2}(1 - e^{-as} - e^{-2as} + e^{-3as}).$

3. Show that the *rectified sine wave* $|\sin t|$ is given by

$$|\sin t| = \sin t + 2\sum_{j=1}^{\infty} h(t - j\pi)\sin(t - j\pi)$$

and that its transform is

$$\pounds\,|\sin t| = \frac{1}{s^2 + 1}\left(1 + 2\sum_{j=1}^{\infty} e^{-j\pi s}\right) = \frac{1}{s^2 + 1}\coth\frac{\pi s}{2}.$$

4. Show that one element of the rectified sine wave $|\sin t|$ is

$$g(t) = \sin t + h(t - \pi)\sin(t - \pi) \text{ and } G(s) = \frac{1 + e^{-\pi s}}{s^2 + 1}.$$

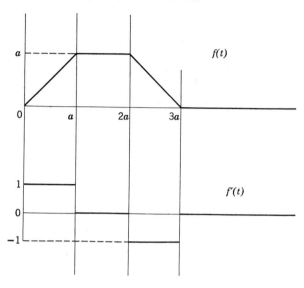

Fig. 71i

Use (8) to find $\mathcal{L} |\sin t|$ as given in Problem 3.

Use VI of Table B to derive $\mathcal{L} |\sin bt|$ as given in Table C.

5. Confirm the results given for the Morse dot function in Table C.

6. Confirm the results given for the rectified sine half-wave in Table C.

7. Confirm the results given for the sawtooth function in Table C.

8. Solve the equation

$$y'' + 2y' + y = 1 - 2h(t - 1) + h(t - 2), \qquad y(0) = 1, \qquad y'(0) = 0.$$

9. Solve the equation

$$y' + 2y + \int_0^t y(\tau)\, d\tau = 1 - h(t - 1), \qquad y(0) = 1.$$

10. Prove that

$$h(t - a) * f(t) = h(t - a) \int_0^{t-a} f(x)\, dx$$

11. Prove that

$$h(t - a) * h(t - b) = (t - a - b)h(t - a - b).$$

12. Prove that the triangular wave whose element $g(t)$ is given in Problem 1 has the transform

$$\frac{1}{s^2}(1 - 2e^{-as} + 2e^{-3as} - 2e^{-5as} + 2e^{-7as} - \cdots) = \frac{1}{s^2}\frac{(1 - e^{-as})^2}{1 + e^{-2as}}.$$

72. RESPONSE TO UNIT FUNCTION

In the differential equation

(1) $f(D)y = \varphi(t)$

$f(D)$ is a polynomial in $D = d/dt$. If

$$f(D) = a_0 D^n + a_1 D^{n-1} + \cdots + a_{n-1}D + a_n,$$

let the initial conditions be

(2) $y(0) = y'(0) = \cdots = y^{(n-1)}(0) = 0.$

The solution $y(t)$ of the system (1-2) is called the *response* to the *driving function* $\varphi(t)$. If $\varphi(t)$ is replaced by the unit function $h(t)$, the corresponding solution $y_1(t)$ is called the response to the unit function. When $y_1(t)$ is known, $y(t)$ may be computed from the following

Theorem. *If $y_1(t)$ is the response to the unit function $h(t)$ in the system (1-2), the response to the driving function $\varphi(t)$ is given by*

(3) $y(t) = y_1(t) * \varphi'(t) + \varphi(0)y_1(t).$

PROOF. The transform of the system (1-2) is

$$(a_0 s^n + a_1 s^{n-1} + \cdots + a_{n-1}s + a_n)Y(s) = \Phi(s)$$

and

(4) $Y(s) = \dfrac{\Phi(s)}{f(s)}.$

When $\varphi(t)$ is replaced by $h(t)$, we must replace $\Phi(s)$ by $\pounds\{h(t)\} = 1/s$. Thus the response $y_1(t)$ to the unit function has the transform

(5) $Y_1(s) = \dfrac{1}{sf(s)}.$

From (4) and (5) we have

$$Y(s) = Y_1(s) \cdot s\Phi(s)$$

or since

$$\pounds\{\varphi'(t)\} = s\Phi(s) - \varphi(0),$$
$$Y(s) = Y_1(s) \cdot \pounds\{\varphi'(t)\} + \varphi(0)Y_1(s).$$

The convolution theorem now gives $y(t)$ in accordance with (3).

Example. For the system

$$y'' + y = \sin t, \qquad y(0) = y'(0) = 0,$$

the response to the unit function is

$$y_1 = 1 - \cos t.$$

Hence the response to the driving function $\varphi(t) = \sin t$ is

$$y = (1 - \cos t) * \cos t + 0$$

$$= \int_0^t \cos x \, dx - \int_0^t \cos x \cos (t - x) \, dx$$

$$= \sin t - \tfrac{1}{2} (\sin t + t \cos t)$$

$$= \tfrac{1}{2} (\sin t - t \cos t).$$

73. UNIT IMPULSE OR DIRAC SYMBOL

The function

$$\delta_a(t) = \begin{cases} 1/\varepsilon & a < t < a + \varepsilon \\ 0 & t < a \quad \text{or} \quad t > a + \varepsilon \end{cases}$$

is called a unit impulse if ε is small; for in mechanics the impulse of the force $1/\varepsilon$ which acts for a brief interval ε is defined as $(1/\varepsilon)\varepsilon = 1$. In terms of unit functions

$$\delta_a(t) = \frac{1}{\varepsilon} [h(t - a) - h(t - a - \varepsilon)]$$

and the transform

(1)′
$$\pounds\{_a(\delta t)\} = \frac{1}{\varepsilon} \left[\frac{e^{-as}}{s} - \frac{e^{-(a+\varepsilon)s}}{s} \right] = \frac{e^{-as}}{s} \cdot \frac{1 - e^{-\varepsilon s}}{\varepsilon}.$$

As $\varepsilon \to 0$, $\delta_a(t) \to \delta(t - a)$, the *Dirac symbol*, which may be regarded as a distribution of values which are zero everywhere except at $t = a$ where the value is infinite; on the right Hospital's rule shows that $(1 - e^{-\varepsilon s})/\varepsilon \to s$. Thus the limiting form of (1)′ as $\varepsilon \to 0$ is

(1)
$$\pounds\{\delta(t - a)\} = e^{-as}.$$

This equation assigns the property

(2)
$$\int_0^\infty e^{-st} \delta(t - a) \, dt = e^{-as}$$

to the Dirac symbol.

If $f(x)$ is any integrable function which is continuous at a, we have also the more general *sifting property*

(3)
$$\int_0^\infty f(t) \delta(t - a) \, dt = f(a).$$

To justify (3), apply the mean-value theorem for integrals‡ to

$$\int_0^\infty f(t)\,\delta_a(t)\,dt = \frac{1}{\varepsilon}\int_a^{a+\varepsilon} f(t)\,dt = \frac{1}{\varepsilon}(a+\varepsilon-a)\mu = \mu$$

where μ lies between the greatest and least values of $f(t)$ in the interval $a \leqq t \leqq a+\varepsilon$; as $\varepsilon \to 0$, $\delta_a(t) \to \delta(t-a)$, $\mu \to f(a)$ and we obtain (3). Note that (2) is the special case $f(t) = e^{-st}$ of (3).

The derivative of the Heaviside function $h'(t-a)$ is zero everywhere except at $t = a$ where it is not defined. If we apply formula (68.1) to $h'(t-a)$, we have

$$£\{h'(t-a)\} = s£\{h(t-a)\} - h(-a) = e^{-as}.$$

Thus $h'(t-a)$ and $\delta(t-a)$ have the same Laplace transform.

The use of the Dirac symbol or "function" $\delta(t-a)$ may be justified by the theory of distributions.† In the theory of beams a load P "concentrated" at the point $x = a$ may be represented by $P\,\delta(x-a)$ in the flexural differential equation.

If we define $f(t) = 0$ when $t < 0$, the sifting property (3) shows that

$$\int_0^t \delta(x)f(t-x)\,dx = \int_0^\infty \delta(x)f(t-x)\,dx = f(t-0) = f(t);$$

therefore *the Dirac symbol is the multiplicative unit in convolution:*

(4) $$\delta(t) * f(t) = f(t).$$

Since $£\{\delta(t)\} = e^0 = 1$ from (1), equation (4) is in agreement with the convolution theorem of § 70.

An infinite series of Dirac symbols

$$\sum_{j=0}^\infty \delta(t-jp) = \delta(t) + \delta(t-p) + \delta(t-2p) + \cdots$$

spaced at equal distances p, has the Laplace transform

$$1 + e^{-ps} + e^{-2ps} + \cdots = \frac{1}{1-e^{-ps}},$$

or

(5) $$£\left\{\sum_{j=0}^\infty \delta(t-jp)\right\} = \frac{1}{1-e^{-ps}}.$$

Hence, if the convolution theorem is applicable,

$$£^{-1}\left\{\frac{G(s)}{1-e^{-ps}}\right\} = \sum_{j=0}^\infty \delta(t-jp) * g(t) = \sum_{j=0}^\infty g(t-jp) = f(t)$$

---

‡ *Advanced Calculus*, p. 258.
† Cf. B. Friedman, *Principles and Techniques of Applied Mathematics*, John Wiley and Sons, New York, 1956.

where $f(t)$ is a function of period p whose function element is $g(t)$. This agrees with the transform of a periodic function given in (71.8).

We shall see in Chapter 11 that the Dirac symbol is the multiplicative unit in an algebra whose elements contain operators as well as functions. This algebra of Mikusiński provides the simplest justification for the rigorous use of $\delta(t)$.

74. DEFLECTION OF BEAMS

Let $y(x)$ denote the downward deflection at a point distant x from one end of a uniform beam caused by distributed or concentrated loads on the

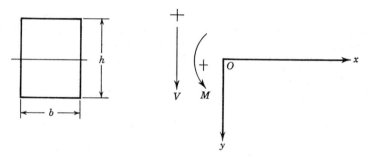

Fig. 74a, b   Sign conventions for moment and shear.

beam. If the beam is only slightly deformed by the loads, it can be shown that if $M(x)$ is the bending moment at the cross-section x, $y(x)$ satisfies the differential equation

(1) $$EIy'' = M(x),$$

where E is Young's modulus (lb/in²) of the cross-section and I is the moment of inertia (in⁴) of the area A of the cross-section at x with respect to the neutral axis (a horizontal line through the centroid of A).* Thus for a rectangular beam of breadth b, height h inches (Fig. 74a)

$$I = 2\int_0^{h/2} y^2 b \, dy = \frac{2b}{3} y^3 \Big|_0^{h/2} = \frac{bh^3}{12} \text{ in}^4.$$

If $V(x)$ is the shearing force at x, $\Delta M = V(x)\,\Delta x$ and

(2) $$\frac{dM}{dx} = V(x)$$

if signs are chosen as in Figure 74b. Moreover, if $w(x)$ is the downward

---

* See, for example, F. Seely and J. O. Smith, *Resistance of Materials*, Chap. V, John Wiley and Sons, New York, 1956; S. Timoshenko, *Strength of Materials*, Chap. V, Van Nostrand, New York, 1940.

load per unit length along the beam, $\Delta V = w(x)\,\Delta x$ and

(3)
$$\frac{dV}{dx} = w(x).$$

From (1), (2), and (3) we now have the differential equation

(4)
$$EI\,y^{\mathrm{iv}} = w(x),$$

or if $z = EIy$,

(5)
$$z^{\mathrm{iv}} = w(x).$$

Moreover, from (1) and (2)

(6)
$$z''(x) = M(x),\qquad z'''(x) = V(x).$$

If the end $x = 0$ is freely supported,

$$z(0) = 0,\qquad z'' = M(0) = 0,\qquad z'''(0) = V(0),$$

the reaction at the left support. If the beam is horizontally restrained at the end $x = 0$,

$$z(0) = 0,\qquad z'(0) = 0,\qquad z''(0) = M(0),\qquad z'''(0) = V(0)$$

where $M(0)$ and $V(0)$ must be determined. For a beam of length c, the end conditions at $x = c$ must be formulated in similar fashion. See the following examples for details.

Example. 1 Simply Supported Beam with a Concentrated Load (Fig. 74c).
Neglecting the weight of the beam, equation (5) for the load P at $x = a$ becomes

(i)
$$z^{\mathrm{iv}} = P\delta(x - a)$$

with the end conditions

(ii)　　$z(0) = 0,\qquad z''(0) = M_0 = 0,$
　　　　　$z'''(0) = V_0,$*

(iii)　　$z(c) = 0,\qquad z''(0) = 0.$

The transform of (i) is

$$s^4 Z - s^2 z'(0) - V_0 = Pe^{-as},$$

$$Z = \frac{z'(0)}{s^2} + \frac{V_0}{s^4} + P\frac{e^{-as}}{s^4}.$$

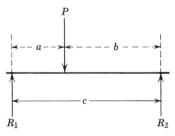

Fig. 74c Simple beam with concentrated load.

Transforming back,

(iv)
$$z(x) = z'(0)x + V_0\frac{x^3}{6} + P\frac{(x-a)^3}{6}\,h(x-a),$$

$$z''(x) = \qquad V_0 x \ + P(x-a)h(x-a).$$

---

* We write $V(0) = V_0$, $M(0) = M_0$.

The conditions (iii) now give

$$0 = z'(0)c + V_0 \frac{c^3}{6} + P \frac{b^3}{6},$$

$$0 = \qquad V_0 c \ + Pb,$$

whence

(v) $\qquad V_0 = -\frac{b}{c} P, \qquad z'(0) = \frac{P}{6} \frac{b}{c} (c^2 - b^2) = \frac{1}{6} \frac{ab}{c} (c + b)P.$

The *upward* reactions at the supports are

$$R_1 = -V_0 = \frac{b}{c} P, \qquad R_2 = P - \frac{b}{c} P = \frac{a}{c} P.$$

As a check, note that R_2 is obtained from R_1 by an interchange of a and b.

With the values given in (v), equation (iv) gives the elastic curve of the beam:

(vi) $\qquad EIy = \frac{P}{6} \left\{ \frac{ab(c + b)}{c} x - \frac{b}{c} x^3 + (x - a)^3 h(x - a) \right\}.$

The deflection $y(a)$ under the load is given by

$$EIy(a) = \frac{1}{6} P \frac{a^2 b}{c} (c + b - a) = \frac{1}{3} P \frac{a^2 b^2}{c}.$$

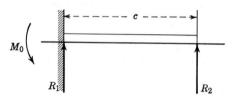

Fig. 74d   Built-in beam with uniform load.

*Example 2. **Uniformly Loaded Beam Restrained Horizontally at One End.***
(Fig. 74d). For a uniform load of w lb/in² equation (5) becomes

(i) $\qquad\qquad\qquad\qquad z^{\mathrm{iv}} = w \qquad (z = EIy)$

with the end conditions

(ii) $\qquad z(0) = 0, \qquad z'(0) = 0, \qquad z''(0) = M_0, \qquad z'''(0) = V_0;$

(iii) $\qquad\qquad\qquad\qquad z(c) = 0, \qquad z''(c) = 0.$

The transform of (i) is

$$s^4 Z - sM_0 - V_0 = \frac{w}{s},$$

$$Z = \frac{M_0}{s^3} + \frac{V_0}{s^4} + \frac{w}{s^5}.$$

Transforming back, we have

(iv)
$$z(x) = M_0 \frac{x^2}{2} + V_0 \frac{x^3}{6} + w \frac{x^4}{24},$$

$$z'(x) = M_0 x + V_0 \frac{x^2}{2} + w \frac{x^3}{6},$$

$$z''(x) = M_0 + V_0 x + \tfrac{1}{2} w x^2.$$

The conditions (iii) now give

$$0 = \tfrac{1}{2} M_0 + \tfrac{1}{6} V_0 c + \tfrac{1}{24} w c^2,$$
$$0 = M_0 + V_0 c + \tfrac{1}{2} w c^2,$$

whence

(v)
$$M_0 = \tfrac{1}{8} w c^2, \qquad V_0 = -\tfrac{5}{8} w c.$$

Equation (iv) now gives the elastic curve

(vi)
$$EIy = \frac{w}{48} (3c^2 x^2 - 5cx^3 + 2x^4)$$

The *upward* reactions at the supports are

$$R_1 = -V_0 = \tfrac{5}{8} w c, \qquad R_2 = wc - \tfrac{5}{8} w c = \tfrac{3}{8} w c.$$

Since $z' = 0$ when $8x^2 + 15cx + 6c^2 = 0$ the greatest deflection occurs at $x = 0.579c$, and may be computed from (vi).

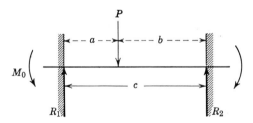

Fig. 74e   Doubly built-in beam with concentrated load.

Example 3. Beam Horizontally Restrained at Both Ends ("built-in") with a Concentrated Load. (Fig. 74e). Neglecting the weight of the beam, equation (5) becomes

(i)
$$z^{\mathrm{iv}} = P\delta(x - a)$$

with the end conditions

(ii) $z(0) = 0, \qquad z'(0) = 0, \qquad z''(0) = M_0, \qquad z'''(0) = V_0,$

(iii) $z(c) = 0, \qquad z''(c) = 0 \qquad (c = a + b).$

The transform of (i) is

$$s^4 Z - M_0 s - V_0 = P e^{-as},$$

$$Z = \frac{M_0}{s^3} + \frac{V_0}{s^4} + \frac{P e^{-as}}{s^4}.$$

Transforming back, we have

(iv)
$$z(x) = M_0 \frac{x^2}{2} + V_0 \frac{x^3}{6} + P \frac{(x - a)^3}{6} h(x - a),$$

$$z'(x) = M_0 x + V_0 \frac{x^2}{2} + P \frac{(x - a)^2}{2} h(x - a).$$

The conditions (iii) now give

$$0 = M_0 \frac{c^2}{2} + V_0 \frac{c^3}{6} + P \frac{b^3}{6} \quad \text{or} \quad 3M_0 + V_0 c = -P \frac{b^3}{c^2},$$

$$0 = M_0 c + V_0 \frac{c^2}{2} + P \frac{b^2}{2} \quad \text{or} \quad 2M_0 + V_0 c = -P \frac{b^2}{c}.$$

These equations give

(v)
$$M_0 = P \frac{ab^2}{c^2}, \qquad V_0 = -P \frac{b^2}{c^3} (3a + b).$$

The *upward* reactions at the supports are

$$R_1 = -V_0 = P \frac{b^2}{c^3} (3a + b), \qquad R_2 = P - R_1 = P \frac{a^2}{c^3} (3b + a).$$

As a check, note that R_2 may be obtained from R_1 by interchanging a and b.

With the values given in (v), equation (iv) gives the elastic curve. The deflection $y(a)$ under the load is given by

$$EIy(a) = M_0 \frac{a^2}{2} + V_0 \frac{a^3}{6} = \frac{1}{3} P \frac{a^3 b^3}{c^3}.$$

75. DISCONTINUOUS INPUT

We now consider the linear equation

(1)
$$x'' + P(t)x' + Q(t)x = R(t)$$

in which the independent variable t is usually the *time* in applications. When $P(t)$ and $Q(t)$ are continuous but $R(t)$ is only piecewise continuous, a function $x(t)$ is called a *solution* of this equation if
1° the derivative $x'(t)$ is continuous,
2° $x''(t)$ exists at all points where $R(t)$ is continuous,
3° $x(t)$ satisfies the equation where $R(t)$ is continuous.

If the initial conditions are

(2)
$$x(0) = x_0, \qquad x'(0) = x_0',$$

we can infer the existence and unicity of the solution in any finite interval $[0, b]$ in the following way. Divide this interval into a finite number of subintervals $[0, t_1], [t_1, t_2], \ldots, [t_n, b]$ in each of which $R(t)$ is continuous.

The existence theorem of § 26 guarantees a unique solution $x_0(t)$ of the system (1)–(2) in the interval $[0, t_1]$. Use this solution to get new end conditions

$$(3) \qquad x(t_1) = x_0(t_1), \qquad x'(t_1) = x_0'(t_1),$$

and solve the system (1)–(3) in the interval $[t_1, t_2]$ to get $x_1(t)$. Use this in turn to get the end conditions

$$(4) \qquad x(t_2) = x_1(t_2), \qquad x'(t_2) = x_1'(t_2)$$

and solve the system (1)–(4) in the interval $[t_2, t_3]$ to get $x_2(t)$. Proceeding in this way we eventually get a solution $x(t)$ of the system (1)–(2) in the interval $[0, b]$ which is made up of the functions $x_0(t), x_1(t), \ldots, x_n(t)$ over their respective intervals; and from the way in which the end conditions were imposed, we see that $x(t)$ is unique, continuous, and has a continuous derivative $x'(t)$ throughout the interval $[0, b]$. Moreover, $x(t)$ satisfies (1) except at the points $t_1, t_2, \ldots$ where $R(t)$ is discontinuous. At these points $x''(t)$ does not exist and, as the equation shows, has precisely the same discontinuities as the input function $R(t)$.

When P and Q are constants, the solution of the system (1)–(2), obtained from the Laplace transform $X(s)$, is the unique solution in the sense specified above. Note that the equations (68.1) and (68.2) for transforming derivatives apply when the derivatives in question are piecewise continuous.

To contrast a piecewise solution with the Laplace solution consider the harmonic motion with a square wave input of period 2π ($f_1(t)$ of Table C with $a = \pi$):

$$(5) \quad x'' + x = h(t) + 2\sum_{j=1}^{\infty}(-1)^j h(t - j\pi), \qquad x(0) = 1, \ x'(0) = 0.$$

We seek a function $x(t)$ with a continuous derivative $x'(t)$ which satisfies the initial conditions and the equation

$$x'' + x = (-1)^n$$

in every interval $n\pi \leqq t < (n + 1)\pi$.

In the interval $[0, \pi]$, the solution for the given conditions is $x_0(t) = 1$.
In the interval $[\pi, 2\pi]$, we solve the system

$$x'' + x = -1, \qquad x(\pi) = 1, \qquad x'(\pi) = 0,$$

and find

$$x_1(t) = -1 - 2\cos t.$$

In the interval $[2\pi, 3\pi]$, we solve the system

$$x'' + x = 1, \qquad x(2\pi) = -3, \qquad x'(2\pi) = 0$$

and find

$$x_2(t) = 1 - 4\cos t.$$

Note that each piece of the solution has its *initial* conditions determined by the *final* values of the preceding piece. Proceeding in this manner, we can extend the solution to as large values of t as desired, but the method is tedious and does not readily lend itself to general results.

Consider now the Laplace transform of the system (5):

$$s^2 X - s + X = \frac{1}{s} + \frac{2}{s} \sum_{j=1}^{\infty} (-1)^j e^{-j\pi s},$$

$$X = \frac{1}{s} + \frac{2}{s(s^2 + 1)} \sum_{j=1}^{\infty} (-1)^j e^{-j\pi s}.$$

Since

$$\pounds^{-1}\left\{\frac{1}{s(s^2 + 1)}\right\} = \pounds^{-1}\left\{\frac{1}{s} - \frac{s}{s^2 + 1}\right\} = 1 - \cos t,$$

we have

$$x(t) = 1 + 2 \sum_{j=1}^{\infty} (-1)^j [1 - \cos (t - j\pi)] h(t - j\pi).$$

When t lies in the interval $n\pi \leqq t < (n + 1)\pi$, $h(t - j\pi) = 1$ for $j = 1, 2, \ldots, n$ but is zero when $j > n$; hence the solution on this interval is

$$x_n(t) = 1 + 2 \sum_{j=1}^{n} (-1)^j [1 - \cos (t - j\pi)]$$

or since $\cos (t - j\pi) = (-1)^j \cos t$,

$$x_n(t) = 1 + 2 \sum_{j=1}^{n} (-1)^j - 2 \cos t \sum_{j=1}^{n} 1$$
$$= 1 + (-1)^n - 1 - 2n \cos t$$

or, finally,

(6) $$x_n(t) = (-1)^n - 2n \cos t.$$

The function $x_0(t) = 1$ fulfills the initial conditions, and since

$$x_n(n\pi) = (-1)^n - 2n(-1)^n = (1 - 2n)(-1)^n$$
$$x_{n-1}(n\pi) = (-1)^{n-1} - 2(n - 1)(-1)^n = (1 - 2n)(-1)^n,$$

it is also continuous at the points $n\pi$. The derivative $x_n'(t)$ is zero at these points and is also continuous. But $x_n''(t) = 2n \cos t$ has a jump of $2(-1)^n$ at $t = n\pi$, precisely the jump of the square wave there.

We see, moreover, that the general formula (6) agrees with the functions obtained piecewise for $n = 0, 1, 2$. The increase of $x_n(t)$ without limit is due to resonance; for the natural period of the simple harmonic motion $x'' + x = 0$ coincides with the impressed period 2π of the square wave.

Example 1. *Integro-differential Equation with Square Wave Input.*

(i)
$$x' + 4x + 3\int_0^t x\,dt = h(t) + 2\sum_{j=1}^{\infty}(-1)^j\,h(t-j).$$

The input function is $f_1(t)$ of Table C with $a = 1$. If $x(0) = 0$, the transform of (i) is

$$sX + 4X + \frac{3X}{s} = \frac{1}{s} + \frac{2}{s}\sum_{j=1}^{\infty}(-1)^j\,e^{-js},$$

whence

$$X(s) = \frac{1}{(s+1)(s+3)} + \frac{2}{(s+1)(s+3)}\sum_{j=1}^{\infty}(-1)^j e^{-js}.$$

Since

$$\pounds^{-1}\left\{\frac{1}{(s+1)(s+3)}\right\} = \pounds^{-1}\left\{\frac{\frac{1}{2}}{s+1} - \frac{\frac{1}{2}}{s+3}\right\} = \frac{1}{2}(e^{-t} - e^{-3t})$$

we have, on applying VIII of Table B,

$$x(t) = \tfrac{1}{2}(e^{-t} - e^{-3t}) + \sum_{j=1}^{\infty}(-1)^j[e^{-(t-j)} - e^{-3(t-j)}]h(t-j).$$

If t lies in the interval $n \leqq t \leqq n + 1$,

$$h(t-j) = \begin{cases} 1 & j \leqq n \\ 0 & j > n; \end{cases}$$

hence in this interval $x(t)$ equals

$$x_n(t) = \tfrac{1}{2}(e^{-t} - e^{-3t}) + e^{-t}\sum_{j=1}^{n}(-1)^j e^j - e^{-3t}\sum_{j=1}^{n}(-1)^j e^{3j}.$$

Replacing the sums of the geometric series by

$$\frac{e}{e+1}[(-1)^n e^n - 1], \qquad \frac{e^3}{e^3+1}[(-1)^n e^{3n} - 1]$$

we have

(ii)
$$x_n(t) = \frac{1}{2}(e^{-t} - e^{-3t}) + \frac{e}{e+1}[(-1)^n e^{-(t-n)} - e^{-t}]$$

$$- \frac{e^3}{e^3+1}[(-1)^n e^{-3(t-n)} - e^{-3t}].$$

The transient part of $x_n(t)$,

$$\mathrm{Tr}\,x(t) = \frac{1}{2}(e^{-t} - e^{-3t}) - \frac{e}{e+1}e^{-t} + \frac{e^3}{e^3+1}e^{-3t},$$

$$= \frac{1}{2}\frac{e^3-1}{e^3+1}e^{-3t} - \frac{1}{2}\frac{e-1}{e+1}e^{-t}$$

$$= (\tfrac{1}{2}\tanh\tfrac{3}{2})e^{-3t} - (\tfrac{1}{2}\tanh\tfrac{1}{2})e^{-t},$$

is the same function of t in each interval; we therefore drop the subscript n.

The graph of the transient is shown in Figure 75a.

The remaining terms of (ii) yield the steady-state solution:

$$\xi_n(\tau) = (-1)^n \left[\frac{e}{e+1} e^{-\tau} - \frac{e^3}{e^3+1} e^{-3\tau} \right]$$

where $\tau = t - n$ varies from $\tau = 0$ to $\tau = 1$ in each interval of length 1. This

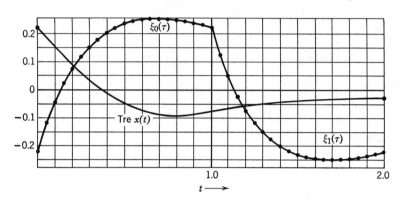

Fig. 75a, b   Steady wave of period 2 and transient.

is a wave of period 2, the same as the square wave input. Since

$$\xi_0(0) = \xi_1(1) = -\frac{e^2 - e}{e^3 + 1} = -0.2216,$$

$$\xi_0(1) = \xi_1(0) = \frac{e^2 - e}{e^3 + 1} = 0.2216,$$

the complete wave formed by $\xi_0(\tau)$ and $\xi_1(\tau)$ is continuous but has a cusp at the center where the slope changes sign (Fig. 75b). Note that

$$x(0) = \text{Tr } x(0) + \xi_0(0) = 0,$$

thus fulfilling the initial condition.

Example 2. ***Damped Harmonic Motion Disturbed by a Morse-Dot Input*** ($f_3(t)$ of Table C with $a = \pi$):

(i) $$x'' + 2x' + 10x = \sum_{j=0}^{\infty} (-1)^j h(t - j\pi).$$

If the initial conditions are

$$x(0) = \alpha, \qquad x'(0) = \beta,$$

the transform of (i) is

$$(s^2 + 2s + 10)X = \alpha s + 2\alpha + \beta + \frac{1}{s} \sum_{j=0}^{\infty} (-1)^j e^{-j\pi s}.$$

Now

$$\mathcal{L}^{-1}\left\{\frac{\alpha(s+1)+\alpha+\beta}{(s+1)^2+9}\right\} = e^{-t}\left(\alpha \cos 3t + \frac{\alpha+\beta}{3} \sin 3t\right) = g(t),$$

$$\mathcal{L}^{-1}\left\{\frac{1}{s(s^2+2s+10)}\right\} = \frac{1}{10}\mathcal{L}^{-1}\left\{\frac{1}{s} - \frac{s+2}{s^2+2s+10}\right\}$$

$$= \tfrac{1}{10}[1 - e^{-t}(\cos 3t + \tfrac{1}{3}\sin 3t)]$$

$$= \tfrac{1}{10}[1 - f(t)]$$

where

$$f(t) = e^{-t}(\cos 3t + \tfrac{1}{3}\sin 3t).$$

Thus we have

$$x(t) = g(t) + \tfrac{1}{10}\sum_{j=0}^{\infty}(-1)^j([1-f(t-j\pi)])h(t-j\pi).$$

If we stop the summation at $j = n$, we obtain $x(t)$ in the interval $n\pi \leqq t < (n+1)\pi$. Since

$$f(t-j\pi) = e^{j\pi}e^{-t}(-1)^j(\cos 3t + \tfrac{1}{3}\sin 3t) = (-1)^j e^{j\pi}f(t)$$

we have

$$x_n(t) = g(t) + \tfrac{1}{10}\sum_{j=0}^{n}(-1)^j - \tfrac{1}{10}f(t)\sum_{j=0}^{n}e^{j\pi}.$$

Now

$$\sum_{j=0}^{n}(-1)^j = \frac{1-(-1)^{n+1}}{2}, \qquad \sum_{j=0}^{n}e^{j\pi} = \frac{e^{(n+1)\pi}-1}{e^\pi - 1},$$

and hence

(ii) $$x_n(t) = g(t) + \frac{1}{10}\frac{1+(-1)^n}{2} - \frac{1}{10}f(t)\frac{e^{(n+1)\pi}-1}{e^\pi-1}.$$

As $t \to \infty$, $g(t)$ and $f(t) \to 0$; hence the transient part of $x(t)$ is

(iii) $$\text{Tr } x(t) = g(t) + \frac{1}{10}\frac{f(t)}{e^\pi-1}.$$

The remaining terms form the steady-state wave

$$\xi_n(t) = \begin{cases} \dfrac{1}{10}\left[1 - \dfrac{e^\pi}{e^\pi-1}e^{-(t-n)\pi}\left(\cos 3t + \dfrac{1}{3}\sin 3t\right)\right], & n \text{ even} \\[4mm] -\dfrac{1}{10}\dfrac{e^\pi}{e^\pi-1}e^{-(t-n\pi)}\left(\cos 3t + \dfrac{1}{3}\sin 3t\right), & n \text{ odd.} \end{cases}$$

The complete wave has the period 2π. This is clearly shown by putting $\tau = t - n\pi$ and noting that

$$\cos 3t = (-1)^n \cos 3\tau, \qquad \sin 3t = (-1)^n \sin 3\tau.$$

Thus we have

(iv) $$\begin{cases} \xi_0(\tau) = \dfrac{1}{10}\left[1 - \dfrac{e^\pi}{e^\pi-1}f(\tau)\right] \\[4mm] \xi_1(\tau) = \dfrac{1}{10}\dfrac{e^\pi}{e^\pi-1}f(\tau) \end{cases}$$

and

(v)
$$\xi_0(\tau) + \xi_1(\tau) = \tfrac{1}{10}.$$

Since $f(0) = 1, f(\pi) = -e^{-\pi}$, we have

$$\xi_0(0) = -\frac{1}{10(e^\pi - 1)} = \xi_1(\pi),$$

$$\xi_0(\pi) = \frac{e^\pi}{10(e^\pi - 1)} = \xi_1(0),$$

showing that the wave is continuous. However, since

$$f'(\tau) = -\frac{10}{3} e^{-\tau} \sin 3\tau, \qquad f'(0) = f'(\pi) = 0,$$

the slope of the wave is also continuous, being zero at the midpoint.

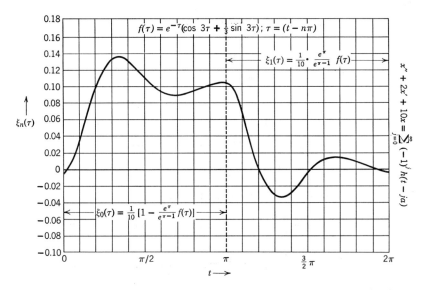

Fig. 75c Steady-state output of a harmonic oscillator having a Morse-dot input.

To graph the wave we first plot $\xi_1(\tau)$ ($0 \leq \tau \leq \pi$) from (iv) and then use (v) to plot $\xi_0(\tau)$ by reflecting $\xi_1(\tau)$ in the line $y = \tfrac{1}{10}$ (Fig. 75c). The extremes of $\xi_1(\tau)$ occur at $\tau = 0, \pi/3, 2\pi/3, \pi$ and these determine the extremes of $\xi_0(\tau)$.

The initial values α, β enter only through the function $g(t)$ in the transient. Since

$$g(0) = \alpha, g'(0) = \beta; \quad f(0) = 1, f'(0) = 0,$$

the solution $x(t)$ satisfies the initial conditions.

Example 3. *Harmonic Motion Disturbed by a Rectified Sine Wave Input:*

(i) $$x'' + x = |\sin t|, \qquad x(0) = x'(0) = 0.$$

The transform (§ 71, Ex. 4) is

$$(s^2 + 1)X = \frac{1}{s^2 + 1}\left(1 + 2\sum_{j=1}^{\infty} e^{-j\pi s}\right),$$

$$X = \frac{1}{(s^2 + 1)^2}\left(1 + 2\sum_{j=1}^{\infty} e^{-j\pi s}\right).$$

Now

$$\mathcal{L}^{-1}\left\{\frac{1}{(s^2 + 1)^2}\right\} = \frac{1}{2}(\sin t - t\cos t) = \frac{1}{2}\varphi(t);$$

$$x(t) = \tfrac{1}{2}\varphi(t) + \sum_{j=1}^{\infty} h(t - j\pi)\varphi(t - j\pi).$$

As before, the values of $x(t)$ in the interval $n\pi < t < (n + 1)\pi$ are obtained by stopping the summation at $j = n$. Since

$$\varphi(t - j\pi) = \sin(t - j\pi) - (t - j\pi)\cos(t - j\pi)$$
$$= (-1)^j(\sin t - (t - j\pi)\cos t),$$
$$h(t - j\pi) = 1, \qquad t > j\pi \qquad (j = 1, 2, \ldots, n),$$

we have

$$x_n(t) = \tfrac{1}{2}(\sin t - t\cos t) +$$
$$(\sin t - t\cos t)\sum_{j=1}^{n}(-1)^j + \pi\cos t\sum_{j=1}^{n}j(-1)^j$$

where the sums are computed by using nos. 3 and 5 of the table in § 81:

$$\sum_{j=1}^{n}(-1)^j = \frac{(-1)^n - 1}{2}, \quad \sum_{j=1}^{n}j(-1)^j = (-1)^n\frac{n}{2} + \frac{(-1)^n - 1}{4}.$$

Thus when $n\pi < t < (n + 1)\pi$,

(ii) $$x_n(t) = \frac{(-1)^n}{2}\left[\sin t - t\cos t + \pi\left(n + \frac{1}{2}\right)\cos t\right] - \frac{\pi}{4}\cos t.$$

Both $x(t)$ and $x'(t)$ are continuous and $x'(n\pi) = 0$.
To show the nature of this function, put $t = n\pi + \tau$; then $x(\tau)$ becomes

$$\frac{1}{2}\left[\sin \tau - (n\pi + \tau)\cos \tau + \pi\left(n + \frac{1}{2}\right)\cos \tau\right] - \frac{\pi}{4}(-1)^n\cos \tau$$

or

(iii) $$x_n(\tau) = \frac{1}{2}(\sin \tau - \tau\cos \tau) + \frac{\pi}{4}(1 - (-1)^n)\cos \tau.$$

According as n is even or odd, the last term is 0 or $(\pi/2)\cos\tau$. The two components of the graph and their resultant are shown in Figure 75d, a smooth wave that is repeated in every interval from $n\pi$ to $(n+2)\pi$ (n even). Note that there is no resonance effect. Explain this by considering the nature of the driving force.

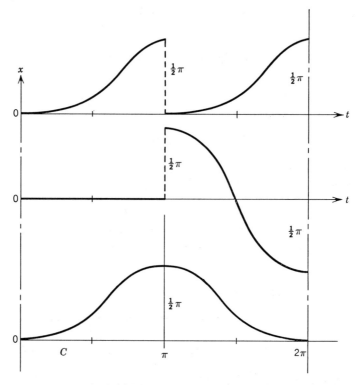

Fig. 75d Steady wave output of harmonic oscillator with rectified sine input.

Example 4. Harmonic Motion Disturbed by Periodic Impulses. We consider the equation

$$x'' + x = \sum_{j=1}^{\infty} \delta(t - j\pi), \qquad x(0) = 0, x'(0) = 1,$$

in which the interval between impulses is the half period π of the simple harmonic motion given by $x'' + x = 0$. Transforming by (73.1), we find

$$X(s) = \frac{1}{s^2 + 1} \sum_{j=0}^{\infty} e^{-j\pi s}, \qquad \text{(lower limit 0)},$$

$$x(t) = \sum_{j=0}^{\infty} h(t - j\pi) \sin(t - j\pi).$$

In the interval $n\pi < t < (n + 1)\pi$,

$$x_n(t) = \sum_{j=0}^{n} (-1)^j \sin t = \sin t \frac{(-1)^n + 1}{2},$$

so that

$$x_n(t) = \begin{cases} \sin t & n \text{ even.} \\ 0 & n \text{ odd.} \end{cases}$$

Graphically, $x(t)$ is a half-wave rectification of $\sin t$. There is no resonance effect. If the impulses are spaced at intervals of 2π,

$$x'' + x = \sum_{j=1}^{\infty} \delta(t - 2j\pi),$$

$$X = \frac{1}{s^2 + 1} \sum_{j=0}^{\infty} e^{-2j\pi s},$$

$$x(t) = \sum_{j=0}^{\infty} h(t - 2j\pi) \sin (t - 2j\pi).$$

Thus when $n\pi < t < (n + 1)\pi$,

$$x_n(t) = \sum_{j=0}^{n} \sin t = (n + 1) \sin t.$$

Explain the resonance in this case.

ALTERNATIVE PROCEDURE

The differential equation

(7) $$P(D)x = f(t), \qquad D = d/dt,$$

in which $P(D)$ is a polynomial in D of degree n, and $f(t)$ is a piece-wise continuous function of period p, always admits a periodic solution $w(t)$ of class $\mathscr{C}^{n-1}$ and period p, provided the zeros of $P(s)$ are not poles of $F(s) = \mathcal{L}\{f(t)\}.$* If the Laplace transform of (7) is

(8) $$P(s)X = Q(s) + F(s),$$

the initial conditions

(9) $$x(0) = \alpha, \qquad x'(0) = \beta, \ldots, x^{(n-1)}(0) = \zeta,$$

that produce this wave enter in $Q(s)$ and may be uniquely determined.

---

* L. Brand, *Periodic Solutions of Linear Differential Equations* (not published as yet).

If we admit the existence of the wave $w(t)$, its transform $W(s)$ must satisfy

$$(8)' \qquad\qquad P(s)W = Q(s) + F(s),$$

and for every zero s_j of $P(s)$ we have

$$(10) \qquad\qquad Q(s_j) = -F(s_j).$$

When $P(s)$ has n simple zeros, these n equations determine the *wave conditions* (9) uniquely if $F(s_j)$ remains finite for all s_j.

When $P(s)$ has a double zero s_j, $P(s_j) = P'(s_j) = 0$, and in addition to (10) we have

$$(11) \qquad\qquad Q'(s_j) = -F'(s_j).$$

Here, however, we only shall consider problems in which all zeros of $P(s)$ are simple.

When $f(t)$ is piecewise continuous, this method avoids the summations of the previous method and is notably simpler. To show this we again solve

Example 3. $x'' + x = |\sin t|, \qquad x(0) = x'(0) = 0.$
First, we find the conditions

$$x(0) = \alpha, \qquad x'(0) = \beta$$

that yield a wave of period π — the period of $|\sin t|$. From Table C we have

$$F(s) = \pounds\, |\sin t| = \frac{\coth \pi s/2}{s^2 + 1}.$$

The differential equation transforms into

$$(s^2 + 1)X = \alpha s + \beta + F(s).$$

Here $Q(s) = \alpha s + \beta$ and $P(s) = s^2 + 1$ has the zeros $\pm i$; but since $F(i)$ has the form $0/0$, we use Hospital's rule to find

$$\lim_{s \to i} F(s) = \lim_{s \to i} \frac{\pi/2}{2s\, \sinh^2 \pi s/2} = \frac{\pi}{4i^3 \sin^2 \pi/2} = \frac{\pi}{4} i.$$

Equation (10) now gives

$$\alpha i + \beta = \tfrac{1}{4}\pi i; \qquad \alpha = \tfrac{1}{4}\pi,\ \beta = 0.$$

We now solve

$$x'' + x = \sin \tau, \qquad x(0) = \tfrac{1}{4}\pi, \qquad x(0) = 0$$

in the interval $0 \leq \tau \leq \pi$ and find

$$x(\tau) = \tfrac{1}{2} \sin \tau - \tfrac{1}{2}\tau \cos \tau + \tfrac{1}{4}\pi \cos \tau.$$

This is a smooth wave of period π, having maxima of $\pi/4$ when $t = n\pi$, minima of $\tfrac{1}{2}$ midway between, and central symmetry about $\tau = \pi/2$.

To obtain the solution for the given initial conditions, we must add to this wave the solution of

$$x'' + x = 0, \qquad x(0) = -\tfrac{1}{4}\pi, \qquad x'(0) = 0,$$

namely, $x = -\tfrac{1}{4}\pi \cos \tau$. This is a wave of period 2π; hence, when $0 \leqq t \leqq \pi$ we add $-\tfrac{1}{4}\pi \cos\tau$ to $x(\tau)$; and when $\pi \leqq t \leqq 2\pi$, we add $-\tfrac{1}{4}\pi \cos(\pi + \tau) = \tfrac{1}{4}\pi \cos \tau$ to $x(\tau)$. The result is the smooth wave of period 2π:

$$x_0(\tau) = \tfrac{1}{2} \sin \tau - \tfrac{1}{2}\tau \cos \tau,$$

$$x_1(\tau) = \tfrac{1}{2} \sin \tau - \tfrac{1}{2}\tau \cos \tau + \tfrac{1}{2}\pi \cos \tau, \qquad\qquad 0 \leqq \tau \leqq \pi,$$

in agreement with our former result.

PROBLEMS

1. Harmonic motion with Morse-dot input of the same period ($f_3(t)$ with $a = \pi$):

$$x'' + x = \sum_{j=0}^{\infty} (-1)^j h(t - j\pi), \qquad x(0) = x'(0) = 0.$$

Show that in the interval $n\pi \leqq t \leqq (n + 1)\pi$, $x(t)$ equals

$$x_n(t) = \frac{1 + (-1)^n}{2} - (n + 1) \cos t$$

and that $x(t)$ and $x'(t)$ are continuous functions.

2. First-order equation with square wave input $f_1(t)$ of period $2a$:

$$x' + bx = h(t) + 2 \sum_{j=1}^{\infty} (-1)^j h(t - ja), \qquad x(0) = x_0.$$

Show that in the interval $na \leqq t \leqq (n + 1)a$

$$x_n(t) = \begin{cases} \left(x_0 - \dfrac{1}{b}\right)e^{-bt} + \dfrac{1}{b} + \dfrac{2}{b} e^{-bt} \dfrac{e^{ab}}{1 + e^{ab}} (1 - e^{abn}) \\[2mm] \left(x_0 - \dfrac{1}{b}\right)e^{-bt} - \dfrac{1}{b} + \dfrac{2}{b} e^{-bt} \dfrac{e^{ab}}{1 + e^{ab}} (1 + e^{abn}) \end{cases}$$

according as n is even or odd; and that the transient

$$\text{Tr } x(t) = x_0 + \frac{1}{b} \tanh \frac{ab}{2} e^{-bt},$$

and that the steady-state solution in the interval $na \leqq t \leqq (n + 1)a$ is

$$\xi_n(\tau) = (-1)^n \frac{1}{b}\left[1 - \frac{2e^{ab}}{1 + e^{ab}} e^{-b\tau}\right], \qquad \tau = t - na.$$

Verify that the complete wave formed by $\xi_0(\tau)$ and $\xi_1(\tau)$ is continuous but has a cusp at the center where the slope changes sign.

Plot the graph with $a = \tfrac{1}{2}$, $b = 2$.

3. Integro-differential equation with Morse-dot input of period 2 ($f_3(t)$ with $a = 1$):

$$x' + 3x + 2 \int_0^t x \, dt = 1 + \sum_{j=1}^{\infty} (-1)^j h(t - 1), \qquad x(0) = 1.$$

Show that the transient

$$\text{Tr } x(t) = e^{-2t} - \frac{e}{e + 1} e^{-t} + \frac{e^2}{e^2 + 1} e^{-2t}$$

and that the steady-state solution in the interval $n \leqq t \leqq n + 1$ is

$$\xi_n(\tau) = (-1)^n \left[\frac{e}{e + 1} e^{-\tau} - \frac{e^2}{e^2 + 1} e^{-2\tau} \right], \qquad \tau = t - n.$$

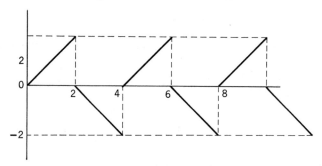

Fig. 75e   Discontinuous input.

Verify the continuity of the wave by showing that $\xi_0(0) = \xi_1(1)$, $\xi_0(1) = \xi_1(0)$.

4. Solve $x' + x = f(t), \qquad x(0) = -1,$

where $f(t)$ is the function of period 4 shown in Figure 75e (Mikusiński, ref. 12). Show that the solution is the triangular wave given by

$$\xi_n(t) = (-1)^n(t - 2n - 1), \qquad 2n \leqq t \leqq 2(n + 1),$$

and the transient is lacking. Use the alternative method.

5. Integro-differential equation with the sawtooth function $f_4(t)$ with $a = 1$ as input:

$$x' + 3x + 2 \int_0^t x \, dt = t - \sum_{j=1}^{\infty} h(t - j), \qquad x(0) = 1.$$

Show that the transient

$$\text{Tr } x(t) = \frac{3e^2 - 5}{2e^2 - 2} e^{-2t} - \frac{e - 2}{e - 1} e^{-t}$$

and that the steady-state solution in the interval $n \leqq t \leqq n + 1$ is

$$\xi(\tau) = \frac{1}{2} + \frac{e^2}{e^2 - 1} e^{-2\tau} - \frac{e}{e - 1} e^{-\tau}, \qquad \tau = t - n.$$

Verify the continuity of $\xi(\tau)$ and $\xi'(\tau)$ by showing that $\xi(0) = \xi(1)$ and $\xi'(0) = \xi'(1)$.

6. Solve Example 3 by piecewise integration and show that in the interval $[2n\pi, (2n + 1)\pi]$

$$x_{2n}(t) = \tfrac{1}{2}(\sin t - t \cos t) + n\pi \cos t,$$

and in the interval $[(2n + 1)\pi, (2n + 2)\pi]$

$$x_{2n+1}(t) = -\tfrac{1}{2}(\sin t - t \cos t) - (n + 1)\pi \cos t.$$

Show that these results agree with equation (iii) of Example 3.

In the following problems apply the alternative method to find the wave conditions and the resulting wave.

7. $x'' - x = f_1(t)$, a square wave of period $2a$.

$$x_n(\tau) = (-1)^n \left[\frac{\cosh (\tau - a)}{\cosh \tfrac{1}{2}a} - 1 \right], \qquad 0 \le \tau \le a.$$

8. $x'' + x = f_1(t)$, a square wave of period $2a$.

$$x_n(\tau) = (-1)^n \left[1 - \frac{\cos (\tau - a)}{\cos \tfrac{1}{2}a} \right], \qquad 0 \le \tau \le a.$$

9. When $f_1(t)$ in Problem 8 is a square wave of period π, show that the conditions $x(0) = 1$, $x'(0) = 0$, yield the wave of period 2π:

$$\begin{aligned}
x_0(t) &= 1 & 0 &\le t \le \tfrac{1}{2}\pi, \\
x_1(t) &= 2 \sin t - 1 & \tfrac{1}{2}\pi &\le t \le \pi, \\
x_2(t) &= 1 + 2 \cos t + 2 \sin t & \pi &\le t \le \tfrac{3}{2}\pi, \\
x_3(t) &= 2 \cos t - 1 & \tfrac{3}{2}\pi &\le t \le 2\pi.
\end{aligned}$$

Show that the conditions $x(0) = 0$, $x'(0) = -1$, yield the wave of period π:

$$x_n(\tau) = (-1)^n(1 - \cos \tau - \sin \tau), \qquad 0 \le \tau \le \tfrac{1}{2}\pi.$$

Deduce the former wave from this one.

10. In Example 4 show that the conditions $y(0) = 0$, $y'(0) = \tfrac{1}{2}$ yield a wave of period π. Find the wave.

76. THE SERIES *RLC* CIRCUIT

We now consider the equation of § 61

(1) $$L\frac{di}{dt} + Ri + \frac{1}{C} \int_0^t i \, dt = E_0 \sin \omega t, \qquad i(0) = 0,$$

from the standpoint of the Laplace transformation. We assume that there is no charge q on the capacitor when $t = 0$; then $q = \dfrac{1}{C} \displaystyle\int_0^t i \, dt$.

To simplify the calculation we replace $\sin \omega t$ by

$$e^{j\omega t} = \cos \omega t + j \sin \omega t \qquad (j = \sqrt{-1})$$

and take the imaginary part of the resulting complex solution. The transform of (1)

$$sLI + RI + \frac{I}{Cs} = \frac{E_0}{s - j\omega}$$

yields

(2)
$$I = \frac{E_0}{\left(Ls + R + \dfrac{1}{Cs}\right)(s - j\omega)}.$$

The steady current corresponds to the partial fraction with denominator $s - j\omega$; its numerator is

$$\frac{E_0}{L\omega j + R + \dfrac{1}{C\omega j}} = \frac{E_0}{R + j\left(\omega L - \dfrac{1}{\omega C}\right)} = \frac{E_0}{Ze^{j\alpha}} \qquad (67.3)$$

where

$$Z^2 = R^2 + \left(\omega L - \frac{1}{\omega C}\right)^2, \qquad \tan \alpha = \frac{\omega L - \dfrac{1}{\omega C}}{R}$$

give the impedance Z and phase angle α in agreement with § 61. The quadratic factor $s^2 + (R/L)s + (1/CL)$ leads to transients containing $\exp(-Rt/2L)$. Now

$$\mathcal{L}^{-1}\left(\frac{E_0}{Ze^{j\alpha}} \frac{1}{s - j\omega}\right) = \frac{E_0}{Z} \frac{e^{j\omega t}}{e^{j\alpha}} = \frac{E_0}{Z} e^{j(\omega t - \alpha)}$$

and the imaginary part of this expression gives the steady current

(3)
$$i_s(t) = \frac{E_0}{Z} \sin(\omega t - \alpha).$$

PROBLEMS

1. Show that $x' + x = |\sin t|$ has the pure wave solution of period π,

$$x(\tau) = \frac{e^\pi}{e^\pi - 1} e^{-\tau} + \tfrac{1}{2}(\sin \tau - \cos \tau), \qquad 0 \leqq \tau \leqq \pi,$$

when $x(0) = \tfrac{1}{2} \coth \pi/2$.

2. In equation (75.7) let $f(t + a) = -f(t)$. Prove that the equation has a wave solution $w(t)$ of period $2a$ such that $w(t + a) = -w(t)$.

CHAPTER 8

$$\sum_{x=a}^{b} f(x) = \Delta^{-1}f(x) \Big|_{a}^{b+1}$$

Linear Difference Equations

77. DIFFERENCES AND ANTIDIFFERENCES

If $f(x)$ is a function of a real variable x, its difference $\Delta f(x)$ is defined as

(1) $$\Delta f(x) = f(x + 1) - f(x).*$$

The second and higher differences are defined in an obvious way. Thus the second difference

$$\Delta^2 f(x) = \Delta(\Delta f(x)) = f(x + 2) - 2f(x + 1) + f(x).$$

If $\omega(x)$ is an arbitrary periodic function of period 1,

$$\Delta\omega(x) = \omega(x + 1) - \omega(x) = 0.$$

Conversely, if $\Delta f(x) = 0$, $f(x)$ is a periodic function of period 1. We shall call such functions *periodics;* these include, in particular, the constants. Thus each of the following equations

$$\Delta f(x) = \Delta g(x), \qquad f(x) = g(x) + \omega(x),$$

implies the other.

The difference operator Δ is *linear*; that is,

(2) $$\Delta\{f(x) + g(x)\} = \Delta f(x) + \Delta g(x), \qquad \Delta\{cf(x)\} = c\,\Delta f(x).$$

If $\Delta F(x) = f(x)$, $F(x)$ is called an *antidifference* of $f(x)$ and denoted by $\Delta^{-1}f(x)$. The most general antidifference of $f(x)$ is $F(x) + \omega$, but in tables the additive ω is usually omitted. Note that

$$\Delta\Delta^{-1}f(x) = f(x), \qquad \Delta^{-1}\,\Delta F(x) = f(x) + \omega.$$

---

* Here the difference of the independent variable x is $\Delta x = 1$. If $\Delta x = h$, the difference

$$\Delta_h f(x) = f(x + h) - f(x).$$

If we put $x = ht$, and take $\Delta t = 1$, then $\Delta x = h$ and $\Delta_h f(x) = \Delta f(ht)$, $\Delta t = 1$.

337

Thus $\Delta\Delta^{-1} = 1 \neq \Delta^{-1}\Delta$. The operators Δ and Δ^{-1} do not commute.*

Two operators are said to be *equivalent* (symbol $=$) when they produce the same result on any function to which they are applicable.

Example 1. $\Delta^{-1}1 = x$.

$$\Delta x = (x+1) - x = 1.$$

Apply Δ^{-1} to this equation; then $x + \omega = \Delta^{-1}1$.

Example 2. $\Delta^{-1}x = \frac{1}{2}x(x-1)$.

$$\Delta x^2 = (x^2 + 2x + 1) - x^2 = 2x + 1.$$

On applying Δ^{-1} we have

$$x^2 + \omega = 2\Delta^{-1}x + x, \qquad \Delta^{-1}x = \frac{1}{2}(x^2 - x).$$

(3)   ***Example 3.*** $\Delta^{-1}a^x = \dfrac{a^x}{a-1}$, $a \neq 1$.

$$\Delta a^x = a^{x+1} - a^x = a^x(a-1).$$

On applying Δ^{-1} we have

$$a^x + \omega = (a-1)\Delta^{-1}a^x.$$

In particular, $\Delta 2^x = 2^x$ and $\Delta^{-1}2^x = 2^x$. Thus in the difference calculus 2^x is the analog of e^x in the differential calculus: but $\frac{1}{2}(2^x + 2^{-x})$, $\frac{1}{2}(2^x - 2^{-x})$ are not analogs of $\cosh x$ and $\sinh x$ since $\Delta 2^{-x} = -\frac{1}{2}2^{-x}$.

(4)   ***Example 4.*** $\Delta^{-1}(xa^x) = \dfrac{a^x}{a-1}\left(x - \dfrac{a}{a-1}\right)$, $a \neq 1$.

$$\Delta(xa^x) = (x+1)a^{x+1} - xa^x = xa^x(a-1) + a^{x+1}.$$

Apply Δ^{-1} and use (3):

$$xa^x + \omega = (a-1)\Delta^{-1}(xa^x) + \frac{a^{x+1}}{a-1}.$$

$$(a-1)\Delta^{-1}(xa^x) = a^x\left(x - \frac{a}{a-1}\right).$$

This gives the stated result.

Example 5. $\Delta^{-1}\cos(ax+b)$, $\Delta^{-1}\sin(ax+b)$.

$$\cos(ax+b) + i\sin(ax+b) = e^{iax}e^{ib},$$
$$\Delta\cos(ax+b) + i\,\Delta\sin(ax+b) = (e^{ia}-1)e^{i(ax+b)}$$
$$= 2i\,\frac{e^{ia/2} - e^{-ia/2}}{2i}\,e^{ia/2}e^{i(ax+b)}$$
$$= 2i\sin\frac{a}{2}\exp i(ax + \tfrac{1}{2}a + b).$$

---

* In the differential calculus

$$DD^{-1}f(x) = f(x), \qquad D^{-1}Df(x) = f(x) + C;$$

and $DD^{-1} = 1 \neq D^{-1}D$. The operators D and D^{-1} do not commute.

Equate real and imaginary parts:

$$(5) \qquad \Delta \cos (ax + b) = -2 \sin \frac{a}{2} \sin \left(ax + \frac{a}{2} + b \right),$$

$$(6) \qquad \Delta \sin (ax + b) = 2 \sin \frac{a}{2} \cos \left(ax + \frac{a}{2} + b \right).$$

From (6)

$$\Delta \sin \left(ax - \frac{a}{2} + b \right) = 2 \sin \frac{a}{2} \cos (ax + b),$$

$$(7) \qquad \Delta^{-1} \cos (ax + b) = \frac{\sin \left(ax + b - \dfrac{a}{2} \right)}{2 \sin \dfrac{a}{2}}.$$

Similarly from (5) we get

$$(8) \qquad \Delta^{-1} \sin (ax + b) = - \frac{\cos \left(ax + b - \dfrac{a}{2} \right)}{2 \sin \dfrac{a}{2}}.$$

PROBLEMS

1. If $c(x) = 2^{x/2} \cos \frac{1}{4}\pi x$, $s(x) = 2^{x/2} \sin \frac{1}{4}\pi x$, show that

$$\Delta c(x) = -s(x), \qquad \Delta s(x) = c(x).$$

2. From the identity

$$\cosh (ax + b) + \sin (ax + b) = e^{ax} e^b$$

deduce

$$(9) \qquad \Delta^{-1} \cosh (ax + b) = \frac{\sinh \left(ax + b - \dfrac{a}{2} \right)}{2 \sinh \dfrac{a}{2}},$$

$$(10) \qquad \Delta^{-1} \sinh (ax + b) = \frac{\cosh \left(ax + b - \dfrac{a}{2} \right)}{2 \sinh \dfrac{a}{2}}.$$

3. From $\Delta^{-1}(e^{inx}/a^x)$ deduce

$$\Delta^{-1} \frac{\cos nx}{a^x} = \frac{1}{a^{x-1}} \frac{\cos n(x - 1) - a \cos nx}{1 - 2a \cos n + a^2},$$

$$\Delta^{-1} \frac{\sin nx}{a^x} = \frac{1}{a^{x-1}} \frac{\sin n(x - 1) - a \sin nx}{1 - 2a \cos n + a^2}.$$

4. $\Delta^{-1}\log x = \log \Gamma(x)$.

5. $\Delta^{-1}(-1)^{x+1}x = \frac{1}{4}(-1)^x(2x - 1)$.

6. Show that $\dbinom{n}{x} + \dbinom{n}{x+1} = \dbinom{n+1}{x+1}$ and hence

$$\Delta^{-1}(-1)^x\binom{n}{x} = (-1)^{x+1}\binom{n-1}{x-1}.$$

78. FACTORIAL POWERS

When a function $f(x)$ is given, we define the corresponding factorial expression

(F) $\qquad (f(x))^{[n]} = f(x)f(x-1)f(x-2)\cdots f(x-n+1)$

as a product of n function values. Note however that $5^{[3]}$ is *not defined* unless $f(x)$ and the value of x for which $f(x) = 5$, are given. Thus if $f(x) = 2x+1, f(2) = 5, f(1) = 3, f(0) = 1$ and $5^{[3]} = 15$; but if $f(x) = 3x - 1, f(2) = 5, f(1) = 2, f(0) = -1$ and $5^{[3]} = -10$. This fact limits the usefulness of factorial expressions.

But when $f(x) = x$, the corresponding factorial expression, written

(1) $\qquad x^{(n)} = x(x-1)(x-2)\cdots(x-n+1),$

is free from this defect. Thus $5^{(3)} = 5\cdot4\cdot3 = 60$ without ambiguity. In the difference calculus the *factorial powers* $x^{(n)}$ play a role analogous to x^n in the differential calculus: corresponding to $Dx^n = nx^{n-1}$ we now shall find that

$$\Delta x^{(n)} = nx^{(n-1)}.$$

Definition (1) leads to the functional equation

(A) $\qquad x^{(m+n)} = x^{m}(x - m)^{(n)} = x^{(n)}(x - n)^{(m)}$

for factorial powers with positive index. Just as the functional equation

$$x^{m+n} = x^m x^n$$

for ordinary powers is used to define the meaning of zero, negative, rational, and eventually all real exponents, we use (A) to obtain a definition of $x^{(n)}$ for all real n. We therefore *postulate* the truth of (A) for all real values of m and n.

When $m = 0$, (A) becomes $x^{(n)} = x^{(0)}x^{(n)}$; hence if $x \neq 0$,

(2) $\qquad\qquad\qquad\qquad x^{(0)} = 1.$

When $m = -n$, we have

$$x^{(0)} = x^{(-n)}(x+n)^{(n)} \quad \text{or} \quad x^{(-n)} = \frac{1}{(x+n)^n}.$$

Hence if n is a positive integer and $x \neq 0$, we have from (1)

$$(3) \qquad x^{(-n)} = \frac{1}{(x + 1)(x + 2) \cdots (x + n)}.$$

Thus (2), (3) and (4) define factorial powers for all integral indices provided $x \neq 0$. We shall see that we can remove this last proviso.

Next let x be any real number and consider the function $f(x) = x^{(x)}$. Letting $m = 1$, $n = x - 1$ in (A) we have

$$f(x) = x^{(x)} = x(x - 1)^{(x-1)} = xf(x - 1).$$

But the gamma function $\Gamma(x)$ (§ 66) has the functional equation $\Gamma(x + 1) = x\Gamma(x)$. Hence when n is not a negative integer, we define

$$(4) \qquad x^{(x)} = \Gamma(x + 1), \qquad x \neq -1, -2, \ldots .$$

When $x = 0$ this gives $0^{(0)} = \Gamma(1) = 1$; we may therefore remove the restriction $x \neq 0$ in definitions (2) and (3); thus

$$0^{(0)} = 1, \qquad 0^{(-n)} = \frac{1}{n!}$$

in sharp contrast with ordinary powers for which 0^0 is indeterminate and 0^{-n} has no meaning.

Again from (A) we have

$$x^{(x)} = x^{(n+x-n)} = x^{(n)}(x - n)^{(x-n)};$$

using (4), we can now give the *general definition* of the factorial power

$$(5) \qquad x^{(n)} = \frac{\Gamma(x + 1)}{\Gamma(x + 1 - n)}$$

for all real values of x and n for which the gamma functions exist. This definition comprises all cases if we agree that when the gamma function is infinite (for arguments $0, -1, -2, \ldots$),

$$(6) \qquad \lim x^{(n)} = \lim_{\varepsilon \to 0} (x + \varepsilon)^{(n)}.$$

Thus from (5), $(-1)^{(2)} = \Gamma(0)/\Gamma(-2)$ is not defined; but from (6)

$$(-1)^{(2)} = \lim_{\varepsilon \to 0} (\varepsilon - 1)^{(2)} = \lim_{\varepsilon \to 0} \frac{\Gamma(\varepsilon)}{\Gamma(\varepsilon - 2)} = \lim_{\varepsilon \to 0} (\varepsilon - 1)(\varepsilon - 2) = 2!$$

in agreement with (1).

The basic functional equation (A) for the factorial power follows at once from (5) and the identity

$$\frac{\Gamma(x+1)}{\Gamma(x+1-m-n)} = \frac{\Gamma(x+1)}{\Gamma(x+1-m)}\frac{\Gamma(x-m+1)}{\Gamma(x-m+1-n)}.$$

By taking $n = -m$ in (A) we get the important special case

$$(7) \qquad x^m(x-m)^{(-m)} = x((-m)(x+m)^{(m)} = 1.$$

We next compute $\Delta(x+c)^{(n)}$ using definition (5) and the functional equation $\Gamma(x+1) = x\Gamma(x)$ of the gamma function:

$$\begin{aligned}
\Delta(x+c)^{(n)} &= (x+c+1)^{(n)} - (x+c)^{(n)}\\
&= \frac{\Gamma(x+c+2)}{\Gamma(x+c+2-n)} - \frac{\Gamma(x+c+1)}{\Gamma(x+c+1-n)}\\
&= \frac{\Gamma(x+c+1)}{\Gamma(x+c+1-n)}\left(\frac{x+c+1}{x+c+1-n} - 1\right)\\
&= n\frac{\Gamma(x+c+1)}{\Gamma(x+c+2-n)}.
\end{aligned}$$

Since $x+c+2-n = x+c+1-(n-1)$, we have

$$(8) \qquad \Delta(x+c)^{(n)} = n(x+c)^{(n-1)}.$$

The corresponding antidifference is

$$(9) \qquad \Delta^{-1}(x+c)^{(n)} = \frac{(x+c)^{(n+1)}}{n+1} + \omega, \qquad n \neq -1.$$

Using definition (F), the factorial expression

$$\begin{aligned}
(ax+b)^{[n]} &= (ax+b)(a(x-1)+b)\cdots(a(x-n+1)+b)\\
&= a^n\left(x+\frac{b}{a}\right)\left(x-1+\frac{b}{a}\right)\cdots\left(x-n+1+\frac{b}{a}\right),
\end{aligned}$$

$$(10) \qquad (ax+b)^{[n]} = a^n\left(x+\frac{b}{a}\right)^{(n)};$$

hence from (8)

$$(11) \qquad \Delta(ax+b)^{[n]} = na^n\left(x+\frac{b}{a}\right)^{(n-1)} = na(ax+b)^{[n-1]}.$$

The corresponding antidifference is

$$(12) \qquad \Delta^{-1}(ax+b)^{[n]} = \frac{(ax+b)^{[n+1]}}{a(n+1)}, \qquad n \neq -1.$$

Any polynomial $f(x)$ of degree n can be expressed as a polynomial in factorial powers by means of a formula analogous to a finite Maclaurin expansion:

$$(13) \qquad f(x) = f(0) + \frac{\Delta f(0)}{1!} x + \frac{\Delta^2 f(0)}{2!} x^{(2)} + \cdots + \frac{\Delta^n f(0)}{n!} x^{(n)}.$$

PROOF. Write the polynomial

$$f(x) = a_0 + a_1 x + a_2 x^{(2)} + \cdots + a_n x^{(n)}.$$

Then $f(0) = a_0$. Now difference $f(x)$ k times; then from (8)

$$\Delta^k f(x) = k! \, a_k + \text{terms in } x, \quad x^{(2)}, \ldots, x^{(n-k)},$$

and on putting $x = 0$ we get

$$\Delta^k f(0) = k! \, a_k.$$

Table 78 Sterling Numbers (second kind)

n \ k	(1)	(2)	(3)	(4)	(5)	(6)	(7)
1	1						
2	1	1					
3	1	3	1				
4	1	7	6	1			
5	1	15	25	10	1		
6	1	31	90	65	15	1	
7	1	63	301	350	140	21	1

For example, let $f(x) = 2 + 3x + x^3$. Then $\Delta f = 3x^2 + 3x + 4$, $\Delta^2 f = 6x + 6$, $\Delta^3 f = 6$; thus $a_0 = 2$, $a_1 = 4$, $a_2 = 6/2 = 3$, $a_3 = 6/6 = 1$ and

$$f(x) = 2 + 4x + 3x^{(2)} + x^{(3)}.$$

Conversions of this kind are readily made from a table of *Sterling numbers* $S_k{}^n$ which express the powers x^n in terms of factorial powers:

$$(14) \qquad x^n = \sum_{k=1}^{n} S_k{}^n x^{(k)}.$$

For example, $x^4 = x + 7x^{(2)} + 6x^{(3)} + x^{(4)}$.

From (14) we have

$$x^{n+1} = \sum_{k=1}^{n} (x - k + k) S_k{}^n x^{(k)} = \sum_{k=1}^{n} S_k{}^n (x^{(k+1)} + k x^{(k)}).$$

On equating the coefficients of $x^{(k)}$ in both members we have

(15) $$S_k^{n+1} = S_{k-1}^n + kS_k^n.$$

The above table was constructed from this relation. It simplifies the conversion of polynomials in x^k into polynomials in $x^{(k)}$. Thus $2 + 3x + x^3 = 2 + 3x + (x + 3x^{(2)} + x^{(3)})$.

Example 1. $\Delta^{-1}x^2$.

From the table $x^2 = x + x^{(2)}$; using (9)

$$\Delta^{-1}x^2 = \frac{x^{(2)}}{2} + \frac{x^{(3)}}{3} = \frac{1}{6}x(x - 1)(2x - 1).$$

Example 2. $\Delta^{-1}\dfrac{1}{x(x + 1)}$.

From (3), $1/x(x + 1) = (x - 1)^{(-2)}$; using (9)

$$\Delta^{-1}\frac{1}{x(x + 1)} = \frac{(x - 1)^{(-1)}}{-1} = -\frac{1}{x}.$$

Example 3. $\Delta^{-1}\left(\dfrac{1}{x^2 - 1}\right)$.

$$\frac{1}{(x - 1)(x + 1)} = \frac{(x - 1) + 1}{(x - 1)x(x + 1)} = (x - 1)^{-2} + (x - 2)^{-3}$$

$$\Delta^{-1}\left(\frac{1}{x^2 - 1}\right) = \frac{(x - 1)^{-1}}{-1} + \frac{(x - 2)^{-2}}{-2} = -\frac{1}{x} - \frac{1}{2(x - 1)x} = \frac{1 - 2x}{2x(x - 1)}.$$

Example 4. $\Delta^{-1}\dfrac{1}{x(x + 3)}$.

$$\frac{1}{x(x + 3)} = \frac{(x + 1)(x + 2)}{x(x + 1)(x + 2)(x + 3)} = \frac{x(x + 1) + 2x + 2}{x(x + 1)(x + 2)(x + 3)}$$

$$= (x + 1)^{(-2)} + 2x^{(-3)} + 2(x - 1)^{(-4)}.$$

Using (9), we now have

$$\Delta^{-1}\frac{1}{x(x + 3)} = -(x + 1)^{(-1)} - x^{(-2)} - \tfrac{2}{3}(x - 1)^{(-3)}.$$

Example 5. The *binomial coefficient* $\dbinom{x}{n}$ for real x and integral $n \geqq 0$ is defined as

(16) $$\binom{x}{0} = 1; \qquad \binom{x}{n} = \frac{x^{(n)}}{n!}, \qquad n = 1, 2, 3, \ldots .$$

Show that

$$\binom{x}{n} = \binom{x - 1}{n - 1} + \binom{x - 1}{n},$$

$$\Delta\binom{x}{n} = \binom{x}{n - 1}, \qquad \Delta^{-1}\binom{x}{n} = \binom{x}{n + 1}.$$

PROBLEMS

1. Find $\Delta^{-1}(2x)^{(3)}$ and $\Delta^{-1}(2x)^{[3]}$.
2. Find $\Delta^{-1}(2x + 1)(2x + 3)$.

3. Find $\Delta^{-1} \dfrac{x + 3}{x(x + 1)(x + 2)}$.

4. Find $\Delta^{-1}x\dbinom{x}{3}$.

5. Plot the curve $y = 0^{(x)}$, the "sidewinder".

79. BERNOULLI NUMBERS AND POLYNOMIALS

The Bernoulli numbers B_k are defined by the symbolic identity

(1)
$$\frac{t}{e^t - 1} = e^{Bt} = \sum_{n=0}^{\infty} \frac{B^n}{n!} t^n \overset{*}{}$$

in which B^n is replaced by B_n. From (1) we have also

(2)
$$t = e^{(B+1)t} - e^{Bt} = \sum_{n=0}^{\infty} \frac{(B + 1)^n - B^n}{n!} t^n$$

in the same symbolic sense; now $(B + 1)^n$ must be replaced by its binomial expansion and after canceling B^n, we write B_k instead of B^k. On equating coefficients of t^n in both members, we have

(3)
$$(B + 1)^n - B^n = 0, \qquad n = 2, 3, 4, \ldots,$$

whereas for $n = 0, 1$, we have the identities

$$1 - 1 = 0, \qquad (B_1 + 1) - B_1 = 1.$$

Equation (3) is now used as a recurrence relation for computing the *Bernoulli numbers B_k.* Thus we have

$$2B_1 + 1 = 0, \qquad B_1 = -\tfrac{1}{2}$$
$$3B_2 + 3B_1 + 1 = 0, \qquad B_2 = \tfrac{1}{6}$$
$$4B_3 + 6B_2 + 4B_1 + 1 = 0, \qquad B_3 = 0$$
$$5B_4 + 10B_3 + 10B_2 + 5B_1 + 1 = 0, \qquad B_4 = -\tfrac{1}{30}$$

and so on. Further Bernoulli numbers are given in the brief list:

$$B_1 = -\tfrac{1}{2}, \quad B_2 = \tfrac{1}{6}, \quad B_4 = -\tfrac{1}{30}, \quad B_6 = \tfrac{1}{42}, \quad B_8 = -\tfrac{1}{30}, \quad B_{10} = \tfrac{5}{66},$$
$$B_{12} = -\tfrac{691}{2730}, \ B_{14} = \tfrac{7}{6}, \ B_{16} = -\tfrac{3617}{510}, \ B_{18} = \tfrac{43867}{798}, \ B_{20} = -\tfrac{174611}{330}.$$

---

* This is the Maclaurin series for the function $f(t) = t/(e^t - 1)$ when we define $f(0) = 1$. It converges in the interval $|t| < 2\pi$. See *Advanced Calculus*, § 211, p 486.

Except for B_1, all Bernoulli numbers of odd index are zero. Then $-t/2$ will be the only odd power in the series (1), and consequently the function

$$\varphi(t) = \frac{t}{2} + \frac{t}{e^t - 1} = \frac{t}{2}\frac{e^t + 1}{e^t - 1} = \frac{t}{2}\coth\frac{t}{2}$$

must be *even;* that is, $\varphi(-t) = \varphi(t)$. This property is readily verified; hence

$$(4) \qquad\qquad B_{2n+1} = 0, \qquad n = 1, 2, 3, \ldots .$$

The Bernoulli polynomials $B_n(x)$ are defined by the symbolic identity

$$(5) \qquad\qquad B_n(x) = (x + B)^n;$$

where again B^k is replaced by B_k after expanding $(x + B)^n$. We thus obtain

$$B_0(x) = 1$$
$$B_1(x) = x - \tfrac{1}{2}$$
$$B_2(x) = x^2 - x + \tfrac{1}{6}$$
$$B_3(x) = x^3 - \tfrac{3}{2}x^2 + \tfrac{1}{2}x = x(x - 1)(x - \tfrac{1}{2})$$
$$B_4(x) = x^4 - 2x^3 + x^2 - \tfrac{1}{30}$$
$$B_5(x) = x^5 - \tfrac{5}{2}x^4 + \tfrac{5}{3}x^3 - \tfrac{1}{6}x = x(x - 1)(x - \tfrac{1}{2})(x^2 - x - \tfrac{1}{3})$$
$$B_6(x) = x^6 - 3x^5 + \tfrac{5}{2}x^4 - \tfrac{1}{2}x^2 + \tfrac{1}{42}$$

and so on. From (5), $B_n(0) = B_n$; thus $B_5 = 0$, $B_6 = \tfrac{1}{42}$.

The Bernoulli polynomials have the properties:

$$(6) \qquad\qquad B_n(1 - x) = (-1)^n B_n(x),$$

$$(7) \qquad\qquad DB_n(x) = nB_{n-1}(x),$$

$$(8) \qquad\qquad \Delta B_n(x) = nx^{n-1},$$

$$(9) \qquad\qquad \Delta^{-1}x^n = \frac{B_{n+1}(x)}{n + 1}, \qquad n \neq -1.$$

Proof of (6): From (5)

$$B_n(1 - x) = (-1)^n[x - (B + 1)]^n$$

$$= (-1)^n \sum_{k=0}^{n}\binom{n}{k}x^{n-k}(-1)^k(B + 1)^k.$$

Now $\qquad (-1)^k(B + 1)^k = B^k, \qquad k = 0, 1, 2, 3, \ldots ;$

for even k this follows from (3); for odd $k > 1$, $B_k = 0$ and hence $(B + 1)^k = 0$ from (3); finally, for $k = 1$, $-(B_1 + 1) = B_1$ since $B_1 = -\tfrac{1}{2}$.

Thus we have

$$B_n(1 - x) = (-1)^n \sum_{k=0}^{n} \binom{n}{k} x^{n-k} B^k = (-1)^n B_n(x).$$

Proof of (7). Differentiate equation (5):

$$DB_n(x) = n(x + B)^{n-1} = nB_{n-1}(x).$$

Proof of (8). Difference equation (5):

$$\Delta B_n(x) = (x + 1 + B)^n - (x + B)^n$$

$$= \sum_{k=0}^{n} \binom{n}{k} x^{n-k}[(1 + B)^n - B^n]$$

$$= \binom{n}{1} x^{n-1} = nx^{n-1},$$

for $(1 + B^n) - B^n = 0$ except when $n = 1$, and then $(1 + B_1) - B_1 = 1$.
Proof of (9). Apply Δ^{-1} to $\Delta B_{n+1}(x) = (n + 1)x^n$.

80. PSI FUNCTION

In the differential calculus the formula $D^{-1}x^n = x^{n+1}/(n + 1)$ fails
when $n = -1$ and a new function $\log x$ is defined so that

$$D \log x = \frac{1}{x}, \qquad D^{-1}\frac{1}{x} = \log x + C.$$

Similarly, in the difference calculus the formula $\Delta^{-1}x^{(n)} = x^{(n+1)}/(n + 1)$
fails when $n = -1$ and a new function $\Psi(x)$ is defined so that

$$\Delta\Psi(x) = \frac{1}{x}, \qquad \Delta^{-1}\frac{1}{x} = \Psi(x) + C.$$

The *psi function* is defined as

(1) $$\Psi(x) = D \log \Gamma(x) = \frac{\Gamma'(x)}{\Gamma(x)}.$$

We may now find $\Delta\Psi(x)$ by taking logarithms of the functional equation

$$\Gamma(x + 1) = x\Gamma(x),$$

$$\log \Gamma(x + 1) = \log x + \log \Gamma(x),$$

and then differentiating:

$$\frac{\Gamma'(x + 1)}{\Gamma(x + 1)} = \frac{1}{x} + \frac{\Gamma'(x)}{\Gamma(x)}.$$

The last two equations state that

(2) $$\Delta \log \Gamma(x) = \log x,$$

(3) $$\Delta \Psi(x) = \frac{1}{x} \, ;$$

and on differentiating (3)

(4) $$\Delta \Psi'(x) = -\frac{1}{x^2}.$$

We thus have the important antidifferences:

(2)′ $$\Delta^{-1} \log x = \log \Gamma(x),$$

(3)′ $$\Delta^{-1} \frac{1}{x} = \Psi(x),$$

(4)′ $$\Delta^{-1} \frac{1}{x^2} = -\Psi'(x).$$

Repeated differentiation of (3) gives

(5) $$\Delta \Psi^{(n)}(x) = (-1)^n \frac{n!}{x^{n+1}},$$

(5)′ $$\Delta^{-1} \frac{1}{x^{n+1}} = \frac{(-1)^n}{n!} \Psi^{(n)}(x).$$

It is readily shown that (2) and (3) hold when x is replaced by $x + a$; and this also is true for the formulas (4) to (5)′ deduced from them. Let the reader verify this fact.

Pairman defined the *digamma function* $\mathsf{F}(x)$ as $D \log \Gamma(x + 1)$; hence

(6) $$\Psi(x) = \mathsf{F}(x - 1).$$

Thus $\Psi(x)$ may be evaluated from tables of the digamma function.*
Finally, from (66.16),

(7) $$\Psi(1) = \Gamma'(1) = -\gamma = -0.57721 \ 56649 \cdots,$$

where γ is *Euler's constant*.

---

* E. Pairman, *Tables of the Digamma and Trigamma Functions*. Tracts for Computers Cambridge University Press, 1919.
Digamma (F) is an obsolete Greek letter.

81. FINITE SUMS

The sum $\sum_{x=a}^{b} f(x)$, where a and $b \geq a$ are integers, may be computed at once if the antiderivative $F(x) = \Delta^{-1}f(x)$ is known.

Fundamental Theorem. *If $\Delta F(x) = f(x)$ and a, $b \geq a$ are integers, then*

(1) $$\sum_{x=a}^{b} f(x) = \Delta^{-1}f(x)\Big|_{a}^{b+1} = F(b+1) - F(a).$$

PROOF. By hypothesis the sum

$$\sum_{x=a}^{b} f(x) = \sum_{x=a}^{b} [F(x+1) - F(x)].$$

Let $b = a + n$; then

$$\sum_{x=a}^{a+n} f(x) = F(a+1) - F(a)$$
$$+ F(a+2) - F(a+1)$$
$$+ \cdots$$
$$+ F(a+n) - F(a+n-1)$$
$$+ F(a+n+1) - F(a+n).$$

In this sum all terms cancel except the second and second last and we obtain (1).

Since

$$\Delta \sum_{t=a}^{x-1} f(t) = \Delta[F(x) - F(a)] = f(x),$$

(2) $$\Delta^{-1}f(x) = \sum_{t=a}^{x-1} f(t).$$

For this reason we call the operation Δ^{-1} *summing.* Δ^{-1} is analogous to the antiderivative D^{-1} which denotes indefinite integration.

In order that equation (1) still hold good when $b = a$ and $b = a - 1$, we adopt the conventions:

$$\sum_{x=a}^{a} f(x) = F(a+1) - F(a) = \Delta F(a) = f(a),$$

$$\sum_{x=a}^{a-1} f(x) = F(a) - F(a) = 0.$$

This extension of the Σ symbol must always be kept in mind when sums are evaluated by (1). For example, if $f(x) = x + 1$,

$$\sum_{t=0}^{n-1}(t + 1) = \frac{t^{(2)}}{2} + t \Big|_0^n = \frac{n(n - 1)}{2} + n = \frac{n(n + 1)}{2}.$$

Now $\frac{1}{2}n(n + 1)$ is $1 = f(0)$ when $n = 1$, 0 when $n = 0$, as our convention stipulates, although the sigmas on the left are meaningless. The convention also affords a simple check on sum formulas.

Table 81   Differences and Antidifferences

No.	$f(x)$	$\Delta f(x)$	$\Delta^{-1}f(x)$
1	1	0	x
2	a^x	$(a - 1)a^x$	$\dfrac{a^x}{a - 1} \quad a \neq 1$
3	$(-1)^x$	$2(-1)^{x+1}$	$\frac{1}{2}(-1)^{x+1}$
4	xa^x	$(a - 1)xa^x + a^{x+1}$	$\dfrac{a^x}{a - 1}\left(x - \dfrac{a}{a - 1}\right) \quad a \neq 1$
5	$x(-1)^x$	$(-1)^{x+1}(1 + 2x)$	$\frac{1}{2}(-1)^{x+1}(x - \frac{1}{2})$
6	$(x + b)^{(n)}$	$n(x + b)^{(n-1)}$	$\dfrac{(x + b)^{(n+1)}}{n + 1} \quad n \neq -1$
7	$\dbinom{x}{n} = \dfrac{x^{(n)}}{n!}$	$\dbinom{x}{n - 1}$	$\dbinom{x}{n + 1}$
8	$(ax + b)^{[n]}$	$n\,a(ax + b)^{[n]}$	$\dfrac{(ax + b)^{[n+1]}}{a(n + 1)}$
9	$\cos(ax + b)$	$-2\sin\dfrac{a}{2}\sin\left(ax + b + \dfrac{a}{2}\right)$	$\dfrac{\sin\left(ax + b - \dfrac{a}{2}\right)}{2\sin\frac{1}{2}a}$
10	$\sin(ax + b)$	$2\sin\dfrac{a}{2}\cos\left(ax + b + \dfrac{a}{2}\right)$	$-\dfrac{\cos\left(ax + b - \dfrac{a}{2}\right)}{2\sin\frac{1}{2}a}$
11	$B_n(x) = (x + B)^n$	nx^{n-1}	
12	x^n		$\dfrac{B_{n+1}(x)}{n + 1} \quad n \neq -1$
13	$\log(x + a)$	$\log\left(1 + \dfrac{1}{x + a}\right)$	$\log \Gamma(x + a)$
14	$\dfrac{1}{x + a}$	$-(x + a - 1)^{(-2)}$	$\Psi(x + a)$
15	$\dfrac{1}{(x + a)^2}$		$-\Psi'(x + a)$

Example 1. **Geometric Series.**

$$S_n = \sum_{x=0}^{n-1} ar^x = \frac{ar^x}{r-1}\Big|_0^n = a\frac{r^n - 1}{r-1}.$$

Example 2. **Arithmetic Series.**

$$S_n = \sum_{x=0}^{n-1}(a + bx) = ax + \tfrac{1}{2}bx^{(2)}\Big|_0^n = an + \tfrac{1}{2}bn(n-1).$$

Example 3. **Series of Squares.**

$$S_n = \sum_{x=1}^{n} x^2 = \sum_{x=1}^{n}(x + x^{(2)}) = \frac{x^{(2)}}{2} + \frac{x^{(3)}}{3}\Big|_1^{n+1}$$

$$= \tfrac{1}{2}(n+1)n - \tfrac{1}{3}(n+1)n(n-1)$$

$$= \tfrac{1}{6}n(n+1)(2n+1).$$

Example 4. **Series of Cubes.**

$$S_n = \sum_{x=1}^{n} x^3 = \sum_{x=1}^{n}(x + 3x^{(2)} + x^{(3)}) \qquad \text{(Table 78)}$$

$$= \frac{x^{(2)}}{2} + x^{(3)} + \frac{x^{(4)}}{4}\Big|_1^{n+1}$$

$$= \tfrac{1}{2}(n+1)n + (n+1)n(n-1) + \tfrac{1}{4}(n+1)n(n-1)(n-2)$$

$$= \tfrac{1}{4}n^2(n+1)^2.$$

When a list of Bernoulli polynomials is available, we may use No. 12 to compute the sums of powers Σx^k. Thus in the above example

$$\sum_{x=1}^{n} x^3 = \frac{B_4(x)}{4}\Big|_1^{n+1} = \frac{B_4(n+1) - B_4(0)}{4}$$

$$= \tfrac{1}{4}[(n+1)^4 - 2(n+1)^2 + (n+1)^2]$$

$$= \tfrac{1}{4}n^2(n+1)^2.$$

With $x = 0$ as lower limit the result is the same; for $B_4(1) = B_4(0)$ from (79.6).

Example 5. **Series of Cosines.**

$$S_n = \sum_{x=1}^{n} \cos xa = \frac{\sin a(x - \tfrac{1}{2})}{2\sin\tfrac{1}{2}a}\Big|_1^{n+1}$$

$$= \frac{\sin(n + \tfrac{1}{2})a - \sin\tfrac{1}{2}a}{2\sin\tfrac{1}{2}a}$$

$$= \frac{\sin\tfrac{1}{2}na\cos\tfrac{1}{2}(n+1)a}{\sin\tfrac{1}{2}a}.$$

Example 6. $1\cdot 3\cdot 4 + 2\cdot 4\cdot 5 + 3\cdot 5\cdot 6 + \cdots$. The general term $x(x+2)(x+3)$ may be written

$$(x+1)(x+2)(x+3) - (x+2)(x+3) = (x+3)^{(3)} - (x+3)^{(2)};$$

$$S_n = \left[\frac{(x+3)^{(4)}}{4} - \frac{(x+3)^{(3)}}{3}\right]_1^{n+1} = \frac{(n+4)^{(4)}}{4} - \frac{(n+4)^{(3)}}{3} + 2.$$

Example 7. $1 - 2 + 3 - 4 + 5 - 6 + \cdots$.

$$S_n = -\sum_{x=1}^{n} (-1)^x x = \frac{(-1)^x}{2}(x - \tfrac{1}{2})\Big|_1^{n+1} = \frac{(-1)^{n+1}}{2}(n + \tfrac{1}{2}) + \tfrac{1}{4}$$

on using No. 5. Thus the sum is $-n/2$ or $(n + 1)/2$ according as n is even or odd. For example,

$$1 - 2 + 3 - \cdots + 99 = \tfrac{1}{2}(99 + \tfrac{1}{2}) + \tfrac{1}{4} = 50.$$

Example 8. $1 \cdot 3 \cdot 5 + 3 \cdot 5 \cdot 7 + 5 \cdot 7 \cdot 9 + \cdots$. The general term is

$$(2x - 1)(2x + 1)(2x + 3) = (2x + 3)^{[3]} = 8(x + \tfrac{1}{2})^{(3)}$$

$$S_n = \sum_{x=1}^{n} (2x + 3)^{[3]} = \frac{(2x + 3)^{[4]}}{8}\Big|_1^{n+1} \qquad\qquad \text{(No. 8)}$$

$$= \tfrac{1}{8}(2x + 3)(2x + 1)(2x - 1)(2x - 3)\Big|_1^{n+1}$$

$$= \tfrac{1}{8}\{(2n + 5)(2xn + 3)(2n + 1)(2n - 1) + 15\}.$$

It is imperative to replace $(2x + 3)^{[4]}$ by its defined value before substituting; for $(5)^{[4]}$ is not defined and $5^{(4)} = 120$ is wrong. Factorial expressions may be avoided by summing $8(x + \tfrac{3}{2})^{(3)}$ and using No. 6 of the table.

Example 9. $\dfrac{1}{1 \cdot 3 \cdot 5} + \dfrac{1}{3 \cdot 5 \cdot 7} + \dfrac{1}{5 \cdot 7 \cdot 9} + \cdots$.
The general term is

$$\frac{1}{(2x - 1)(2x + 1)(2x + 3)} = \frac{1}{8(x - \tfrac{1}{2})(x + \tfrac{1}{2})(x + \tfrac{3}{2})} = \frac{1}{8}(x - \tfrac{3}{2})^{(-3)}$$

$$S_n = \frac{1}{8}\sum_{x=1}^{n}(x - \tfrac{3}{2})^{(-3)} = \frac{1}{8}\frac{(x - \tfrac{3}{2})^{(-2)}}{-2}\Big|_1^{n+1}$$

$$= \frac{1}{16}[(-\tfrac{1}{2})^{(-2)} - (n - \tfrac{1}{2})^{(-2)}]$$

$$= \frac{1}{16}\left[\frac{1}{\tfrac{1}{2} \cdot \tfrac{3}{2}} - \frac{1}{(n + \tfrac{1}{2})(n + \tfrac{3}{2})}\right]$$

$$= \frac{1}{4}\left[\frac{1}{3} - \frac{1}{(2n + 1)(2n + 3)}\right].$$

As $n \to \infty$, $S_n \to \tfrac{1}{12}$.

PROBLEMS

1. $\displaystyle\sum_{x=1}^{n} \frac{1}{x(x + 1)} = \frac{n}{n + 1}$.

2. $\displaystyle\sum_{x=1}^{n} \frac{1}{x(x + 1)(x + 2)} = \frac{1}{4} - \frac{1}{2(n + 1)(n + 2)}$.

3. $\displaystyle\sum_{x=1}^{\infty} xa^x = \frac{a}{(1 - a)^2}$, $a \neq 1$.   (Ex. 77.4)

4. $\sum_{x=1}^{n} (x + 1)2^x = n2^{n+1}.$

5. $\sum_{x=1}^{n} \frac{x + 1}{2^x} = 3 - \frac{n + 3}{2^n}.$

6. $\sum_{x=1}^{n} \frac{x + 3}{x(x + 1)(x + 2)} = \frac{5}{4} - \frac{2n + 5}{2(n + 1)(n + 2)}.$

7. $\sum_{x=0}^{n-1} \cos (2x + 1)c = \frac{\sin 2nc}{2 \sin c}.$

8. $\sum_{x=2}^{100} \frac{1}{x^2 - 1} = \frac{3}{4} - \frac{201}{20200}.$ (Ex. 78.3)

9. $\sum_{x=1}^{n} x^4 = \frac{n(n + 1)}{30} (6n^3 + 9n^2 + n - 1).$

10. $\sum_{x=1}^{n} \cos \frac{\pi}{n} x = -1;$ $\sum_{x=1}^{n} \sin \frac{\pi}{n} x = \cot \frac{\pi}{2n}.$

11. $\sum_{x=1}^{\infty} x^2 a^x = \frac{a(a + 1)}{(1 - a)^3},$ $a \neq 1.$ (cf. Ex. 77.4)

12. $\sum_{x=1}^{\infty} \frac{1}{x(x + 3)} = \frac{11}{18}.$ (Ex. 78.4)

13. $\sum_{x=1}^{n} x(n - x) = \binom{n + 1}{3}.$

14. $\sum_{x=1}^{n} (2x - 1)^2 = \frac{n(4n^2 - 1)}{3}.$

15. Sum $\sum_{x=1}^{n} (-1)^x e^{ixa}$ using (2) and take real and imaginary parts to obtain

$$\sum_{x=1}^{n} (-1)^{x-1} \cos xa = \frac{\cos \frac{1}{2}a - (-1)^n \cos (n + \frac{1}{2})a}{\cos \frac{1}{2}a},$$

$$\sum_{x=1}^{n} (-1)^{x-1} \sin xa = \frac{\sin \frac{1}{2}a - (-1)^n \sin (n + \frac{1}{2})a}{\cos \frac{1}{2}a},   (a \neq k\pi).$$

16. Show that the sums of Problem 15 are valid when sin, cos are changed to sinh, cosh.

17. Where the sum convention applies, use it to check the problems above.

82.   LINEAR DIFFERENCE EQUATIONS OF FIRST ORDER

Let S denote a set of real numbers x. The set S may include all real numbers; or it may be restricted to the integers, or the non-negative integers, or only the positive integers. Then if the function $y(x)$ is defined over the set S, an equation relating that value of y and one or more of its differences $\Delta y, \Delta^2 y, \ldots$ is called a *difference equation*.

If the equation relates y and Δy, as in

$$\Delta y(x) + xy(x) = 2x^2,$$

it is of the *first order*. It is usually advantageous to put $\Delta y = y(x + 1) - y(x)$; the equation above then becomes

$$y(x + 1) + (x - 1)y(x) = 2x^2.$$

The equation

(1) $$y(x + 1) - p(x)y(x) = q(x),$$

where $p(x)$ and $q(x)$ are functions defined over a set S, is the general *linear* equation of the first order. We shall solve (1) when for some initial value $x = \alpha$, $y(\alpha)$ is given, say $y(\alpha) = y_0$. Then the set S consists of the numbers α, $\alpha + 1$, $\alpha + 2$, ... ; α is usually an integer, as 0 or 1, but this is not an essential requirement. Now from (1)

$$y(\alpha + 1) = p(\alpha)y_0 + q(\alpha) \qquad = y_1 \text{ (say)},$$
$$y(\alpha + 2) = p(\alpha + 1)y_1 + q(\alpha + 1) = y_2,$$

and so on, so that $y(x)$ is uniquely determined for each number of the set S provided $p(x)$ and $q(x)$ are defined on S. Thus the existence and unicity of a solution of (1) for which $y(\alpha) = y_0$ is known in advance.

Before attacking the *complete* equation (1) we shall solve the *reduced* equation

(2) $$y(x + 1) - p(x)y(x) = 0, \qquad y(\alpha) = y_0.$$

From (2) we have

$$y(x) = p(x - 1)y(x - 1)$$
$$y(x - 1) = p(x - 2)y(x - 2)$$
$$\cdot$$
$$\cdot \quad \cdot \quad \cdot \quad \cdot \quad \cdot \quad \cdot \quad \cdot \quad \cdot$$
$$\cdot$$
$$y(\alpha + 1) = p(\alpha)y(\alpha).$$

On multiplying these $x - \alpha$ equations together, all the y's cancel except $y(x)$ and $y(\alpha) = y_0$; we thus obtain

(3) $$y(x) = y_0 p(\alpha)p(\alpha + 1) \cdots p(x - 1) = y_0 P(x).$$

where $P(x)$ denotes the product of $x - \alpha$ factors $p(t)$:

(4) $$P(x) = \prod_{t=\alpha}^{x-1} p(t), \qquad P(\alpha) = 1.$$

The value $P(\alpha) = 1$ is necessary so that (3) still holds when $x = \alpha$.

From (3) we have

$$(5) \qquad \Delta\left(\frac{y(x)}{P(x)}\right) = \frac{y(x+1)}{P(x+1)} - \frac{y(x)}{P(x)} = \Delta y_0 = 0.$$

This equation is equivalent to (2) and shows that the *multiplier* $1/P(x+1)$ converts (2) into the *exact* equation (5). Using this fact we now solve the complete equation (1) by multiplying it by $1/P(x+1)$. Then, in view of (2), we have

$$\Delta\left(\frac{y(x)}{P(x)}\right) = \frac{q(x)}{P(x+1)} \, ;$$

hence the general solution of (1) is

$$(6) \qquad y(x) = P(x) \, \Delta^{-1}\left(\frac{q(x)}{P(x+1)}\right) + cP(x).$$

Putting $q(x) = 0$, we have $cP(x)$ as the general solution of the reduced equation; and when $c = 0$, the first term in (6) is a particular solution of the complete equation. Note the striking analogy in procedure and in the final result with the solution of the linear differential equation in § 16.

To obtain the unique solution for which $y(\alpha) = y_0$, determine c in (6) by putting $x = \alpha$, $y(\alpha) = y_0$.

Example 1. Let $y(x)$ denote the number of permutations of n different letters taken x at a time. Then from *each* permutation of x letters we can get $n - x$ permutations of $x + 1$ letters by placing one of the $n - x$ remaining letters at the end. Thus

$$y(x+1) = (n-x)y(x), \qquad y(1) = n;$$

$$P(x) = \prod_{t=1}^{x-1} (n-t) = (n-1)(n-2)\cdots(n-x+1),$$

and from (3)

$$y(x) = nP(x) = n(n-1)\cdots(n-x+1) = n^{(x)}.$$

Example 2. Let $y(x)$ denote the number of combinations of n different letters taken x at a time. Then from each combination of x letters we may get a combination of $x + 1$ letters by adding one of the $n - x$ remaining letters. But this procedure gives every one of $y(x + 1)$ combinations $x + 1$ times. Thus

$$y(x+1) = \frac{n-x}{x+1} y(x), \qquad y(1) = n;$$

$$P(x) = \prod_{t=1}^{x-1} \frac{n-t}{t+1} = \frac{(n-1)(n-2)\cdots(n-x+1)}{2 \cdot 3 \cdots x},$$

and

$$y(x) = nP(x) = \frac{n(n-1)\cdots(n-x+1)}{x!} = \binom{n}{x}.$$

Example 3. Solve the complete equation over the set of positive integers:

$$y(x + 1) - xy(x) = (x + 1)!, \qquad y(1) = 2.$$

$$P(x) = \prod_{t=1}^{x-1} x = 1 \;\cdot\; 2 \cdots (x - 1) = (x - 1)!$$

and from (6)

$$y(x) = (x - 1)! \, \Delta^{-1} \frac{(x + 1)!}{x!} + \omega(x - 1)!$$

$$= (x - 1)! \, \Delta^{-1}(x + 1) + \omega(x - 1)!$$

$$= (x - 1)! \, \frac{(x + 1)^{(2)}}{2} + \omega(x - 1)!,$$

$$y(x) = \tfrac{1}{2}(x + 1)! + \omega(x - 1)!.$$

To find ω, put $x = 1$; then $2 = 1 + \omega$, $\omega = 1$, and

$$y(x) = \tfrac{1}{2}(x + 1)! + (x - 1)!.$$

Example 4. Find the general solution of the equation

$$y(x + 1) + y(x) = -(x + 1)$$

over the set $1, 2, 3, \ldots$.

$$P(x) = \prod_{t=1}^{x-1} (-1) = (-1)^{x-1}$$

$$y(x) = (-1)^{x-1} \, \Delta^{-1} \left(\frac{-(x + 1)}{(-1)^x} \right) + \omega(-1)^{x-1}$$

$$= (-1)^{x-1} \, \Delta^{-1}((-1)^{x+1} (x + 1)) + \omega(-1)^{x-1}$$

$$= (-1)^{x-1} \frac{(-1)^{x+1}}{-2} (x + 1 - \tfrac{1}{2}) + \omega(-1)^{x-1}$$

$$y(x) = -\tfrac{1}{2}(x + \tfrac{1}{2}) + \omega(-1)^{x-1}.$$

Check. Verify that the two terms are solutions of the complete and reduced equations, respectively.

PROBLEMS

1. $y(x + 1) = ay(x), \qquad y(0) = 1.$
2. $y(x + 1) - y(x) = x, \qquad y(2) = 1.$
3. $y(x + 1) = xy(x), \qquad y(1) = 0.$

4. $y(x + 1) = \dfrac{x + a}{x} y(x), \qquad y(1) = 1.$

5. $y(x + 1) = \dfrac{n + x}{x + 1} y(x), \qquad y(1) = n;$ $y(x)$ is the number of combinations of n letters taken x at a time when repetition is allowed.

6. $y(x + 1) = \dfrac{2x + 1}{2x + 2} y(x), \qquad y(1) = \tfrac{1}{2}.$

7. $x^2 y(x + 1) = 2(x + 1)y(x),$ $y(1) = 2.$

8. $y(x + 1) - 2y(x) = 2^x \dfrac{x^{(3)}}{3!}.$

9. $y(x + 1) - ay(x) = b,$ $a \neq 1.$

10. $y(x + 1) - ay(x) = \dfrac{a^x}{(x + 1)^2},$ $y(1) = 1.$

11. $y(x + 1) - ay(x) = \cos nx$ (cf. Prob. 77.3).
12. $y(x + 1) - pa^{2x}y(x) = qa^{x^2},$ p, q const.
13. $y(x + 1) - (x + 1)y(x) = 2^x(1 - x).$
14. $(x + 1)y(x + 1) + xy(x) = 2x - 3,$ $y(1) = 1.$
15. Show that

$$p(x)y(x + 1)y(x) + q(x)y(x + 1) + r(x)y(x) = 0$$

is linear in $1/y(x).$

83. EXACT EQUATIONS

The linear form in the left member of

(1) $p_0(x)y(x + 2) + p_1(x)y(x + 1) + p_2(x)y(x) = 0$

is said to be *exact* when it can be expressed as the perfect difference of a linear form of order one, say

$$\Delta\{f(x)y(x + 1) + g(x)y(x)\}.$$

Since this difference equals

$$f(x + 1)y(x + 2) + \{g(x + 1) - f(x)\}y(x + 1) - g(x)y(x),$$

when (1) is exact, we must have

$$\begin{aligned}
p_0(x) &= f(x + 1), \\
p_1(x) &= g(x + 1) - f(x), \\
p_2(x) &= -g(x).
\end{aligned}$$

These equations imply the necessary condition for exactness:

(2) $p_0(x) + p_1(x + 1) + p_2(x + 2) = 0.$

Since $f(x) = p_0(x - 1),$ $g(x) = -p_2(x),$ equation (1) then becomes

(3) $\Delta\{p_0(x - 1)y(x + 1) - p_2(x)y(x)\} = 0.$

The condition (2) is also sufficient to ensure the exactness of (1). When it is fulfilled, (3) reduces to (1) when the difference is computed; for the coefficient of $y(x + 1)$ is then

$$-p_0(x - 1) - p_2(x + 1) = p_1(x).$$

A function $\lambda(x)$ is said to be a *multiplier* (or *summation factor*) of a difference equation if the equation multiplied by $\lambda(x)$ is exact. In view of (2), $\lambda(x)$ will be a multiplier of (1) when $\lambda(x)$ satisfies the condition

$$\lambda(x)p_0(x) + \lambda(x+1)p_1(x+1) + \lambda(x+2)p_2(x+2) = 0,$$

that is, when $\lambda(x)$ is a solution of

(4) $\qquad p_2(x+2)z(x+2) + p_1(x+1)z(x+1) + p_0(x)z(x) = 0,$

the equation *adjoint* to (1).

The adjoint of (4) is therefore

(5) $\quad p_0(x+2)y(x+2) + p_1(x+2)y(x+1) + p_2(x+2)y(x) = 0.$

This is essentially the same equation as (1); for if we put $t = x + 2$, it becomes

$$p_0(t)y(t) + p_1(t)y(t-1) + p_2(t)y(t-2) = 0.$$

These results generalize in an obvious way to the linear equation of order n

(6) $\qquad p_0(x)y(x+n) + p_1(x)y(x+n-1) + \cdots + p_n(x)y(x) = 0$

for which the exactness condition is

(7) $\qquad p_0(x) + p_1(x+1) + \cdots + p_n(x+n) = 0.$

In particular, the equation of the first order

(8) $\qquad\qquad p_0(x)y(x+1) + p_1(x)y(x) = 0$

is evidently exact when

(9) $\qquad\qquad p_0(x) + p_1(x+1) = 0;$

then (8) becomes $\Delta[p_1(x)y(x)] = 0$ and its solution is

(10) $\qquad\qquad p_1(x)y(x) = \omega, \qquad$ a periodic.

The adjoint of (8) is

$$p_1(x+1)z(x+1) + p_0(x)z(x) = 0.$$

For example, the equations

(11) (12) $\quad y(x+1) - xy(x) = 0, \qquad (x+1)z(x+1) - z(x) = 0$

are adjoint to each other. The functional equation

(13) $\qquad\qquad\qquad \Gamma(x+1) = x\Gamma(x) \qquad\qquad\qquad$ (66.4)

shows that

(11)' (12)' $y(x) = \omega\Gamma(x)$, $z(x) = \dfrac{\omega}{\Gamma(x+1)}$,

are solutions of (11) and (12).

Equation (13) shows that the following equations have the given multipliers $\lambda(x)$:

(14) $y(x+1) - (x-a)y(x) = 0$, $\lambda(x) = \dfrac{1}{\Gamma(x-a+1)}$;

(15) $(x-b)y(x+1) - y(x) = 0$, $\lambda(x) = \Gamma(x-b)$;

(16) $(x-b)y(x+1) - (x-a)y(x) = 0$, $\lambda(x) = \dfrac{\Gamma(x-b)}{\Gamma(x-a+1)}$.

Thus (16) becomes

(16)' $\Delta\left\{\dfrac{\Gamma(x-b)}{\Gamma(x-a)}\,y(x)\right\} = 0$ and $y(x) = \omega\,\dfrac{\Gamma(x-a)}{\Gamma(x-b)}$.

By inspection, we have

(17) $y(x+1) - ky(x) = 0$, $\lambda(x) = 1/k^{x+1}$;

(17)' $y(x) = \omega k^x$.

An equation with polynomial coefficients such as

(18) $\alpha(x-a_1)\cdots(x-a_m)y(x+1) - \beta(x-b_1)\cdots(x-b_n)y(x) = 0$

has a multiplier which can be formed as above:

(19) $\lambda(x) = \dfrac{\alpha^x\Gamma(x-a_1)\cdots\Gamma(x-a_m)}{\beta^{x+1}\Gamma(x-b_1+1)\cdots\Gamma(x-b_n+1)}$.

When multiplied by $\lambda(x)$, (18) becomes

(20) $\Delta\left\{\dfrac{\alpha^x\Gamma(x-a_1)\cdots\Gamma(x-a_m)}{\beta^x\Gamma(x-b_1)\cdots\Gamma(x-b_n)}\,y(x)\right\} = 0$,

an exact equation whose general solution is

(21) $y(x) = \omega\,\dfrac{\beta^x\Gamma(x-b_1)\cdots\Gamma(x-b_n)}{\alpha^x\Gamma(x-a_1)\cdots\Gamma(x-a_n)}$.

If the connecting sign in (18) is $+$, replace β by $-\beta$.

Example 1. $y(x+2) + (x+1)y(x+1) - xy(x) = 0$.
The adjoint equation is

$$-(x+2)z(x+2) + (x+2)z(x+1) + z(x) = 0$$

or $(x+2)\,\Delta z(x+1) - z(x) = 0$.

Evidently $z = x + 2 \ (\Delta z = 1)$ is a solution. Hence

$$(x + 2)y(x + 2) + (x + 2)(x + 1)y(x + 1) - (x + 2)x\, y(x) = 0$$

is exact; and since $p_0(x) = x + 2$, $q_0(x) = -(x + 2)x$, we have from (3)

$$(x + 1)y(x + 1) + x(x + 2)y(x) = \omega_1.$$

This in turn admits the multiplier

$$\lambda(x) = \frac{\Gamma(x + 1)}{(-1)^{x+1}\Gamma(x + 1)\Gamma(x + 3)} = \frac{(-1)^{x+1}}{\Gamma(x + 3)} \tag{19}$$

and yields the equation

$$\Delta\left\{\frac{(-1)^x x y(x)}{\Gamma(x + 2)}\right\} = \omega_1 \frac{(-1)^{x+1}}{\Gamma(x + 3)}$$

whose solution is

$$\frac{(-1)^x x y(x)}{\Gamma(x + 2)} = \omega_1 \sum_{t=a}^{x-1} \frac{(-1)^{t+1}}{(t + 3)} + \omega_2. \tag{81.2}$$

Since $\Gamma(x + 2)/x = (x + 1)\Gamma(x)$, this may be written

$$y(x) = \omega_1(-1)^x(x + 1)\Gamma(x)\sum_{t=a}^{x-1} \frac{(-1)^{t+1}}{\Gamma(t + 3)} + \omega_2(-1)^x(x + 1)\Gamma(x).$$

Over the set of positive integers $\{n\}$ we have

$$y(n) = (-1)^n(n + 1)(n - 1)!\left[\omega_1\sum_{t=1}^{n-1} \frac{(-1)^{t+1}}{(t + 2)!} + \omega_2\right].$$

Keeping in mind the summation conventions (§ 81), ω_1 and ω_2 are given by

$$y(1) = -2\omega_2, \qquad y(2) = \tfrac{1}{2}\omega_1 + 3\omega_2.$$

Example 2. $(x + 1)(x + 2)y(x + 2) - y(x) = 0$. The adjoint equation

$$-z(x + 2) + (x + 2)(x + 1)z(x) = 0$$

has the obvious particular solution $\lambda(x) = \Gamma(x + 1)$. Multiplying by $\Gamma(x + 1)$ yields the exact equation

$$\Gamma(x + 3)y(x + 2) - \Gamma(x + 1)y(x) = 0$$

in which $p_0(x) = \Gamma(x + 3)$, $p_2(x) = -\Gamma(x + 1)$. Its solution, given by (3), is

$$\Gamma(x + 2)y(x + 1) + \Gamma(x + 1)y(x) = \omega_1.$$

Multiplication by $(-1)^{x+1}$ converts this into

$$\Delta\{(-1)^x \Gamma(x + 1)y(x)\} = -\omega_1(-1)^x$$

whence

$$(-1)^x \Gamma(x + 1)y(x) = \tfrac{1}{2}\omega_1(-1)^x + \omega_2 \tag{Table 81,3}$$

$$\Gamma(x + 1)y(x) = \tfrac{1}{2}\omega_1 + \omega_2(-1)^x.$$

Thus $1/\Gamma(x + 1)$ and $(-1)^x/\Gamma(x + 1)$ form a solution basis for the equation.

PROBLEMS

Find multipliers for the equations and solve:
1. $y(x + 1) + (x - 1)(x + 1)y(x) = 0.$
2. $2x(x + 1)y(x + 1) - (x - 1)y(x) = 0.$
3. $(x + 3)y(x + 1) - 2(x + 2)(x + 1)y(x) = 0.$
4. $y(x + 1) + x^2(x - 1)y(x) = 0.$
Prove exact and solve:
5. $xy(x + 2) - (x - 2)y(x) = 0;$ $y(0) = 1, y(-1) = 2.$
6. $y(x + 2) - xy(x + 1) + (x - 2)y(x) = 0;$ $y(3) = 1, y(4) = 2.$
7. In Problem 6 find $y(5)$ and $y(6)$ from the solution and check by finding
their values directly from the equation.
8. In Example 1 find the solution for which $y(1) = 2, y(2) = 3,$ and check
by finding $y(3)$ and $y(4)$ from solution and equation.
Solve the equations:
9. $(x + 2)y(x + 2) - xy(x + 1) - y(x) = 0.$

10. $2y(x + 2) - \dfrac{x + 3}{x + 1}(x + 1) + \dfrac{1}{x}y(x) = 0.$

[2^x is a solution of the adjoint equation.]

84. LINEAR DIFFERENCE EQUATION OF SECOND ORDER

The general linear equation of the second order is

(1) $y(x + 2) + p(x)y(x + 1) + q(x)y(x) = r(x).$

For some initial value $x = \alpha$, let $y(\alpha)$ and $y(\alpha + 1)$ be given, say

(2) $y(\alpha) = y_0,$ $y(\alpha + 1) = y_1.$

We shall now consider solutions of (1) over the set S consisting of the
numbers $\alpha, \alpha + 1, \alpha + 2, \ldots$. We then have the following

Existence Theorem. *Let the functions $p(x)$, $q(x)$, $r(x)$ be defined over the set
S: $\alpha, \alpha + 1, \alpha + 2, \ldots$. Then there exists a unique solution $y(x)$ of
equation* (1) *over S, which satisfies the conditions* (2).
    PROOF. Put $x = \alpha, \alpha + 1, \alpha + 2, \ldots$ successively in (1); then

$$y(\alpha + 2) = r(\alpha) - y_1 p(\alpha) - y_0 q(\alpha) = y_2 \quad \text{(say)},$$
$$y(\alpha + 3) = r(\alpha + 1) - y_2 p(\alpha + 1) - y_1 q(\alpha + 1) = y_3,$$

and so on, so that $y(x)$ is uniquely determined for each number of the
set S.
    Corresponding to the *complete equation* (1) we have the *reduced* equation

(3) $y(x + 2) + p(x)y(x + 1) + q(x)y(x) = 0.$

We now call any function which has the same value over the set S a *constant*. We then have the obvious analog of Theorem 26.2:

Theorem. *If $u(x)$ and $v(x)$ are solutions of the reduced equation* (3), *then*

$$(4) \qquad\qquad y(x) = c_1 u(x) + c_2 v(x)$$

with arbitrary constants c_1, c_2, is also a solution.

When $v = ku$, the solution (4) reduces to $y = (c_1 + kc_2)u = Cu$ which has but one essential constant. But when v is not a multiple of u, we shall see in the next section that all solutions of (3) are included in (4). Then (4) is the general solution of (3).

Let the reader show that when $p(x)/q(x)$, $r(x)/q(x)$ are defined over the set S': α, $\alpha - 1$, $\alpha - 2$, $\ldots$, there exists a unique solution $y(x)$ of equation (1) over S, which satisfies the conditions $y(\alpha) = y_0$, $y(\alpha - 1) = y_1$.

85. CASORATI DETERMINANT

The *Casorati determinant** (or simply *Casoratian*) of n functions $f_1(x)$, $f_2(x)$, $\ldots$, $f_n(x)$ is defined as

$$K(x) = \begin{vmatrix} f_1(x) & f_2(x) & \cdots & f_n(x) \\ f_1(x+1) & f_2(x+1) & \cdots & f_n(x+1) \\ \cdots & \cdots & \cdots & \cdots \\ f_1(x+n-1) & f_2(x+n-1) & \cdots & f_n(x+n-1) \end{vmatrix}$$

We shall also write

$$K(x) = K(f_1, f_2, \ldots, f_n)$$

when the functions need to be specified.

In the theory of difference equations the Casoratian plays the role of the Wronskian in differential equations. Thus we have the analog of Theorem 27.1.

Theorem 1. *A necessary condition that a set of functions be linearly dependent on a set S: α_1, $\alpha + 1$, $\alpha + 2$, $\ldots$, is that their Casoratian vanish identically on S.*

Corollary. *A sufficient condition that a set of functions be linearly independent on a set S: α, $\alpha + 1$, $\alpha + 2$, $\ldots$, is that their Casoratian does not vanish identically on S.*

---

* First used by the Italian mathematician Felice Casorati (1835–1890) who recognized the many analogies between difference and differential equations.

We also have the analog of Theorem 27.2.

Theorem 2. *If the functions $f(x)$ and $g(x)$ are linearly dependent on a set S:
$\alpha, \alpha + 1, \alpha + 2, \ldots, K(f, g) \equiv 0$ over I.*

*Conversely, if $K(f, g) \equiv 0$ over S and one function is never zero on S,
then $f(x)$ and $g(x)$ are linearly dependent on S.*

PROOF. The first part is included in Theorem 1, but an independent
proof is simple. Let $c_1 f + c_2 g \equiv 0$ and $c_2 \neq 0$ on S; then if $k = -c_1/c_2$,

$$g(x) = kf(x) \quad \text{and} \quad K(f, g) = \begin{vmatrix} f(x) & kf(x) \\ f(x + 1) & kf(x + 1) \end{vmatrix} = 0.$$

As to the converse, let $K(f, g) = 0$ and $f(x) \neq 0$ on S; then

$$(1) \qquad \frac{K(f, g)}{f(x)f(x + 1)} = \frac{f(x)g(x + 1) - g(x)f(x + 1)}{f(x)f(x + 1)} = \Delta\left(\frac{g(x)}{f(x)}\right) = 0$$

and $g(x)/f(x) = c$. Thus $cf(x) - 1 \cdot g(x) \equiv 0$ on S and the functions are
linearly dependent.

86. THE REDUCED EQUATION

If $u(x)$ and $v(x)$ are solutions of the reduced equation

$$(1) \qquad y(x + 2) + p(x)y(x + 1) + q(x)y(x) = 0,$$

their Casoratian $K(x)$ satisfies the equation

$$(2) \qquad K(x + 1) = q(x)K(x).$$

PROOF. In the Casoratian

$$K(x + 1) = \begin{vmatrix} u(x + 1) & v(x + 1) \\ u(x + 2) & v(x + 2) \end{vmatrix}$$

replace $u(x + 2)$ and $v(x + 2)$ by their values from equation (1) and add
$p(x)$ times the first row to the second; then

$$K(x + 1) = \begin{vmatrix} u(x + 1) & v(x + 1) \\ -q(x)u(x) & -q(x)v(x) \end{vmatrix} = q(x)K(x).$$

If $u(x)$ and $v(x)$ are linearly dependent, $K(x) \equiv 0$ and (2) is trivial.
But if $K(\alpha) \neq 0$, $u(x)$ and $v(x)$ are linearly independent by Theorem 85.1:
then if $q(x) \neq 0$ over the set S: $\alpha, \alpha + 1, \alpha + 2, \ldots, K(x) \neq 0$ over S.

If $u(x)$ and $v(x)$ are solutions of (1) that satisfy the conditions

$$u(\alpha) = 1, \, u(\alpha + 1) = 0; \qquad v(\alpha) = 0, \, v(\alpha + 1) = 1;$$

then $K(\alpha) = 1$ and $u(x)$ and $v(x)$ are linearly independent.

Any two linearly independent solutions of (1) for which $K(\alpha) \neq 0$ are said to form a *fundamental system* in view of the following

Theorem. *If $u(x)$ and $v(x)$ are a fundamental system of solutions of the reduced equation (1) on the set S: $\alpha, \alpha + 1, \alpha + 2, \ldots$, every solution of this equation is included in*

(3) $$y(x) = c_1 u(x) + c_2 v(x)$$

when the constants are suitably chosen.

PROOF. Let $y(x)$ be any solution of (1); and let $y(\alpha) = y_0, y(\alpha + 1) = y_1$. Choose c_1 and c_2 so that

$$c_1 u(\alpha) + c_2 v(\alpha) = y_0,$$

$$c_1 u(\alpha + 1) + c_2 v(\alpha + 1) = y_1.$$

This is always possible since these linear equations in c_1, c_2 have as their determinant the Casorati $K(\alpha) \neq 0$. With these values of c_1 and c_2 the two solutions of (1)

$$c_1 u(x) + c_2 v(x) \quad \text{and} \quad y(x)$$

have the same values when $x = \alpha$ and $x = \alpha + 1$. But the existence theorem of § 84 states that there is only *one* solution of equation (1) taking on these values at α, thus proving (3).

If $u(x)$ and $v(x)$ are a fundamental system of solutions of (1), so are also

$$U = au + bv, \qquad V = cu + dv \quad \text{if} \quad \begin{vmatrix} a & b \\ c & d \end{vmatrix} \neq 0.$$

For, as in § 28, we have

$$K(U, V) = \begin{vmatrix} a & b \\ c & d \end{vmatrix} K(u, v).$$

Equation (2) is a linear difference equation of the first order which may be solved for $K(x)$ as soon as $K(\alpha)$ is specified. The formula (82.3) now gives

(4) $$K(x) = K(\alpha)Q(x); \qquad Q(x) = \prod_{t=\alpha}^{x-1} q(t), \qquad Q(\alpha) = 1.$$

When one solution $u(x)$ of the reduced equation is known, a second $v(x)$ may be found so that $u(x), v(x)$ form a fundamental system. For from (85.1)

$$K(x) = K(u, v) = u(x)u(x + 1) \Delta\left(\frac{v(x)}{u(x)}\right)$$

and hence from (4)

(5) $$\Delta \frac{v(x)}{u(x)} = K(\alpha)\frac{Q(x)}{u(x)u(x + 1)}.$$

Now apply Δ^{-1} to (5); we then have

(6) $$v(x) = K(\alpha)u(x)\Delta^{-1}\left(\frac{Q(x)}{u(x)u(x + 1)}\right);$$

or we may sum (5) from α to x:

(7) $$\frac{v(x + 1)}{u(x + 1)} - \frac{v(\alpha)}{u(\alpha)} = K(\alpha)\sum_{t=\alpha}^{x}\frac{Q(x)}{u(x)u(x + 1)}.$$

A difference equation having the fundamental system $u(x)$, $v(x)$ is

(8) $$\begin{vmatrix} y(x) & u(x) & v(x) \\ y(x + 1) & u(x + 1) & v(x + 1) \\ y(x + 2) & u(x + 2) & v(x + 2) \end{vmatrix} = 0;$$

for the determinant vanishes when $y = u$ or v. Denote the Casoratian $K(u, v)$ by $K(x)$; then on expanding (8) we have

(9) $$K(x)y(x + 2) - \begin{vmatrix} u(x) & v(x) \\ u(x + 2) & v(x + 2) \end{vmatrix}y(x + 1) + K(x + 1)y(x) = 0.$$

Since u and v satisfy (1), the determinant reduces to $-p(t)K(x)$ and $K(x + 1) = q(x)K(x)$ from (2). Thus equation (9) is simply equation (1) multiplied by $K(x)$.

Example 1. By inspection we find that $u = (x - 1)!$ is a solution of

$$y(x + 2) - x(x + 1)y(x) = 0$$

over the set $1, 2, 3, \ldots$. We now use (6) to find a second solution $v(x)$. Here $q(x) = -x(x + 1)$,

$$Q(x) = (-1)^{x-1}\prod_{t=1}^{x-1}t(t + 1) = (-1)^{x-1}(x - 1)! \, x!,$$

$$\frac{Q(x)}{u(x)u(x + 1)} = (-1)^{x-1}\frac{(x - 1)! \, x!}{(x - 1)! \, x!} = (-1)^{x-1},$$

$$\Delta^{-1}(-1)^{x-1} = -\tfrac{1}{2}(-1)^{x-1} = \tfrac{1}{2}(-1)^x, \qquad (\S 81, \text{ no. } 2')$$

and finally,

$$v(x) = K(x - 1)! \, \tfrac{1}{2}(-1)^x = C(-1)^x(x - 1)!.$$

The solutions $u = (x - 1)!$, $v = (-1)^x(x - 1)!$ form a fundamental system since

$$K(1) = \begin{vmatrix} u(1) & v(1) \\ u(2) & v(2) \end{vmatrix} = \begin{vmatrix} 1 & -1 \\ 1 & 1 \end{vmatrix} = 2.$$

Example 2. A *complete permutation* or *derangement* of the n numbers 1, 2, ..., n is one that leaves no number fixed. Find the number of derangements $y(n)$ of the first n numbers.

$y(n)$ may be obtained from $y(n - 1)$ and $y(n - 2)$ as follows:

(i) In each derangement of $y(n - 1)$ put n in place 1, 2, ..., $n - 1$ successively and the displaced number last: this produces $(n - 1)y(n - 1)$ permutations of $y(n)$.

(1) The derangements $p(n - 1)$ with one number k fixed amount to $p(n - 2)$. In each of these put n in place of k, and k last: this produces $(n - 1)y(n - 2)$ permutations of $y(n)$.

Thus $y(n) = (n - 1)y(n - 1) + (n - 1)y(n - 2)$. Evidently $y(1) = 0, y(2) = 1$; and with these conditions we must solve

(i) $$y(x + 2) - (x + 1)y(x + 1) - (x + 1)y(x) = 0.$$

One solution is $u(x) = x!$ To find a second solution we have

$$Q(x) = (-1)^{x-1}\prod_{t=1}^{x-1} (t + 1) = (-1)^{x-1} x!$$

and from (6) with $K = 1$,

$$\frac{v(x)}{x!} = \Delta^{-1}\frac{(-1)^{x-1}}{(x + 1)!} = \sum_{t=1}^{x-1}\frac{(-1)^{t-1}}{(t + 1)!} = \frac{1}{2!} - \frac{1}{3!} + \cdots + \frac{(-1)^x}{x!},$$

with $v(1) = 0$ (§ 81). The general solution is

$$y(x) = c_1 u(x) + c_2 v(x);$$

and from the initial conditions $c_1 = 0, c_2 = 1$. Thus $y(x) = v(x)$; or

$$y(x) = x!\left(\frac{1}{2!} - \frac{1}{3!} + \cdots + \frac{(-1)^x}{x!}\right) \qquad (x > 1)$$

$$= x^{(x-2)} - x^{(x-3)} + \cdots + (-1)^x x^{(0)}.$$

For example,

$$y(5) = 5^{(3)} - 5^{(2)} + 5^{(1)} - 5^{(0)} = 60 - 20 + 5 - 1 = 44.$$

Note that the *ratio* of complete to total permutations $y(x)/x! \to 1/e$ as $x \to \infty$.

In a large state each soldier is numbered beginning with 1; if all were put in a line, the probability that none would occupy the place denoted by his number is practically e^{-1}; for the Maclaurin series for e^{-1} rapidly converges.

The derangements D_n of n numbers may be neatly expressed as the permanent of an n-square matrix A whose elements are $a(i, j)$. The *permanent* is defined as

$$\text{per } A = \sum a(1, i_1)a(2, i_2) \cdots a(n, i_n),$$

where the sum is extended over all permutations $(i_1, i_2, \ldots, i_n)$ of 1, 2, $\ldots$, n. The permanent differs from a determinant in that all products are treated alike, whereas in det A the products with odd permutations $(i_1, i_2, \ldots, i_n)$ are altered in sign. With this definition it is easy to verify that

$$D_n = \text{per } (J_n - I_n),$$

where J_n is the n-square matrix whose elements are all 1, and I_n is the unit matrix.

Since permanents occur in combinatorial mathematics, we list a few of their simpler properties.

1. A permanent is not altered by permuting its rows or columns.
2. If D is a diagonal matrix, per $DA = $ per D per A.
3. Permanents admit the Laplace expansion in which the cofactor of any element is the permanent of its minor. Thus

$$\text{per} \begin{pmatrix} -1 & 0 & 2 \\ 1 & 1 & 2 \\ 2 & 3 & 4 \end{pmatrix} = -\text{per} \begin{pmatrix} 1 & 2 \\ 3 & 4 \end{pmatrix} + 2\,\text{per} \begin{pmatrix} 1 & 1 \\ 2 & 3 \end{pmatrix} = -10 + 10 = 0.$$

PROBLEMS

1. Check equation (1) when $x = \alpha$.
Find a second solution (v) of the following equations when the first (u) is given.
2. $y(x + 2) - 7y(x + 1) + 6y(x) = 0, \qquad u = 1.$
3. $y(x + 2) - 4y(x + 1) + 4y(x) = 0, \qquad u = 2^x.$
4. $x(x + 1)y(x + 2) - 2x(x + 2)y(x + 1) + (x + 1)(x + 2)y(x) = 0,$
    $u = x.$
5. $(x + 1)^2 y(x + 2) - (2x + 1)(x + 2)y(x + 1) + (x + 1)(x + 2)y(x) = 0,$
    $u = x.$
6. $(x + 2)y(x + 2) - (x + 1)y(x + 1) - y(x) = 0, \qquad u = 1.$
7. If a hatcheck girl has 50 hats and returns them all at random, what is the probability that no man gets his own hat?

87. THE COMPLETE EQUATION

If $y(x)$ and $y_1(x)$ are two solutions of the complete equation (84.1),

(1) $$y(x + 2) + p(x)y(x + 1) + q(x)y(x) = r(x),$$
$$y_1(x + 2) + p(x)y_1(x + 1) + q(x)y_1(x) = r(x).$$

On subtracting this from (1), we see that $y(x) - y_1(x)$ satisfies the reduced equation

$$(2) \qquad y(x + 2) + p(x)y(x + 1) + q(x)y(x) = 0$$

and must be included in its general solution

$$(3) \qquad y_0(x) = c_1 u(x) + c_2 v(x),$$

given in the preceding article.

Fundamental Theorem. *The general solution of the complete equation is the sum of the general solution $y_0(x)$ of the reduced equation and any particular solution $y_1(x)$ of the complete equation*

$$(4) \qquad y(x) = y_0(x) + y_1(x).$$

The part $y_0(x)$ given in (3) contains the arbitrary constants. Any particular solution of (1) may be chosen as $y_1(x)$; but, naturally, it should be chosen as simple as possible.

If $u(x)$ is a solution of the *reduced* equation (2), a second solution $v(x)$ may be found (§ 86) so that $u(x)$, $v(x)$ form a fundamental system. We may now solve the complete equation by making use of

Theorem 2. *If $u(x)$, $v(x)$ form a fundamental system of the reduced equation (2), this equation admits the multipliers*

$$(5) \qquad \lambda(x) = \frac{u(x + 1)}{K(x + 1)}, \qquad \mu(x) = \frac{v(x + 1)}{K(x + 1)},$$

where $K(x)$ is the Casoratian $K(u, v)$.

PROOF. The equations

$$(6) \qquad \Delta \frac{K(u, y)}{K(u, v)} = 0, \qquad \Delta \frac{K(v, y)}{K(u, v)} = 0,$$

both have the solutions $u(x)$, $v(x)$; for when $y = u$ or v, the fractions in (6) are either 0 or ± 1. Now the coefficients of $y(x + 2)$ in these equations are $\lambda(x)$ and $\mu(x)$ given in (5); for

$$\Delta \frac{K(u, y)}{K(u, v)} = \Delta \left(\frac{u(x)y(x + 1) - y(x)u(x + 1)}{K(x)} \right)$$

$$= \frac{u(x + 1)}{K(x + 2)} y(x + 2) + \cdots$$

and similarly for the other equation. Since the *exact* equations (6) are necessarily multiples of equation (2),* it is clear that $\lambda(x)$, $\mu(x)$ are multipliers of this equation.

We can now solve the complete equation (1) by converting it into an exact equation in two ways. If we multiply (1) by $\lambda(x)$, it becomes

$$\Delta\left(\frac{u(x)y(x+1) - u(x+1)y(x)}{K(x)}\right) = \frac{u(x+1)}{K(x+1)}r(x)$$

and hence on "integration",

$$(7)\quad \frac{u(x)y(x+1) - u(x+1)y(x)}{K(x)} = \Delta^{-1}\left(\frac{u(x+1)}{K(x+1)}r(x)\right) + c_2.$$

Using the multiplier $\mu(x)$ we get, in similar fashion,

$$(8)\quad \frac{v(x)y(x+1) - v(x+1)y(x)}{K(x)} = \Delta^{-1}\left(\frac{v(x+1)}{K(x+1)}r(x)\right) - c_1,$$

where c_2 and $-c_1$ are arbitrary constants. From these first "integrals" of (1) we now obtain $y(x)$ by eliminating $y(x+1)$. Multiply (7) by $v(x)$, (8) by $-u(x)$, and add the resulting equations; the left member then reduces to $y(x)$ and we obtain the general solution of (1):

$$(9)\ y(x) = v(x)\Delta^{-1}\left(\frac{u(x+1)}{K(x+1)}r(x)\right) - u(x)\Delta^{-1}\left(\frac{v(x+1)}{K(x+1)}r(x)\right) + y_0(x).$$

Here $y_0(x)$ is the general solution (3) of the reduced equation; and the other terms give $y_1(x)$, a particular solution of the complete equation.

Compare the above deduction with that given in § 30 for differential equations. To strengthen the analogy we shall next obtain (9) by Lagrange's *variation of parameters*, a method also used in § 30. To this end let

$$(10)\qquad y(x) = A(x)u(x) + B(x)v(x).$$

Then

$$y(x+1) = A(x+1)u(x+1) + B(x+1)v(x+1)$$

where

$$A(x+1) = A(x) + \Delta A, \qquad B(x+1) = B(x) + \Delta B.$$

---

* Two equations in the form (2), with 1 as leading coefficient and which admit the fundamental system u, v must be precisely the same (why?). Hence if u and v satisfy

$$(2)'\qquad p_0(x)y(x+2) + p_1(x)y(x+1) + p_2(x)y(x) = 0,$$

$p_1/p_0 = p, p_2/p_0 = q$; that is, equation (2)' is equation (2) multiplied by p_0.

If we now impose a *first* condition

(11) $u(x + 1) \, \Delta A + v(x + 1) \, \Delta B = 0$

on the disposable functions $A(x)$, $B(x)$, we shall have

(12) $y(x + 1) = A(x)y(x + 1) + B(x)v(x + 1).$

From (12) we have

(13) $y(x + 2) = A(x)u(x + 2) + B(x)v(x + 2)$
$$+ u(x + 2) \, \Delta A + v(x + 2) \, \Delta B;$$

we now impose a *second* condition on $A(x)$, $B(x)$ by requiring that (10) be a solution of (1). Multiply (10) by $q(x)$, (12) by $p(x)$, and add to (13); then since $u(x)$ and $v(x)$ are solutions of (2), we have

(14) $u(x + 2) \, \Delta A + v(x + 2) \, \Delta B = r(x).$

ΔA and ΔB are now determined from the linear equations (11) and (14) whose determinant is the Casoratian $K(x + 1)$ of u and v; we thus obtain

$$\Delta A = \frac{-v(x + 1)}{K(x + 1)} r(x), \qquad \Delta B = \frac{u(x + 1)}{K(x + 1)} r(x),$$

and then $A(x)$, $B(x)$ by summing. The final result is again the precise solution of (1) given in (9).

Example. Find the general solution of

$$x(x + 1)y(x + 2) - 2x(x + 2)y(x + 1) + (x + 1)(x + 2)y(x) = (x + 2)^{(3)}$$

given the solution $u = x$ of the reduced equation.

First, find a second solution v of the reduced equation by the method of § 86:

$$q(x) = \frac{x + 2}{x}, \qquad Q(x) = \prod_{t=1}^{x-1} \frac{t + 2}{t} = \frac{1}{2} x(x + 1),$$

$$\frac{Q(x)}{x(x + 1)} = \frac{1}{2}, \qquad v = K(1)x \cdot \tfrac{1}{2}x = x^2 \quad \text{if} \quad K(1) = 2.$$

The Casoratian of u, v is

$$K(x) = \begin{vmatrix} x & x + 1 \\ x^2 & (x + 1)^2 \end{vmatrix} = x(x + 1) > 0 \quad \text{on the set } 1, 2, 3, \dots ,$$

$$r(x) = \frac{(x + 2)(x + 1)x}{x(x + 1)} = x + 2;$$

$$\frac{u(x + 1)}{K(x + 1)} r(x) = 1, \qquad \Delta^{-1} 1 = x,$$

$$\frac{v(x + 1)}{K(x + 1)} r(x) = x + 1, \qquad \Delta^{-1}(x + 1) = \frac{(x + 1)^{(2)}}{2}$$

omitting constants. Formula (9) now gives the particular solution

$$x^2 \cdot x - x \frac{(x + 1)x}{2} = \tfrac{1}{2}x^3 - \tfrac{1}{2}x^2.$$

Since x^2 satisfies the reduced equation, the simplest particular solution is $y_1 = \tfrac{1}{2}x^3$. The general solution is therefore

$$y(x) = c_1 x + c_2 x^2 + \tfrac{1}{2}x^3.$$

PROBLEMS

Find the general solution, given the solution $u(x)$ of the reduced equation.
1. $y(x + 2) - 7y(x + 1) + 6y(x) = x,$ $u = 1$ (Prob. 86.2).
2. $y(x + 2) - x(x + 1)y(x) = 2(x + 1)!,$ $u = (x - 1)!$ (Ex. 86).

88. LINEAR DIFFERENCE EQUATIONS

The linear equation of the first order

$$y(x + 1) - p(x)y(x) = q(x)$$

over the set S: $\alpha, \alpha + 1, \alpha + 2, \ldots$ admits the multiplier $1/P(x + 1)$, where

$$P(x) = \prod_{t=\alpha}^{x-1} p(t), \qquad P(\alpha) = 1.$$

When multiplied by $1/p(x + 1)$, it becomes

$$\Delta \frac{y(x)}{P(x)} = \frac{q(x)}{P(x + 1)}$$

from which follows the general solution

$$y(x) = P(x) \Delta^{-1} \frac{q(x)}{P(x + 1)} + cP(x).$$

The linear equation of the second order

$$y(x + 2) + p(x)y(x + 1) + q(x)y(x) = r(x)$$

can be solved if a particular solution $u(x)$ of the reduced equation

$$y(x + 2) + p(x)y(x + 1) + q(x)y(x) = 0$$

is known. A second solution $v(x)$, independent of $u(x)$ is then given by

$$v(x) = Ku(x) \Delta^{-1}\left(\frac{Q(x)}{u(x)u(x + 1)} \right)$$

where

$$Q(x) = \prod_{t=\alpha}^{x-1} q(t), \qquad Q(\alpha) = 1.$$

The general solution of the reduced equation is then

$$y_0(x) = c_1 u(x) + c_2 v(x).$$

The complete equation now has the general solution

$$y(x) = c_1 u(x) + c_2 v(x) + y_1(x),$$

where $y_1(x)$ is any one of its particular solutions—the simpler the better.

To find $y_1(x)$ we make use of the fact that if $K(x)$ is the Casoratian of $u(x)$ and $v(x)$,

$$\lambda(x) = \frac{u(x+1)}{K(x+1)} \quad \text{and} \quad \mu(x) = \frac{v(x+1)}{K(x+1)}$$

are multipliers. These multipliers yield two first "integrals" of the complete equation; and if $y(x)$ is eliminated from these, we obtain a particular solution in the form

$$y_1(x) = v(x) \Delta^{-1}\left[\frac{u(x+1)}{K(x+1)} r(x)\right] - u(x) \Delta^{-1}\left[\frac{v(x+1)}{K(x+1)} r(x)\right].$$

This precise particular solution may also be obtained by variation of parameters.

The analogy with linear differential equations is striking and complete, the Casoratian playing the role of the Wronskian.

CHAPTER 9

$$(E - a)^{-1} = a^{x-1}\Delta^{-1}a^{-x}$$

Linear Difference Equations
with Constant Coefficients

89. THE OPERATOR E

The operation E is defined by

(1) $Ey(x) = y(x + 1).$

Since $y(x + 1) = y(x) + \Delta y(x) = (1 + \Delta)y(x)$, we have the operational equation

(2) $E = 1 + \Delta.$

Repetitions of E are written as powers; thus

$$E^2 y(x) = Ey(x + 1) = y(x + 2)$$

and, in general, for any positive integer n

$$E^n y(x) = y(x + n).$$

If we expand $E^n = (1 + \Delta)^n$ by the binomial theorem, we obtain

(3) $y(n + x) = \sum_{k=0}^{n} \binom{n}{k} \Delta^k y(x),$

a formula due to Newton.

The complete difference equation of order n with constant coefficients

(4)
$$ay_0(x + n) + a_1 y(x + n - 1) + \cdots + a_{n-1}y(x + 1) + a_n y(n) = \varphi(x),$$

in which a_0 and $a_n \neq 0$, may be written

$$(a_0 E^n + a_1 E^{n-1} + \cdots + a_{n-1}E + a_n)y(x) = \varphi(x);$$

or, denoting the operator polynomial by $f(E)$,

(5) $f(E)y(x) = \varphi(x).$

The general solution of the reduced equation

$$(6) \qquad f(E)y(x) = 0$$

may be written down at once as soon as the roots of the *characteristic equation*

$$(7) \qquad f(r) = 0$$

are known. If these roots are $r_1, r_2, \ldots, r_n$, then

$$f(r) = a_0(r - r_1)(r - r_2) \cdots (r - r_n),$$

and similarly,

$$f(E) = a_0(E - r_1)(E - r_2) \cdots (E - r_n).$$

The factors $E - r_i$ commute with each other; for

$$(E - a)(E - b)y(x) = (E - a)[y(x + 1) - by(x)]$$
$$= y(x + 2) - by(x + 1) - ay(x + 1) + aby(x),$$

and this expression is unaltered by an interchange of a and b.

The reduced equation now becomes

$$(8) \qquad (E - r_1)(E - r_2) \cdots (E - r_n)y(x) = 0.$$

Since the factors commute, any one of them may be brought to bear on $y(x)$; thus a solution of $(E - r_i)y(x) = 0$ is also a particular solution of (8). For a root a of multiplicity k, $(E - a)^k$ may be brought to bear on $y(x)$, so that (8) may be written

$$(9) \qquad g(E)(E - a)^k y(x) = 0.$$

Then a solution of

$$(10) \qquad (E - a)^k y(x) = 0$$

is also a solution of (9). The general solution of the reduced equation may be built up from the solutions of equations of this type. To solve them in a simple and elegant way we next develop an operational formula, the *power shift*.

90. THE POWER SHIFT

We first prove the special case

$$(1) \qquad f(E)a^x = f(a)a^x$$

where $f(E)$ is a polynomial in E. The operator E is linear; for obviously

$$E(y + z) = Ey + Ez, \qquad E(cy) = cEy.$$

Since $f(E)$ is a sum of powers of E multiplied by constants, it will suffice to prove (1) when $f(E) = E^k$. This proof, however, is immediate, for $E^k a^x = a^{x+k} = a^k a^x$.

Now if X denotes an arbitrary function of x, the general power shift is expressed by

(2) $$f(E)(a^x X) = a^x f(aE) X.$$

Here the *power* a^x is shifted before the operator just as in the exponential shift (36.1), the exponent e^{ax} is shifted before the operator. Again it will suffice to prove (2) when $f(E) = E^k$, and this proof follows from

$$E[y(x)z(x)] = y(x + 1)z(x + 1) = Ey \cdot Ez.$$

Thus we have from (1)

$$E^k(a^x X) = (E^k a^x)(E^k X) = a^x a^k(E^k X) = a^x(aE)^k X,$$

which is formula (2) when $f(E) = E^k$.

The operator Δ^{-1} is defined by $\Delta\Delta^{-1} = 1$; hence $(E - 1)(E - 1)^{-1} = 1$. More generally, the operator $(E - a)^{-1}$ is defined by

$$(E - a)(E - a)^{-1} = 1.$$

We can now show that the power shift

$$(E - a)^{-1} a^x X = a^x(aE - a)^{-1} X = a^{x-1} \Delta^{-1} X$$

is valid for all functions X; that is,

$$(E - a)^{-1} a^x = a^{x-1} \Delta^{-1},$$

(3) $$(E - a)^{-1} = a^{x-1} \Delta^{-1} a^{-x}.$$

PROOF. Apply $E - a$ to (3); then

$$\begin{aligned}
(E - a)(E - a)^{-1} &= (E - a)a^{x-1} \Delta^{-1} a^{-x} \\
&= a^{x-1}(aE - a) \Delta^{-1} a^{-x} \\
&= a^x \Delta\Delta^{-1} a^{-x} \\
&= a^x a^{-x} = 1.
\end{aligned}$$

Thus $(E - a)^{-1}$ means:

Multiply by a^{-x}, sum, and then multiply by a^{x-1}.

Ws shall see that (3) virtually contains the entire theory of the linear difference equation with constant coefficients.

Applying $(E - a)^{-1}$ twice gives

$$(E - a)^{-2} = a^{x-1} \Delta^{-1} a^{-x} \cdot a^{x-1} \Delta^{-1} a^{-x} = a^{x-2} \Delta^{-2} a^{-x},$$

and, in general,

(4) $$(E - a)^{-k} = a^{x-k} \Delta^{-k} a^{-x}.$$

Example 1. The power shift may be used to compute antidifferences. Thus if $a \neq 1$,

$$\begin{aligned}
\Delta^{-1} x^2 a^x &= (E - 1)^{-1} x a^x & (\Delta = E - 1) \\
&= a^x (aE - 1)^{-1} x \\
&= a^x (a - 1 + a\Delta)^{-1} x & (E = \Delta + 1) \\
&= \frac{a^x}{a - 1} \frac{1}{1 + \dfrac{a}{a - 1} \Delta} x \\
&= \frac{a^x}{a - 1} \left(1 - \frac{a}{a - 1} \Delta\right) x & (\text{cf. } \S 42)
\end{aligned}$$

$$\Delta^{-1} x^2 a^x = \frac{a^x}{a - 1} \left(x - \frac{a}{a - 1}\right) \qquad (\text{Table 81, 4}).$$

Example 2. $y(x + 1) - ay(x) = q(x)$. This is the linear equation (82.1) with $p(x) = a$. Writing it $(E - a)y(x) = q(x)$,

$$\begin{aligned}
y(x) &= (E - a)^{-1} q(x) \\
&= a^{x-1} \Delta^{-1} a^{-x} \cdot q(x) \\
&= a^{x-1} \Delta^{-1} \left(\frac{q(x)}{a^x}\right) + c a^{x-1}.
\end{aligned}$$

This agrees with (82.6) when $P = a^{x-1}$.

Example 3. $y(x + 2) - 4y(x + 1) + 4y(x) = x 2^x$.

$$\begin{aligned}
(E - 2)^2 y &= x 2^x \\
y &= 2^{x-2} \Delta^{-2} 2^{-x} \cdot x 2^x \\
&= 2^{x-2} \Delta^{-2} x \\
&= 2^{x-2} \Delta^{-1}(\tfrac{1}{2} x^{(2)} + c_1) \\
&= 2^{x-2}(\tfrac{1}{6} x^{(3)} + c_1 x + c_2)
\end{aligned}$$

or $$y(x) = 2^x(\tfrac{1}{24} x^{(3)} + c_1 x + c_2)$$

where the arbitrary constants are altered.

Example 4. $y(x + 2) - y(x) = 1$, $y(0) = 1$, $y(1) = 2$; find $y(100)$. The equation is $(E - 1)(E + 1)y = 1$; hence

$$\begin{aligned}
y &= (-1)^{x-1} \Delta^{-1}(-1)^{-x} \cdot \Delta^{-1} \cdot 1 \\
&= (-1)^{x-1} \Delta^{-1}(-1)^{-x}(x + c_1) \\
&= (-1)^{x-1}\left[\tfrac{1}{2}(-1)^{x+1}(x - \tfrac{1}{2}) + \frac{c_1}{2}(-1)^{x+1} + c_2\right] \qquad (\text{Table 81, 5, 3}) \\
&= \frac{1}{2} x - \frac{1}{4} + \frac{c_1}{2} + c_2(-1)^{x-1}
\end{aligned}$$

or, on altering the form of the constants,

$$y(x) = \tfrac{1}{2}x + c_1 + c_2(-1)^x.$$

From the initial conditions

$$c_1 + c_2 = 1, \quad c_1 - c_2 = \tfrac{3}{2}; \qquad c_1 = \tfrac{5}{4}, \quad c_2 = -\tfrac{1}{4};$$
$$y(x) = \tfrac{1}{2}x + \tfrac{5}{4} - \tfrac{1}{4}(-1)^x,$$
$$y(100) = 50 + \tfrac{5}{4} - \tfrac{1}{4} = 51.$$

Example 5. Prove that n straight coplanar lines, no two parallel, no three concurrent, divide the plane into $\tfrac{1}{2}(n^2 + n + 2)$ parts.

PROOF. Let $y(x)$ denote the number of parts into which x straight lines divide the plane. Then for $x + 1$ lines

$$y(x + 1) = y(x) + x + 1;$$

for as the last line enters from infinity, it will divide a region into two at each intersection, producing x new regions, plus one more after the last intersection. (Convince yourself with a figure if necessary.) Thus we must solve

$$(E - 1)y(x) = x + 1, \qquad y(1) = 2.$$

Since $E - 1 = \Delta$,

$$y(x) = \Delta^{-1}(x + 1) = \frac{x^{(2)}}{2} + x + c,$$

$$2 = 0 + 1 + c, \qquad c = 1;$$

$$y(x) = \frac{x(x - 1)}{2} + x + 1 = \tfrac{1}{2}(x^2 + x + 2).$$

PROBLEMS

1. Use the power shift to prove:

$$\Delta^{-1}(x^2 2^x) = (x^2 - 4x + 6)2^x.$$

2. $\Delta^{-1}(x^{(3)}a^x) = (\alpha - 1)(x^{(3)} - 3\alpha x^{(2)} + 6\alpha^2 x - 6\alpha^3)$ where $\alpha = a/(a - 1)$.

Find $y(x)$ in Problems 3, 4, and 5.

3. $y(x + 1) + 3y(x) = x, \qquad y(0) = 1.$

4. $y(x + 2) - 3y(x + 1) + 2y(x) = -1, \qquad y(0) = 2, y(1) = 4.$

5. $y(x + 2) - 4y(x + 1) + 3y(x) = 3^x.$

6. Prove that a particular solution of

(i) $\qquad\qquad f(E)y = a^x \quad$ is $\quad a^x/f(a) \quad$ if $\quad f(a) \neq 0;$

(ii) $\qquad\qquad f(E)y = 1 \quad$ is $\quad 1/f(1) \quad$ if $\quad f(1) \neq 0.$

7. Prove that a particular solution of

$$(E - a)^n y = a^x \quad \text{is} \quad a^{x-n}\frac{x^{(n)}}{n!}$$

8. Prove that $\cos \alpha x$ and $\sin \alpha x$ are solutions of

$$(E^2 - 2E \cos \alpha + 1)y = 0.$$

9. Prove that n circles in a plane, each cutting all the others, no three con-current, divide the plane into $n^2 - n + 2$ parts.

10. A line is divided by x points into $y_1(x) = x + 1$ parts, and $\Delta y_1(x) = 1$. A plane is divided by x lines, none parallel, no three copunctal, into $y_2(x)$ parts, and $\Delta y_2(x) = y_1(x)$ (see Example 5).

Conjecture: Space is divided by x planes, none parallel, no four copunctal, into $y_3(x)$ parts such that

$$\Delta y_3(x) = y_2(x).$$

Prove this, and find $y_3(x)$.

91. THE REDUCED EQUATION

To solve the reduced equation of order n,

$$(1) \qquad\qquad f(E)y(x) = 0,$$

we must find the roots $r_1, r_2, \ldots, r_n$ of characteristic equation

$$(2) \qquad\qquad f(r) = 0.$$

If (2) has a k-fold root a, $f(r)$ will have $(r - a)^k$ as a factor, $f(E)$ will have $(E - a)^k$ as a factor, and this factor may be brought to bear directly on y:

$$(1)' \qquad\qquad g(E)(E - a)^k y = 0.$$

Evidently any solution of

$$(3) \qquad\qquad (E - a)^k y = 0, \qquad a \neq 0*$$

is also a solution of (1)' or (1).

We seek a solution of (3) of the form

$$(4) \qquad\qquad y = a^x X$$

where X is a function to be determined. Substituting (4) in (3) and using the power shift gives

$$a^x(aE - a)^k X = a^{x+1} \Delta^k X = 0,$$

or since $a \neq 0$, $\Delta^k X = 0$. Therefore

$$X = \Delta^{-k}0 = P_{k-1}(x),$$

---

* If $a = 0$, E^k would be a factor of $f(E)$ and (1) would be an equation of order $n - k$ in $E^k y = y(x + k)$.

a polynomial of degree $k - 1$ having k arbitrary constants for coefficients; for

$$\Delta^{-1} 0 = c_1, \qquad \Delta^{-2} 0 = c_1 x + c_2, \qquad \Delta^{-3} 0 = \tfrac{1}{2} c_1 x^{(2)} + c_2 x + c_3,$$

and so on, and each factorial power $x^{(j)}$ is a polynomial of degree j (§ 78).

Corresponding to every real k-fold root a we thus obtain a solution of (1) of the form

$$(5) \qquad\qquad a^x (c_1 x^{k-1} + c_2 x^{k-2} + \cdots + c_{k-1} x + c_k).$$

This discloses the fact that

$$a^x, \; x a^x, \; x^2 a^x, \; \ldots, \; x^{k-1} a^x$$

are all particular solutions of (1). Moreover, they are linearly independent since $1, x, x^2, \ldots, x^{k-1}$ are linearly independent (§ 37).

In particular, for every simple root a of the characteristic equation the reduced equation has the corresponding solution $c a^x$.

Next, suppose that equation (2)—having *real* coefficients—has two k-fold conjugate complex roots $a e^{ib}$, $a e^{-ib}$. For these roots the corresponding solutions of (1) are

$$(6) \qquad\qquad a^x e^{ibx} P(x), \qquad a^x e^{-ibx} Q(x),$$

where $P(x)$ and $Q(x)$ are polynomials of degree $k - 1$, each containing k arbitrary constants. Now

$$e^{ibx} = \cos bx + i \sin bx, \qquad e^{-ibx} = \cos bx - i \sin bx;$$

the sum of solutions (6), which is also a solution of (1), may therefore be written

$$a^x (P + Q) \cos bx + i a^x (P - Q) \sin bx.$$

Now if $p(x)$ and $q(x)$ are arbitrary *real* polynomials of degree $k - 1$, choose

$$P = \tfrac{1}{2}(p - iq), \qquad Q = \tfrac{1}{2}(p + iq).$$

Then

$$P + Q = p, \qquad i(P - Q) = q,$$

and the solution corresponding to the k-fold complex roots $a e^{\pm ib}$ becomes

$$(7) \qquad\qquad a^x \{ p_{k-1}(x) \cos bx + q_{k-1}(x) \sin bx \}$$

in which we have restored the subscript to indicate degree. Note that there are $2k$ real arbitrary constants in (7), k in each polynomial.

For a simple complex pair $a e^{\pm ib}$, the solution (7) reduces to

$$(8) \qquad\qquad a^x (c_1 \cos bx + c_2 \sin bx).$$

We summarize these results in Table 91.

The last entry includes all the others; for when $k = 1$ it reduces to the third; when $b = 0$ it reduces to the second; and when $b = 0$ and $k = 1$ it reduces to the first.

Table 91

Roots of f(r) = 0		Solution
Real	simple	ca^x
$(a \neq 0)$	k-fold	$a^x P_{k-1}(x)$
Complex	simple	$a^x(c_1 \cos bx + c_2 \sin bx)$
$ae^{\pm ib}$		
$(a > 0)$	k-fold	$a^x\{P_{k-1}(x) \cos bx + Q_{k-1}(x) \sin bx\}$

To obtain the general solution $y_0(x)$ of the difference equation $f(E)y = 0$ of order n:

(i) Find the roots of $f(r) = 0$.

(ii) Write the contribution of each root to the solution from the table above.

(iii) Add these contributions to get $y_0(x)$ which will then contain exactly n arbitrary constants. The n functions they multiply form a *solution basis* for the equation.

Example 1. Consider an equation $f(E)y = 0$ of order ten; and let $f(r) = 0$ have the ten roots

$$-3, 1, 1, 1, \pm i, 2 \pm 3i, 2 \pm 3i.$$

This corresponds to Example 37.1 except that the triple root 0 is replaced by the triple root 1, for triple zero is now inadmissible as it would reduce the order of the equation from 10 to 7.

When the complex roots are replaced by $e^{\pm i\pi/2}$ and $\sqrt{13}\, e^{\pm ib}$ ($b = \tan^{-1} \frac{3}{2}$), the roots correspond to the particular solutions:

$$c_1(-3)^x, \quad c_2 + c_3 x + c_4 x^2, \quad c_5 \cos\frac{\pi}{2}x + c_6 \sin\frac{\pi}{2}x,$$

$$(\sqrt{13})^x(c_7 + c_8 x)\cos bx, \quad (\sqrt{13})^x(c_9 + c_{10}x)\sin bx.$$

The general solution is the sum of these solutions and contains ten arbitrary constants.

Example 2. Find an operator (fE) which nullifies the function (cf. Ex. 37.2)

$$\varphi(x) = 4 - 3^x + 7x(-1)^x + 3(-1)^x \cos 2x.$$

SOLUTION. From Table 91 we obtain the factors of $f(E)$ which nullify the separate terms of $\varphi(x)$. Omitting the constant coefficients of the terms, we have

Term	Roots	Factor
1	1	$E - 1 (\Delta)$
3^x	3	$E - 3$
$x(-1)^x$	$-1, -1$	$(E + 1)^2$
$(-1)^x \cos 2x =$	$e^{\pm i(\pi - 2)} =$	$(E + \cos 2)^2 + \sin^2 2 =$
$\cos (\pi - 2)x$	$-\cos 2 \pm i \sin 2$	$E^2 + 2 \cos 2E + 1$

In the last term, $a = -1$ is inadmissible since a must be positive; we therefore replace $(-1)^x \cos 2x$ by $\cos (\pi - 2)x$ and put $a = 1$, $b = \pi - 2$ to find the corresponding roots $e^{\pm i(\pi - 2)} = -\cos 2 \pm i \sin 2$. Thus

$$f(E) = (E - 1)(E - 3)(E + 1)^2(E^2 + 2 \cos 2\, E + 1)$$

is the nullifying operator.

Example 3. Fibonacci Sequence. The famous sequence 0, 1, 1, 2, 3, 5, 8, 13, ... plays a role in phyllotaxy, the arrangement of leaves along a plant stem.* After the initial values $y(0) = 0$, $y(1) = 1$, each term is the sum of the two preceding:

$$y(x + 2) = y(x + 1) + y(x) \quad \text{or} \quad (E^2 - E - 1)y = 0.$$

The equation $r^2 - r - 1 = 0$ has the roots $\frac{1}{2} \pm \frac{1}{2}\sqrt{5}$; hence the general solution is

$$y(x) = c_1 \left(\frac{1 + \sqrt{5}}{2}\right)^x + c_2 \left(\frac{1 - \sqrt{5}}{2}\right)^x.$$

From the initial values we have

$$c_1 + c_2 = 0, \quad c_1 - c_2 = \frac{2}{\sqrt{5}}; \quad c_1 = -c_2 = \frac{1}{\sqrt{5}}.$$

Thus when $x = n$,

$$y(n) = \frac{1}{\sqrt{5}}\left[\left(\frac{1 + \sqrt{5}}{2}\right)^n - \left(\frac{1 - \sqrt{5}}{2}\right)^n\right].$$

This can be put in a very stylish form by writing $\sinh \alpha = \frac{1}{2}$, $\cosh \alpha = \sqrt{5}/2$, which is permissible since $\frac{5}{4} - \frac{1}{4} = 1$. Then

$$y(n) = \frac{1}{2 \cosh \alpha} [(\cosh \alpha + \sinh \alpha)^n + (-1)^{n+1} (\cosh \alpha - \sinh \alpha)^n]$$

$$= \frac{e^{n\alpha} + (-1)^{n+1}e^{-n\alpha}}{2 \cosh \alpha}.$$

---

* Cf. Thompson, D. W., *On Growth and Form*, Cambridge, 1952, Chapter 14. Coxeter, H. C. M., *Introduction to Geometry*, Wiley, New York, 1961, p. 169.

Therefore, according as n is even or odd,

$$y(n) = \frac{\sinh n\alpha}{\cosh \alpha} \quad \text{or} \quad \frac{\cosh n\alpha}{\cosh \alpha}.$$

The reader may prove that

$$\lim_{n \to \infty} \frac{y_{n+1}}{y_n} = e^\alpha = \frac{1 + \sqrt{5}}{2}.$$

PROBLEMS

1–12. Find the general solution of Problems 1–12 in § 37 when D is replaced by E.

Find a nullifying operator in Problems 13 to 15.

13. $x^2 3^x - x^3 \sin x + 2x + 3$.

14. $x \cos x + 3 \sin x + 4(-1)^x \cos x$.

15. $2x^3 + x - 3 + (x^2 + 2)(-2)^x + 3 \sin 2x$.

16. Solve $(E^3 - E^2 - 4E + 4)y = 0$ if

$$y(0) = 1, \qquad y(1) = 0, \qquad y(2) = 2.$$

17. Solve the Fibonacci difference equation

$$(E^2 - E - 1)y = 0 \quad \text{when} \quad y(0) = 2, \quad y(1) = 1.$$

18. Solve the difference equation

$$(E^2 - E + 1)y = 0 \quad \text{when} \quad y(0) = y(1) = 1.$$

92. EQUATION OF SECOND ORDER

The equation

$$(aE^2 + bE + c)y(x) = 0 \qquad (a, c \neq 0)$$

has the characteristic quadratic

$$ar^2 + br + c = 0.$$

Its roots may be real and distinct, real and equal, or conjugate complex.

Case 1. $b^2 - 4ac > 0$.

The distinct roots

$$\frac{-b \pm \sqrt{b^2 - 4ac}}{2a} = \alpha \pm \beta \text{ are real and} \neq 0.$$

The independent solutions are

$$(1) \qquad u = (\alpha + \beta)^x, \qquad v = (\alpha - \beta)^x.$$

Case 2. $b^2 - 4ac = 0$.

Double root $\alpha = -b/2a$. The independent solutions are

(2) $$u = \alpha^x, \qquad v = x\alpha^x.$$

Case 3. $b^2 - 4ac < 0$.

The complex roots

$$\frac{-b \pm i\sqrt{4ac - b^2}}{2a} = \alpha e^{\pm i\beta} \text{ are conjugate and } \alpha > 0.$$

The independent solutions are

(3) $$u = \alpha^x \cos \beta x, \qquad v = \alpha^x \sin \beta x.$$

In the solution of the complete equation

(4) $$(aE^2 + bE + c)y(x) = \varphi(x)$$

we shall use a solution $v(x)$ of the reduced equation which satisfies the conditions

(5) $$v(0) = 0, \qquad v(1) = 1.$$

In the three cases we have, respectively,

(1)′ $$v(x) = \frac{(\alpha + \beta)^x - (\alpha - \beta)^x}{2\beta}$$

(2)′ $$v(x) = x\alpha^{x-1}$$

(3)′ $$v(x) = \frac{\alpha^{x-1} \sin \beta x}{\sin \beta}.$$

Example. $(E^2 - 2E - 2)y(x) = 0$. The characteristic equation $r^2 - 2r - 2 = 0$ has the roots $1 \pm i = \sqrt{2}\, e^{\pm \pi i/2}$. The independent solutions are

$$2^{x/2} \cos \frac{\pi}{2} x, \qquad 2^{x/2} \sin \frac{\pi}{2} x.$$

The appropriate $v(x)$ from (3)′ is

$$v(x) = \alpha^{(x-1)/2} \sin \frac{\pi}{2} x.$$

93. THE PARTICULAR SOLUTION

Theorem 1 of § 39 has the following analog:

Theorem. *Let $v(x)$ be a solution of the reduced equation*

(1) $$y(x + 2) + by(x + 1) + cy(x) = 0$$

which satisfies the conditions

$$v(0) = 0, \qquad v(1) = 1.$$

Then the solution $y_1(x)$ of the complete equation

(2) $$y(x + 2) + by(x + 1) + cy(x) = \varphi(x)$$

which satisfies the conditions

$$y_1(\alpha) = 0, \qquad y_1(\alpha + 1) = 0$$

is given by

(3) $$y_1(x) = \sum_{t=\alpha}^{x-1} \varphi(t)v(x - t - 1) = [\Delta^{-1}\varphi(t)v(x - t - 1)]_{t=\alpha}^{x}.$$

PROOF. We have

$$y_1(x + 1) = \sum_{t=\alpha}^{x} \varphi(t)v(x - t)$$

$$= \varphi(x)v(0) + \sum_{t=\alpha}^{x-1} \varphi(t)v(x - t),$$

(4) $$y_1(x + 1) = \sum_{t=\alpha}^{x-1} \varphi(t)v(x - t);$$

$$y_1(x + 2) = \sum_{t=\alpha}^{x} \varphi(t)v(x + 1 - t)$$

$$= \varphi(x)v(1) + \sum_{t=\alpha}^{x-1} \varphi(t)v(x + 1 - t),$$

(5) $$y_1(x + 2) = \varphi(x) + \sum_{t=\alpha}^{x-1} \varphi(t)v(x + 1 - t).$$

Now multiply (3) by c, (4) by b, and add the resulting equations to (5). Then

$$y_1(x + 2) + by_1(x + 1) + cy_1(x) = \varphi(x);$$

for the sum (in which $\xi = x - t + 1$)

$$\sum_{t=\alpha}^{x-1} \varphi(t)\{v(\xi + 2) + bv(\xi + 1) + cv(\xi)\} = 0,$$

since $v(x)$ is a solution of (1). Moreover, we have $y_1(\alpha) = 0, y_1(\alpha + 1) = 0$ from (3) and (4), because of the sum convention of § 81.

The statement and proof of the analog of Theorem 2 of § 39 is left to the reader (Prob. 6).

Example 1. $(E^2 - 3E + 2)y(x) = x.$ The characteristic equation

$$(r - 1)(r - 2) = 0$$

has the roots 1, 2, and to apply the theorem, the appropriate

$$v(x) = 2^x - 1.$$

From (3) we have

$$y_1(x) = [\Delta^{-1}t(2^{x-t-1} - 1)]_{t=0}^x$$

$$= [2^{x-1}\Delta^{-1}t(\tfrac{1}{2})^t - \Delta^{-1}t]_{t=0}^x$$

$$= \left[2^{x-1}\frac{(\tfrac{1}{2})^t}{-\tfrac{1}{2}}(t + 1) - \frac{t(t - 1)}{2}\right]_{t=0}^x \qquad \text{(Table 81, 4)}$$

$$= -(x + 1) - \frac{x(x - 1)}{2} + 2^x$$

$$= 2^x - \tfrac{1}{2}(x^2 + x + 2).$$

Check: $y_1(0) = 1 - 1 = 0$, $y_1(1) = 2 - 2 = 0$.

Example 2. $(E^2 - 1)y(x) = 1$. The characteristic equation $r^2 - 1 = 0$ has the roots ± 1, and the appropriate

$$v(x) = \tfrac{1}{2}[1 - (-1)^x]$$

$$y_1(x) = \tfrac{1}{2}[\Delta^{-1}[1 - (-1)^{x-t-1}]]_{t=0}^x$$

$$= \tfrac{1}{2}[\Delta^{-1}1 + (-1)^x\Delta^{-1}(-1)^t]_{t=0}^x$$

$$= \tfrac{1}{2}\left[t + (-1)^x\frac{(-1)^t}{-2}\right]_{t=0}^x \qquad \text{(Table 81, 2)}$$

$$= \tfrac{1}{2}x - \tfrac{1}{4} + \tfrac{1}{4}(-1)^x.$$

Check. $y_1(0) = \tfrac{1}{4} - \tfrac{1}{4} = 0$, $\qquad y_1(1) = \tfrac{1}{2} - \tfrac{1}{4} - \tfrac{1}{4} = 0$.

PROBLEMS

Find $y_1(x)$ from equation (3).
1. $(E^2 - 3E + 2)y = 1$.
2. $(E^2 - 3E + 2)y = 3^x$.
3. $(E - 1)^2 y = x^2$.
4. $(E^2 + 1)y = 1$.
5. $(E^2 - 1)y = 1$.
6. $(E^2 - 1)(E + 1)y = 1$; $y(0) = y(1) = 0$, $y(2) = 1$.
State and prove the analog of Theorem 2 of § 39; then use it to solve the preceding equation.

94. METHOD OF UNDETERMINED COEFFICIENTS

This method is always applicable when the right member $\varphi(x)$ of the complete equation

(1) $$f(E)y(x) = \varphi(x)$$

consists of terms included in Table 91. In this case we can always find an operator $g(E)$ which nullifies $\varphi(x)$, as explained in Example 91.2. Thus all solutions of the complete equation (1) are included in the general solution of

$$(2) \qquad\qquad g(E)f(E)y = 0,$$

a reduced equation of higher order. This determines the *form* of all particular solutions of (1).

Procedure

Let $f(r) = 0$ have m roots $r_1, r_2, \ldots, r_m$; from them construct the complementary function

$$(3) \qquad\qquad y_0(x) = c_1 u_1 + c_2 u_2 + \cdots + c_m u_m.$$

If $g(s) = 0$ has the n roots $s_1, s_2, \ldots, s_n$, the characteristic equation of (2),

$$g(s)f(s) = 0$$

has the $m + n$ roots $r_1, r_2, \ldots, r_m, s_1, \ldots, s_n$. From the set r, s, construct the general solution of (2); besides the terms in $y_0(x)$ it will contain n *new* terms

$$(4) \qquad\qquad Av_1 + Bv_2 + \cdots + Kv_n.$$

That particular solution of (1) which does not contain the functions u_i in $y_0(x)$ (which contribute nothing to $\varphi(x)$ since $f(E)u_i(x) = 0$) is given by (4) when the "undetermined constants" $A, B, \ldots$ are properly determined. To find them, substitute

$$(5) \qquad\qquad y(x) = Av_1 + Bv_2 + \cdots + Kv_n$$

in the left member of (1) and equate the coefficients of like functions on both sides. There are two cases.

Case 1. None of the roots r occurs in the set S.

In this case equation (5) is the general solution of $g(E)y = 0$. Then the functions v_i are those that occur in $\varphi(x)$ plus all those that result from them by repeated differencing (or repeated $E = 1 + \Delta$). Thus from $\cos x$ we have $E \cos x = \cos(x + 1)$ which is a linear combination of $\cos x$ and $\sin x$.

Case 2. Some of the roots r occur in the set S.

The set r, s now contains roots of higher multiplicity than either component set. From the set r, s form the general solution of $g(E)f(E)y = 0$, discard all the functions u_i in $y_0(x)$, and use the remaining functions v_i to find the proper form (5) of the particular solution.

Example 1. Find a particular solution of

$$(E^2 - 3E + 2)y = 2(-1)^x + \cos x.$$

From $r^2 - 3r + 2 = 0$, $r = 1, 2$. The roots of the operator that nullifies the right member are $s = -1$, $e^{\pm i} = \cos 1 \pm i \sin 1$. Since the set s has no roots in common with the set r, we seek a particular solution of the form

$$
\begin{array}{r|l}
2 & y_1 = A(-1)^x + B \cos x \qquad\qquad + C \sin x; \\
-3 & Ey_1 = -A(-1)^x + B \cos (x + 1) + C \sin (x + 1), \\
1 & E^2 y_1 = A(-1)^x + B \cos (x + 2) + C \sin (x + 2).
\end{array}
$$

These equations are multiplied by 2, −3, 1 respectively and added. On the left we have

$$2(-1)^x + \cos x;$$

and on the right

$$6A(-1)^x + B[2 \cos x - 3 \cos (x + 1) + \cos (x + 2)]$$
$$+ C[2 \sin x - 3 \sin (x + 1) + \sin (x + 2)].$$

Thus $A = \frac{1}{3}$. Using the addition theorems for the cosine and sine, we find that the term in $\cos x$ is

$$B(2 - 3 \cos 1 + \cos 2) - C(3 \sin 1 - \sin 2) = 1,$$

and the term in $\sin x$

$$B(3 \sin 1 - \sin 2) + C(2 - 3 \cos 1 + \cos 2) = 0.$$

The determinant of these equations reduces to

$$d = (2 - 2 \cos 1)(5 - 4 \cos 1) \neq 0;$$

and their solution is

$$B = \frac{2 - 3 \cos 1 + \cos 2}{d}, \qquad C = \frac{\sin 2 - 3 \sin 1}{d}.$$

With these values of A, B, C, the particular solution y_1 is determined.

The method is cumbersome when $\varphi(x)$ contains sines or cosines, and operational methods are much simpler (§ 94).

Example 2. Solve the equation

$$(E^2 - 4E + 3)y = x4^x.$$

From $r^2 - 4r + 3 = 0$, $r = 1, 3$. The roots of the nullifying operator are $s = 4, 4$; hence we assume

$$
\begin{array}{r|l}
3 & y_1 = (Ax + B)4^x; \\
-4 & Ey_1 = (Ax + A + B)4 \cdot 4^x \\
1 & E^2 y_1 = (Ax + 2A + B)16 \cdot 4^x.
\end{array}
$$

Multiply these equations by 3, −4, 1 respectively and add; we have

$$x4^x = (3A - 16A + 16A)x4^x + (3B - 16A - 16B + 32A + 16B)4^x.$$

Equating the coefficients of like functions,

$$3A = 1, \qquad 3B + 16A = 0; \qquad A = \tfrac{1}{3}, \quad B = -\tfrac{16}{9}.$$

The particular solution

$$y_1 = \tfrac{1}{9}(3x - 16)4^x;$$

and the general solution

$$y = c_1 + c_2 3^x + y_1.$$

Example 3. Find a particular solution of

$$(E^3 - E^2 - 4E + 4)y = 1 + x + 2^x.$$

From $(r - 1)(r - 2)(r + 2) = 0$, $r = 1, 2, -2$. The roots of the nullifying operator are $s = 1, 1, 2$. The set $1, 1, 1, 2, 2, -2$ corresponds to the functions

$$1, x, x^2, 2^x, x2^x, (-2)^x.$$

Discard $1, x, (-2)^x$ corresponding to the roots r and assume

$$
\begin{array}{r|l}
4 & y_1 = Ax \qquad\quad + Bx^2 \qquad\qquad + Cx2^x \\
-4 & Ey_1 = A(x + 1) + B(x + 1)^2 + C(2x + 2)2^x \\
-1 & E^2 y_1 = A(x + 2) + B(x + 2)^2 + C(4x + 8)2^x \\
1 & E^3 y_1 = A(x + 3) + B(x + 3)^2 + C(8x + 24)2^x.
\end{array}
$$

On adding these equations when multiplied as shown, we have

$$1 + x + 2^x = -3A - 6Bx + B + 8C\,2^x;$$
$$B - 3A = 1, \qquad -6B = 1, \qquad 8C = 1;$$

hence $C = \tfrac{1}{8}$, $B = -\tfrac{1}{6}$, $A = -\tfrac{7}{18}$ and

$$y_1 = -\tfrac{7}{18}x - \tfrac{1}{6}x^2 + \tfrac{1}{8}x2^x.$$

PROBLEMS

Find the general solution.
1. $(E^2 - 7E + 6)y = x$.
2. $(E^2 - 4E + 4)y = 1 + (-1)^x + 2^x$.
3. $(E^2 + 1)y = \cos(\pi/2)x$.
4. $(E^2 + 1)y = \sin(\pi/2)x$.
5. $(E^2 - 5E + 6)y = t^2$.
6. Find the solution of Problem 5 when $y(0) = 1$, $y(1) = -1$.

95. OPERATIONAL METHODS

The power shifts

$$(1) \qquad\qquad f(E)a^x = a^x f(a)$$
$$(2) \qquad\qquad f(E)a^x X = a^x f(aE)X$$

and their inverses

(3)
$$\frac{1}{f(E)} a^x = \frac{a^x}{f(a)}, \qquad f(a) \neq 0,$$

(4)
$$\frac{1}{f(E)} (a^x X) = a^x \frac{1}{f(aE)} X,$$

afford the simplest and most powerful methods of finding particular solutions corresponding to the terms a^x or $e^{iax} = \cos ax + i \sin ax$. To prove (3) and (4), apply $f(E)$ to both members, use (1) and (2), and obtain an identity.

Note that (1) is a special case of (2); for the polynomial operator

$$f(aE) = f(a + a\Delta) = f(a) + \text{terms in } \Delta$$

applied to $X = 1$ gives $f(a)$.

Formula (3) cannot be used when $f(a) = 0$. In this case, write

$$f(E) = (E - a)^k g(E), \qquad g(a) \neq 0;$$

then

$$
\begin{aligned}
\frac{1}{f(E)} a^x &= \frac{1}{(E-a)^k} \cdot \frac{1}{g(E)} a^x = \frac{1}{(E-a)^k} \frac{a^x}{g(a)} \\
&= \frac{a^x}{g(a)} \frac{1}{(aE-a)^k} \cdot 1 = \frac{a^{x-k}}{g(a)} \frac{1}{(E-1)^k} 1 \\
&= \frac{a^{x-k}}{g(a)} \Delta^{-k} 1 = \frac{a^{x-k}}{g(a)} \frac{x^{(k)}}{k!};
\end{aligned}
$$

hence

(5)
$$\frac{1}{(E-a)^k g(E)} a^x = \frac{a^{x-k}}{g(a)} \frac{x^{(k)}}{k!}, \qquad g(a) \neq 0.$$

The *process*, rather than the formula, should be remembered.

To find a particular solution corresponding to a polynomial $\varphi(x)$ of degree n in the complete equation, apply the method given in § 42 for the operator $1/f(D)$ to the operator

$$\frac{1}{f(E)} = \frac{1}{f(1 + \Delta)} = \frac{1}{F(\Delta)} = \frac{1}{F(0)} + b_1 \Delta + b_2 \Delta^2 + \cdots + b_n \Delta^n,$$

stopping at the term in Δ^n, for higher powers of Δ nullify $\varphi(x)$. If $F(0) = 0$, write

$$F(\Delta) = \Delta^k g(\Delta), \qquad g(0) \neq 0$$

$$\frac{1}{F(\Delta)} = \Delta^{-k} \left(\frac{1}{g(0)} + b_1 \Delta + \cdots + b_n \Delta^n \right).$$

The validity of these steps follows from precisely the same reasoning used before. Moreover the proof of the pudding is in the eating, and any alleged solution (however obtained) can always be checked for accuracy. We proceed to solve seriatim the examples of the preceding article.

Example 1. $(E - 1)(E - 2)y = 2(-1)^x + \cos x.$
For the term $2(-1)^x$ apply (3):

$$y_1 = 2 \cdot \frac{1}{(E - 1)(E - 2)} (-1)^x = 2 \frac{(-1)^x}{(-2)(-3)} = \tfrac{1}{3}(-1)^x.$$

For the term $\cos x$, replace $\cos x$ by e^{ix}:

$$Y_1 = \frac{e^{ix}}{(e^i - 1)(e^i - 2)} \qquad \text{(apply (3))}$$

$$= \frac{e^{ix}(e^{-i} - 1)(e^{-i} - 2)}{(e^i - 1)(e^{-i} - 1)(e^i - 2)(e^{-i} - 2)} \qquad \text{(to find real part)}$$

where $e^{-i} - 1$, $e^{-i} - 2$ are conjugates of $e^i - 1$, $e^i - 2$. Since

$$(e^i - 1)(e^{-i} - 1) = 2 - (e^i + e^{-i}) = 2 + 2 \cos 1,$$
$$(e^i - 2)(e^{-i} - 2) = 5 - 2(e^i + e^{-i}) = 5 - 4 \cos 1,$$
$$Y_1 = \frac{e^{i(x-2)} - 3e^{i(x-1)} + 2e^{ix}}{(2 + 2 \cos 1)(5 - 4 \cos 1)},$$
$$y_1 = \text{Re } Y = \frac{\cos (x - 2) - 3 \cos (x - 1) + 2 \cos x}{2(1 + 2 \cos 1)(5 - 4 \cos 1)}.$$

This agrees with the solution of Exercise 94.1, but we have avoided a morass of calculation by an elegant approach. Remember that mathematics is an art as well as a science!

Example 2. $(E - 1)(E - 3)y = x4^x.$

$$y_1 = \frac{1}{(E - 1)(E - 3)} x4^x$$

$$= 4^x \frac{1}{(4E - 1)(4E - 3)} x \qquad \text{(shift } 4^x\text{)}$$

$$= 4^x \frac{1}{(3 + 4\Delta)(1 + 4\Delta)} x \qquad (E = 1 + \Delta)$$

$$= \frac{4^x}{3} \frac{1}{(1 + \tfrac{4}{3}\Delta)(1 + 4\Delta)^x} \qquad \text{(make leading term 1)}$$

$$= \frac{4^x}{3} (1 - \tfrac{4}{3}\Delta)(1 - 4\Delta)x \qquad \text{(stop at term in } \Delta\text{)}$$

$$= \frac{4^x}{3} \left(1 - \frac{16}{3} \Delta\right) x \qquad \text{(discard } \Delta^2\text{)}$$

$$= \frac{4^x}{3} \left(x - \frac{16}{3}\right) \qquad (\Delta x = 1)$$

in agreement with Exercise 94.2.

Example 3. $(E - 1)(E - 2)(E + 2)y = 1 + x + 2^x$. For the term 2^x, apply (3) in part, then shift:

$$y_1 = \frac{1}{E - 2} \cdot \frac{1}{(E - 1)(E + 2)} 2^x$$

$$= \frac{1}{E - 2} \frac{2^x}{4} \qquad \text{[apply (3)]}$$

$$= \frac{2^x}{4} \frac{1}{2E - 2} 1 \qquad \text{(shift)}$$

$$= \frac{2^x}{8} \Delta^{-1} 1 = \frac{x 2^x}{8}.$$

For the terms $1 + x$, write

$$(E - 1)(E - 2)(E + 2) = \Delta(\Delta - 1)(\Delta + 3):$$

$$y_1 = -\tfrac{1}{3} \Delta^{-1} \frac{1}{(1 - \Delta)(1 + \tfrac{1}{3}\Delta)} (1 + x) \qquad \text{(leading term 1)}$$

$$= -\tfrac{1}{3} \Delta^{-1} (1 + \Delta)(1 - \tfrac{1}{3}\Delta)(1 + x) \qquad \text{(stop at } \Delta)$$

$$= -\tfrac{1}{3} \Delta^{-1} (1 + \tfrac{2}{3}\Delta)(1 + x) \qquad \text{(discard } \Delta^2)$$

$$= -\tfrac{1}{3} \Delta^{-1} (1 + x + \tfrac{2}{3}) \qquad (\Delta x = 1)$$

$$= -\tfrac{1}{3} \left(\frac{5}{3} x + \frac{x^{(2)}}{2} \right) \qquad (\Delta^{-1} x = \tfrac{1}{2} x^{(2)})$$

$$= -\tfrac{1}{3} \left(\frac{5}{3} x + \frac{x^2 - x}{2} \right) \qquad [x^{(2)} = x(x - 1)]$$

$$= -\frac{7}{18} x - \frac{1}{6} x^2.$$

The sum of these solutions agrees with Exercise 94.3.

PROBLEMS

Find the general solution.
1. $(E - 3)y = 2 \sin 2x$.
2. $(3E - 1)y = x^2$.
3. $(E - 2)(E - 3)y = x + 1$.
4. $(E - 1)(E - 6)y = x$.
5. $(E - 2)^3 y = 2x^{(3)} - 3x$.
6. $(E - 2)^2 y = x 2^x$.
7. $(E^2 - 6E + 4)y = 10$.
8. $(E^2 + E + 1)y = x^2 + x + 1$.
9. $(E^2 + 2E + 5)y = 5x^{(2)} + 13x + 6$.
10. $(E - 1)(E - 2)^3 y = x^2 2^x$.
11. $(E^2 + 1)y = \cos x$.
12. $(E^2 + 1)y = \sin x$.
13. $(E - 2)^2 y = 1 + (-1)^x + 2^x$.

14. $(E^2 + 1)y = \cos \dfrac{\pi}{2} x.$

15. $(E^2 + 1)y = \sin \dfrac{\pi}{2} x.$

16. $(E^2 - 2E, \cos \alpha + 1)y(x) = \cos \alpha x$ or $\sin \alpha x.$

17. $(aE^2 + bE - a - b)y(x) = k.$

96.   RICCATI TYPES

The nonlinear difference equation of Riccati type

(1) $$ay(x)y(x + 1) + by(x) + c = 0$$

may be reduced to the linear equation of the second order

(2) $$az(x + 2) + bz(x + 1) + cz(x) = 0$$

by the substitution $y(x) = z(x + 1)/z(x)$.
  More generally,

(3) $$y(x + 1) = \frac{ay(x) + b}{cy(x) + d}, \qquad c \neq 0, \qquad D = \begin{vmatrix} a & b \\ c & d \end{vmatrix} \neq 0$$

may be reduced to the form

(4) $$z(x + 1) = 2\alpha - \frac{\beta}{z(x)}, \qquad 2\alpha = \frac{a + d}{c}, \qquad \beta = \frac{D}{c^2}$$

by the substitution $y(x) = z(x) - d/c$. This equation is now in the form (1), namely

(4)′ $$z(x + 1)z(x) - 2\alpha z(x) + \beta = 0;$$

and the substitution $w(x) = z(x + 1)/z(x)$ reduces it to

(5) $$w(x + 2) - 2\alpha w(x + 1) + \beta w(x) = 0.$$

Example 1.

(i) $$y(x + 1) = 2 - \frac{2}{y(x)}.$$

With $y(x) = z(x + 1)/z(x)$ the equation becomes

(ii) $$z(x + 2) - 2z(x + 1) + 2z(x) = 0.$$

The characteristic equation $r^2 - 2r + 2 = 0$ has the conjugate complex roots $1 \pm i = \sqrt{2}\, e^{i\pi/4}$, and the general solution of (ii) is

$$z(x) = 2^{x/2}\left(c_1 \cos \frac{\pi}{4} x + c_2 \sin \frac{\pi}{4} x\right).$$

Hence (i) has the general solution

(iii)
$$y(x) = \sqrt{2} \, \frac{c_1 \cos \frac{\pi}{4}(x+1) + c_2 \sin \frac{\pi}{4}(x+1)}{c_1 \cos \frac{\pi}{4}x + c_2 \sin \frac{\pi}{4}x}.$$

If we determine γ in the interval $-\frac{1}{2}\pi < \gamma \leq \frac{1}{2}\pi$ so that

$$\frac{\cos \gamma}{c_1} = \frac{\sin \gamma}{c_2} \quad \text{or} \quad \tan \gamma = \frac{c_2}{c_1},$$

(iii) takes the form

(iv)
$$y(x) = \sqrt{2} \, \frac{\cos \left[\frac{\pi}{4}(x+1) - \gamma \right]}{\cos \left(\frac{\pi}{4}x - \gamma \right)} = 1 - \tan \left(\frac{\pi}{4}x - \gamma \right).$$

in which γ plays the role of an arbitrary constant. Since $\tan \theta$ has the period π, $y(x)$ has the period 4: $y(x+4) = y(x)$.

Example 2.

(i)
$$y(x) + 1 = 4 - \frac{4}{y(x)}.$$

With $y(x) = z(x+1)/z(x)$, the equation becomes

(ii)
$$z(x+2) - 4z(x+1) + 4z(x) = 0.$$

The characteristic equation $k^2 - 4k + 4 = (k-2)^2 = 0$ now has equal roots 2, 2; and the general solution of (ii) is

$$z(x) = (c_1 + c_2 x)2^x.$$

Hence (i) has the general solution

(iii)
$$y(x) = 2 \, \frac{c_1 + c_2(x+1)}{c_1 + c_2 x} = 2 + \frac{2c_2}{c_1 + c_2 x}.$$

Evidently $y(x) \to 2$ as $x \to \infty$, irrespective of the initial value $y(1)$.

PROBLEMS

Find the general solution $y(x)$, giving the period if $y(x)$ is periodic or $\lim_{x \to \infty} y(x)$ if the limit exists.

1. $y(x+1) = 1 - \dfrac{1}{y(x)}$.

2. $y(x+1) = 1 + \dfrac{2}{y(x)}$, $y(1) = 1$.

3. $y(x+1) = 3 - \dfrac{3}{y(x)}$.

4. $y(x + 1) = \dfrac{y(x)}{1 + y(x)}$, $y(1) = \alpha$.

5. $y(x + 1) = \dfrac{y(x) + 4}{y(x) + 1}$, $y(0) = 1$.

6. $y(x)y(x + 1) - 2y(x) - 3 = 0$, $y(0) = 1$.

7. $[2x - y(x)]y(x + 1) = x(x + 1)$, $y(1) = 3$.

97. MACLAURIN TRANSFORM

If the terms of the sequence $\{f(t)\}$ are used as the coefficients of x^t in a power series, we obtain a function $F(x)$ defined by the Maclaurin expansion

$$(\mathcal{M}) \qquad\qquad F(x) = \sum_{t=0}^{\infty} f(t)x^t, \qquad |x| < R,$$

which will converge in some interval $-R < x < R$. We shall call $F(x)$ the Maclaurin transform of $f(t)$. Since the Maclaurin series for $F(x)$, namely

$$F(x) = \sum_{t=0}^{\infty} \frac{F^{(t)}(0)}{t!} x^t$$

is unique, the inverse transformation is

$$(\mathcal{M}^{-1}) \qquad\qquad f(t) = \frac{F^{(t)}(0)}{t!}.$$

We shall write

$$F(x) = \mathcal{M}\{f(t)\}, \qquad f(t) = \mathcal{M}^{-1}\{F(x)\},$$

and regard the functions $f(t)$ and $F(t)$ as transform pairs. Function $F(x)$ is called the *generating function* of the sequence $\{f(t)\}$.

Each Maclaurin expansion yields a transform pair; for example, from $e^x = \sum_{t=0}^{\infty} x^t/t!$ we have

$$e^x = \mathcal{M}\left\{\frac{1}{t!}\right\}, \qquad \frac{1}{t!} = \mathcal{M}^{-1}\{e^x\}.$$

Note that the Maclaurin transformation is linear; that is,

$$\mathcal{M}\{f + g\} = \mathcal{M}\{f\} + \mathcal{M}\{g\}, \qquad M\{cf\} = c\mathcal{M}\{f\}.$$

If the power series $(\mathcal{M})$ converges when $|x| < R$, the series obtained by differentiating or integrating the series term by term has the same radius of convergence R;* and within the interval $|x| < R$ the new series converges to $F'(x)$ or $\displaystyle\int_0^x F(x)\,dx$, respectively.† We use these facts to build up a

---

* However the convergence at $x = \pm R$ may be altered. Differentiation tends to exclude endpoints, integration to include them. Why?

† *Advanced Calculus*, §§ 181–183.

useful set of transform pairs, beginning with the simple geometric series

(1) $$\mathcal{M}\{1\} = \sum_{t=0}^{\infty} x^t = (1 - x)^{-1}, \qquad |x| < 1;$$

(2) $$\mathcal{M}\{k^t\} = \sum_{t=0}^{\infty} (kx)^t = (1 - kx)^{-1}, \qquad |x| < k^{-1}.$$

Differentiate ($\mathcal{M}$) n times; then

$$D^n F(x) = \sum_{t=0}^{\infty} f(t)t(t - 1) \cdots (t - n + 1)x^{t-n} = \sum_{t=0}^{\infty} t^{(n)} f(t) x^{t-n}.$$

We may use this equation in two ways.

First, when written

$$x^n D^n F(x) = \sum_{t=0}^{\infty} t^{(n)} f(t) x^t,$$

(3) $$\mathcal{M}\{t^{(n)} f(t)\} = x^n D^n F(x), \qquad |x| < R.$$

Second, since $t^{(n)} = 0$ when $t < n$, we may start the summation at $t = n$ and make the change of index $t = s + n$; then

$$D^n F(x) = \sum_{s=0}^{\infty} (s + n)^{(n)} f(s + n) x^s.$$

Since the choice of index letter is immaterial, we may replace s by t and write

(4) $$\mathcal{M}\{(t + n)^{(n)} f(t + n)\} = D^n F(x), \qquad |x| < R.$$

If the operator xD is applied n times to the series ($\mathcal{M}$), we have

$$(xD)^n F(x) = \sum_{t=0}^{\infty} t^n f(t) x^t,$$

for $(xD)x^t = tx^t$; thus

(5) $$\mathcal{M}\{t^n f(t)\} = (xD)^n F(x), \qquad |x| < R.$$

Note, however, that $(xD)^n \neq x^n D^n$.

By specializing the function $f(t)$ we can use (3), (4), and (5) to obtain a number of useful transforms.

With $f(t) = 1$, $F(x) = (1 - x)^{-1}$, we get

(3.1) $$\mathcal{M}\{t^{(n)}\} = n!\, x^n (1 - x)^{-n-1},$$

(4.1) $$\mathcal{M}\{(t + n)^{(n)}\} = n!\, (1 - x)^{-n-1},$$

(5.1) $$\mathcal{M}\{t^n\} = (xD)^n (1 - x)^{-1}, \qquad |x| < 1.$$

For $n = 1, 2$, (5.1) gives

(6) $$\mathscr{M}\{t\} = x(1 - x)^{-2},$$

(7) $$\mathscr{M}\{t^2\} = x(1 + x)(1 - x)^{-2}.$$

In general,

$$\mathscr{M}\{t^n\} = xP_n(x)(1 - x)^{-n-1},$$

where $P_n(x)$ is a polynomial of degree n that satisfies the recurrence relation

$$P_{n+1}(x) = (nx + 1)P_n(x) + x(1 - x)P_n{}'(x), \qquad P_1 = 1.$$

With $f(t) = k^t$, $F(x) = (1 - kx)^{-1}$, we get

(3.2) $$\mathscr{M}\{t^{(n)}k^t\} = n!\, k^n x^n (1 - kx)^{-n-1},$$

(4.2) $$\mathscr{M}\{(t + n)^{(n)}k^t\} = n!\,(1 - kx)^{-n-1},$$

(5.2) $$\mathscr{M}\{t^n k^t\} = (xD)^n(1 - kx)^{-1}, \qquad |x| < k^{-1}.$$

For $n = 1, 2$, (5.2) becomes

(8) $$\mathscr{M}\{tk^t\} = kx(1 - kx)^{-2},$$

(9) $$\mathscr{M}\{t^2 k^t\} = kx(1 + kx)(1 - kx)^{-3}.$$

If we replace x by kx in $(\mathscr{M})$,

$$F(kx) = \sum_{t=0}^{\infty} f(t)k^t x^t,$$

(10) $$\mathscr{M}\{k^t f(t)\} = F(kx).$$

From (2) we have

$$\mathscr{M}\{e^{ax}\} = (1 - e^a x)^{-1}, \qquad |x| < e^{-a}.$$

The linearity of $\mathscr{M}$ now gives

(11) $$\mathscr{M}\{\cosh at\} = \frac{1 - x \cosh a}{1 - 2x \cosh a + x^2},$$

(12) $$\mathscr{M}\{\sinh at\} = \frac{x \sinh a}{1 - 2x \cosh a + x^2}, \qquad |x| < e^{-a}.$$

On replacing a by ia and using

$$\cosh(iax) = \cos ax, \qquad \sinh(iax) = i \sin ax,$$

we have also

(13) $$\mathscr{M}\{\cos at\} = \frac{1 - x \cos a}{1 - 2x \cos a + x^2},$$

(14) $$\mathscr{M}\{\sin at\} = \frac{x \sin a}{1 - 2x \cos a + x^2}, \qquad |x| < 1.$$

If we integrate series $(\mathcal{M})$ term by term and then divide by x, we have

$$\frac{1}{x}\int_0^x F(x)\, dx = \sum_{t=0}^{\infty} \frac{f(t)}{t+1}\, x^t,$$

(15) $$\mathcal{M}\left\{\frac{f(t)}{t+1}\right\} = \frac{1}{x}\int_0^x (Fx)\, dx, \qquad |x| < R.$$

For example, if $f(t) = k^t$,

(16) $$\mathcal{M}\left\{\frac{k^t}{t+1}\right\} = \frac{1}{x}\int_0^x \frac{dx}{1-kx} = -\frac{1}{kx}\log(1-kx), \qquad |x| < k^{-1}.$$

In particular, for $k = 1$ and -1

(17) $$\mathcal{M}\left\{\frac{1}{t+1}\right\} = -\frac{\log(1-x)}{x},$$

(18) $$\mathcal{M}\left\{\frac{(-1)^t}{t+1}\right\} = \frac{\log(1+x)}{x}, \qquad |x| < 1.$$

From the binomial expansion

$$(1+x)^r = \sum_{t=0}^{\infty} \binom{r}{t} x^t,$$

(19) $$\mathcal{M}\left\{\binom{r}{t}\right\} = (1+x)^r, \qquad |x| < 1.$$

When n is a positive integer, $\binom{t}{n} = t^{(n)}/n!$; hence (3.1) may be written

(20) $$\mathcal{M}\left\{\binom{t}{n}\right\} = x^n(1-x)^{-n-1}.$$

Finally, to transform a difference equation we need the transform of $f(t+n)$. Now

$$\mathcal{M}\{f(t+n)\} = \sum_{t=0}^{\infty} f(t+n)x^t = \sum_{s=n}^{\infty} f(s)x^{s-n}, \qquad s = t+n;$$

on reverting to the index t, we find the last sum to be

$$x^{-n}\sum_{t=n}^{\infty} f(t)x^t = x^{-n}\left(\sum_{t=0}^{\infty} f(t)x^t - \sum_{t=0}^{n-1} f(t)x^t\right);$$

hence

(21) $$\mathcal{M}\{f(t+n)\} = x^{-n}\left[F(x) - \sum_{t=0}^{n-1} f(t)x^t\right],$$

a formula which requires the knowledge of n initial values, $f(0), f(1), \ldots, f(n-1)$.

We shall also need

$$\mathcal{M}\{f(t-n)\} = \sum_{t=0}^{\infty} f(t-n)x^t = \sum_{s=-n}^{\infty} f(s)x^{s+n}, \qquad s = t - n.$$

(22) $$\mathcal{M}\{f(t-n)\} = x^n \left[\sum_{t=-n}^{-1} f(t)x^t + F(x) \right].$$

When $f(t) = 0$ for $t < 0$, this gives

(23) $$\mathcal{M}\{f(t-n)\} = x^n F(x), \qquad f(-) = 0.$$

If $f(t) \neq 0$ when $t < 0$, we have from (22):

(24) $$\mathcal{M}\{f(t-1)\} = xF(x) + f(-1),$$

(25) $$\mathcal{M}\{f(t-2)\} = x^2 F(x) + f(-2) + xf(-1),$$

and so on.†

98. CONVOLUTION

If the power series

$$F(x) = \sum_{t=0}^{\infty} f(t)x^t = f(0) + f(1)x + f(2)x^2 + \cdots$$

$$G(x) = \sum_{t=0}^{\infty} g(t)x^t = g(0) + g(1)x + g(2)x^2 + \cdots$$

both converge in the interval $|x| < R$ (the smaller of their radii of convergence), they also converge absolutely at any point of this interval. Hence their Cauchy product converges to $F(x)G(x)$ in the interval $|x| < R$.‡ The coefficient of x^t in this product is

$$f(0)g(t) + f(1)g(t-1) + \cdots + f(t)g(0) = \sum_{\tau=0}^{t} f(\tau)g(t-\tau).$$

Hence if we define the *convolution* of $f(t)$ and $g(t)$ as

(1) $$f * g = \sum_{\tau=0}^{t} f(\tau)g(t-\tau),$$

---

† Tomlinson Fort in the *American Mathematical Monthly*, vol. 62, no. 9, 1955, defines the *Dirichlet transform* as

$$\mathcal{D}\{f(t)\} = \sum_{t=0}^{\infty} m^{-st}f(t).$$

The list of transforms given by Fort may be obtained from their Maclaurin analogs by replacing x by m^{-s}.

‡ *Advanced Calculus*, § 183.

we have

(2) $$\mathcal{M}\{f * g\} = F(x)G(x).$$

An interchange of f and g in (1) does not alter the sum; hence the convolution is commutative

(3) $$f * g = g * f.$$

The convolution is also associative

(4) $$(f * g) * h = f * (g * h),$$

a property that readily follows from (2).

The convolution

(5) $$f * 1 = \sum_{\tau=0}^{t} f(\tau) = f(0) + f(1) + \cdots + f(t)$$

is the sum of $t + 1$ terms of the series for $F(x)$; and since $\mathcal{M}(1) = (1 - x)^{-1}$, we have from (2)

(6) $$\sum_{\tau=0}^{t} f(\tau) = \frac{F(x)}{1 - x}.$$

Thus if $f(t) = 1$, the sum is $t + 1$ and

$$\mathcal{M}\{t + 1\} = (1 - x)^{-2}.$$

Now let $\Delta^{-1}f(t)$ denote that antidifference of $f(t)$ *which vanishes for* $t = 0$; then from (81.2)

$$\Delta^{-1}f(t) = \sum_{\tau=0}^{t-1} f(\tau)$$

and (6) may be written

$$\mathcal{M}\{\Delta^{-1}f(t)\} + \mathcal{M}\{f(t)\} = \frac{F(x)}{1 - x},$$

or, since $F(x) = \mathcal{M}\{f(t)\}$,

(7) $$\mathcal{M}\{\Delta^{-1}f(t)\} = \frac{x}{1 - x} \mathcal{M}\{f(t)\}.$$

Example. If $f(t) = k^t$, $\mathcal{M}\{f\} = (1 - kx)^{-1}$ and

$$\mathcal{M}\{\Delta^{-1}k^t\} = \frac{x}{(1 - x)(1 - kx)} = \frac{1}{k - 1}\left(\frac{1}{1 - kx} - \frac{1}{1 - x}\right),$$

$$\Delta^{-1}k^t = \frac{1}{k - 1}(k^t - 1), \qquad k \neq 1.$$

Note that this antidifference vanishes for $t = 0$.

PROBLEMS

1. Show that
   (a) $1 * 1 = t + 1$,
   (b) $1 * t = \frac{1}{2}t(t + 1) = (t + 1)^{(2)}/2!$,
   (c) $t * t = (t + 1)^{(3)}/3!$,
and in each case verify equation (2).

2. From $\Delta f = f(t + 1) - f(t)$, show that

$$\mathscr{M}\{\Delta f\} = (x^{-1} - 1)\mathscr{M}\{f\} - x^{-1}f(0).$$

3. If $\Delta \varphi(t) = f(t)$, show that

$$\mathscr{M}\{\varphi(t)\} = \frac{x\mathscr{M}(f) + \varphi(0)}{1 - x}.$$

When $\varphi(0) = 0$, this reduces to (7).

4. Prove directly that

$$(f * g) * h = f * (g * h).$$

5. If $1 * 1 * \cdots$ to n factors is written $(1 *)^n$, show that

$$(1 *)^3 = \frac{(t + 2)^{(2)}}{2!}, \qquad (1 *)^{n+1} = \frac{(t + n)^{(n)}}{n!}.$$

[Cf. Prob. 1a].

6. Prove that $(t *)^3 = (t + 2)^{(5)}/5!$.

99. GENERATING FUNCTIONS

If $F(x)$ is the sum of the convergent power series,

$$F(x) = \sum_{t=0}^{\infty} f(t)x^t,$$

$F(x)$ is said to be the *generating function* of the sequence $f(0), f(1), \ldots$.
When the sequence is defined by a difference equation with initial conditions, its generating function can often be found by use of Tables 99a and 99b.

For example, the sequence defined by

(1) $af(t + 2) + bf(t + 1) + cf(t) = 0, \qquad f(0) = \alpha, \qquad f(1) = \beta,$

has the transform

$$ax^{-2}(F - \alpha - \beta x) + bx^{-1}(F - \alpha) + cF = 0;$$

its generating function is therefore

(2) $$F(x) = \frac{a\alpha + (a\beta + b\alpha)x}{a + bx + cx^2}.$$

Thus for the Fibonacci numbers (Ex. 97.3) 0, 1, 1, 2, 3, 5, . . . ,

$$f(t + 2) - f(t + 1) - f(t) = 0, \quad f(0) = 0, \quad f(1) = 1;$$

with $a = 1$, $b = c = -1$, $\alpha = 0$, $\beta = 1$, we get their generating function

$$(3) \quad F(x) = \frac{x}{1 - x - x^2} = 0 + x + x^2 + 2x^3 + 3x^4 + 5x^5 + \cdots.$$

The generating function is a convenient carryall for the entire sequence.

Table 99a   Generating Functions: Operations

No.	$f(t)$	$F(x) = \sum_{t=0}^{\infty} f(t)x^t$	Source
I	$f(t + n) = E^n f(t)$	$x^{-n}[F(x) - \sum_{t=0}^{n-1} f(t)x^t]$	97.17
	$f(t + 1)$	$x^{-1}[F(x) - f(0)]$	
	$f(t + 2)$	$x^{-2}[F(x) - f(0) - f(1)x]$	
II	$f(t - n) = E^{-n}f(t)$	$x^n[F(x) + \sum_{t=-n}^{-1} f(t)x^t]$	97.22
	$f(t - 1)$	$xF(x) + f(-1)$	
	$f(t - 2)$	$x^2F(x) + xf(-1) + f(-2)$	
III	$t^{(n)}f(t)$	$x^n D^n F(x)$	97.3
	$tf(t)$	$xF'(x)$	
	$t(t - 1)f(t)$	$x^2F''(x)$	
VI	$(t + n)^{(n)}f(t + n)$	$D^n F(x)$	97.4
	$(t + 1)f(t + 1)$	$F'(x)$	
	$(t + 2)(t + 1)f(t + 2)$	$F''(x)$	
V	$t^n f(t)$	$(xD)^n F(x)$	97.5
	$t^2 f(t)$	$xF'(x) + x^2 F''(x)$	
	$t^3 f(t)$	$xF'(x) + 3x^2 F''(x) + x^3 F'''(x)$	
VI	$\dfrac{f(t)}{t + 1}$	$\dfrac{1}{x} \int_0^x F(x)\,dx$	97.15
VII	$k^t f(t)$	$F(kx)$	97.10
VIII	$f(t) * g(t)$	$F(x)G(x)$	98.2
IX	$\Delta f(t)$	$x^{-1}[(1 - x)F(x) - f(0)]$	no. I
X	$\Delta^{-1}f(t)$	$x(1 - x)^{-1}F(x)$	98.7

Table 99b Generating Functions
Special Functions

No.	$f(t)$	$F(x) = \sum_{t=0}^{\infty} f(t)x^t$	Convergence
1	1	$(1-x)^{-1}$	$\|x\| < 1$
2	$t+1$	$(1-x)^{-2}$	
3	$(t+2)(t+1) = (t+2)^{(2)}$	$2(1-x)^{-3}$	
4	$(t+n)^{(n)}$	$n!(1-x)^{-n-1}$	
5	t	$x(1-x)^{-2}$	
6	$t(t-1) = t^{(2)}$	$2x^2(1-x)^{-3}$	
7	$t^{(n)}$	$n!x^n(1-x)^{-n-1}$	
8	t^2	$x(1+x)(1-x)^{-3}$	
9	t^3	$x(1+4x+x^2)(1-x)^{-4}$	
10	t^n	$xP_n(x)(1-x)^{-n-1}$ \quad (cf. §97)	
11	k^t	$(1-kx)^{-1}$	$\|x\| < k^{-1}$
12	$(t+1)k^t$	$(1-kx)^{-2}$	
13	$(t+n)^{(n)}k^t$	$n!(1-kx)^{-n-1}$	
14	tk^t	$kx(1-kx)^{-2}$	
15	t^2k^t	$kx(1+kx)(1-kx)^{-3}$	
16	e^{at}	$(1-e^a x)^{-1}$	$\|x\| < e^{-a}$
17	$\cosh at$	$\dfrac{1 - x\cosh a}{1 - 2x\cosh a + x^2}$	
18	$\sinh at$	$\dfrac{x\sinh a}{1 - 2x\cosh a + x^2}$	
19	$\cos at$	$\dfrac{1 - x\cos a}{1 - 2x\cos a + x^2}$	$\|x\| < 1$
20	$\sin at$	$\dfrac{x\sin a}{1 - 2x\cos a + x^2}$	
21	$k^t \cos at$	$\dfrac{1 - kx\cos a}{1 - 2kx\cos a + k^2x^2}$	$\|x\| < k^{-1}$
22	$k^t \sin at$	$\dfrac{kx\sin a}{1 - 2kx\cos a + k^2x^2}$	
23	$k^t \cos\dfrac{\pi}{2}t$	$\dfrac{1}{1 + k^2x^2}$	$\|x\| < k^{-1}$
24	$k^t \sin\dfrac{\pi}{2}t$	$\dfrac{kx}{1 + k^2x^2}$	$\|x\| < k^{-1}$
25	$\dfrac{k^t}{t!}$	e^{kx}	all x

Table 99b *continued*

No.	$f(t)$	$F(x) = \sum\limits_{t=0}^{\infty} f(t)x^t$		Convergence
26	$\dfrac{1}{(2t)!}$	$\cosh \sqrt{x}$		all x
27	$\dbinom{2t}{t}$	$(1 - 4x)^{-1/2}$		$|x| < \frac{1}{4}$
28	$\dbinom{2t-1}{t}$	$\frac{1}{2}(1 - 4x)^{-1/2}$		$|x| < \frac{1}{4}$
29	$\dbinom{r}{t}$	$(1 + x)^r$		$|x| < 1$
30	$(-1)^t \dbinom{r}{t}$	$(1 - x)^r$		$|x| < 1$
31	$\dbinom{t}{n}$	$x^n(1 - x)^{-n-1}$		$|x| < 1$
32	$\dfrac{1}{t + 1}$	$\dfrac{-\log(1 - x)}{x}$		$|x| < 1$
33	$\dfrac{(-1)^t}{t + 1}$	$\dfrac{\log(1 + x)}{x}$		$|x| < 1$
34	$\dfrac{B_t}{t!}$	$\dfrac{x}{e^x - 1}$	(§ 79)	$|x| < 2\pi$
35	f_n (Fibonacci nos.)	$\dfrac{x}{1 - x - x^2}$	(§ 99)	$|x| < \frac{1}{2}(\sqrt{5} - 1)$

Example 1. $t * t = \dfrac{1}{3!}(t + 1)^{(3)}$.

Proof $\mathscr{M}\{t\} = x(1 - x)^{-2}$ no. 5 in Table
$\mathscr{M}\{t * t\} = x^2(1 - x)^{-4}$ op. VIII
$3!\mathscr{M}\{t * t\} = 3!\, x^2(1 - x)^{-4}$
$\phantom{3!\mathscr{M}\{t * t\}} = x^{-1}\mathscr{M}\{t^{(3)}\}$ no. 7
$\phantom{3!\mathscr{M}\{t * t\}} = \mathscr{M}(t + 1)^{(3)}$.   op. I

Example 2. $\Delta^{-1}k^t = (k^t - 1)/(k - 1)$.

Proof. $\mathscr{M}\{k^t\} = (1 - kx)^{-1}$ no. 11

$\mathscr{M}\{\Delta^{-1}k^t\} = \dfrac{x}{(1 - kx)(1 - x)}$ op. X

$\phantom{\mathscr{M}\{\Delta^{-1}k^t\}} = \dfrac{1}{k - 1}\left(\dfrac{1}{1 - kx} - \dfrac{1}{1 - x}\right)$

$\phantom{\mathscr{M}\{\Delta^{-1}k^t\}} = \dfrac{1}{k - 1}\,\mathscr{M}\{k^t - 1\}$.

100. EQUATIONS WITH CONSTANT COEFFICIENTS

To solve the difference equation

$$f(E)y(t) = \varphi(t),$$

let $\mathcal{M}\{y(t)\} = Y(x)$ and transform the terms of the left member using

$$\mathcal{M}\{E^n y\} = x^{-n}\left[Y(x) - \sum_{t=0}^{n-1} y(t)x^t \right]$$

with the appropriate initial values of $y(t)$. The right member is transformed in accordance with Table 99b for special functions. Solve the resulting equation for $Y(x)$ and use the table again to find $y(t)$. If some terms do not appear in the list of special functions, Table 99a for operations must be used to produce the desired function. Examples 3 and 4 illustrate the procedure. The answer may be checked by finding a few terms of the solution sequence and comparing them with those found from the equation.

The formulas of I for transforming $E^n y$ will give $x^{-n}f(x)$ as the coefficient of Y in the transform of equation (1). Now if $r_1, r_2, \ldots, r_n$ are the roots of the characteristic equation $f(r) = 0$, we have the factorization

$$x^{-n}f(x) = x^{-n}(x - r_1)(x - r_2) \cdots (x - r_n)$$

$$= (1 - r_1 x)(1 - r_2 x) \cdots (1 - r_n x)$$

which is most useful in obtaining partial fractions which appear in Table 99b of special transforms. See the following examples 2 and 5.

Example 1. $y(t + 1) + 3y(t) = t;$ $\quad y(0) = 1.$
Transform

$$x^{-1}(Y - 1) + 3Y = \frac{x}{(1 - x)^2}.$$

Multiply by x and solve for $Y(x)$:

$$Y(x) = \frac{2x^2 - 2x + 1}{(1 + 3x)(1 - x)^2} = \frac{\frac{17}{16}}{1 + 3x} - \frac{\frac{15}{16}}{1 - x} + \frac{\frac{1}{4}}{(1 - x)^2}.$$

Transform back, using nos. 12, 1, 2:

$$y(t) = \frac{17}{16}(-3)^t - \frac{5}{16} + \frac{1}{4}(t + 1)$$

$$= \frac{17}{16}(-3)^t - \frac{1}{16} + \frac{t}{4}.$$

Example 2. $y(t + 2) - 3y(t + 1) + 2y(t) = -1;$ $y(0) = 2, y(1) = 4.$

Transform:

$$x^{-2}(Y - 2 - 4x) - 3x^{-1}(Y - 2) + 2Y = \frac{-1}{1 - x}.$$

Multiply by x^2 and solve for $F(x)$:

$$Y(x) = \frac{x^2 - 4x + 2}{(1 - x^2)(1 - 2x)} = \frac{1}{(1 - x)^2} + \frac{1}{1 - 2x}.$$

Transforming back, using nos. 2, 12:

$$y(t) = t + 1 + 2^t.$$

Example 3. $y(t + 2) - 2y(t + 1) + 2y(t) = 0, \qquad y(0) = 0, \qquad y(1) = 1.$

$$x^{-2}(Y - x) - 2x^{-1}Y + 2Y = 0,$$

$$Y - x - 2xY + 2x^2Y = 0,$$

$$Y(x) = \frac{x}{1 - 2x + 2x^2}.$$

From no. 20 we have (see note)

$$\mathscr{M}\{k^t \sin at\} = \frac{kx \sin a}{1 - 2kx \cos a + k^2x^2}.$$

Comparing with $Y(x)$ we have $k^2 = 2, k = \sqrt{2}$;

$$k \cos a = 1, \qquad a = \frac{\pi}{4}; \qquad k \sin a = 1; \qquad \text{and}$$

$$y(t) = 2^{t/2} \sin \frac{\pi}{4} t.$$

Solution sequence: $0, 1, 2, 2, 0, -4, -8, -8, \ldots .$

Example 4. $y(t + 2) + y(t) = \cos \frac{\pi}{2} t, \qquad y(0) = 1, y(1) = 0.$

$$x^{-2}(Y - 1) + Y = \frac{1}{1 + x^2},$$

$$Y(x) = \frac{1}{1 + x^2} + \frac{x^2}{1 + x^2}.$$

Since $\mathscr{M}[t \cos (\pi/2)x] = xD(1 + x^2)^{-1} = -2x^2/(1 + x^2)^2$, from III,

$$y(t) = \cos \frac{\pi}{2} t - \frac{1}{2} t \cos \frac{\pi}{2} t = \left(1 - \frac{1}{2} t\right) \cos \frac{\pi}{2} t.$$

Solution sequence: $1, 0, 0, 0, -1, 0, 2, 0, -3, 0, 4, \ldots .$

Example 5. $y(t + 2) - y(t + 1) - y(t) = 0, \qquad y(0) = 0, \; y(1) = 1.$
This is the Fibonacci equation of Exercise 91.3. The transform is

$$x^{-2}(Y - x) + x^{-1}Y - Y = 0$$

or

$$(1 - x - x^2)Y = x.$$

Since $\alpha = (1 + \sqrt{5})/2$, $\beta = (1 - \sqrt{5})/2$ are the roots of the characteristic equation $r^2 - r - 1 = 0$, we have

$$Y = \frac{x}{(1 - \alpha x)(1 - \beta x)} = \frac{1}{\alpha - \beta}\left[\frac{1}{1 - \alpha x} - \frac{1}{1 - \beta x}\right]$$

$$y(t) = \frac{1}{\sqrt{5}}(\alpha^t - \beta^t)$$

in agreement with Example 91.3.

PROBLEMS

1. $y(t + 1) + y(t) = 0,$ $y(0) = 1.$

2. $y(t + 1) + y(t) = 1,$ $y(0) = 1.$

3. $y(t + 2) - y(t + 1) - y(t) = 0,$ $y(0) = 2, y(1) = 1.$

4. $y(t + 2) + 3y(t + 1) + 2y(t) = 0,$ $y(0) = 0, y(1) = 1.$

5. $y(t + 2) + 8y(t + 1) - 9y(t) = 0,$ $y(0) = y(1) = 0.$

6. $y(t + 2) - 3y(t + 1) + y(t) = 0,$ $y(0) = 0, y(1) = 1.$

7. $y(t + 2) - 5y(t + 1) + 6y(t) = t,$ $y(0) = y(1) = 0.$

8. $y(t + 2) + k^2 y(t) = 0,$ $y(0) = \alpha, y(1) = \beta.$

9. $y(t + 2) + y(t + 1) + y(t) = t^2 + t + 1,$ $y(0) = 0, y(1) = 1.$

10. $y(t + 2) + 3y(t + 1) + 2y(t) = 1,$ $y(0) = 1, y(1) = 0.$

11. $y(t + 2) - y(t + 1) + y(t) = 0,$ $y(0) = y(1) = 1.$

12. $y(t + 3) - y(t + 2) - y(t + 1) + y(t) = 1,$ $y(0) = y(1) = y(2) = 1.$

13. $2y(t + 2) - 2y(t + 1) + y(t) = \dfrac{1 + (-1)^t}{2},$ $y(0) = 1, y(1) = 0.$

14. $y(t + 2) + y(t) = \sin\dfrac{\pi}{2} t,$ $y(0) = 1, y(1) = 0.$

101. STABILITY

A difference equation with constant coefficients

$$(1) \qquad f(E)y = (a_0 E^n + a_1 E^{n-1} + \cdots + a_{n-1}E + a_n)y = 0$$

is said to be *stable* when all of its solutions are transients, that is, approach zero as $x \to \infty$. It is said to be *metastable* if all members of its solution basis that are not transients remain bounded for $t \geq 0$. An examination of Table 91 shows that all functions of the solution basis are included in

$$a^x x^j \cos bx, \qquad a^x x^j \sin bx,$$

where a is the absolute value of a root of the characteristic equation

$$(2) \qquad f(r) = a_0 r^n + a_1 r^{n-1} + \cdots + a_{n-1}r + a_n = 0$$

and j is a non-negative integer. Evidently equation (1) is stable iff all roots of (2) have absolute values less than 1; and it is metastable iff all multiple roots ($j \neq 0$) have absolute values less than 1 and all simple roots ($j = 0$) have the absolute value 1.

When equation (1) is stable, all roots of equation (2) must lie inside the unit circle $|z| = 1$ of the complex plane. Necessary and sufficient conditions for this in determinant form are given by Morris Marden, *The Geometry of the Zeros of a Polynomial in a Complex Variable*, Chapter X, Mathematical Surveys, no. III, Am. Math. Soc., 1949, New York.

Example. $2y(t + 2) - 2y(t + 1) + y(t) = [1 + (-1)^t]/2$. The characteristic equation $2r^2 - 2r + 1 = 0$ has the roots $\frac{1}{2}(1 + i) = (1/\sqrt{2}) \exp (i\pi/4)$. By the method of undetermined coefficients we find the particular solution $\frac{1}{2} + \frac{1}{10}(-1)^t$. Hence the general solution is

$$y(t) = \left(\frac{1}{\sqrt{2}}\right)^t \left(c_1 \cos \frac{\pi}{4} t + c_2 \sin \frac{\pi}{4} t\right) + \frac{1}{2} + \frac{1}{10}(-1)^t.$$

Since $(1/\sqrt{2})^t \to 0$ as $t \to \infty$, the first two terms are transient and the solution ultimately tends to the steady-state "wave" $\frac{1}{2} + \frac{1}{10}(-1)^t$ of period 2, namely a repetition of $\frac{3}{5}$ and $\frac{2}{5}$ (cf. Appendix 3).

The initial values $y(0)$ and $y(1)$ determine c_1 and c_2; but since the terms with these constants tend to zero, the solution approaches the same steady-state irrespective of the initial conditions.

102. EQUATIONS WITH VARIABLE COEFFICIENTS

We transform the equation as usual, relying on the table of operations in dealing with terms having variable coefficients. This procedure will introduce derivatives, so that the transformed difference equation is an ordinary differential equation. In solving this, initial conditions such as

$$(1) \qquad\qquad F(0) = f(0), \qquad F'(0) = f(1),$$

derived from ($\mathscr{M}^{-1}$) for $t = 0, 1$, are used to determine the arbitrary constants.

Example 1. $(t + 1)y(t + 1) - (n - t)y(t) = 0, \; y(0) = 1$.
Transform, using Op. IV and III:

$$Y' - nY + xY' = 0,$$

$$\frac{Y'}{Y} = \frac{n}{1 + x}.$$

$$\log Y = n \log (1 + x) + \log A,$$

$$Y(x) = A(1 + x)^n.$$

To find A, put $x = 0$; then since $Y(0) = y(0) = 1$, $A = 1$ and

$$Y(x) = (1 + x)^n,$$

$$y(t) = \binom{n}{t} \quad \text{from no. 28 of Table 99b.}$$

Example 2. $2(t + 1)y(t + 1) - (2t + 1)y(t) = 0$, $y(0) = 1$.
Transform, using op. IV and III:

$$2Y' - 2xY' - Y = 0,$$

$$\frac{Y'}{Y} = \frac{1}{2(1 - x)},$$

$$\log Y = \log A - \tfrac{1}{2} \log (1 - x),$$

$$Y(x) = A(1 - x)^{-\frac{1}{2}}.$$

To find A put $x = 0$; then $Y(0) = y(0) = 1 = A$ and

$$Y(x) = (1 - x)^{-\frac{1}{2}}.$$

From no. 29 of Table 99b,

$$y(t) = (-1)^t \binom{-\frac{1}{2}}{t}$$

$$= (-1)^t \frac{(-\frac{1}{2})(-\frac{3}{2}) \cdots (t - \frac{1}{2})}{t!}, \quad (t \text{ factors})$$

$$= \frac{1 \cdot 3 \cdot 5 \cdots (2t - 1)}{2^t t!},$$

$$= \frac{1 \cdot 2 \cdot 3 \cdot 4 \cdots (2t - 1)(2t)}{2^t 2^t t!},$$

$$y(t) = \frac{1}{4^t} \binom{2t}{t}.$$

Example 3. $2t(2t - 1)y(t) - (2t - 3)^2 y(t - 1) + (2t - 5)y(t - 2) = 0$,
$y(0) = 1$, $y(1) = \frac{1}{2}$.
With $z(t) = (2t - 1)y(t)$, the equation can be written

$$2t\, z(t) - (2t - 3)z(t - 1) + z(t - 2) = 0, \qquad z(0) = -1, z(1) = \tfrac{1}{2}.$$

This equation shows that $z(-t) = 0$, $t = 1, 2, \ldots$, that op. II becomes
$\mathcal{M}\{f(t - n)\} = x^n F(x)$.
Writing the last equation

$$2t\, z(t) - 2(t - 1)z(t - 1) + z(t - 1) + z(t - 2) = 0.$$

we find the transform

$$2xZ' - 2x^2 Z' + xZ + x^2 Z = 0;$$

$$\frac{Z'}{Z} = \frac{1}{2} \frac{x + 1}{x - 1} = \frac{1}{2} + \frac{1}{x - 1},$$

$$\log Z = \log A + \tfrac{1}{2}x + \log (x - 1),$$

$$Z(x) = A(x - 1)e^{x/2}.$$

Since $Z(0) = z(0) = -1$, $-1 = -A$, we have $A = 1$ and

$$Z = (x - 1)e^{x/2}.$$

From $z(t) = 2ty(t) - y(t)$, we have

$$Z = 2xY' - Y;$$

hence

$$2xY' - Y = (x - 1)e^{x/2},$$

$$Y' - \frac{1}{2x}\,Y = \frac{1}{2}\left(1 - \frac{1}{x}\right)e^{x/2},$$

a linear equation having $x^{-1/2}$ as multiplier. Thus we have (§ 16)

$$\frac{d}{dx}\,[x^{-1/2}\,Y] = \frac{1}{2}\,(x^{-1/2} - x^{-3/2})e^{x/2}$$

and on integration

$$x^{-1/2}\,Y = x^{-1/2}e^{x/2} + B,$$

$$Y(x) = e^{x/2} + Bx^{1/2}.$$

Since $Y(0) = y(0) = 1$, $B = 0$; thus

$$Y(x) = e^{x/2}, \qquad y(t) = \frac{1}{2^t t!}.$$

This satisfies the condition $y(1) = \frac{1}{2}$, which was used in getting $z(-1) = 0$.

103. LAURENT TRANSFORM

The series of negative powers

$$(\mathcal{N}) \qquad\qquad F_1(x) = \sum_{t=1}^{\infty} f(t)x^{-t} = \mathcal{N}\{f(t)\}$$

defines the Laurent transform* of the sequence $f(t)$. It bears a close analogy to the Laplace transform, x^{-t} corresponding to e^{-st}. If the Maclaurin transform

$$(\mathcal{M}) \qquad\qquad F(x) = \sum_{t=0}^{n} f(t)x^{t} = \mathcal{M}\{f(t)\}$$

is known, we have the connecting relation

$$(1) \qquad\qquad F_1(x) = F(x^{-1}) - f(0).$$

---

* Lawden, D. F., On the Solution of Difference Equations, *Math. Gazette* **36**, 193–196, 1952.

   Aseltine, J. A., *Transform Methods in Linear System Analysis*, Chap. 16. Aseltine's definition differs from that of Lawden in that the Laurent series includes the constant term.

For example,

$$\mathcal{N}\{k^t\} = \left(1 - \frac{k}{x}\right)^{-1} - 1 = k(x - k)^{-1}.$$

Moreover, if series $(\mathcal{M})$ converges when $|x| < R$, series $(\mathcal{N})$ will converge when $|x| > 1/R$.

A brief table of transforms is appended (Table 103) which the reader can regard as a set of problems.

Table 103 Laurent Transforms
Operations

No.	$f(t)$	$F(x) = \sum_{t=1}^{\infty} f(t)x^{-t}$
I	$f(t + n)$	$x^n\left[F(x) - \sum_{t=1}^{n} f(t)x^{-t}\right]$
	$f(t + 1)$	$xF(x) - f(1)$
	$f(t + 2)$	$x^2F(x) - xf(1) - f(2)$
II	$f(t - n)$	$x^{-n}F(x)$ if $f(t) = 0, t \leqq 0.$
III	$(t - 1)^{(n)}f(t - n)$	$(-1)^n D^n F(x)$
	$(t - 1)f(t - 1)$	$-F'(x)$
IV	$(t + n - 1)^{(n)}f(t)$	$-(1)^n x^n D^n F(x)$
	$tf(t)$	$-xF'(x)$
V	$t^n f(t)$	$(-1)^n(xD)^n F(x)$
	$t^2 f(t)$	$xF'(x) + x^2 F(x)$
VI	$\dfrac{f(t)}{t}$	$\displaystyle\int_x^{\infty} \frac{F(x)}{x}\,dx$
VII	$k^t f(t)$	$F\left(\dfrac{x}{k}\right)$
VIII	$f(t) * g(t)$	$F(x)G(x)$

		Special Functions	Convergence
1	1	$(x - 1)^{-1}$	$|x| > 1$
2	$t - 1$	$(x - 1)^{-2}$	
3	t	$x(x - 1)^{-2}$	
4	t^2	$x(x + 1)(x - 1)^{-3}$	
5	k^t	$k(x - k)^{-1}$	$|x| > k$
6	tk^t	$kx(x - k)^{-2}$	
7	$\dfrac{1}{t!}$	$e^{1/x} - 1$	all x
8	$1/t$	$\log \dfrac{x}{x - 1}$	$|x| > 1$

104. COMPLETE LAURENT TRANSFORM

The Maclaurin and Laurent series used thus far transform a sequence with the initial term, $f(0)$ or $f(1)$, respectively. A *complete sequence* ... $f(-1), f(0), f(1), \ldots$ extending indefinitely to the left and right may be transformed by the complete Laurent series

$$(\mathscr{T}) \qquad\qquad \mathscr{T}\{f(t)\} = \sum_{t=-\infty}^{\infty} f(t)x^t = F(x).$$

Here we have the simple formulas

$$(1) \qquad\qquad \mathscr{T}\{f(t+n)\} = x^{-n}F(x),$$

$$(2) \qquad\qquad \mathscr{T}\{f(t-n)\} = x^n F(x).$$

Their proof is immediate; thus if $s = t + n$,

$$\sum_{t=-\infty}^{\infty} f(t+n)x^t = \sum_{s=-\infty}^{\infty} f(s)x^{s-n} = x^{-n}F(x).$$

Moreover, on differentiating $(\mathscr{T})$ we have

$$(3) \qquad\qquad \mathscr{T}\{tf(t)\} = xF'(x).$$

We shall not pursue this matter further; but we shall use the foregoing formulas to obtain the generating function of the Bessel functions $J_t(z)$ which are defined for all integral values of z and satisfy the well-known recurrence relation

$$(4) \qquad\qquad J_{t-1}(z) + J_{t+1}(z) = \frac{2t}{z} J_t(z). \qquad\qquad (126.10)$$

If $\mathscr{T}\{J_t(z)\} = F(x, z)$, this transforms into

$$(5) \qquad\qquad (x^{-1} + x)F(x, z) = \frac{2}{z} xF'(x, z)$$

with z held constant. Thus

$$\frac{F'(x, z)}{F(x, z)} = \frac{z}{2}\left(1 + \frac{1}{x^2}\right),$$

$$\log F(x, z) = \frac{z}{2}\left(x - \frac{1}{x}\right) + \log A,$$

$$(6) \qquad\qquad F(x, z) = A \exp \frac{z}{2}\left(x - \frac{1}{x}\right).$$

Since $J_t(0) = 0$ $(t \neq 0)$, $J_0(0) = 1$, we have

$$F(x, 0) = \sum_{t=-\infty}^{\infty} J_t(0) = J_0(0) = 1 = A.$$

The generating function for the Bessel functions is therefore

(7) $$\exp \tfrac{1}{2}z(x - x^{-1}) = \sum_{t=-\infty}^{\infty} J_t(z)x^t.$$

This derivation is merely *heuristic*, for the convergence and operations performed on the Laurent series are open to question. The process of discovery (Greek *heuriskein*, to discover) employed here is as important as the *proof* of this result which will be given later (§ 132).

PROBLEMS

1. Prove the binomial theorem for factorial powers:

$$(x + a)^{(n)} = \sum_{k=0}^{n} \binom{n}{k} x^{(k)} a^{(n-k)}. \quad \text{[Use (78.13).]}$$

In the following problems show that the *Newton series* (in factorial powers) satisfies the given difference equation and converges to the function in the stated interval. In each case, first find the initial values.

2. $2^x = \sum_{k=0}^{\infty} \dfrac{x^{(k)}}{k!}$, $\qquad\qquad x > -1; \quad \Delta y = y.$

3. $2^{x-1} = \sum_{k=0}^{\infty} \dfrac{x^{(2k)}}{(2k)!}$, $\qquad\qquad x > 0; \quad \Delta^2 y = y.$

4. $2^{x-1} = \sum_{k=0}^{\infty} \dfrac{x^{(2k+1)}}{(2k + 1)!}$, $\qquad\qquad x > 0; \quad \Delta^2 y = y.$

5. $0 = \sum_{k=0}^{\infty} (-1)^k \dfrac{x^{(k)}}{k!}$, $\qquad\qquad x > 0; \quad \Delta y = -y.$

6. $2^{x/2} \cos \dfrac{\pi}{4} x = \sum_{k=0}^{\infty} (-1)^k \dfrac{x^{(2k)}}{(2k)!}$, $\qquad x > -1; \quad \Delta^2 y = -y.$

7. $2^{x/2} \sin \dfrac{\pi}{4} x = \sum_{k=0}^{\infty} (-1)^k \dfrac{x^{(2k+1)}}{(2k + 1)!}$, $\quad x > -1; \quad \Delta^2 y = -y.$

8. $\dfrac{2}{3} 3^{x/2} \cos \dfrac{\pi}{6} x = \sum_{k=0}^{\infty} (-1)^k \dfrac{x^{(3k)}}{(3k)!}$, $\qquad x > 0; \quad \Delta^3 y = -y.$

CHAPTER 10

$$\boxed{f(\vartheta)y + x^s g(\vartheta)y = 0.}$$

Solutions in Series

105. ORDINARY AND SINGULAR POINTS

We shall now find solutions of the linear equation

(1) $$y'' + P(x)y' + Q(x)y = 0$$

in the form

(2) $$y(x) = x^\lambda \sum_{n=0}^{\infty} c_n(x - a)^n,$$

where λ is a suitably chosen number called the *index* of the solution.

If $P(x)$ and $Q(x)$ are *analytic* at the point a, they may be represented by Taylor series in powers of $x - a$ which converge within the circle $|x - a| = r$, which passes through the nearest singular point of the function in question.* The point a is then called an *ordinary point* of equation (1).

However if either $P(x)$ and $Q(x)$ become infinite at a (i.e., have a *pole* at a), the equation is said to have a *singular point* at a. If the poles of $P(x)$ and $Q(x)$ are at most of the first and second orders respectively, the point a is called a *regular singular point* of the equation. Then the functions

(3) $$p(x) = (x - a)P(x), \qquad q(x) = (x - a)^2 Q(x)$$

are analytic at a and may be expanded in Taylor series. A singular point which is not regular is termed *irregular*.

A singular point at a may be brought to the origin by the change of variable $t = x - a$. It will therefore suffice to discuss series solutions of equation (1) at the origin. If the origin is an ordinary or a regular singular point, we multiply equation (1) by x^2; in view of (3) it then becomes

(4) $$x^2 y'' + p(x)xy' + q(x)y = 0.$$

---

* *Advanced Calculus*, § 207. The facts are most simply stated when x is regarded as a complex variable and the singularities of $P(x)$, $Q(x)$ are marked in the complex plane.

Now $p(x)$ and $q(x)$ are analytic at $x = 0$ and admit the Maclaurin expansions

(5)
$$p(x) = \sum_{n=0}^{\infty} p_n x^n, \qquad q(x) = \sum_{n=0}^{\infty} q_n x^n.$$

If $x = 0$ is an ordinary point, equations (3) (with $a = 0$) show that

(6)
$$p_0 = 0, \qquad q_0 = q_1 = 0.$$

To find the character of the point at infinity, make the change of independent variable $x = 1/t$; then

(7)
$$y' = \frac{dy}{dx} = \frac{dy/dt}{dx/dt} = \frac{\dot{y}}{-1/t^2} = -t^2 \dot{y},$$

(8)
$$y'' = \frac{dy'}{dx} = \frac{-t^2 \ddot{y} - 2t\dot{y}}{-1/t^2} = t^4 \ddot{y} + 2t^3 \dot{y},$$

where $\dot{y}$ and $\ddot{y}$ denote derivatives with respect to t. Since $x = \infty$ maps into $t = 0$, $x = \infty$ is said to be an ordinary or a singular point of the original equation according as $t = 0$ is an ordinary or a singular point of the transformed equation.

106. THE OPERATOR $\vartheta = xD$

In obtaining series solutions of differential equations, the calculations are simplified by using the operator

(1)
$$\vartheta = xD = x\frac{d}{dx}$$

introduced in § 43. In this article we derived the *power shift* formulas

(2)
$$f(\vartheta)x^a X = x^a f(\vartheta + a)X,$$

(3)
$$f(\vartheta)x^a = f(a)x^a.$$

Here $f(\vartheta)$ is a polynomial in ϑ; and (3) follows from (2) when we put $X = 1$ and $f(\vartheta + a) = f(a) +$ terms in powers of ϑ. We also found that D and ϑ are connected by the relation (43.5):

(4)
$$x^n D^n = \vartheta(\vartheta - 1) \cdots (\vartheta - n + 1) = \vartheta^{(n)}.$$

To reduce equations of the second order to the *theta form*, we need only the special formulas

(5)
$$xD = \vartheta, \qquad x^2 D^2 = \vartheta(\vartheta - 1).$$

Example 1. Reduce to the theta form

(i) $$x^2(1 - x)y'' - 3xy' + 2xy = 0.$$

Using equations (5) we have

$$[\vartheta(\vartheta - 1) - 3\vartheta]y - x[\vartheta(\vartheta - 1) + 2]y = 0$$

or

(ii) $$\vartheta(\vartheta - 4)y - x(\vartheta + 1)(\vartheta - 2)y = 0.$$

To make the change of variable $t = ax^m$ in an equation in theta form, we have

$$x\frac{d}{dx} = x\frac{dt}{dx}\frac{d}{dt} = x \cdot amx^{m-1}\frac{d}{dt} = mt\frac{d}{dt}.$$

Let $\dot\vartheta = t\,d/dt$; then if

(6) $$t = ax^m, \qquad \vartheta = m\dot\vartheta.$$

The substitution $x = 1/t$ is made to find solutions of a differential equation valid for large x (small t); then from (6)

(7) $$t = x^{-1}, \qquad \vartheta = -\dot\vartheta.$$

Example 2. In equation (ii), put $x = 1/t$; then

$$-\dot\vartheta(-\dot\vartheta - 4)y - \frac{1}{t}(-\dot\vartheta + 1)(-\dot\vartheta + 2)y = 0$$

(iii) $$(\dot\vartheta - 1)(\dot\vartheta - 2)y - t\dot\vartheta(\dot\vartheta + 4)y = 0.$$

Example 3. In the equation

$$\vartheta(\vartheta - 4)y - x^2(\vartheta - 1)(\vartheta - 2)y = 0,$$

make the change of variable $t = x^2$; then $\vartheta = 2\dot\vartheta$ and the equation becomes

$$2\dot\vartheta(2\dot\vartheta - 4)y - t(2\dot\vartheta - 1)(2\dot\vartheta - 2)y = 0$$

or

$$\dot\vartheta(\dot\vartheta - 2)y - t(\dot\vartheta - \tfrac{1}{2})(\dot\vartheta - 1)y = 0.$$

PROBLEMS

1. Prove directly that

$$\vartheta^n x^a = a^n x^a, \qquad f(\vartheta)x^a = f(a)x^a$$

where $f(\vartheta)$ is a polynomial in ϑ.

2. When $x = 1/t$, show that equation (i) becomes

$$t^2(t - 1)\ddot y + t(5t - 2)\dot y + 2y = 0.$$

Convert this to the ϑ-form and again obtain (iii).

3. Find all (finite or infinite) regular singular points of equation (i).

4. From $\vartheta = xD$ show that

$$(\vartheta + a)(\vartheta + b) = x^2 D^2 + (a + b + 1)xD + ab.$$

Hence transform (iii) back to (i).

5. Show that

$$\vartheta(\vartheta - 1)y - x^2(\vartheta + 1)(\vartheta + 3)y = 0$$

has the D-form

$$(1 - x^2)y'' - 5xy' - 3y = 0.$$

6. Show that the equation

$$\vartheta(\vartheta - 1)y - x^2(\vartheta - a)(\vartheta - b)y = 0$$

has an ordinary point at $x = 0$ and regular singular points at $x = \pm 1$.

107. INDICIAL EQUATION

For an ordinary or regular singular point at $x = 0$, the equation

$$\{x^2 D^2 + p(x)xD + q(x)\}y = 0$$

becomes

(1)
$$\{\vartheta(\vartheta - 1) + p(x)\vartheta + q(x)\}y = 0$$

on using equations (106.5). Here $p(x)$ and $q(x)$ are analytic at $x = 0$ and may be represented by the power series

(2)
$$p(x) = \sum_{n=0}^{\infty} p_n x^n, \qquad q(x) = \sum_{n=0}^{\infty} q_n x^n$$

that converge in some neighborhood of $x = 0$. We now attempt to satisfy (1) with a series of the form

(3)
$$y(x) = \sum_{n=0}^{\infty} c_n x^{\lambda+n}$$

when the *index* λ is suitably chosen. Substituting (3) in (1) and noting that

$$\vartheta x^{\lambda+n} = (\lambda + n)x^{\lambda+n}, \qquad \vartheta(\vartheta - 1)x^{\lambda+n} = (\lambda + n)(\lambda + n - 1)x^{\lambda+n},$$

we obtain, on dividing out x^λ,

$$\sum_{n=0}^{\infty} (\lambda + n)(\lambda + n - 1)c_n x^n + p(x)\sum_{n=0}^{\infty} (\lambda + n)c_n x^n + q(x)\sum_{n=0}^{\infty} c_n x^n = 0.$$

Here $p(x)$ and $q(x)$ must be replaced by the series in (2); the second and third terms then involve the Cauchy product (or convolution) of the sequences

$$\begin{Bmatrix} p_0 & p_1 & p_2 & , & \cdots \\ \lambda c_0 & (\lambda + 1)c_1 & (\lambda + 2)c_2, & \cdots \end{Bmatrix} \quad \text{and} \quad \begin{Bmatrix} q_0 & q_1 & q_2 & \cdots \\ c_0 & c_1 & c_2 & \cdots \end{Bmatrix}.$$

Choose $c_0 \neq 0$ at pleasure; the constant term of the series ($n = 0$) will then vanish if λ satisfies

(4) $$F(\lambda) = \lambda(\lambda - 1) + p_0\lambda + q_0 = 0.$$

The roots λ_1, λ_2 of this quadratic are the *indices* of our problem, and (4) is called the indicial equation.

Choose an index λ; then the term in x ($n = 1$) will vanish if

$$\{(\lambda + 1)\lambda + p_0(\lambda + 1) + q_0\}c_1 + (p_1\lambda + q_1)c_0 = 0,$$

or

(5) $$F(\lambda + 1)c_1 + (p_1\lambda + q_1)c_0 = 0.$$

The term in x^2 ($n = 2$) will vanish if

$$\{(\lambda + 2)(\lambda + 1) + p_0(\lambda + 2) + q_0\}c_2$$
$$+ \{p_1(\lambda + 1) + q_1\}c_1 + (p_2\lambda + q_2)c_0 = 0,$$

or

(6) $$F(\lambda + 2)c_2 + \{p_1(\lambda + 1) + q_1\}c_1 + (p_2\lambda + q_2)c_0 = 0.$$

In general, the term in x^n will vanish if

(7) $$F(\lambda + n)c_n + (*)c_{n-1} + \cdots + (*)c_1 + (*)c_0 = 0.$$

Thus (5) determines c_1 if $F(\lambda + 1) \neq 0$; then (6) determines c_2 if $F(\lambda + 2) \neq 0$; and, in general, when $c_0, c_1, \ldots, c_{n-1}$ are known, (7) determines c_n if $F(\lambda + n) \neq 0$. Thus if

(8) $$F(\lambda) = 0, \qquad F(\lambda + n) \neq 0, \qquad n = 1, 2, 3, \ldots,$$

we can choose $c_0 \neq 0$ arbitrarily (say $c_0 = 1$) and then find the coefficients $c_1, c_2, \ldots$ of the series for the index λ.

Since $F(\lambda) = 0$ only when $\lambda = \lambda_1$ or λ_2, the conditions (8) will be met for $\lambda = \lambda_1$ if $\lambda_1 \geq \lambda_2$. Thus the foregoing process always yields a solution $y_1(x)$ corresponding to the larger index. If $\lambda_1 - \lambda_2 \neq 0, 1, 2, \ldots$, this process will also yield a second solution $y_2(x)$ corresponding to the smaller index λ_2. The general solution is then $Ay_1(x) + By_2(x)$. When $\lambda_1 = \lambda_2$ there is only one solution of type (3); a second independent solution must then be sought by other means [cf. (28.7) and § 111].

Since equation (7) usually grows more complicated with increasing n, tedious calculations may be expected. Moreover, c_n for general n can only be regarded as known when c_n is expressed as a function of n. Fortunately most of the classical differential equations, which have arisen from problems in physics, have a relatively simple theta form; and for these c_n can be computed as a function of n from a *two-term recurrence relation*.

For a regular singular point the indices need not be integers, and the series (3) is a power series multiplied by x^λ. But for an *ordinary point* we have seen that $p_0 = 0, q_0 = q_1 = 0$ (105.6) and hence the indicial equation reduces to

(9) $$F(\lambda) = \lambda(\lambda - 1) = 0.$$

The indices at an ordinary point are therefore $\lambda_1 = 1, \lambda_2 = 0$ and the foregoing process always gives $y_1(x)$. Although $\lambda_1 - \lambda_2 = 1$, the process also gives $y_2(x)$; for with $\lambda = 0$, (5) assumes the form

(10) $$F(1)c_1 + q_1 c_0 = 0,$$

which is satisfied identically since $F(1) = 0$ and $q_1 = 0$. Thus we can choose $c_0 = 0$ and c_1 at pleasure and then determine the successive co-efficients seriatim. The two solutions for the ordinary point $x = 0$ are thus *power series* which converge in a circle about the origin, passing through the nearest singular point (real or complex) of the differential equation. The circle of convergence, however, *may* pass through a more remote singular point and even include the entire finite plane.

A nonlogarithmic solution at a regular singular point has the form x^λ times a power series, and this series will still converge in a circle about the origin with a radius extending at least to the nearest singular point of the equation. Of course if $\lambda < 0$, the factor x^λ will make the solution become infinite at the origin; but the power series multiplied by x^λ will still converge in the circle punctured at the origin.

For a regular singular point at $x = 0$ the indicial equation will be $\lambda(\lambda - 1) = 0$, provided $p_0 = q_0 = 0$; but now $q_1 \neq 0$ since $q(x)$ cannot have a double zero at the origin if it is a singular point. Then equation (10) cannot be solved for c_1, and we shall see that the solution for the smaller index involves $\log x$.

108. EQUATIONS WITH TWO-TERM RECURRENCE RELATION

Many important classical differential equations, such as the hypergeometric, confluent hypergeometric, and the equations of Legendre, Bessel, Hermite, Laguerre, and Chebyshev assume the simple theta form

(1) $$f(\vartheta)y + x^s g(\vartheta)y = 0$$

where $f(\vartheta)$ and $g(\vartheta)$ are polynomials whose degree does not exceed 2 and s is a positive integer. The reduction to the form (1) is made by using the formulas

$$xD = \vartheta, \qquad x^2 D^2 = \vartheta(\vartheta - 1).$$

The form (1) has five merits:

1. The *indicial equation* for the point $x = 0$ is

(2)
$$f(\lambda) = 0.$$

2. The *skip number* by which the powers in the solution series advance is s. Thus if λ is a root of (2), the corresponding solution has the form

(3)
$$y(x) = x^\lambda \sum_{n=0}^{\infty} c_n x^{sn} = \sum_{n=0}^{\infty} c_n x^{\lambda+sn}.$$

3. The *two-term recurrence relation* for the coefficients c_n may be written down at once; see equation (6) below.

4. The recurrence relation gives the ratio c_{n+1}/c_n whose limiting value determines the convergence interval of the power series $\Sigma\, c_n x^{sn}$.

5. The transformation $x = 1/t$, $\vartheta = -\dot\vartheta$ gives the equation

(4)
$$g(-\vartheta)y + t^s f(-\vartheta)y = 0,$$

which yields solutions about $t = 0$ $(x = \infty)$ having indices given by the roots of

(5)
$$g(-\lambda) = 0,$$

and which are valid for large x.

To obtain the solution corresponding to an index λ, substitute the series (3) in equation (1). Using the power shift

$$f(\vartheta)x^a = f(a)x^a, \tag{106.3}$$

we obtain

$$\sum_{n=0}^{\infty} f(\lambda + sn)c_n x^{\lambda+sn} + \sum_{n=0}^{\infty} g(\lambda + sn)c_n x^{\lambda+sn+s} = 0.$$

The first sum for $n = 0$ gives the constant term $f(\lambda)c_0 x^\lambda$; to make this vanish choose λ as a root of equation (2). The first sum now starts with $n = 1$. If we put $m = n + 1$ in the second sum, it becomes

$$\sum_{m=1}^{\infty} g(\lambda + sm - s)c_{m-1} x^{\lambda+sm}.$$

Since any letter may be used as summation variable, replace m by n. Then both series may be combined; and after canceling x^λ we have

$$\sum_{n=1}^{\infty} \{f(\lambda + sn)c_n + g(\lambda + sn - s)c_{n-1}\}x^{sn} = 0.$$

In order that this power series vanish identically in some interval about $x = 0$, the coefficients of x^{sn} must vanish for $n = 1, 2, 3, \ldots$. We thus obtain the two-term recurrence relation

$$(6) \qquad f(\lambda + sn)c_n + g(\lambda + sn - s)c_{n-1} = 0, \qquad n \geq 1.$$

Choose c_0 arbitrarily and use (6) to compute $c_1, c_2, \ldots$ in turn. This can certainly be done for the index $\lambda_1 \geq \lambda_2$, because then $f(sn + \lambda_1) \neq 0$ for $n \geq 1$. Indeed we can find a *formula* for c_n by solving the difference equation (6).

If $\lambda_1 = \lambda_2$, there is only one series solution of the form (3). A second solution involving $\log x$ can then be obtained (cf. § 111).

If $\lambda_1 - \lambda_2 = ms$ (a multiple of s), the calculation of c_m for the smaller index λ_2 may fail; for $f(sm + \lambda_2) = f(\lambda_1) = 0$, and unless the second term in (6) is also zero, this equation cannot be satisfied. Here a second solution will again involve $\log x$ (cf. § 112). But if equation (6) is satisfied identically when $n = m$, a solution of form (3) for the smaller index can be found. This is always the case if $x = 0$ is an ordinary point of the differential equation (§ 107).

The power series $\Sigma\, c_n x^{sn}$ in (3) will converge in a circle about $x = 0$ in the complex plane passing through the nearest singular point of the differential equation, and this circle will cut off an interval about $x = 0$ on the axis of reals. The convergence interval, however, may be larger; its exact length may be found by applying the ratio test.* Using (5) we have

$$\left| \frac{c_n x^{sn}}{c_{n-1} x^{sn-s}} \right| = \left| \frac{c_n}{c_{n-1}} \right| |x|^s = \left| \frac{g(\lambda + sn - s)}{f(\lambda + sn)} \right| |x|^s.$$

The series will converge when the limit of this ratio < 1, that is, when

$$|x|^s < \lim_{n \to \infty} \left| \frac{f(\lambda + sn)}{g(\lambda + sn - s)} \right|.$$

Since the numerator and denominator are polynomials in n, this limit is ∞ or 0 according as the degree of f is greater or less than the degree of g. But if f and g are of the same degree, say $f(n) = an^2 + \cdots$, $g(n) = bn^2 + \cdots$, the limit is $|a/b|$. Therefore, the series for the index λ:

Converges absolutely for all x if $\deg f > \deg g$,

Converges absolutely for $|x| < \sqrt[s]{|a/b|}$ if $\deg f = \deg g$,

Diverges for all $x \neq 0$ if $\deg f < \deg g$.

When $x = \pm \sqrt[s]{|a/b|}$, the convergence must be determined by more refined tests. Owing to the factor x^λ the series, (3) will not exist at $x = 0$ if $\lambda < 0$.

---

* *Advanced Calculus*, § 29.

Finally, to obtain solutions of equation (1) valid for large x, put $x = 1/t$, $\vartheta = -\dot\vartheta$ (106.7); then

(4) $$g(-\dot\vartheta)y + t^s f(-\dot\vartheta)y = 0.$$

This shows that the indicial equation for $t = 0$ $(x = \infty)$ is $g(-\lambda) = 0$.

Example 1. $y'' - y = 0$.
The point $x = 0$ is ordinary. Multiply by x^2 to get

(i) $$\vartheta(\vartheta - 1)y - x^2 y = 0.$$

The indicial equation is $\lambda(\lambda - 1) = 0$ and the indices $\lambda_1 = 1$, $\lambda_2 = 0$. The skip number $s = 2$ and $\lambda_1 - \lambda_2$ is not a multiple of s. Therefore, to each index there corresponds a solution in power series. Thus for

$$\lambda_2 = 0: \qquad y_2 = \sum_{n=0}^{\infty} c_n x^{2n}.$$

Since $f(\lambda) = \lambda(\lambda - 1)$, $g(\lambda) = -1$, the recurrence relation (6)

$$f(2n)c_n - g(2n - 2)c_{n-1} = 0$$

becomes

$$2n(2n - 1)c_n = c_{n-1}.$$

Thus $$(2n - 2)(2n - 3)c_{n-1} = c_{n-2},$$

$$\begin{matrix} \cdot & \cdot & \cdot & \cdot \\ \cdot & \cdot & \cdot & \cdot \\ \cdot & \cdot & \cdot & \cdot \end{matrix}$$

$$(2) \qquad (1) \qquad c_1 \; = c_0.$$

Multiply the n equations together; then

$$(2n)!c_n = c_0,$$

and if $c_0 = 1$, we have

$$y_2 = \sum_{n=0}^{\infty} \frac{x^{2n}}{(2n)!} = \cosh x.$$

For the index

$$\lambda_1 = 1, \qquad y_1 = \sum_{n=0}^{\infty} c_n x^{2n+1},$$

we have the recurrence relation

$$(2n + 1)(2n)c_n = c_0;$$

and we find

$$(2n + 1)! \, c_n = c_0 = 1,$$

$$y_1 = \sum_{n=0}^{\infty} \frac{x^{2n+1}}{(2n + 1)!} = \sinh x.$$

The equation has no finite singular points; and the series converge for all x.

Example 2. $x^2 y'' + x(x + 1)y' - y = 0$.
The only finite singularity is a regular singular point at $x = 0$. The theta form

(ii) $$(\vartheta^2 - 1)y + x\vartheta y = 0$$

gives the indicial equation $\lambda^2 - 1 = 0$ and the skip number $s = 1$. The indices are $\lambda_1 = 1$, $\lambda_2 = -1$ and $\lambda_1 - \lambda_2 = 2$ is a multiple of s. Nevertheless the corresponding solutions y_1 and y_2 are power series multiplied by x and x^{-1}, respectively. This is the expected behavior for $\lambda_1 = 1$.

Consider, now, the smaller index

$$\lambda_2 = -1: \qquad y_2 = \sum_{n=0}^{\infty} c_n x^{n-1}.$$

Since $f(\lambda) = \lambda^2 - 1$, $g(\lambda) = \lambda$, the recurrence relation (6)

$$f(n-1)c_n + g(n-2)c_{n-1} = 0,$$

becomes

$$n(n-2)c_n + (n-2)c_{n-1} = 0.$$

With $c_0 = 1$ we have

$$-c_1 - c_0 = 0, \qquad c_1 = -1$$
$$0c_2 + 0 = 0, \qquad c_2 \text{ is arbitrary.}$$

If we take $c_2 = 0$ we have the solution

$$y_2 = c_0 x^{-1} + c_1 = 1 - \frac{1}{x} = \frac{x-1}{x}.$$

If we cancel $n - 2$ in the recurrence relation, $nc_n + c_{n-1} = 0$. If we choose $c_0 = 1$, $c_1 = -1$, $c_2 = \frac{1}{2}$ to satisfy this relation, we find $c_n = (-1)^n/n!$ and get the second solution

$$\tilde{y}_2 = \sum_{n=0}^{\infty} (-1)^n \frac{x^{n-1}}{n!} = \frac{e^{-x}}{x}$$

for $\lambda_2 = -1$. Since y_2 and $\tilde{y}_2$ are linearly independent, the general solution of (ii) is $y = x^{-1}\{A(1 - x) + Be^{-x}\}$.

For $\lambda_1 = 1$, the usual procedure gives the solution

$$y_1 = \frac{1}{x}(e^{-x} - x + 1) = \tilde{y}_2 - y_2.$$

Example 3. $xy'' - y = 0$.

The only finite singularity is a regular singular point at $x = 0$. Multiply by x to get the theta form:

(iii) $$\vartheta(\vartheta - 1)y - xy = 0.$$

The indicial equation is $\lambda(\lambda - 1) = 0$ and the skip number $s = 1$. The indices are $\lambda_1 = 1$, $\lambda_2 = 0$ and $\lambda_1 - \lambda_2 = 1$ is a multiple of s.

For the larger index

$$\lambda_1 = 1, \qquad y_1 = \sum_{n=0}^{\infty} c_n x^{n+1}.$$

Since $f(\lambda) = \lambda(\lambda - 1)$, $g(\lambda) = -1$, the recurrence relation (6)

$$f(n+1)c_n - c_{n-1} = 0$$

becomes

$$(n+1)nc_n = c_{n-1}.$$

Thus
$$n(n - 1)c_{n-1} = c_{n-2}$$
$$\cdot \qquad \cdot$$
$$\cdot \qquad \cdot$$
$$\cdot \qquad \cdot$$
$$1 \cdot 2 \qquad c_1 = c_0.$$

Multiply these $n + 1$ equations together; then

$$(n + 1)!\,n!\,c_n = c_0.$$

Thus if $c_0 = 1$, we have the solution

$$y_1 = \sum_{n=0}^{\infty} \frac{x^{n+1}}{(n + 1)!\,n!}.$$

For the smaller index

$$\lambda_2 = 0, \qquad y_2 = \sum_{n=0}^{\infty} c_n x^n, \qquad c_0 \neq 0.$$

The recurrence relation is now

$$f(n)c_n - c_{n-1} = 0$$

or

$$n(n - 1)c_n = c_{n-1}.$$

For $n = 1$ this gives the contradiction $1 \cdot 0\, c_1 = c_0$. The assumption of a second-power series solution for $\lambda_2 = 0$ is therefore untenable. We shall see in Exercise 112.1 that a second solution, independent of y_1, involves $\log x$.

109. ORDINARY POINTS

We have shown (§ 107) that both solutions for an ordinary point at $x = 0$ are power series with indices $\lambda_1 = 1$, $\lambda_2 = 0$. If we regard x as a complex variable, the series converge in a circle about $x = 0$ passing through the nearest singular point of the equation. The series, however, may converge in a larger circle or even in the entire plane.

Example. $(1 - x^2)y'' - 6xy' - 4y = 0$.
This equation has regular singular points at ± 1 and no others in the finite plane. The origin is an ordinary point. The theta form

(i) $\vartheta(\vartheta - 1)y - x^2(\vartheta + 1)(\vartheta + 4) = 0$

gives the indicial equation $\lambda(\lambda - 1) = 0$ and the skip number $s = 2$.

$$\lambda_2 = 0: \qquad y_2 = \sum_{n=0}^{\infty} c_n x^{2n}.$$

Since $f(\lambda) = \lambda(\lambda - 1)$, $g(\lambda) = -(\lambda + 1)(\lambda + 4)$, the recurrence relation (108.6)

$$f(2n)c_n + g(2n - 2)c_{n-1} = 0$$

becomes

$$2n(2n - 1)c_n = (2n - 1)(2n + 2)c_{n-1}$$

or on canceling $2(2n - 1) \neq 0$, we have

$$nc_n = (n + 1)c_{n-1}.$$

Thus
$$(n - 1)c_{n-1} = nc_{n-2}$$

$$
\begin{array}{cc}
\cdot & \cdot \\
\cdot & \cdot \\
\cdot & \cdot
\end{array}
$$

$$2c_2 = 3c_1$$
$$1c_2 = 2c_0,$$

and on multiplying these n equations together, we find after cancellation

$$c_n = (n + 1)c_0.$$

With $c_0 = 1$ this gives the series solution

$$y_2 = \sum_{n=0}^{\infty} (n + 1)x^{2n} = (1 - x^2)^{-2}.$$

This value is obtained by differentiating the geometric series

$$(1 - x)^{-1} = \sum_{n=0}^{\infty} x^n, \qquad |x| < 1:$$

$$(1 - x)^{-2} = \sum_{n=1}^{\infty} nx^{n-1} = \sum_{n=0}^{\infty} (n + 1)x^n,$$

and replacing x by x^2. Of course a simple closed form such as this is not, in general, available.

$$\lambda_1 = 1: \qquad y_1 = \sum_{n=0}^{\infty} c_n x^{2n+1}.$$

The recurrence relation

$$f(2n + 1)c_n + g(2n - 1)c_{n-1} = 0$$

now becomes

$$(2n + 1)(2n)c_n = (2n)(2n + 3)c_{n-1},$$

or on canceling $2n$,

$$(2n + 1)c_n = (2n + 3)c_{n-1}, \qquad n > 0.$$

Thus
$$(2n - 1)c_{n-1} = (2n + 1)c_{n-2}$$

$$
\begin{array}{cc}
\cdot & \cdot \\
\cdot & \cdot \\
\cdot & \cdot
\end{array}
$$

$$5c_2 = 7c_1$$
$$3c_1 = 5c_0.$$

On multiplying these equations together we find that everything cancels except $3c_n$ on the left and $(2n + 3)c_0$ on the right. Thus taking $c_0 = 3$ we have $c_n = 2n + 3$ and

$$y_1 = \sum_{n=0}^{\infty} (2n + 3)x^{2n+1} = 2x \sum_{n=0}^{\infty} (n + 1)x^{2n} + x \sum_{n=0}^{\infty} x^{2n}$$

or
$$y_1 = 2x(1 - x^2)^{-2} + x(1 - x^2)^{-1} = (3x - x^3)(1 - x^2)^{-2}.$$

The series for y_1 and y_2 both converge in the interval $|x| < 1$ of the real axis cut off by the unit circle about the origin and passing through the singular points ± 1 of the equation.

PROBLEMS

Reduce to the theta form and find solutions for each index.

1. $y'' - xy = 0$.   **2.** $(x^2 - 1)y'' - xy' + y = 0$.
3. $y'' + xy' + 3y = 0$.   **4.** $(1 + x^2)y'' + 2xy' - 2y = 0$.
5. $y'' + 2xy' - 8y = 0$.   **6.** $y'' + x^2y' - 4xy = 0$.
7. $y'' + 3xy' + 3y = 0$.   **8.** $y'' + xy' + y = 0$.
9. $y'' - 2xy' + 6y = 0$.   **10.** $(1 - x^2)y'' - 5xy' - 3y = 0$.
11. $y'' - xy' - ay = 0$.   **12.** $y''' + x^2y'' + 5xy' + 3y = 0$.
13. $y' - xy = 1$, $y(0) = 0$.

[Differentiate to obtain $y'' - xy' - y = 0$, reduce to the theta form, and obtain the solution of index 1 since $y(0) = 0$. From the given equation $y'(0) = 1$, $c_0 = 1$.]

110. REGULAR SINGULAR POINTS

Let $x = 0$ be a regular singular point with indices λ_1 and λ_2, where $\lambda_1 \geqq \lambda_2$. The solutions for λ_1 will be x^{λ_1} times a power series, and the power series will at least converge in a circle with the origin as center and passing through the nearest of the other singularities of the equation.

If $\lambda_1 - \lambda_2$ is not a multiple of the skip number s, the solution for the index λ_2 will be x^{λ_2} times a power series. This power series will also converge in a circle about the origin through the nearest singularity. If, however, $\lambda_2 = \lambda_1$, the second solution will involve $\log x$; and if $\lambda_1 - \lambda_2 = ms$, the second solution will also involve $\log x$ unless the recurrence relation is identically satisfied when $n = m$. This nonlogarithmic case is illustrated in Example 2.

Example 1. $xy'' + (\frac{1}{2} - x)y' - \frac{1}{2}y = 0$.

The only finite singularity $x = 0$ is regular. Multiply the equation by x to get the theta form

(i) $$\vartheta(\vartheta - \tfrac{1}{2})y - x(\vartheta + \tfrac{1}{2})y = 0.$$

The indicial equation $\lambda(\lambda - \frac{1}{2}) = 0$ gives the indices $\lambda_1 = \frac{1}{2}$ $\lambda_2 = 0$ and their difference is not a multiple of the skip number $s = 1$. The solution y_2 is a power series, whereas y_1 is a power series multiplied by $x^{1/2}$.

$$\lambda_2 = 0: \qquad y_2 = \sum_{n=0}^{\infty} c_n x^n.$$

This gives the recurrence relation

$$n(n - \tfrac{1}{2})c_n - (n - \tfrac{1}{2})c_{n-1} = 0$$

or

$$nc_n = c_{n-1}.$$

With $c_0 = 1$ we have $c_n = 1/n!$ and

$$y_2 = \sum_{n=0}^{\infty} \frac{x^n}{n!} = e^x$$

$$\lambda_1 = \tfrac{1}{2}: \qquad y_1 = \sum_{n=0}^{\infty} c_n x^{n+\frac{1}{2}}.$$

The recurrence relation is now

$$(n + \tfrac{1}{2})nc_n - nc_{n-1} = 0, \qquad n > 0,$$

or

$$(2n + 1)c_n = 2c_{n-1}.$$

Thus

$$(2n - 1)c_{n-1} = 2c_{n-2}$$

$$\cdots \cdots$$

$$5c_2 = 2c_1$$

$$3c_1 = 2c_0.$$

On multiplying these equations, we find with $c_0 = 1$,

$$3 \cdot 5 \cdots (2n + 1)c_n = 2^n \qquad c_n = \frac{2^n}{(2n + 1)!!}$$

where $(2n + 1)!!$ denotes the product of all *odd* numbers from 1 to $2n + 1$.*
The corresponding solution

$$y_1 = x^{\frac{1}{2}} \sum_{n=0}^{\infty} \frac{2^n}{(2n)!!} x^n.$$

As expected, the series for y_1 and y_2 converge for all values of x.

Example 2. $x(1 - x)y'' - 3y' + 2y = 0.$
Both $x = 0$ and $x = 1$ are regular singularities. Multiply the equation by x to get the theta form

(ii) $$\vartheta(\vartheta - 4)y - x(\vartheta - 2)(\vartheta + 1)y = 0.$$

Thus $f(\lambda) = \lambda(\lambda - 4)$, $g(\lambda) = -(\lambda - 2)(\lambda + 1)$; the indices $\lambda_1 = 4$, $\lambda_2 = 0$, and $s = 1$. Since $\lambda_1 - \lambda_2$ is a multiple of s, a solution with $\log x$ may occur.

$$\lambda_1 = 4: \qquad y_1 = \sum_{n=0}^{\infty} c_n x^{n+4}.$$

The recurrence relation (108.6)

$$f(n + 4)c_n + g(n + 3)c_{n-1} = 0$$

becomes

$$(n + 4)nc_n - (n + 1)(n + 4)c_{n-1} = 0$$

or

$$nc_n = (n + 1)c_{n-1}.$$

---

* Similarly, $(2n)!!$ denotes the product of all *even* numbers from 2 to $2n$.

With $c_0 = 1$ we have $c_n = n + 1$ and

$$y_1 = x^4 \sum_{n=0}^{\infty} (n + 1)x^n = x^4(1 - x)^{-2} \qquad \text{(Ex. 109)}.$$

$$\lambda_2 = 0: \qquad y_2 = \sum_{n=0}^{\infty} c_n x^n.$$

The recurrence relation

$$f(n)c_n + g(n - 1)c_{n-1} = 0$$

becomes

$$n(n - 4)c_n - (n - 3)nc_{n-1} = 0$$

or

$$(n - 4)c_n = (n - 3)c_{n-1}, \qquad n > 0.$$

We have

$$3c_1 = 2c_0, \qquad 2c_2 = c_1, \qquad c_3 = 0, \qquad 0 \cdot c_4 = 0,$$

so that c_4 is arbitrary.

If we take $c_4 = 0$, $c_n = 0$ $(n > 2)$; and if $c_0 = 3$, then $c_1 = 2$, $c_2 = 1$ and the corresponding solution is

$$y_2 = 3 + 2x + x^2.$$

If we take $c_4 = 1$, we have

$$c_5 = 2, \qquad c_6 = 3, \quad \text{and} \quad c_n = n - 3 \qquad (n > 3).$$

The corresponding solution is now

$$\tilde{y}_2 = 3 + 2x + x^2 + \sum_{n=4}^{\infty} (n - 3)x^n$$

$$= y_2 + \sum_{m=0}^{\infty} (m + 1)x^{m+4} \qquad (n = m + 4).$$

Thus $\tilde{y}_2 = y_2 + y_1$ is included in the general solution $y = Ay_1 + By_2$.

Note that both y_1 and y_2 could have been found from the smaller index $\lambda_2 = 0$. Although the series for y_1 converges within a unit circle about the origin (passing through the singular point $x = 1$), the solution y_2 is valid for all x.

PROBLEMS

Reduce to the theta form and find solutions for each index.

1. $x^2y'' - xy' - 4x^4y = 0$.

2. $2xy'' + y' + y = 0$.

3. $xy'' + 2y' - xy = 0$.

4. $x^2y'' - 2xy' + (2 + x^2)y = 0$.

5. $xy'' + (x^2 - 3)y' - 2xy = 0$.

6. $x^2y'' + x(1 + x)y' - y = 0$.

7. Show that the general solution of Problem 6 is $y = \dfrac{1}{x}[Ae^{-x} + B(1 - x)]$. Find that solution for which $y(1) = 0$, $y'(1) = 1$.

8. $x^2(1 - x)y'' + 2x(2 - x)y' + 2(1 + x)y = 0$.

9. $xy'' - y' - 4x^3y = 0$. Find a solution not identically zero for which $y(0) = y'(0) = 0$. Explain. (Cf. the existence theorem of § 26.)

111. EQUAL INDICES

When the equation

(1) $$L(y) = \{f(\vartheta) + x^s g(\vartheta)\}y = 0*$$

has equal indices λ_1 at $x = 0$, λ_1 is a double root of $f(\lambda) = 0$ and

(2) $$f(\lambda_1) = 0, \qquad f'(\lambda_1) = 0.$$

One solution $y_1(x)$ may be found in the usual manner. To find a second, let

(3) $$y(x, \lambda) = \sum_{n=0}^{\infty} c_n(\lambda) x^{\lambda+sn}$$

where λ is a variable parameter. If we substitute (3) in the equation (1), we have

(4) $$L(y) = \sum_{n=0}^{\infty} \{c_n f(\lambda + sn) x^{\lambda+sn} + c_n g(\lambda + sn) x^{\lambda+sn+s}\}$$

$$= c_0 f(\lambda) x^\lambda + \sum_{n=1}^{\infty} \{c_n f(\lambda + sn) + c_{n-1} g(\lambda + sn - s)\} x^{\lambda+sn}.$$

Now choose $c_0 = 1$ and let $c_n(\lambda)$ be a solution of the recurrence relation

$$c_n f(\lambda + sn) + c_{n-1} g(\lambda + sn - s) = 0.$$

Then from (3) we have

(5) $$L\{y(x, \lambda)\} = c_0 f(\lambda) x^\lambda, \qquad c_0 = 1.$$

Differentiate this relation with respect to λ: then

(6) $$L\left\{\frac{\partial y}{\partial \lambda}\right\} = f(\lambda) x^\lambda \log x + f'(\lambda) x^\lambda.$$

From equations (2) the right members of both (5) and (6) vanish when $\lambda = \lambda_1$. Thus a first solution of (1) is given by

(7) $$y_1 = y(x, \lambda_1) = \sum_{n=0}^{\infty} c_n(\lambda_1) x^{\lambda_1+sn}.$$

To obtain a second, differentiate (3) with respect to λ and then put $\lambda = \lambda_1$:

$$\frac{\partial y}{\partial \lambda} = \sum_{n=0}^{\infty} \{c_n(\lambda) x^{\lambda+sn} \log x + c_n'(\lambda) x^{\lambda+sn}\},$$

(8) $$y_2 = y_1 \log x + \sum_{n=1}^{\infty} c_n'(\lambda_1) x^{\lambda_1+sn}$$

where $c_0'(\lambda_1) = 0$ since $c_0 = 1$.

---

* L denotes the linear operator in braces.

The general solution is $y = Ay_1 + By_2$.

In writing the logarithmic solution the notation

$$(9) \qquad \Omega_n = 1 + \frac{1}{2} + \frac{1}{3} + \cdots + \frac{1}{n}$$

for the sum of n terms of the harmonic series is often convenient; then $\Omega_1 = 1$ and by convention $\Omega_0 = 0$.

Example 1. Bessel's Equation of Order Zero.

$$xy'' + y' + xy = 0 \quad \text{or} \quad \vartheta^2 y + x^2 y = 0.$$

Assume

$$y(\lambda) = \sum_{n=0}^{\infty} c_n(\lambda) x^{\lambda + 2n}, \qquad c_0 = 1.$$

The recurrence relation is then

$$(\lambda + 2n)^2 c_n = -c_{n-1}$$

$$\cdot$$
$$\cdot$$
$$\cdot$$

$$(\lambda + 4)^2 c_2 = -c_1$$

$$(\lambda + 2)^2 c_1 = -1;$$

and on multiplying these equations together

$$c_n(\lambda) = \frac{(-1)^n}{(\lambda + 2)^2 (\lambda + 4)^2 \cdots (\lambda + 2n)^2}, \qquad n > 0.$$

By logarithmic differentiation,

$$\frac{c_n'(\lambda)}{c_n(\lambda)} = -\frac{2}{\lambda + 2} - \frac{2}{\lambda + 4} - \cdots - \frac{2}{\lambda + 2n};$$

hence

$$c_n(0) = \frac{(-1)^n}{2^2 4^2 \cdots (2n)^2} = \frac{(-1)^n}{2^{2n}(n!)^2},$$

$$\frac{c_n'(0)}{c_n(0)} = -\left(1 + \frac{1}{2} + \cdots + \frac{1}{n}\right) = -\Omega_n,$$

$$c_n'(0) = -(-1)^n \frac{\Omega_n}{2^{2n}(n!)^2}, \qquad n > 0.$$

$$y_1 = y(0) = \sum_{n=0}^{\infty} \frac{(-1)^n}{2^{2n}(n!)^2} x^{2n} = J_0(x),$$

$$y_2 = y_1 \log x - \sum_{n=1}^{\infty} \frac{(-1)^n \Omega_n}{2^{2n}(n!)^2} x^{2n} = K_0(x) \qquad \text{from (8).}$$

The notation $J_0(x)$ is standard for the power series solution; $K_0(x)$ is an independent second solution. The general solution of Bessel's equation of order zero is

$$y = AJ_0(x) + BK_0(x)$$

but Neumann's logarithmic solution denoted by $Y_0(x)$ (§ 125) is commonly used instead of $K_0(x)$.

Example 2. $x(x - 1)y'' + (2x - 1)y' - 2y = 0.$
Multiply by x to obtain the theta form

$$\vartheta^2 y - x(\vartheta - 1)(\vartheta + 2)y = 0.$$

The equation has equal indices 0, 0 at $x = 0$. Assume

$$y = \sum_{n=0}^{\infty} c_n x^{\lambda+n}, \qquad c_0 = 1.$$

The recurrence relation is then

$$(\lambda + n)^2 c_n = (\lambda + n - 2)(\lambda + n + 1)c_{n-1}$$
$$(\lambda + n - 1)^2 c_{n-1} = (\lambda + n - 3)(\lambda + n)c_{n-2}$$
$$(\lambda + n - 2)^2 c_{n-2} = (\lambda + n - 4)(\lambda + n - 1)c_{n-3}$$
$$\cdots\cdots\cdots\cdots\cdots\cdots\cdots\cdots\cdots\cdots\cdots$$
$$(\lambda + 4)^2 c_4 = (\lambda + 2)(\lambda + 5)c_3$$
$$(\lambda + 3)^2 c_3 = (\lambda + 1)(\lambda + 4)c_2$$
$$(\lambda + 2)^2 c_2 = \lambda(\lambda + 3)c_1$$
$$(\lambda + 1)^2 c_1 = (\lambda - 1)(\lambda + 2)c_0.$$

With $c_0 = 1$, the last equation gives

$$c_1(\lambda) = \frac{(\lambda - 1)(\lambda + 2)}{(\lambda + 1)^2}.$$

On multiplying all n equations together, some terms in the first two and last two equations survive; these give

$$c_n(\lambda) = \frac{(\lambda + n + 1)\lambda(\lambda - 1)}{(\lambda + n)(\lambda + n - 1)(\lambda + 1)}, \qquad n > 1.$$

Logarithmic differentiation now gives

$$\frac{c_1'(\lambda)}{c_1(\lambda)} = \frac{1}{\lambda - 1} + \frac{1}{\lambda + 2} - \frac{2}{\lambda + 1}$$

$$\frac{c_n'(\lambda)}{c_n(\lambda)} = \frac{1}{\lambda + n + 1} + \frac{1}{\lambda} + \frac{1}{\lambda - 1} - \frac{1}{\lambda + n} - \frac{1}{\lambda + n - 1} - \frac{1}{\lambda + 1}.$$

Multiply by $c_n(\lambda)$ and then let $\lambda \to 0$:

$$c_1'(0) = c_1(0)(-1 + \tfrac{1}{2} - 2) = -2(-\tfrac{5}{2}) = 5$$

$$c_n'(0) = \lim_{\lambda \to 0} \frac{(\lambda + n + 1)(\lambda - 1)}{(\lambda + n)(\lambda + n - 1)(\lambda + 1)} = -\frac{n + 1}{n(n - 1)}, \qquad n > 1.$$

When $\lambda = 0$ we have $c_0 = 1$, $c_1 = -2$ and $c_n = 0$ ($n > 1$); thus one solution is

$$y_1 = 1 - 2x.$$

From (6) we obtain the second solution:

$$y_2 = y_1 \log x + \sum_{n=1}^{\infty} c_n{'}(0)x^n$$

$$= (1 - 2x) \log x + 5x - \sum_{n=2}^{\infty} \frac{n+1}{n(n-1)} x^n.$$

We can confirm this solution by putting $u = 1 - 2x$ in the formula (28.8) for a second solution v. Since

$$P = \frac{1 - 2x}{x(1 - x)} = \frac{1}{x} - \frac{1}{1 - x}, \qquad \int P\, dx = \log x(1 - x),$$

$$v = (1 - 2x) \int \frac{dx}{x(1 - x)(1 - 2x)^2}$$

$$= (1 - 2x) \int \left\{ \frac{-1}{1 - x} - \frac{1}{x} - \frac{4}{(1 - 2x)^2} \right\} dx$$

$$= (1 - 2x)\{\log (1 - x) - \log x\} - 2.$$

Now the solution

$$-2u - v = (1 - 2x) \log x + 4x - (1 - 2x) \log (1 - x)$$

proves to be the same as y_2; for the series in y_2 is

$$\sum_{n=2}^{\infty} \left(\frac{2}{n+1} - \frac{1}{n} \right) x^n = x + (1 - 2x) \log (1 - x).$$

PROBLEMS

Obtain the solutions given for the following equations.

1. $xy'' + (1 + x)y' + y = 0$.

$$y_1 = e^{-x}, \qquad y_2 = e^{-x} \log x - \sum_{n=1}^{\infty} \frac{\Omega_n}{n!} x^n. \qquad \left[\Omega_n = 1 + \frac{1}{2} + \cdots \frac{1}{n} \right].$$

2. $x(1 - x)y'' + (1 - 5x)y' - 4y = 0$.

$$y_1 = \sum_{n=0}^{\infty} (n + 1)^2 x^n, \qquad y_2 = y_1 \log x - 2 \sum_{n=1}^{\infty} n(n + 1)x^n.$$

3. $x^2 y'' + x(x - 1)y' + (1 - x)y = 0$.

$$y_1 = x; \qquad y_2 = x \log x + \sum_{n=1}^{\infty} \frac{(-1)^n}{nn!} x^{n+1}.$$

4. $xy'' + (1 - x)y' - y = 0$.

$$y_1 = e^x, \qquad y_2 = e^x \log x - \sum_{n=1}^{\infty} \frac{\Omega_n}{n!} x^n.$$

112. UNEQUAL INDICES: LOGARITHMIC CASE

When the equation

(1) $$L(y) = \{f(\vartheta) + x^s g(\vartheta)\}y = 0$$

has indices that differ by an integral multiple of s, say

$$\lambda_1 = \lambda_2 + sm, \qquad m \text{ a positive integer,}$$

the solution y_1 for the larger index λ_1 is found as before. The solution for smaller index λ_2 depends on the character of the equation for c_m

(2) $$f(\lambda + sm)c_m + g(\lambda + sm - s)c_{m-1} = 0,$$

when $\lambda = \lambda_2$. Since $f(\lambda_2 + sm) = f(\lambda_1) = 0$, the equation cannot be satisfied unless the second term is also zero; and then c_m is arbitrary (Ex. 108.2). When the second term is not zero, we shall see that a second solution independent of $y_1(x)$ will contain $\log x$.

As before, we put

(3) $$y(x, \lambda) = \sum_{n=0}^{\infty} c_n(\lambda)x^{\lambda + sn},$$

where λ is a variable parameter, but now choose

$$c_0 = \lambda - \lambda_2.$$

Then it is clear from the recurrence relation that $c_1, c_2, \ldots, c_{m-1}$ all have $\lambda - \lambda_2$ as a factor. Since we can take $f(\lambda) = (\lambda - \lambda_1)(\lambda - \lambda_2)$, we have

$$f(\lambda + sm) = (\lambda - \lambda_2)(\lambda + sm - \lambda_2).$$

Hence in equation (2) both $f(\lambda + sm)$ and c_{m-1} have $\lambda - \lambda_2$ as a factor; and when this factor is divided out, c_m can be determined as a function of λ. Then $c_{m+1}, c_{m+2}, \ldots$ are found as usual and we obtain a sequence starting with $c_0 = \lambda - \lambda_2$ which satisfies the recurrence relation *for an arbitrary* λ.

If we now substitute the series (3) with these values of $c_n(\lambda)$ into equation (1), only the first term ($n = 0$) survives, and as in the preceding article

(4) $$L\{y(x, \lambda)\} = c_0 f(\lambda)x^\lambda, \qquad c_0 = \lambda - \lambda_2.$$

Differentiate this relation with respect to λ: then, since $c_0' = 1$,

(5) $$L\left\{\frac{\partial y}{\partial \lambda}\right\} = f(\lambda)x^\lambda + c_0 f'(\lambda)x^\lambda + c_0 f(\lambda) \log x x^\lambda.$$

When $\lambda = \lambda_2$, the right members of both (4) and (5) vanish. Thus a first solution of (1) is given by

(6)
$$y_2 = y(x, \lambda_2) = \sum_{n=0}^{\infty} c_n(\lambda_2)x^{\lambda_2+sn}.$$

To obtain a second, differentiate (3) with respect to λ and then put $\lambda = \lambda_2$:

$$\frac{\partial y}{\partial \lambda} = \sum_{n=0}^{\infty} \{c_n(\lambda)x^{\lambda+sn} \log x + c_n'(\lambda)x^{\lambda+sn}\},$$

(7)
$$y_3 = y_2 \log x + \sum_{n=0}^{\infty} c_n'(\lambda_2)x^{\lambda +sn}.$$

Since $c_0 = \lambda - \lambda_2$, $c_0' = 1$. After finding $c_n(\lambda)$, $c_n'(\lambda)$ is best found by logarithmic differentiation as in the following example. The terms up to $c_m'(\lambda)$ will follow a pattern different from those thereafter and considerable care is needed to ensure exact results.

The solution y_2 proves to be merely a multiple of the solution y_1 for the larger index. Since y_2 and y_3 are linearly independent, the general solution is $y = Ay_2 + By_3$.

Example 1. $xy'' - y = 0$ (Ex. 108.3).
In Exercise 108.3 we found the theta form

(i)
$$\vartheta(\vartheta - 1)y - xy = 0$$

and the power series solution y_1 for the larger index $\lambda_1 = 1$. We also saw that a power series solution for the smaller index $\lambda_2 = 0$ was impossible.
To find y_2 and y_3, assume that

$$y(\lambda) = \sum_{n=0}^{\infty} c_n x^{\lambda+n}, \qquad c_0 = \lambda - \lambda_2 = \lambda = c_0.$$

Substitution in (i) gives the recurrence relation when $n > 0$:

$$(\lambda + n)(\lambda + n - 1)c_n \quad = c_{n-1}.$$

$$(\lambda + n - 1)(\lambda + n - 2)c_{n-1} = c_{n-2}$$

$$\begin{array}{ccc} \cdot & \cdot & \cdot \\ \cdot & \cdot & \cdot \\ \cdot & \cdot & \cdot \end{array}$$

$$(\lambda + 2) \cdot (\lambda + 1) \quad c_2 \quad = c_1$$

$$(\lambda + 1) \cdot \lambda \quad\quad c_1 \quad = \lambda.$$

On multiplying these equations together we find

$$(\lambda + n)(\lambda + n - 1)^2 \cdots (\lambda + 1)^2 c_n = 1.$$

Thus

$$c_n(\lambda) = \frac{1}{(\lambda + n)(\lambda + n - 1)^2 \cdots (\lambda + 1)^2}, \qquad n > 1;$$

and by logarithmic differentiation

$$\frac{c_n'(\lambda)}{c_n(\lambda)} = \frac{-1}{\lambda + n} - \frac{2}{\lambda + n - 1} \cdots - \frac{2}{\lambda + 2} - \frac{2}{\lambda + 1}.$$

As $\lambda \to 0$, we have

$$c_n(0) = \frac{1}{n(n-1)^2 \cdots 2^2 1^2} = \frac{1}{n!\,(n-1)!}, \qquad n > 1,$$

$$\frac{c_n'(0)}{c_n(0)} = -\left[\frac{1}{n} + \frac{2}{n-1} + \frac{2}{n-2} + \cdots + \frac{2}{2} + \frac{2}{1}\right] = -(\Omega_n + \Omega_{n-1})$$

where $\Omega_n = 1 + \frac{1}{2} + \cdots + \frac{1}{n}$. Hence

$$c_n'(0) = -\frac{\Omega_n + \Omega_{n-1}}{n!\,(n-1)}, \qquad n > 1;$$

For $n = 0$,

$$c_0(\lambda) = \lambda, \quad c_0'(\lambda) = 1; \qquad c_0(0) = 0, \quad c_0'(0) = 1;$$

for $n = 1$

$$c_1(\lambda) = (\lambda + 1)^{-1}, \quad c_1'(\lambda) = -(\lambda + 1)^{-2}; \qquad c_1(0) = 1, \quad c_1'(0) = -1.$$

From these results we have

$$y_2 = \sum_{n=0}^{\infty} c_n(0)x^n = \sum_{n=1}^{\infty} \frac{x^n}{n!\,(n-1)!}$$

with the usual convention that $0! = 1$; and

$$y_3 = y_2 \log x + \sum_{n=0}^{\infty} c_n'(0)x^n$$

$$= y_2 \log x + 1 - x - \sum_{n=2}^{\infty} \frac{\Omega_n + \Omega_{n-1}}{n!\,(n-1)!} x^n.$$

The term $-x$ can be assimilated in the sum following if we begin it with $n = 1$ and use the convention $\Omega_0 = 0$.

The solution y_2 coincides with the solution y_1 previously found in Exercise 108.3.

Example 2. Bessel's Equation of Order One.

$$x^2 y'' + xy' + (x^2 - 1)y = 0 \quad \text{or} \quad (\vartheta^2 - 1)y + x^2 y = 0.$$

Indices $\lambda_1 = 1$, $\lambda_2 = -1$, and $\lambda_1 - \lambda_2 = 2 = s$.
Index $\lambda_1 = 1$: assume

$$y_1 = \sum_{n=0}^{\infty} c_n x^{2n+1}, \qquad c_0 = 1.$$

From the recurrence relation

$$2^2 n(n + 1)c_n = -c_{n-1}$$

$$2^2(n - 1)nc_{n-1} = -c_{n-2}$$

$$\begin{array}{ccc} \cdot & & \cdot \\ \cdot & & \cdot \\ \cdot & & \cdot \end{array}$$

$$2^2 \cdot 1 \cdot 2c_1 = -1$$

we find

$$2^{2n} n! \, (n + 1)! \, c_n = (-1)^n;$$

hence

$$y_1 = \sum_{n=0}^{\infty} \frac{(-1)^n}{2^{2n} n!(n + 1)!} x^{2n+1}.$$

However the standard power series solution is $y_1/2$ and is denoted by

$$J_1(x) = \sum_{n=0}^{\infty} \frac{(-1)^n}{n! \, (n + 1)!} \left(\frac{x}{2}\right)^{2n+1}.$$

To find y_2 and y_3 assume

$$y(\lambda) = \sum_{n=0}^{\infty} c_n x^{\lambda+2n}, \qquad c_0 = \lambda + 1.$$

The recurrence relation is now

$$(\lambda + 2n - 1)(\lambda + 2n + 1)c_n = -c_{n-1}$$

$$(\lambda + 2n - 3)(\lambda + 2n - 1)c_{n-1} = -c_{n-2}$$

$$\begin{array}{ccc} \cdot & \cdot & \cdot \\ \cdot & \cdot & \cdot \\ \cdot & \cdot & \cdot \end{array}$$

$$(\lambda + 3) \quad (\lambda + 5)c_2 = -c_1$$

$$(\lambda + 1) \quad (\lambda + 3)c_1 = -(\lambda + 1);$$

and on multiplying these equations together, we have

$$(\lambda + 2n + 1)(\lambda + 2n - 1)^2 \ldots (\lambda + 3)^2 c_n = (-1)^n.$$

Hence

$$c_n(\lambda) = \frac{(-1)^n}{(\lambda + 2n + 1)(\lambda + 2n - 1)^2 \ldots (\lambda + 5)^2(\lambda + 3)^2},$$

$$\frac{c_n'(\lambda)}{c_n(\lambda)} = -\frac{1}{\lambda + 2n + 1} - \frac{2}{\lambda + 2n - 1} - \cdots - \frac{2}{\lambda + 5} - \frac{2}{\lambda + 3}.$$

We now put $\lambda = -1$, the smaller index: then

$$c_n(-1) = \frac{(-1)^n}{(2n)(2n - 2)^2 \cdots 4^2 2^2} = \frac{(-1)^n}{2^{2n-1} n! \, (n - 1)!},$$

$$\frac{c_n'(-1)}{c_n(-1)} = -\left[\frac{1}{2n} + \frac{1}{n - 1} + \cdots + \frac{1}{1}\right] = -\frac{\Omega_n + \Omega_{n-1}}{2},$$

$$c_n'(-1) = -\frac{(-1)^n(\Omega_n + \Omega_{n-1})}{2^{2n} n! \, (n - 1)!}, \qquad n > 1.$$

For $n = 0$,

$$c_0(\lambda) = 1 + \lambda, \quad c_0{}'(\lambda) = 1; \qquad c_0(-1) = 0, \quad c_0{}'(-1) = 1.$$

For $n = 1$,

$$c_1(\lambda) = -(\lambda + 3)^{-1}, \quad c_1{}'(\lambda) = (\lambda + 3)^{-2}; \qquad c_1(-1) = -\tfrac{1}{2}, \quad c_1{}'(-1) = \tfrac{1}{4}.$$

We therefore have the solutions

$$y_2 = y(-1) = \sum_{n=1}^{\infty} \frac{(-1)^n}{2^{2n-1} n! \,(n-1)!}\, x^{2n-1};$$

the sum includes the correct term $-x/2$ when $n = 1$. If we change the summation index by writing $n = m + 1$, we find that

$$y_2 = -\frac{y_1}{2} = -J_1(x);$$

$$y_3 = y_2 \log x + \sum_{n=0}^{\infty} c_n{}'(-1) x^{2n-1}$$

$$= y_2 \log x + x^{-1} + \frac{x}{4} - \sum_{n=2}^{\infty} \frac{(-1)^n (\Omega_n + \Omega_{n-1})}{2^{2n} n! \,(n-1)!}\, x^{2n-1}.$$

The term $x/4$ can be included in the sum beginning with $n = 1$ if we adopt the convention $\Omega_0 = 0$.

The notation $K_1(x) = -y_3$ is used for the logarithmic solution and the general solution is

$$y = A J_1(x) + B K_1(x).$$

However, Neumann's logarithmic solution $Y_1(x)$ (§ 125) is commonly used instead of $K_1(x)$.

PROBLEMS

Obtain the solutions given for the following equations.

1. $x(1 - x)y'' - 3xy' - y = 0.$

$$y_2 = x(1 - x)^{-2}, \qquad y_3 = y_2 \log x + (1 - x)^{-1}.$$

2. With $u = y_1$ in Problem 1, find a second solution v using formula (28.8) and reconcile it with y_3.

3. $xy'' + xy' + y = 0.$

$$y_2 = -xe^{-x}, \quad y_3 = y_2 \log x + 1 + \sum_{n=0}^{\infty} \frac{(-1)^n \Omega_n}{n!}\, x^{n+1}.$$

4. $x^2 y'' + 3xy' + x^2 y = 0.$

$$y_1 = \sum_{n=0}^{\infty} \frac{(-1)^n x^{2n}}{2^{2n} n! \,(n+1)!}, \qquad y_2 = -\tfrac{1}{2} y_1;$$

$$y_3 = y_2 \log x + x^{-2} + \frac{1}{4} + \sum_{n=2}^{\infty} \frac{(-1)^{n+1} (\Omega_n + \Omega_{n-1})}{2^n n! \,(n-1)!}\, x^{2(n-1)}.$$

5. $xy'' - y' + y = 0$.

$$y_1 = 2x^2 \sum_{n=0}^{\infty} \frac{(-1)^n}{n!\,(n+2)!}\, x^n, \qquad y_2 = -\tfrac{1}{2}y_1;$$

$$y_3 = y_1 \log x + 1 + x + \sum_{n=2}^{\infty} (-1)^n \frac{\Omega_n + \Omega_{n-2} - 1}{n!\,(n-2)!}\, x^n.$$

6. $xy'' - xy^1 + y = 0$.

$$y_1 = x, \quad y_2 = -x; \qquad y_3 = -x \log x + 1 + 2x - \sum_{n=2}^{\infty} \frac{x^n}{(n-1)n!}.$$

Verify y_3 by using (28.8) with $u = x$; then

$$v = x \log x - 1 + \sum_{n=2}^{\infty} \frac{x^n}{(n-1)!\,n!} = 2y_1 - y_3.$$

113. POINT AT INFINITY

The transformation $x = 1/t$ maps the region for which $|x| > 1$ onto the region $|t| < 1$. Thus to study the differential equation

(1) $$y'' + Py' + Qy = 0$$

for large x, we put $x = 1/t$; then

$$y' = \frac{dy}{dx} = \frac{dy/dt}{dx/dt} = \frac{\dot{y}}{-t^{-2}} = -t^2 \dot{y},$$

$$y'' = \frac{dy'}{dx} = \frac{dy'/dt}{dx/dt} = -\frac{t^2\ddot{y} + 2t\dot{y}}{-t^{-2}} = t^4\ddot{y} + 2t^3\dot{y},$$

and (1) becomes

$$t^4\ddot{y} + t^2(2t - P)\dot{y} + Qy = 0$$

where $P = P(1/t)$, $Q = Q(1/t)$; hence

(2) $$\ddot{y} + \frac{2t - P}{t^2}\dot{y} + \frac{Q}{t^4} = 0.$$

If $t = 0$ ($x = \infty$) is a regular singular point, the preceding method will give series solutions valid for small t or large x.

To study the equation

(3) $$f(\vartheta)y + x^s g(\vartheta)y = 0$$

for large x, we use

(4) $$x = \frac{1}{t}, \qquad \vartheta = -\dot{\vartheta} \qquad\qquad (106.7)$$

to transform (3) into

(5) $$g(-\dot{\vartheta})y + t^s f(-\dot{\vartheta})y = 0.$$

The indices for $t = 0$ are the roots λ_1, λ_2 of $g(-\lambda) = 0$, and the corresponding solutions are power series multiplied by t^{λ_1} and t^{λ_2}. These series converge within a circle $\mathscr{C}$ about $t = 0$ passing through the nearest singular point of equation (3). If we put $t = 1/x$ in these solutions, the power series become (Laurent) series in negative powers of x that converge *outside* the circle $\mathscr{C}$ and thus give solutions valid for large x.

Example. $x^4 y'' + xy' + 2y = 0$.

The point $x = 0$ is an irregular singular point and the corresponding series solutions diverge. This is apparent from the theta form of the equation

(i) $$(\vartheta + 2)y + x^2 \vartheta(\vartheta - 1)y = 0,$$

since the degree of $f(\lambda) = \lambda + 2$ is smaller than the degree of $g(\lambda) = \lambda(\lambda - 1)$ (§ 108). The transformation (4) changes (i) into

(ii) $$\vartheta(\vartheta + 1)y - t^2(\vartheta - 2)y = 0.$$

The indices for $t = 0$ are $\lambda_1 = 0$, $\lambda_2 = -1$, and since $\lambda_1 - \lambda_2 = 1$ is not a multiple of the skip number 2, both solutions will be nonlogarithmic.

$\lambda_1 = 0$: $$y_1 = \sum_{n=0}^{\infty} c_n t^{2n}.$$

The usual procedure gives the recurrence relation

$$n(2n + 1)c_n = (n - 2)c_{n-1}$$

from which we have $c_0 = 1$, $c_1 = -\frac{1}{3}$, $c_2 = 0$, and $c_n = 0$ when $n > 2$. Thus one solution is

$$y_1 = 1 - \frac{1}{3}t^2 = 1 - \frac{1}{3x^2}, \qquad x > 0.$$

$\lambda_2 = -1$: $$y_2 = \sum_{n=0}^{\infty} c_n t^{2n-1}.$$

The recurrence relation is now

$$2n(2n - 1)c_n = (2n - 5)c_{n-1}$$
$$2(n - 1)(2n - 3)c_{n-1} = (2n - 7)c_{n-2}$$
$$2(n - 2)(2n - 5)c_{n-2} = (2n - 9)c_{n-3}$$

$$\cdot \qquad \cdot \qquad \cdot$$
$$\cdot \qquad \cdot \qquad \cdot$$
$$\cdot \qquad \cdot \qquad \cdot$$

$$2 \cdot 3 \cdot 5\, c_3 = 1\, c_2$$
$$2 \cdot 2 \cdot 3\, c_2 = -1\, c_1$$
$$2 \cdot 1 \cdot 1\, c_1 = -3\, c_0.$$

On multiplying these equations together we find

$$2^n n!\, (2n - 1)(2n - 3)c_n = (-1)(-3)c_0 = 3$$

if $c_0 = 1$; hence

$$y_1 = 3x \sum_{n=0}^{\infty} \frac{x^{-2n}}{2^n n!\, (2n - 1)(2n - 3)} \qquad x > 0.$$

PROBLEMS

Find all nonlogarithmic solutions valid for large x:
1. $x(1 - x)y'' - 3y' + 2y = 0$.
2. $x^4y'' + x(1 - x^2)y' + y = 0$.
3. $2x^2(x - 1)y'' + x(5x - 3)y' + (x + 1)y = 0$.
4. In Problem 3, use (28.8) to obtain a second solution.
5. $x^4y'' + x(x^2 + 1)y' + y = 0$.
6. $y'' - xy' - \lambda y = 0$. [Cf. Prob. 117.6].

114. HYPERGEOMETRIC EQUATION

The hypergeometric (hg) differential equation

(1) $$x(1 - x)y'' + [\gamma - (\alpha + \beta + 1)x]y' - \alpha\beta y = 0$$

contains three constant parameters α, β, γ; but α and β may be inter-changed without altering the equation. The equation obviously has two singular points $x = 0$, $x = 1$ which are both regular. The substitution $x = 1/t$ reveals a third singular point at $t = 0$ or $x = \infty$.

If we write (1) in the form

$$(xD^2 + \gamma D)y + [x^2D^2 + (\alpha + \beta + 1)xD + \alpha\beta]y = 0$$

and multiply by x, it assumes theta form

(2) $$\vartheta(\vartheta + \gamma - 1)y - x(\vartheta + \alpha)(\vartheta + \beta)y = 0,$$

which is in the standard two-term form with

$$f(\lambda) = \lambda(\lambda + \gamma - 1), \qquad g(\lambda) = -(\lambda + \alpha)(\alpha + \beta),$$

and skip number $s = 1$. We shall obtain series solutions for the singular points $0, 1, \infty$.

1° *Singular point $x = 0$.* The indicial equation $f(\lambda) = 0$ has the roots $\lambda_1 = 0$, $\lambda_2 = 1 - \gamma$.
     Index $\lambda_1 = 0$:

$$y_1 = \sum_{n=0}^{\infty} c_n x^n.$$

The recurrence relation

$$f(n)c_n + g(n - 1)c_{n-1} = 0$$

becomes

$$n(n + \gamma - 1)c_n = (n - 1 + \alpha)(n - 1 + \beta)c_{n-1}$$

$$(n - 1)(n + \gamma - 2)c_{n-1} = (n - 2 + \alpha)(n - 2 + \beta)c_{n-2}$$

$$.$$
$$.$$
$$.$$

$$2(1 + \gamma)c_2 = (1 + \alpha)(1 + \beta)c_1$$

$$1(\gamma)c_1 = (\alpha)(\beta)c_0.$$

On multiplying these equations together we find

$$c_n = \frac{\alpha(\alpha + 1) \cdots (\alpha + n - 1)\beta(\beta + 1) \cdots (\beta + n - 1)}{n!} \frac{}{\gamma(\gamma + 1) \cdots (\gamma + n - 1)} c_0,$$

in which the products containing α, β, γ each have n factors. Taking $c_0 = 1$, we obtain the solution for the index 0:

(3) $$y_1 = 1 + \frac{\alpha\beta}{1 \cdot \gamma} x + \frac{\alpha(\alpha + 1)\beta(\beta + 1)}{1 \cdot 2 \;\; \gamma(\gamma + 1)} x^2 + \cdots.$$

This series* converges for $|x| < 1$ and defines the *hypergeometric function*

(4) $$F(\alpha, \beta; \gamma; x) =$$

$$1 + \sum_{n=1}^{\infty} \frac{\alpha(\alpha + 1) \cdots (\alpha + n - 1)\beta(\beta + 1) \cdots (\beta + n - 1)}{\gamma(\gamma + 1) \cdots (\gamma + n - 1)} \frac{}{n!} x^n, \quad |x| < 1.$$

Its derivative may be found by differentiating the series (3) term by term:

(5) $$F'(\alpha, \beta; \gamma; x) = \frac{\alpha\beta}{\gamma} F(\alpha + 1, \beta + 1; \gamma + 1; x), \quad |x| < 1.$$

---

* When γ is zero or a negative integer, the *hypergeometric series* (3) is not defined. With these values of γ excluded, the series converges absolutely when $|x| < 1$, diverges when $|x| > 1$. When $x = \pm 1$, the convergence depends on $r = \gamma - \alpha - \beta$.

$$x = 1: \quad r > 0, \text{ converges absolutely,}$$
$$r \leqq 0, \text{ diverges.}$$

In the case of convergence we have the Gaussian relation

$$F(\alpha, \beta; \gamma; 1) = \frac{\Gamma(\gamma)\Gamma(\gamma - \alpha - \beta)}{\Gamma(\gamma - \alpha)\Gamma(\gamma - \beta)}.$$

$$x = -1: \quad r > 0, \text{ converges absolutely,}$$
$$-1 < r \leqq 0, \text{ converges conditionally,}$$
$$r \leqq -1, \text{ diverges.}$$

When $\beta = \gamma \neq 0$, the β and γ factors in (4) cancel and

$$(6) \qquad F(\alpha, \beta; \beta, x) = 1 + \sum_{n=1}^{\infty} \binom{-\alpha}{n}(-x)^n = (1 - x)^{-\alpha};$$

for $\alpha = 1$ this reduces to the geometric series $1 + x + x^2 + \cdots$; hence the term *hyper*geometric. When $\gamma = \beta = 0$, the hg series becomes indeterminate and we define $F(\alpha, 0; 0; x) = (1 - x)^{-\alpha}$ since this is the limit of (6) as $\beta \to 0$. Here equation (1) has 1 and $(1 - x)^{-\alpha}$ as basic solutions.

When α or β is an integer $k \leq 0$, the hg series terminates and becomes a polynomial of degree k. When γ is an integer ≤ 0, the hg series is not defined and the solution for index 0 involves $\log x$; then y_2 given below provides the series solution of higher index $1 - \gamma$.

Index $\lambda_2 = 1 - \gamma$: $y_2 = x^{1-\gamma}u(x)$ where $u(x)$ is a power series. To find it substitute y_2 in (2), use the power shift to bring $x^{1-\gamma}$ to the left of the operators and divide it out; then

$$(\vartheta + 1 - \gamma)\vartheta u - x(\vartheta + \alpha + 1 - \gamma)(\vartheta + \beta + 1 - \gamma)u = 0.$$

Comparison with (2) shows that u satisfies a hg equation with the parameters

$$\alpha_1 = \alpha + 1 - \gamma, \qquad \beta_1 = \beta + 1 - \gamma, \qquad \gamma_1 = 2 - \gamma.$$

We thus obtain a second solution for the point $x = 0$:

$$(7) \qquad y_2 = x^{1-\gamma}F(\alpha + 1 - \gamma, \beta + 1 - \gamma; 2 - \gamma; x),$$

which is linearly independent of y_1 when $\gamma \neq 1$. But when $\gamma = 1$, both indices are 0 and the second solution must be found by the procedure of § 111.

2° *Singular point $x = 1$.* This singular point is brought to the origin by putting $x = 1 - t$. Denoting t derivatives by $\dot{y}$, $\ddot{y}$, we have

$$y' = -\dot{y}, \qquad y'' = \ddot{y},$$

and (1) becomes

$$(1 - t)t\ddot{y} - [\gamma - (\alpha + \beta + 1)(1 - t)]\dot{y} - \alpha\beta y = 0$$

or

$$t(1 - t)\ddot{y} + [(\alpha + \beta - \gamma + 1) - (\alpha + \beta + 1)t]\dot{y} - \alpha\beta y = 0.$$

Comparison with (1) shows that this equation is hg with the parameters

$$\alpha_2 = \alpha, \qquad \beta_2 = \beta, \qquad \gamma_2 = \alpha + \beta - \gamma + 1.$$

It therefore has two solutions that may be obtained from y_1 and y_2 by replacing α, β, γ, x by $\alpha, \beta, \alpha + \beta - \gamma + 1, t = 1 - x$:

$$(8) \qquad y_3 = F(\alpha, \beta; \alpha + \beta - \gamma + 1; 1 - x),$$
$$(9) \qquad y_4 = (1 - x)^{\gamma - \alpha - \beta}F(\gamma - \beta, \gamma - \alpha; \gamma - \alpha - \beta + 1; 1 - x).$$

The latter is independent of y_3 except when $\gamma = \alpha + \beta$, in which case $y_4 = y_3$.

3° *Singular point $x = \infty$.* This point is brought to the origin by the substitution $x = 1/t$. Then $\vartheta = -\dot\vartheta$ and (2) becomes

(10) $$(\dot\vartheta - \alpha)(\dot\vartheta - \beta)y - t\dot\vartheta(\dot\vartheta - \gamma + 1)y = 0.$$

The indicial equation $(\lambda - \alpha)(\lambda - \beta) = 0$ now has the roots α, β.

For the index α the solution has the form $y_5 = t^\alpha v(t)$. Substituting this in (10) and using the power shift gives the equation satisfied by $v(t)$:

(11) $$\dot\vartheta(\dot\vartheta + \alpha - \beta)v - t(\dot\vartheta + \alpha)(\dot\vartheta + \alpha - \gamma + 1)v = 0.$$

Comparison with (2) shows that this equation is hg with the parameters

$$\alpha_3 = \alpha, \qquad \beta_3 = \alpha - \gamma + 1, \qquad \gamma_3 = \alpha - \beta + 1.$$

Hence $v(t) = F(\alpha_3, \beta_3; \gamma_3; t)$ and we have the solution

(12) $$y_5 = x^{-\alpha}F(\alpha, \alpha - \gamma + 1; \alpha - \beta + 1; x^{-1}).$$

For the index β we obtain another solution by interchanging α and β in (12):

(13) $$y_6 = x^{-\beta}F(\beta, \beta - \gamma + 1; \beta - \alpha + 1; x^{-1});$$

for this interchange does not alter equation (10). If $\alpha = \beta$, $y_6 = y_5$; but when $\alpha \neq \beta$, y_5 and y_6 are linearly independent solutions valid for $|x| > 1$.

Finally, we prove an important property of the hg equation.

Theorem. *If $y(x)$ is a solution of the hg equation with parameters α, β, γ, $y'(x)$ is a solution of a hg equation with parameters $\alpha + 1$, $\beta + 1$, $\gamma + 1$.*

PROOF. If we differentiate equation (1) we have

$$x(1 - x)y''' + (1 - 2x)y'' + [\gamma - (\alpha + \beta + 1)x]y''$$
$$- (\alpha + \beta + 1 + \alpha\beta)y' = 0,$$

and if $y'(x) = z$, this becomes

$$x(1 - x)z'' + [\gamma + 1 - (\alpha + 1 + \beta + 1 + 1)x]z'$$
$$- (\alpha + 1)(\beta + 1)z = 0.$$

Note that (5) is in harmony with this theorem.

Example 1. $x(1 - x)y'' - 3y' + 2y = 0$. This equation, previously considered in Example 110.2, has the theta form of a hg equation:

$$\vartheta(\vartheta - 4)y - x(\vartheta - 2)(\vartheta + 1) = 0$$

whose parameters are

$$\alpha = 1, \qquad \beta = -2, \qquad \gamma = -3.$$

Hence the solutions for the singular point $x = 0$ are

$$y_1 = F(1, -2; -3; x)$$

$$= 1 + \frac{(-2)}{(-3)}x + \frac{(-2)(-1)}{(-3)(-2)}x^2$$

$$= 1 + \tfrac{2}{3}x + \tfrac{1}{3}x^2$$

$$y_2 = x^4 F(5, 2; 5; x) \qquad\qquad \text{from (7),}$$

$$= x^4(1 - x)^{-2} \qquad\qquad \text{from (6).}$$

For the singular point $x = 1$ we have

$$y_3 = F(1, -2; 3; 1 - x) \qquad\qquad \text{from (8),}$$

$$y_4 = (1 - x)^{-2}F(-1, -4; -1; 1 - x) \qquad \text{from (9),}$$

$$= (1 - x)^{-2}x^4 \qquad\qquad \text{from (6).}$$

For the singular point ∞ we have

$$y_5 = x^{-1}F(1, 5; 4; x^{-1}), \qquad\qquad \text{from (12)}$$

$$y_6 = x^2 F(-2, 2; -2; x^{-1}) \qquad\qquad \text{from (13)}$$

$$= x^2(1 - x^{-1})^{-2} = x^4(x - 1)^{-2} \qquad \text{from (6).}$$

Note that $y_2 = y_4 = y_6$ is a solution valid for all $x \neq 1$.

Example 2. $x(1 - x)y'' + (1 - 2x)y' + \tfrac{1}{4}y = 0$. The theta form

$$\vartheta^2 y - x(\vartheta + \tfrac{1}{2})^2 y = 0$$

is that of a hg equation with parameters

$$\alpha = \beta = \tfrac{1}{2}, \qquad \gamma = 1.$$

We find that the six solutions now reduce to three:

$$y_1 = y_2 = F(\tfrac{1}{2}, \tfrac{1}{2}; 1; x)$$

$$y_3 = y_4 = F(\tfrac{1}{2}, \tfrac{1}{2}; 1; 1 - x)$$

$$y_5 = y_6 = x^{-\frac{1}{2}}F(\tfrac{1}{2}, \tfrac{1}{2}; 1; x^{-1})$$

where

$$F(\tfrac{1}{2}, \tfrac{1}{2}; 1; t) = 1 + \sum_{n=1}^{\infty} \left[\frac{(2n - 1)!!}{(2n)!!}\right]^2 t^n.$$

As in all cases of equal indices, the second *independent* solution involves log x.

PROBLEMS

Deduce the following properties of the hg function:

1. $xF(1, 1; 2; -x) = \log(1 + x)$.

2. $2xF(\frac{1}{2}, 1; \frac{3}{2}; x^2) = \log\dfrac{1 + x}{1 - x}$.

3. $xF(\frac{1}{2}, \frac{1}{2}; \frac{3}{2}; x^2) = \arcsin x$.

4. $xF(\frac{1}{2}, 1; \frac{3}{2}; -x^2) = \arctan x$.

5. $F(1, -\frac{1}{2}; \frac{1}{2}; -x^2) = 1 + x \arctan x$.

6. $F(\alpha + 1, \beta; \gamma; x) - F(\alpha, \beta; \gamma; x) = \dfrac{\beta x}{\gamma} F(\alpha + 1, \beta + 1; \gamma + 1; x)$.

7. When $\beta = \gamma = 0$, show that the hg equation (1) has the solution basis 1, $(1 - x)^{-\alpha}$.

8. Compute $F(1, -3; 1; x)$ directly from (3) and verify equation (6).

9. Show that the self-adjoint form of the hg equation (1) is

$$D[x^\gamma(1 - x)^{\alpha+\beta-\gamma+1}y'] + \alpha\beta x^{\gamma-1}(1 - x)^{\alpha+\beta-\gamma}y = 0.$$

10. Show that the factor $\sigma = (1 - x)^\alpha(1 + x)^\beta$ will render *Jacobi's equation*

$$(1 - x^2)y'' + [\beta - \alpha - (\alpha + \beta + 2)x]y' + n(n + \alpha + \beta + 1)y = 0$$

self-adjoint.

115. REDUCTION TO THE HYPERGEOMETRIC EQUATION

The equation

(1) $$(x - a)(x - b)y'' + (cx + d)y' + ey = 0, \qquad a \neq b,$$

has regular singular points at $x = a, b, \infty$. It may be reduced to the hg equation

(2) $$t(1 - t)\ddot{y} + [\gamma - (\alpha + \beta + 1)t]\dot{y} - \alpha\beta y = 0$$

by means of the linear transformation

(3) $$x - a = (b - a)t,$$

which carries $x = a, b, \infty$ into $t = 0, 1, \infty$. Since

$$x - b = (b - a)(t - 1), \qquad dx = (b - a)\,dt,$$

(1) becomes

$$t(t - 1)\ddot{y} + \frac{ca + c(b - a)t + d}{b - a}\dot{y} + ey = 0$$

or, on changing signs throughout,

(4) $$t(1 - t)\ddot{y} + \left[\frac{ac + d}{a - b} - ct\right]\dot{y} - ey = 0.$$

Comparison with (2) shows that (4) is hg with parameters determined by

$$\gamma = \frac{ac + d}{a - b}, \qquad \alpha + \beta +_{,}1 = c, \qquad \alpha\beta = e.$$

As an example, see the reduction of the Legendre equation in § 119.

Any equation whose theta form is

(5) $$(\vartheta + a)(\vartheta + b)y - kx^m(\vartheta + c)(\vartheta + d)y = 0$$

may be reduced to the standard hg form

(6) $$\vartheta(\vartheta + \gamma - 1)y - x(\vartheta + \alpha)(\vartheta + \beta)y = 0$$

by changing variables. To bring the first term to the proper form, put

(7) $$y = x^{-a}u,$$

use the power shift to move x^{-a} before the ϑ operators, and then cancel it from the equation. We thus obtain

(8) $$\vartheta(\vartheta + b - a)u - kx^m(\vartheta + c - a)(\vartheta + d - a)u = 0.$$

To bring the second term to the standard form, put

(9) $$t = kx^m, \qquad \vartheta = m\dot{\vartheta} \qquad (106.6);$$

then after dividing out m^2, we have

(10) $$\dot{\vartheta}\left(\dot{\vartheta} + \frac{b - a}{m}\right)u - t\left(\dot{\vartheta} + \frac{c - a}{m}\right)\left(\dot{\vartheta} + \frac{d - a}{m}\right)u = 0.$$

Comparison with (6) shows that this equation is hg with parameters

$$\alpha = \frac{c - a}{m}, \qquad \beta = \frac{d - a}{m}, \qquad \gamma = \frac{b - a}{m} + 1.$$

Its series solutions are therefore known and may be converted into solutions of (5) by replacing u and t with their values from (7) and (9).

Example. $(1 - x^2)y'' - 2xy' + 12y = 0$. Multiply by x^2 and convert to the theta form

$$\vartheta(\vartheta - 1)y - x^2(\vartheta - 3)(\vartheta + 4)y = 0.$$

With $t = x^2$, $\vartheta = 2\dot{\vartheta}$, this becomes

$$2\dot{\vartheta}(2\dot{\vartheta} - 1)y - t(2\dot{\vartheta} - 3)(2\dot{\vartheta} + 4)y = 0,$$
$$\dot{\vartheta}(\dot{\vartheta} - \tfrac{1}{2})y - t(\dot{\vartheta} - \tfrac{3}{2})(\dot{\vartheta} + 2)y = 0,$$

an hg equation in t with parameters

$$\alpha = 2, \qquad \beta = -\tfrac{3}{2}, \qquad \gamma = \tfrac{1}{2}.$$

The six solutions given in § 114 are

$$y_1 = F(2, -\tfrac{3}{2}; \tfrac{1}{2}; t) = \sum_{n=0}^{\infty} \frac{3(n+1)}{(2n-3)(2n-1)} t^n$$

$$y_2 = t^{\frac{1}{2}} F(\tfrac{5}{2}, -1; \tfrac{3}{2}; t) = t^{\frac{1}{2}}(1 - \tfrac{5}{3}t)$$

$$y_3 = F(2, -\tfrac{3}{2}; 1; 1 - t)$$

$$y_4 = y_3 \quad (\text{since } \gamma = \alpha + \beta)$$

$$y_5 = t^{-2} F(2, \tfrac{5}{2}; \tfrac{9}{2}; t^{-1})$$

$$y_6 = t^{\frac{3}{2}} F(-\tfrac{3}{2}, -1; -\tfrac{5}{2}; t^{-1})$$

$$= t^{\frac{3}{2}}(1 - \tfrac{3}{5}t^{-1}) = t^{\frac{1}{2}}(t - \tfrac{3}{5}) = -\tfrac{5}{3}y_2.$$

These are solutions of the given equation when t is replaced by x^2.

PROBLEMS

Reduce to the hg theta form and find y_1 to y_6 as given in § 114.

1. $(1 + x^2)y'' + 2xy' - 2y = 0.$
2. $(1 - x^2)y'' - xy' + y = 0.$
3. $x(1 - x^2)y'' + (2x^2 - 3)y' - 2xy = 0.$
4. $x^2(1 - x)y'' + 2x(2 - x)y' + 2(1 + x)y = 0.$
5. $(1 - x^2)y'' - 5xy' - 3y = 0.$
6. $(1 - x^2)y'' - xy' + y = 0.$
7. $(1 - x^2)y'' + 2y = 0.$
8. $x(x + 1)y'' + (x - 1)y' - y = 0.$
9. $x(x - 1)y'' + (x - 2)y' - y = 0.$
10. $2x(1 - x)y'' + (1 - x)y' + 3y = 0.$
11. $x(1 - x)y'' + (2 - 3x)y' - y = 0.$
12. $(x^3 + 1)y'' + x^2 y' - 4xy = 0.$
13. $(1 + x^2)y'' - 4xy + 6y = 0.$

116. ORTHOGONAL FUNCTIONS

The set of all functions whose squares are integrable in a fundamental interval $a \leq x \leq b$ and are of positive *norm*,

(1) $$\text{Norm } f = \int_a^b f^2(x) \, dx > 0,$$

is said to constitute a certain function space $\mathscr{F}$. Two functions $f(x)$, $g(x)$

of $\mathscr{F}$ are said to be orthogonal in the interval $[a, b]$ when

$$(2) \qquad \int_a^b f(x)g(x)\, dx = 0.^*$$

The most interesting and important situations occur when any two functions of a countable set have this property. We lay down, therefore, the following generalized definition.

Definition 1. A sequence of real-valued functions $\{\psi_n(x)\}$ of $\mathscr{F}$ is said to be orthogonal in an interval $a \leq x \leq b$ with respect to the *weight function* $\rho(x)$ if

$$(3) \qquad \int_a^b \rho(x)\psi_m(x)\psi_n(x)\, dx = \begin{cases} 0, & m \neq n, \\ h_n, & m = n. \end{cases}$$

If $\rho(x) = 1$, the set $\{\psi_n(x)\}$ is simply called *orthogonal*; and if, in addition, $h_n = 1$, the set is called *orthonormal*.

We shall assume that the weight function $\rho(x) \geq 0$; then $h_n > 0$ and the functions

$$(4) \qquad \varphi_n(x) = \sqrt{\frac{\rho(x)}{h_n}}\, \varphi_n(x)$$

obviously form an orthonormal set. Thus from any set of orthogonal functions in the sense of (3) we can construct an orthonormal set as soon as the constants h_n are known. For the orthonormal set $\{\varphi_n(x)\}$ the relation (3) becomes

$$(5) \qquad \int_a^b \varphi_m(x)\varphi_n(x)\, dx = \delta_{mn},$$

where the *Kronecker delta* $\delta_{mn} = 0$ or 1 according as $m \neq n$ or $m = n$.

An orthogonal set $\{\psi_n(x)\}$ is said to be *complete* when no function of $\mathscr{F}$ is orthogonal to all members of the set. The well-known sine-cosine set $\{1, \sin nx, \cos nx\}$ can be shown to be complete.†

The importance of orthogonal sets $\{\psi_n(x)\}$ is due to the fact that a function $f(x)$ of $\mathscr{F}$ can often be represented by a series expansion $\Sigma c_n \psi_n(x)$

---

* Two vectors f, g in n-space with components f_i, g_i are said to be orthogonal when

$$(2)' \qquad \sum_{i=1}^n f_i g_i = 0.$$

If the functions $f(x), g(x)$ are regarded as vectors with an infinite number of components (their values in the interval), equation (2) is a natural extension of (2)'.

† The Maclaurin series for $f(x)$ is an expansion in terms of the set $1, x, x^2, \ldots$ which is not orthogonal over any interval.

in terms of the functions $\{\psi_n(x)\}$.* In view of (4) it will suffice to consider expansions

(6)
$$f(x) = \sum_{i=1}^{\infty} c_i \varphi_i(x)$$

in terms of the *orthonormal* set $\{\varphi_n(x)\}$. Let us assume that the series in (6) converges uniformly to $f(x)$; then to find c_n multiply (6) by $\varphi_n(x)$ and integrate the series from a to b term by term†; then, in view of (5)

$$\int_a^b f(x)\varphi_n(x)\, dx = \sum_{i=1}^{\infty} c_i \delta_{in} = c_n.$$

This procedure can be justified in many important cases and yields the formula

(7)
$$c_n = \int_a^b f(x)\varphi_n(x)\, dx$$

for the *Fourier constants* c_n of $f(x)$ with respect to the orthonormal system $\{\varphi_n\}$. In any case we say that the series (6) *corresponds* to the function $f(x)$ and write

(8)
$$f(x) \sim \sum_{i=1}^{\infty} c_i \varphi_i(x),$$

irrespective of whether the series converges to $f(x)$ or even converges at all. Thus (8) simply means that the constants c_n have been computed for $f(x)$ by means of formula (7).

Now let $a_1, a_2, \ldots, a_n$ be n arbitrary constants and consider the function

$$\sum_{i=1}^{n} a_i \varphi_i(x) = a_1 \varphi_1(x) + \cdots + a_n \varphi_n(x).$$

We propose to find the values of a_i so that this sum, *for a fixed n*, will be the best approximation to $f(x)$ in the sense of least squares. Thus our problem is to find n constants a_i so that the non-negative integral

$$I_n = \int_a^b \left[f(x) - \sum_{i=1}^{n} a_i \varphi_i(x) \right]^2 dx$$

assumes its least value. On expanding the integrand, we have

$$f^2 + \sum a_i^2 \varphi_i^2 - 2 \sum a_i f \varphi_i + 2 \sum_{i \neq j} a_i a_j \varphi_i \varphi_j;$$

_____

* *Advanced Calculus*, p. 530.
† *Advanced Calculus*, § 181.

hence from (5) and (7) we have

$$I_n = \int_a^b f^2\, dx + \sum_{i=1}^n a_i^2 \int_a^b \varphi_i^2\, dx - 2 \sum_{i=1}^n a_i \int_a^b f\varphi_i\, dx + 0$$

$$= \int_a^b f^2\, dx + \sum_{i=1}^n a_i^2 - 2 \sum_{i=1}^n a_i c_i$$

$$= \int_a^b f^2\, dx + \sum_{i=1}^n (a_i - c_i)^2 - \sum_{i=1}^n c_i^2.$$

Since the first and last terms are fixed, I_n will assume its least value

$$(9) \qquad \min I_n = \int_a^b f^2\, dx - \sum_{i=1}^n c_i^2 \geqq 0$$

when the constants $a_i = c_i$, the Fourier constants of $f(x)$. Note that the terms of the best approximation for a given n are retained in the best approximations for all larger values of n. Moreover, since n can be taken arbitrarily large, (9) also proves *Bessel's inequality*:

$$(10) \qquad \sum_{i=1}^\infty c_i^2 \leqq \int_a^b f^2(x)\, dx.$$

Thus the positive series $\Sigma\, c_i^2$ converges and its terms form a null sequence*: $c_n \to 0$ as $n \to \infty$.

We collect these results in the following

Theorem 1. *Let $\{\varphi_n(x)\}$ be an orthonormal set over $[a, b]$ and $f(x)$ a function of $\mathscr{F}$. Then for any given n.*

$$a_1\varphi_1(x) + a_2\varphi_2(x) + \cdots + a_n\varphi_n(x)$$

is the best approximation to $f(x)$ over $[a, b]$ in the sense of least squares when the constants a_i are the Fourier constants of $f(x)$.

The Fourier constants $\{c_n\}$ form a null sequence and the series of their squares converges to a sum not exceeding norm f.

We add, without proof,

Theorem 2. *When the orthonormal set $\{\varphi_n(x)\}$ is complete, the series of squares of the Fourier constants of any function $f(x)$ of $\mathscr{F}$ converges to norm f:*

$$(11) \qquad \sum_{i=1}^\infty c_i^2 = \int_a^b f^2(x)\, dx.$$

Equation (11) is known as *Parseval's equation*.

---

* *Advanced Calculus.* p. 45.

Example.　*Sine-Cosine Set.*　The set

$$1, \cos x, \sin x, \cos 2x, \sin 2x, \ldots$$

is orthogonal over any interval of length 2π such as $[-\pi, \pi]$. Since $\int_{-\pi}^{\pi} 1 \, dx = 2\pi$
and

$$\int_{-\pi}^{\pi} \sin^2 nx \, dx = \int_{-\pi}^{\pi} \cos^2 nx \, dx = \tfrac{1}{2} \int_{-\pi}^{\pi} (\sin^2 nx + \cos^2 nx) \, dx = \pi,$$

the set

(12)
$$\frac{1}{\sqrt{2\pi}}, \quad \left\{\frac{\cos nx}{\sqrt{\pi}}\right\}, \quad \left\{\frac{\sin nx}{\sqrt{\pi}}\right\}$$

is orthonormal.

With this set it is customary to write

(13)
$$f(x) \sim \tfrac{1}{2}a_0 + \sum_{n=1}^{\infty} (a_n \cos nx + b_n \sin nx).$$

We then find, by the foregoing procedure,

(14)
$$\begin{aligned} a_n \\ b_n \end{aligned} = \frac{1}{\pi} \int_{-\pi}^{\pi} f(x) \begin{aligned} \cos nx \\ \sin nx \end{aligned} \, dx.$$

The first term is written $\tfrac{1}{2}a_0$ so that the formula for a_n applies to a_0.

It can be shown that the sine-cosine set is complete in the space of all square-integrable functions*; hence for all functions of $\mathscr{F}$, Parseval's equation holds. For the orthonormal set (12) the Fourier constants are

$$c_0 = \sqrt{\pi/2} \, a_0, \qquad c_n = \sqrt{\pi} \, a_n, \qquad c_n' = \sqrt{\pi} \, b_n,$$

and Parseval's equation takes the form

(15)
$$\frac{1}{2} a_0{}^2 + \sum_{n=1}^{\infty} (a_n{}^2 + b_n{}^2) = \frac{1}{\pi} \int_{-\pi}^{\pi} f^2(x) \, dx.$$

It can be proved† that if $f(x)$ is piecewise continuous in the interval $[-\pi, \pi]$, its Fourier series (13) converges to

$$\tfrac{1}{2}[f(x+) + f(x-)]$$

at every point where $f(x)$ has right- and left-hand *slopes*. In particular, at every point where $f(x)$ is continuous and has right- and left-hand *derivatives*, its Fourier series will converge to $f(x)$.

In view of this theorem, the Fourier series in Problems 3 to 6 are all valid in the interval $(-\pi, \pi)$.

---

* Cf. Rogosinski, *Fourier Series*, Chelsea, 1950, p. 53. Note that if $f(x)$ is integrable, so is $f^2(x)$, but not conversely (*Advanced Calculus*, § 118).
† *Advanced Calculus*, §§ 222–223.

PROBLEMS

1. If (13) holds as an *equation* and the convergence is uniform, deduce formulas (14).

2. Deduce Parseval's equation (15).

In Problems 3 to 6, verify the Fourier series and find Parseval's equation for functions defined over $(-\pi, \pi)$.

3. The *square wave* of period 2π

$$f_1(x) = \begin{cases} -1 & (-\pi < x < 0) \\ 0 & x = 0 \\ 1 & (0 < x < \pi) \end{cases} = \frac{4}{\pi} \sum_{n=0}^{\infty} \frac{\sin (2n+1)x}{2n+1}.$$

4. $\dfrac{x}{2} = \sum\limits_{n=1}^{\infty} (-1)^{n+1} \dfrac{\sin nx}{n}.$

5. $|x| = \dfrac{\pi}{2} - \dfrac{4}{\pi} \sum\limits_{n=0}^{\infty} \dfrac{\cos (2n+1)x}{(2n+1)^2}.$

6. $x^2 = \dfrac{\pi^2}{3} + 4 \sum\limits_{n=1}^{\infty} (-1)^n \dfrac{\cos nx}{n^2}.$

7. Integrate the series in Problem 3 term by term from 0 to x ($|x| < \pi$) to obtain the series in Problem 5 (*Advanced Calculus* § 227).

8. Integrate the series of Problem 4 term by term from 0 to x ($|x| < \pi$) to obtain the series of Problem 6 (cf. *Advanced Calculus* § 227).

9. If the series $\sum\limits_{n=1}^{\infty} a_n \psi_n(x)$ in terms of the orthogonal system (3) with $\rho(x) = 1$ converges uniformly to $f(x)$, show that

$$a_n = \frac{1}{h_n} \int_a^b f(x) \psi_n(x) \, dx;$$

and that when the system is complete, Parseval's equation becomes

$$\sum_{n=1}^{\infty} h_n a_n^2 = \int_a^b f^2(x) \, dx.$$

10. (a) If $f(x)$ is a function of period $2p$, show that $F(x) = f(px/\pi)$ is a function of period 2π.

(b) In the Fourier series for $F(x)$, make the substitution $x = \pi t/p$ and obtain the series.

$$f(t) = \tfrac{1}{2} a_0 + \sum_{n=1}^{\infty} (a_n \cos n\omega t + b_n \sin n\omega t), \qquad \omega = \frac{\pi}{p},$$

where

$$\begin{matrix} a_n \\ b_n \end{matrix} = \frac{1}{p} \int_{-p}^{p} f(t) \begin{matrix} \cos n\omega t \\ \sin n\omega t \end{matrix} \, dt,$$

and show that Parseval's equation becomes

$$\frac{1}{p} \int_{-p}^{p} f^2(t)\, dt = \tfrac{1}{2}a_0^2 + \sum_{n=1}^{\infty} (a_n^2 + b_n^2).$$

(c) If $f(t)$ is an even function,

$$a_n = \frac{2}{p} \int_0^p f(t)\cos n\omega t\, dt, \qquad b_n = 0;$$

If $f(t)$ is an odd function,

$$b_n = \frac{2}{p} \int_0^p f(t)\sin n\omega t\, dt, \qquad a_n = 0.$$

11. The function $f(t) = 1 - t,\, 0 < t \le 1$.
(a) Expand $f(t)$ in a cosine series by defining $f(t)$ so that it is an even function in $[-1, 1]$. Draw the graph. Find $f(0)$ and $f(\tfrac{1}{2})$.
(b) Expand $f(t)$ in a sine series by defining $f(t)$ so that it is an odd function in $[-1, 1]$. Draw the graph. Find $f(0)$ and $f(\tfrac{1}{2})$.
12. Expand $f(t) = 1 - t,\, -1 < t < 1$, in a Fourier series of period 2. Draw the graph. Find $f(0), f(\tfrac{1}{2}), f(1)$.

117. STURM-LIOUVILLE SYSTEMS

The self-adjoint linear equation of the second order containing a parameter λ,

(1) $$D[p(x)y'] + [q(x) + \lambda\rho(x)]y = 0,$$

is called a Sturm-Liouville equation* in an interval $a \le x \le b$ when subject to certain boundary conditions at its end points. These conditions are various and are given later. We assume that $p(x)$, $p'(x)$, $q(x)$, $\rho(x)$ are real-valued and continuous and $p(x)$, $\rho(x)$ are positive over $[a, b]$; the existence theorem of § 26 then guarantees a continuous solution basis over $[a, b]$. It will appear, however, that the Sturm-Liouville *system*, composed of (1) and the imposed boundary conditions, admits non-zero solutions only when the parameter λ assumes certain discrete *eigenvalues* λ_n. The eigenvalues constitute the *spectrum* of the system and the corresponding non-zero solutions are the *eigenfunctions*.

We now consider the nature of the boundary conditions that must be imposed on equation (1) to ensure an orthogonal set of eigenfunctions on

---

* Jaques Sturm (1803–1855), a Swiss mathematician, is perhaps best remembered for his celebrated theorem on the location of the zeros of a polynomial. The French mathematician Joseph Liouville (1809–1882) founded in 1836 the important periodical *Journal de Mathématiques pures et appliqueés* (often called *Liouville's Journal*). Liouville is famed for his researches in differential equations and complex analysis.

$[a, b]$. If λ, μ are distinct eigenvalues and $u(x)$, $v(x)$ the corresponding eigenfunctions, then

$$D(pu') + (q + \lambda\rho)u = 0,$$
$$D(pv') + (q + \mu\rho)v = 0.$$

Multiply the first equation by $-v$, the second by u, and add them; then

$$uD(pv') - vD(pu') = (\lambda - \mu)\rho uv.$$

If $W(x)$ denotes the Wronskian of u and v,

$$W = uv' - vu', \qquad W' = uv'' - vu'',$$

and the left member becomes $p'W + pW' = D(pW)$; hence the identity

$$(2) \qquad D[p(x)W(x)] = (\lambda - \mu)\rho uv.$$

If we integrate (2) between $x = a$ and $x = b$, then

$$(3) \qquad p(b)W(b) - p(a)W(a) = (\lambda - \mu)\int_a^b \rho uv \, dx.$$

This equation shows how to impose conditions at a and b so that the integral is zero.

We have a *regular system* when

$$1° \qquad W(a) = 0, \qquad W(b) = 0.$$

These conditions are met by imposing the linear boundary conditions

$$(4) \qquad Ay(a) + A'y'(a) = 0 \qquad (A, A') \neq (0, 0),$$
$$(5) \qquad By(b) + B'y'(b) = 0 \qquad (B, B') \neq (0, 0).$$

For the solutions $u(x)$, $v(x)$, (4) implies that

$$Au(a) + A'u'(a) = 0,$$
$$Av(a) + A'v'(a) = 0,$$

and since these equations are satisfied by the non-zero pair (A, A'), their determinant $W(a) = 0$. Similarly, (5) implies that $W(b) = 0$.

In a *periodic system*

$$2° \qquad p(a) = p(b), \qquad W(a) = W(b).$$

When $p(a) = p(b)$, it is sufficient to impose the periodic boundary conditions

$$(6) \qquad y(a) = y(b), \qquad y'(a) = y'(b);$$

for then

$$W(a) = \begin{vmatrix} u(a) & v(a) \\ u'(a) & v'(a) \end{vmatrix} = \begin{vmatrix} u(b) & v(b) \\ u'(b) & v'(b) \end{vmatrix} = W(b).$$

If we only require that $p(x)$, $\rho(x)$ be positive in the *open* interval (a, b), we can also have the *singular systems*:

3° $W(a) = 0,$ $p(b) = 0;$

4° $p(a) = 0,$ $W(b) = 0;$

5° $p(a) = 0,$ $p(b) = 0.$

In case 3° condition (4) yields $W(a) = 0$; in case 4° condition (5) yields $W(b) = 0$. In case 5° the integral in (3) vanishes irrespective of the boundary conditions. To obtain a discrete set of eigenvalues in these cases, we require *bounded* solutions in the interval $[a, b]$. This requirement is often met when polynomial solutions correspond to a discrete set of eigenvalues.

In all five cases the left member of (3) is zero and since $\lambda \neq \mu$, the integral on the right is also zero. We therefore have

Theorem 1. *In the Sturm-Liouville system composed of equation* (1) *and any of the boundary conditions listed in cases* 1° *to* 5°, *any two eigenfunctions corresponding to different eigenvalues are orthogonal in* $[a, b]$ *with respect to the weight function* $\rho(x)$:

(7) $$\int_a^b \rho(x)u(x)v(x)\,dx = 0.$$

As to the eigenvalues we have

Theorem 2. *Under the conditions of Theorem* 1 *the eigenvalues of the Sturm-Liouville system are all real.*

PROOF. Let the eigenvalue $\lambda = \alpha + i\beta$ (α, β real) correspond to the eigenfunction $y = u + iv$ in which u and v are real-valued functions. Then from (1)

$$D[p(u + iv)'] + [q + (\alpha + i\beta)\rho](u + iv) = 0;$$

and if we take the conjugate of the left member we see that $\bar{\lambda} = \alpha - i\beta$ is an eigenvalue with the corresponding eigenfunction $u - iv$. If $\beta \neq 0$, $\lambda \neq \bar{\lambda}$, and from Theorem 1

$$\int_a^b \rho(u + iv)(u - iv)\,dx = \int_a^b \rho(u^2 + v^2)\,dx = 0.$$

But this is impossible since $\rho > 0$ and the integral is positive. Thus $\beta = 0$, $\lambda = \alpha$, and all eigenvalues are real.

Example 1. The regular Sturm-Liouville system

$$y'' + \lambda y = 0; \qquad y(0) = 0, \quad y(\pi) = 0,$$

of case 1° has the end conditions (4–5) with $a = 0$, $b = \pi$ and $A = B = 1$, $A' = B' = 0$.

When $\lambda = -n^2$ (negative), $y = c_1 e^{nx} + c_2 e^{-nx}$, and the conditions are satisfied only when $c_1 = c_2 = 0$.

When $\lambda = 0$, $y = c_1 x + c_2$, and again the conditions require that $c_1 = c_2 = 0$.

When $\lambda = n^2$ (positive),

$$y = c_1 \cos nx + c_2 \sin nx,$$

and the conditions require that $c_1 = 0$ and $\sin n\pi = 0$. Hence $n = 1, 2, 3, \ldots$, and the eigenvalues $\lambda = n^2 = 1, 4, 9, \ldots$ correspond to the eigenfunctions

$$\sin x, \sin 2x, \sin 3x, \ldots .$$

Since $\rho(x) = 1$, Theorem 1 shows that these functions are orthogonal on the interval $[0, \pi]$.

Example 2. The periodic Sturm-Liouville system

$$y'' + \lambda y = 0; \qquad y(-\pi) = y(\pi), \quad y'(-\pi) = y'(\pi)$$

of case 2° has the periodic end conditions (6) with $a = -\pi$, $b = \pi$. As in Example 1, nontrivial solutions occur only when $\lambda = n^2$ (positive) and the conditions require that $\sin n\pi = 0$, but with c_1 and c_2 arbitrary. Thus n must be an integer, and the eigenvalues $\lambda = n^2$ are the squares of the integers. The eigenvalues $\lambda = 0, 1, 4, 9, \ldots$ correspond to the eigenfunctions

$$1, \quad (\cos x, \sin x), \quad (\cos 2x, \sin 2x), \ldots .$$

Since *two* eigenfunctions correspond to each non-zero eigenvalue, we cannot conclude from Theorem 1 that $\cos nx$ and $\sin nx$ are orthogonal on $[-\pi, \pi]$; but since $2 \cos nx \sin nx = \sin 2nx$, this is also true. Thus the functions of the preceding set are orthogonal on the interval $[-\pi, \pi]$.

Example 3. The parametric Bessel equation of order zero is

$$xy'' + y' + \lambda^2 xy = 0 \quad \text{or} \quad \vartheta^2 y + \lambda^2 x^2 y = 0.$$

On putting $t = \lambda x$, $\vartheta = \vartheta$ (106.6), it becomes the standard Bessel equation of order zero

$$\vartheta^2 y - t^2 y = 0 \qquad \text{(Ex. 111.1).}$$

This has a regular singular point at $t = 0$ and admits the continuous solution

$$y = J_0(t) = J_0(\lambda x)$$

for every positive λ.

Consider the now Sturm-Liouville system

(i)　　　　　　　　$D(xy') + \lambda^2 xy = 0, \qquad y(1) = 0,$

over the interval $[0, 1]$ in which

$$p(x) = x, \qquad q(x) = 0, \qquad \rho(x) = x.$$

Since $p(0) = 0$, the system is singular and falls under case 4°. The solution $J_0(\lambda x)$ is continuous and therefore is bounded in $[0, 1]$; and if

$$J_0(\lambda) = 0,$$

it satisfies the condition at $x = 1$. This equation has an infinite number of positive roots $\lambda_1, \lambda_2, \ldots$ (Theorem 130.2); hence $J_0(\lambda_1 x), J_0(\lambda_2 x), \ldots$ are eigenfunctions of the Sturm-Liouville system belonging to the eigenvalues $\lambda_1{}^2, \lambda_2{}^2, \ldots$ [squared because the parameter in (i) is λ^2]. Therefore, by Theorem 1, the functions $J_0(\lambda_n x)$ form an orthogonal system in the interval $[0, 1]$ with the weight function $\rho(x) = x$.

Example 4. The hypergeometric equation

(i) $$x(1 - x)y'' + (1 - 2x)y' + \lambda y = 0$$

has the theta form

$$\vartheta^2 y - x(\vartheta^2 + \vartheta - \lambda)y = 0.$$

Its parameters are $\alpha, \beta, \gamma = 1$ where α, β satisfy

$$(\vartheta + \alpha)(\vartheta + \beta) = \vartheta^2 + \vartheta - \lambda; \qquad \alpha + \beta = 1, \quad \alpha\beta = -\lambda.$$

The solution analytic at $x = 0$ is the hypergeometric series

$$y(x) = F(\alpha, \beta; \gamma; x),$$

for the second solution involves log x (§ 111). The series converges when $-1 \leqq x < 1$, but diverges when $x = 1$ ($\gamma - \alpha - \beta = 0$), (§ 114) unless it terminates. Thus the only *bounded* solutions in $[-1, 1]$ are polynomials. These occur when $\alpha = -n, n = 0, 1, 2, \ldots$; then $\beta = n + 1, \lambda = n(n + 1)$.

Writing (i) in the form

$$D[x(1 - x)y'] + \lambda y = 0$$

shows that (i) is a singular Sturm-Liouville equation of case 5° over $[0, 1]$ with $p = x(1 - x), q = 0, \rho = 1$. The eigenvalues are $\lambda_n = n(n + 1)$, and the eigenfunctions are the polynomials

$$y_n = F(-n, n + 1; 1; x), \qquad n = 0, 1, 2, \ldots ,$$

which form an orthogonal set over $[0, 1]$. The first four are

$$y_0 = 1, \quad y_1 = 1 - 2x, \quad y_2 = 1 - 6x + 6x^2, \quad y_3 = 1 - 12x + 30x^2 - 20x^3.$$

PROBLEMS

In Problems 1 to 4 show that the regular Sturm-Liouville system has the given eigenvalues λ_n, eigenfunctions y_n ($n = 0, 1, 2, \ldots$) and weight function $\rho(x)$.

1. $y'' + \lambda y = 0$; $y(0) = 0, y(\pi/2) = 0$;
   $\lambda_n = 4n^2, y_n = \sin 2nx, \rho = 1$.

2. $y'' + \lambda y = 0$; $y(0) = 0, y(1) = 0$;
   $\lambda_n = n^2\pi^2, y_n = \sin n\pi x, \rho = 1$.

3. $(x^2 y')' + (\lambda/x^2)y = 0$, $y(1) = 0$, $y(2) = 0$;
   $\lambda_n = 4n^2\pi^2$, $y_n = \sin [2n\pi(x - 1)/x]$, $\rho = 1/x^2$.

4. $xy'' + y' + \lambda x^3 y = 0$; $y(0) = 0$, $y(a) = 0$;
   $\lambda_n = 4n^2\pi^2/a^4$, $y_n = \sin (n\pi x^2/a^2)$, $\rho = x$.

5. Show that the system

$$y'' + \lambda^3 xy = 0, \qquad y(0) = 0, \qquad y(1) = 0,$$

has an infinite number of positive eigenvalues and that the eigenfunctions are orthogonal over [0, 1].

[Reduce to the theta form and put $t = \lambda x$ to obtain the *Airy equation*

$$\vartheta(\vartheta - 1)y + t^3 y = 0$$

whose solutions have an infinite number of positive zeros (Prob. 130.5). The solution of index 1, $y = \varphi(t) = \varphi(\lambda x)$, will vanish at $x = 0$ and also at $x = 1$ when λ is a zero of $\varphi(x)$.]

6. Put *Weber's equation* (Heinrich Weber (1842–1913))

$$y'' - xy' - \lambda y = 0$$

in the theta form and find two power series solutions about $x = 0$. Show that these become polynomials when $\lambda = 0, -1, -2, \ldots$. Find the first five of these polynomials with the coefficient 1 for the term of lowest degree.

Reduce the equation to the self-adjoint form (§ 33) and show that the polynomial solutions form an orthogonal set over $[-\infty, \infty]$ with the weight function $\exp(-x^2)$.

118. CHEBYSHEV'S EQUATION*

(1) $$(1 - x^2)y'' - xy' + n^2 y = 0$$

has regular singular points at $x = 1, -1, \infty$. The linear substitution

$$x = 1 - 2t \quad \text{or} \quad t = \tfrac{1}{2}(1 - x)$$

carries these points into $t = 0, 1, \infty$. Since $y' = -\tfrac{1}{2}\dot{y}$, $y'' = \tfrac{1}{4}\ddot{y}$, (1) becomes

(2) $$t(1 - t)\ddot{y} + (\tfrac{1}{2} - t)\dot{y} + n^2 y = 0.$$

Comparison with (114.1) shows that this is a hg equation with $\alpha = n$, $\beta = -n$, $\gamma = \tfrac{1}{2}$. When $n = 0, 1, 2, \ldots$, the series solution

(3) $$T_n(x) = F[n, -n; \tfrac{1}{2}; \tfrac{1}{2}(1 - x)]$$

terminates and is called the *Chebyshev polynomial* of degree n. When $x = 1$, the series reduces to its first term 1; hence for any n

(4) $$T_n(1) = F(n, -n; \tfrac{1}{2}, 0) = 1.$$

Formula (3) gives $T_0(x) = 1$, $T_1(x) = x$, but for higher values of n, $T_n(x)$ is

---

* P. L. Chebyshev (1821–1894), a Russian mathematician famed especially for his contributions to the theory of numbers. His name was formerly transcribed Tschebycheff; hence the notation $T_n(x)$.

best obtained from a recurrence relation. To obtain this put $x = \cos\theta$ in the interval $|x| \le 1$; then since

$$y' = -\frac{y_\theta}{\sin\theta}, \qquad y'' = \frac{y_{\theta\theta}}{\sin^2\theta} - \frac{\cos\theta}{\sin^3\theta}\,y_\theta$$

($y_\theta = dy/d\theta$), equation (1) becomes

(5)
$$\frac{d^2y}{d\theta^2} + n^2y = 0.$$

This equation has the solution basis $\cos n\theta$, $\sin n\theta$. Now by means of DeMoivre's theorem, $\cos n\theta$ may be expressed as a polynomial in $x = \cos\theta$ which has the property (4); for when $x = 1$, $\theta = \cos^{-1}1 = 0$ when we take the principal value ($0 \le \theta \le \pi$). Thus in the interval $-1 \le x \le 1$ we have

(6)
$$T_n(x) = \cos n\theta, \qquad x = \cos\theta.$$

The identity

$$\cos n\theta + \cos(n-2)\theta = 2\cos\theta\cos(n-1)\theta$$

now gives the recurrence relation

(7)
$$T_n(x) + T_{n-2}(x) = 2xT_{n-1}(x).$$

By beginning with $T_0(x) = 1$, $T_1(x) = x$, (7) now gives successively

$$T_2(x) = 2x^2 - 1, \qquad T_3(x) = 4x^3 - 3x, \qquad T_4(x) = 8x^4 - 8x^2 + 1,$$

and so on.

Chebyshev's equation (1) assumes the self-adjoint form

(8)
$$D(\sqrt{1-x^2}\,y') + \frac{n^2}{\sqrt{1-x^2}}\,y = 0$$

when multiplied by the factor

$$\sigma = \frac{1}{P_0}\int\frac{P_1}{P_0}\,dx = \frac{1}{\sqrt{1-x^2}} \qquad (32.8).$$

Comparison with (117.1) shows that

$$p(x) = \sqrt{1-x^2}, \qquad q(x) = 0, \qquad \rho(x) = \frac{1}{\sqrt{1-x^2}}, \qquad \lambda = n^2,$$

and $p(x) = 0$ when $x = \pm 1$. In the interval $[-1, 1]$ we have a singular Sturm-Liouville system under case 5°. For $n = 0, 1, 2, \ldots$, we have the eigenvalues $\lambda = n^2$ and the corresponding eigenfunctions $T_n(x)$. These form an orthogonal set over $[-1, 1]$ with the weight function $(1 - x^2)^{-\frac{1}{2}}$:

(9)
$$\int_{-1}^{1} \frac{T_m(x)T_n(x)}{\sqrt{1 - x^2}} \, dx = \begin{cases} 0, & m \neq n, \\ \frac{1}{2}\pi, & m = n \neq 0, \\ \pi, & m = n = 0. \end{cases}$$

The results when $m = n$ follow after we put $x = \cos \theta$; the integral then becomes

$$\int_0^{\pi} \cos^2 n\theta \, d\theta = \begin{cases} \frac{1}{2}\pi, & m = n \neq 0, \\ \pi, & m = n = 0. \end{cases}$$

The recurrence relation (7) shows that the coefficient of x^n in $T_n(x)$ is 2^{n-1}; hence the polynomials $2^{1-n}T_n(x)$ are *monic*—they begin with x^n. These monic polynomials have the remarkable

Minimax Property. *Among all monic polynomials $P(x)$ of degrees $n > 0$, $2^{1-n}T_n(x)$ deviates least from zero in the interval $[-1, 1]$; that is*

(10)
$$\max_{[-1,1]} |P(x)| \geq \max_{[-1,1]} |2^{1-n}T_n(x)| = 2^{1-n}, \qquad n > 0.$$

PROOF. Since $\max |T_n(x)| = \max |\cos n\theta| = 1$ in $[-1, 1]$, we have the equality in (10). *Assume* now that a monic polynomial $P(x)$ is such that $\max_{[-1,1]} |P(x)| < 2^{1-n}$ in $[-1, 1]$. Now $2^{1-n}T_n(x) = 2^{1-n} \cos n\theta$ takes on alternately positive and negative values $\pm 2^{1-n}$ at the $n + 1$ points $\theta = 0$, $\pi/n, 2\pi/n, \ldots, n\pi/n = \pi$. Hence $Q(x) = T_n(x) - P(x)$ has the same sign as $T_n(x)$ at these points and must change sign n times in the interval $[-1, 1]$. By Rolle's theorem, $Q(x)$ must have n zeros in $[-1, 1]$. But since $Q(x)$ is a polynomial of degree $n - 1$ or less, this is impossible.

PROBLEMS

1. Verify that the substitution $x = \cos \theta$ reduces equation (1) to (5).

2. Use the recurrence relation (7) to show by induction that the highest power in $T_n(x) = 2^{n-1}x^n$ $(n > 0)$.

3. Show that Chebyshev's equation (1) has the theta form

(11)
$$\vartheta(\vartheta - 1) - x^2(\vartheta + n)(\vartheta - n)y = 0,$$

which becomes the hg equation

(12)
$$\vartheta(\vartheta - \tfrac{1}{2})y - t(\vartheta + \tfrac{1}{2}n)(\vartheta - \tfrac{1}{2}n)y = 0$$

when we put $t = x^2$.

4. Show that the hg equation (12) has the polynomial solutions

$$y_1(x) = F\left(\frac{n}{2}, -\frac{n}{2}; \frac{1}{2}; x^2\right)$$

$$y_2(x) = xF\left(\frac{1+n}{2}, \frac{1-n}{2}; \frac{3}{2}; x^2\right)$$

for even and odd n, respectively. Hence show that for $m = 0, 1, 2, \ldots$,

(13)
$$T_{2m}(x) = \frac{F(m, -m; \frac{1}{2}; x^2)}{F(m, -m; \frac{1}{2}; 1)},$$

(14)
$$T_{2m+1}(x) = \frac{xF(m+1, -m; \frac{3}{2}; x^2)}{F(m+1, -m; \frac{3}{2}; 1)}.$$

5. Compute $T_2(x)$, $T_3(x)$, $T_4(x)$, and $T_5(x)$ from the formulas (13) and (14).
6. Deduce the identity

(15)
$$T_{m+n}(x) + T_{m-n}(x) = 2T_m(x)T_n(x)$$

from a corresponding identity for cosines.
    Show that (7) is a special case of (15).
7. Prove the identity

(16)
$$T_m\{T_n(x)\} = T_n\{T_m(x)\} = T_{mn}(x).$$

119. LEGENDRE'S EQUATION*

(1)
$$(1 - x^2)y'' - 2xy' + n(n+1)y = 0$$

has regular singular points at $x = 1, -1, \infty$. The linear substitution

(2)
$$x = 1 - 2t \quad \text{or} \quad t = \tfrac{1}{2}(1 - x)$$

carries these points into $t = 0, 1, \infty$, and the equation becomes hg:

(3)
$$t(1 - t)\ddot{y} + (1 - 2t)\dot{y} + n(n+1)y = 0.$$

Its theta form

$$\vartheta^2 y - t(\vartheta - n)(\vartheta + n + 1)y = 0$$

discloses the parameters

$$\alpha = -n, \qquad \beta = n + 1, \qquad \gamma = 1;$$

and indicial equation $\lambda^2 = 0$ shows that the singular point $t = 0$ has equal indices $0, 0$. One solution

(4)
$$y_1(t) = F(-n, n + 1; 1; t)$$

---

* Adrien-Marie Legendre (1752–1833), a French mathematician who made many important contributions to the theory of numbers and elliptic functions.

is analytic at $t = 0$ but diverges when $t = 1$ since $\gamma - \alpha - \beta = 0$; the second $y_2(t)$ involves log t and may be found by the method of § 111 or by use of formula (28.8). From (3) we have

$$P = \frac{1 - 2t}{t(1 - t)} = \frac{1}{t} - \frac{1}{1 - t}, \qquad \int P \, dt = \log t(1 - t),$$

and hence

(5) $$y_2 = y_1 \int \frac{dt}{t(1 - t)y_1{}^2}.$$

For example, when $n = 0$, $y_1 = 1$ and

$$y_2 = \int \frac{dt}{t(1 - t)} = \log \frac{t}{1 - t} = \log t - \log(1 - t)$$

$$= \log t + t + \frac{t^2}{2} + \frac{t^3}{3} + \cdots.$$

Since equation (3) has singular points at $t = 0, 1$, the solutions y_1 and y_2 for any n are at least valid when $0 < |t| < 1$. The general solution in this range is $c_1 y_1 + c_2 y_2$, but the only *analytic* solution is $c_1 y_1$.

When $n = 0, 1, 2, 3, \ldots$, the hg series in (4) terminates and defines the *Legendre polynomial* $P_n(x)$ of degree n:

(6) $$P_n(x) = F[-n, n + 1; 1; \tfrac{1}{2}(1 - x)].$$

When $x = 1$, the series reduces to its first term 1; hence for any n

(7) $$P_n(1) = F(-n, n + 1; 1, 0) = 1.$$

Formula (6) gives the Legendre polynomials in powers of $\frac{1}{2}(1 - x)$; thus

$$P_2(x) = 1 + \frac{(-2)3}{1} \frac{1 - x}{2} + \frac{(-2)(-1)3 \cdot 4}{1 \cdot 2} \frac{1}{2!} \left(\frac{1 - x}{2}\right)^2 = \frac{1}{2}(3x^2 - 1).$$

We shall obtain methods of computing $P_n(x)$ which are less laborious.

Consider the hg equation whose parameters

$$\alpha_1 = -2n, \qquad \beta_1 = 1, \qquad \gamma_1 = 1 - n$$

are n less than those in (6). When n is a positive integer, γ is zero or a negative integer and the solution $F(-2n, 1; 1 - n; t)$ does not exist. The second solution (114.7) is now

$$t^n F(-n, n + 1; n + 1; t) = t^n (1 - t)^n$$

from (114.6). The nth derivative of this solution is a polynomial of degree n whose constant term is $n!$, and Theorem 114 shows that it satisfies (3)—a hg equation whose parameters are n greater than α_1, β_1, γ_1. But all polynomial solutions of (3) are multiples of $y_1(x)$ in (4); and since $y_1(t)$ has the constant term 1, we must have

$$F(-n, n+1; 1; t) = \dot{D}^n\left[\frac{t^n(1-t)^n}{n!}\right].$$

When we put $t = \frac{1}{2}(1 - x)$, the left member becomes $P_n(x)$; and since

$$x = 1 - 2t, \qquad \dot{D} = \frac{d}{dt} = \frac{dx}{dt}\frac{d}{dx} = -2D,$$

$$\dot{D}^n[t^n(1-t)^n] = (-2)^n D^n\left(\frac{1-x^2}{2^2}\right)^n = \frac{1}{2^n}D^n(x^2-1)^n,$$

we have *Rodrigues' formula* for the Legendre polynomials:

(8)
$$P_n(x) = \frac{1}{n!\,2^n}D^n(x^2-1)^n.$$

For example,

$$P_2(x) = \frac{1}{8}D^2(x^4 - 2x^2 + 1) = \frac{12x^2 - 4}{8} = \frac{1}{2}(3x^2 - 1).$$

From formula (8) we have after n integrations by parts

$$\int_{-1}^{1} P_n{}^2(x)\,dx = \frac{(-1)^n(2n)!}{(n!\,2^n)^2}\int_{-1}^{1}(x^2-1)^n\,dx = 2\frac{(2n-1)!!}{(2n)!!}\int_{0}^{1}(1-x^2)^n\,dx.$$

Putting $x = \cos\theta$, we have*

$$\int_{0}^{1}(1-x^2)^n\,dx = \int_{0}^{\pi/2}\sin^{2n+1}\theta\,d\theta = \frac{(2n)!!}{(2n+1)!!}$$

and hence

(9)
$$\int_{-1}^{1}P_n{}^2(x)\,dx = \frac{2}{2n+1}.$$

Repeated integration by parts also shows that the Legendre polynomials are orthogonal on the interval $[-1, 1]$.† But this property also follows from Theorem 117.1, for when Legendre's equation is written in the self-adjoint form

(10)
$$D[(1-x^2)y'] + n(n+1)y = 0,$$

---

* *Advanced Calculus*, p. 269.
† *Advanced Calculus*, p. 514.

we have a singular Sturm-Liouville system over $[-1, 1]$ with

$$p(x) = 1 - x^2, \qquad q(x) = 0, \qquad \rho(x) = 1, \qquad \lambda = n(n + 1).$$

Since $p(-1) = p(1) = 0$, we are in case 5° of § 117 and *bounded* solutions over $[-1, 1]$ are required. These occur only when $\lambda = n(n + 1)$, $n = 0, 1, 2, \ldots$; these are the eigenvalues and the corresponding eigenfunctions are the Legendre polynomials $P_n(x)$. For other values of λ, the hypergeometric series diverges at $x = 1$. Since $\rho(x) = 1$, the polynomials $P_n(x)$ form an orthogonal set over $[-1, 1]$:

$$(11) \qquad \int_{-1}^{1} P_m(x)P_n(x)\, dx = \begin{cases} 0, & m \neq n, \\ \dfrac{2}{2n + 1}, & m = n. \end{cases}$$

Therefore, the functions

$$(12) \qquad \sqrt{n + \tfrac{1}{2}}\, P_n(x)$$

form an orthonormal set on $[-1, 1]$. From the Weierstrass approximation theorem stating that any continuous function in the interval $[-1, 1]$ can be uniformly approximated by a polynomial $P(x)$ to any assigned degree of accuracy, that is,

$$|f(x) - P(x)| < \varepsilon, \qquad -1 \leq x \leq 1,$$

we can show that the orthonormal set (12) is *complete*.*

When Legendre's equation is multiplied by x^2, it assumes the theta form

$$(13) \qquad \vartheta(\vartheta - 1)y - x^2(\vartheta - n)(\vartheta + n + 1)y = 0.$$

If we now make the change of variable

$$t = x^2, \qquad \vartheta = 2\dot{\vartheta} \qquad\qquad (106.7)$$

and divide the equation by 4, we obtain the hg equation in t

$$(14) \qquad \dot{\vartheta}\left(\dot{\vartheta} - \frac{1}{2}\right)y - t\left(\dot{\vartheta} - \frac{n}{2}\right)\left(\dot{\vartheta} + \frac{n + 1}{2}\right)y = 0$$

with parameters

$$\alpha = -\frac{n}{2}, \qquad \beta = \frac{n + 1}{2}, \qquad \gamma = \frac{1}{2}.$$

Now $t = 0$ ($x = 0$) is an ordinary point with indices 0, $\tfrac{1}{2}$, and admits the series solutions

$$y_1 = F\left(-\frac{n}{2}, \frac{n + 1}{2}; \frac{1}{2}; x^2\right),$$

$$y_2 = xF\left(\frac{1 - n}{2}, \frac{n + 2}{2}; \frac{3}{2}; x^2\right).$$

---

* *Advanced Calculus*, p. 528.

The first terminates when n is an even integer, the second when n is an odd integer. These polynomial solutions must be multiples of $P_n(x)$ for even and odd n, because such solutions are valid everywhere. Since $P_n(1) = 1$, we have therefore

$$(15) \qquad\qquad P_{2m}(x) = \frac{F(-m,\ m + \frac{1}{2};\ \frac{1}{2};\ x^2)}{F(-m,\ m + \frac{1}{2};\ \frac{1}{2};\ 1)}\ ;$$

$$(16) \qquad\qquad P_{2m+1}(x) = \frac{xF(-m,\ m + \frac{3}{2};\ \frac{3}{2};\ x^2)}{F(-m,\ m + \frac{3}{2};\ \frac{3}{2};\ 1)}\ .$$

In these formulas we compute the numerator and divide by its value when $x = 1$. We see also that $P_n(x)$ is an even or odd function according as n is even or odd. Thus we find

$P_0(x) = 1$ $\qquad\qquad\qquad\qquad$ $P_1(x) = x$

$P_2(x) = \frac{1}{2}(3x^2 - 1)$ $\qquad\qquad\quad$ $P_3(x) = \frac{1}{2}(5x^2 - 3x)$

$P_4(x) = \frac{1}{8}(35x^4 - 30x^2 + 3)$ $\qquad$ $P_5(x) = \frac{1}{8}(63x^5 - 70x^3 + 15x)$.

Their graphs, shown in Fig. 119, illustrate the fact that $P_n(x)$ has exactly n simple zeros in the interval $[-1, 1]$—a property we shall prove in § 121.

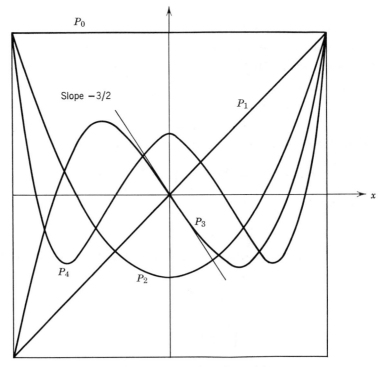

Fig. 119   Legendre polynomials.

PROBLEM

1. When $n = 1$, show that the two solutions of equation (3), given by (4) and (5), are

$$y_1 = 1 - 2t$$

$$y_2 = (1 - 2t) \log \frac{t}{1 - t} + 2$$

$$= (1 - 2t) \log t + 2 + t - \sum_{n=2}^{\infty} \frac{n+1}{n(n-1)} t^n.$$

[Cf. Ex. 111.2 where equation (3) with signs reversed was solved by another method. Show that this y_2 may be derived from the former y_2.]

120. RECURRENCE RELATIONS FOR $P_n(x)$

We can use Rodrigues' formula to obtain several useful recurrence relations. Thus from

$$P_{n+1}(x) = \frac{1}{(n+1)! \, 2^{n+1}} D^{n+1}[(x^2 - 1)^{n+1}]$$

$$= \frac{1}{n! \, 2^n} D^n[x(x^2 - 1)^n],$$

$$P'_{n+1}(x) = \frac{1}{n! \, 2^n} D^{n+1}[x(x^2 - 1)^n].$$

If we compute the derivative by use of Leibniz's theorem* we get

$$P'_{n+1} = \frac{1}{n! \, 2^n} [xD^{n+1}(x^2 - 1)^n + (n+1)D^n(x^2 - 1)^n]$$

$$= xP_n' + (n+1)P_n.$$

But if we compute D^{n+1} as $D^n D$, we have

$$P'_{n+1} = \frac{1}{n! \, 2^n} D^n[(x^2 - 1)^n + 2nx^2(x^2 - 1)^{n-1}]$$

$$= \frac{1}{n! \, 2^n} D^n[(2n + 1)(x^2 - 1)^n + 2n(x^2 - 1)^{n-1}]$$

$$= (2n + 1)P_n + P'_{n-1}.$$

---

* *Advanced Calculus*, p. 110 (5).

We have thus proved the identities

(1) $$(n + 1)P_n = P'_{n+1} - xP'_n,$$

(2) $$(2n + 1)P_n = P'_{n+1} - P'_{n-1};$$

and on subtracting (1) from (2), we have

(3) $$nP_n = xP'_n - P'_{n-1}.$$

We may eliminate the derivatives from these equations as follows: from (1), (2), and (3) we have

$$nP_{n-1} = P'_n - xP'_{n-1},$$
$$-(2n + 1)xP_n = xP'_{n-1} - xP'_{n+1},$$
$$(n + 1)P_{n+1} = xP'_{n+1} - P'_n,$$

and on adding these equations we find the important relation

(4) $$(n + 1)P_{n+1} - (2n + 1)xP_n + nP_{n-1} = 0.$$

From $P_0 = 1$, $P_1 = x$ we may use (4) to find $P_2, P_3, \ldots$ in turn. The reader should verify in this way the values of P_2 to P_5 given in § 119.

From (4) we can find the generating function of $P_n(x)$ by the method of § 99. In harmony with the notation of § 99 we write $P_t(z)$ instead of $P_n(x)$; then (4) becomes

(4)′ $$(t + 1)P_{t+1} - (2t + 1)zP_t + tP_{t-1} = 0.$$

Now if

(5) $$F(x, z) = \sum_{t=0}^{\infty} P_t(z)x^t$$

and we define $P_{-1} = 0$ [which satisfies (4)′ when $t = 0$], we have the transforms from Table 99a:

$$tP_t \sim xF', \quad (t + 1)P_{t+1} \sim F', \quad tP_{t-1} \sim x(xF)' = xF + x^2F',$$

and (4)′ yields the differential equation

$$F' - z(2xF' + F) + x^2F' + xF = 0$$

in which $F' = \partial F/\partial x$ and z is regarded as a constant parameter. Hence

$$\frac{F'}{F} + \frac{x - z}{1 - 2zx + x^2} = 0,$$

and on integration with respect to x, we have

$$\log F + \tfrac{1}{2} \log (1 - 2zx + x^2) = \log C,$$
$$F(x, z) = C(1 - 2zx + x^2)^{-\frac{1}{2}}.$$

When $x = 0$, the series (5) reduces to its first term $P_0(z) = 1 = C$, and the generating function is $(1 - 2zx + x^2)^{-1/2}$. By writing n for t, (5) now becomes

$$(6) \qquad (1 - 2zx + x^2)^{-1/2} = \sum_{n=0}^{\infty} P_n(z)x^n.$$

In particular, when $z = 0$ we have

$$(1 + x^2)^{-1/2} = \sum_{n=0}^{\infty} \binom{-\frac{1}{2}}{n} x^{2n} = \sum_{n=0}^{\infty} P_{2n}(0)x^{2n}$$

since $P_{2n+1}(0) = 0$ (why?); hence

$$(7) \qquad P_{2n}(0) = \binom{-\frac{1}{2}}{n} = (-1)^n \frac{(2n-1)!!}{(2n)!!}.$$

Since $P_n(x)$ is an even or odd function according to the parity of n,

$$P_n(-1) = (-1)^n P_n(1) = (-1)^n.$$

This result also follows from (6) when $z = -1$:

$$(1 + x)^{-1} = \sum_{n=0}^{\infty} (-x)^n = \sum_{n=0}^{\infty} P_n(-1)x^n.$$

PROBLEMS

1. Prove that $P_{2n+1}(0) = 0$.

2. Prove that

$$(2n + 1) \int_x^1 P_n(x) \, dx = P_{n-1}(x) - P_{n+1}(x).$$

3. When $n > 0$, prove that

(a) $\displaystyle \int_0^1 P_n(x) \, dx = \frac{1}{n+1} P_{n-1}(0);$

(b) $\displaystyle \int_0^1 P_{2n}(x) \, dx = 0;$

(c) $\displaystyle \int_0^1 P_{2n+1}(x) \, dx = (-1)^n \frac{(2n-1)!!}{(2n+2)!!}.$

(d) Compute these integrals when $n = 0$.

4. Use (120.1) to prove that

(a) $P'_{2n}(0) = 0;$ (b) $P'_{2n+1}(0) = (-1)^n \dfrac{(2n+1)!!}{(2n)!!}.$

5. When $z = \cos \theta = \frac{1}{2}(e^{i\theta} + e^{-i\theta})$, show that (6) becomes

$$(1 - xe^{i\theta})^{-\frac{1}{2}}(1 - xe^{-i\theta})^{-\frac{1}{2}} = \sum_{n=0}^{\infty} P_n(\cos \theta)x^n.$$

Write the left member as the product of two series and show that

$$P_0(\cos \theta) = 1, \qquad\qquad P_1(\cos \theta) = \cos \theta,$$

$$P_2(\cos \theta) = \tfrac{1}{4}(3 \cos 2\theta + 1), \qquad\qquad P_3(\cos \theta) = \tfrac{1}{8}(5 \cos 3\theta + 3 \cos \theta).$$

121. LEGENDRE EXPANSIONS

Since the Legendre polynomials $\{P_n(x)\}$ form a complete set of orthogonal functions over the interval $[-1, 1]$, we can expand a function which is piecewise smooth in the interval $[-1, 1]$ in a series

$$(1) \qquad f(x) = \sum_{j=0}^{\infty} a_j P_j(x), \qquad a_n = \frac{2n + 1}{2} \int_{-1}^{1} f(x) P_n(x) \, dx.$$

This value of a_n is found by multiplying the series by $P_n(x)$, integrating term by term from -1 to 1, and using equations (119.11).

For such Legendre expansions we have the following basic theorem.

Theorem 1. *Let $f(x)$ be a bounded, integrable function in the interval $[-1, 1]$ and $s_n(x)$ the nth partial sum of the Legendre series. Then if $\sigma_n(x)$ is the nth partial sum of the Fourier cosine series for the function $f(\cos \theta)$ in the interval $[0, \pi]$, then*

$$\lim_{n \to \infty} [s_n(\cos \theta) - \sigma_n(\theta)] = 0$$

and the two expansions converge or diverge together.*

Thus the study of Legendre expansions is reduced to the well-known theory of Fourier series.

According as $g(x)$ is an even or an odd function, we have

$$\int_{-1}^{1} g(x) \, dx = 2 \int_{0}^{1} g(x) \, dx \quad \text{or} \quad 0.\dagger$$

---

* W. H. Young, "Sur le series de polynomes de Legendre," *Compt. Rend.* (*Paris*) **165** (1917), pp. 696–699.

A. Haar, "Reihenentwicklungen nach Legendreschen Polynomen," *Math. Ann.*, **78** (1918) pp. 121–136.

† *Advanced Calculus*, p. 272, Ex. 2.

Hence when $f(x)$ is an even or an odd function, the coefficients a_n in its Legendre expansion given in (1) have the values

$$a_n = \begin{cases} (2n + 1) \int_0^1 f(x) P_n(x) \, dx & \begin{cases} f(x) \text{ even, } n \text{ even} \\ f(x) \text{ odd, } n \text{ odd}; \end{cases} \\ 0 & \begin{cases} f(x) \text{ even, } n \text{ odd} \\ f(x) \text{ odd, } n \text{ even}. \end{cases} \end{cases}$$

Thus Legendre expansions of even or odd functions contain only $P_n(x)$ of even or odd index, respectively.

If $s_{n+1}(x)$ is the $(n + 1)$th partial sum of the Legendre expansion of a function $f(x)$, $s_{n+1}(x)$ is the polynomial of degree n that best approximates $f(x)$ on $[-1, 1]$ in the sense of least squares. This follows from the general theory of expansions in orthogonal functions given in § 116. Thus $s_{n+1}(x)$ is a better polynomial approximation to $f(x)$ on $[-1, 1]$ than the corresponding polynomial given by the Maclaurin series for $f(x)$.

If $f_m(x)$ is a polynomial of degree m, the "best" polynomial approximation to $f_m(x)$ in the sense of least squares is precisely $f_m(x)$; hence the Legendre expansion for $f_m(x)$ is the sum

$$(3) \qquad f_m(x) = \sum_{j=0}^{m} a_j P_j(x),$$

for powers higher than x^m can not occur. Since $a_n = 0$ when $n > m$ in this expansion, then

$$(4) \qquad \int_{-1}^{1} f_m(x) P_n(x) \, dx = 0 \quad \text{when} \quad m < n.$$

It is now easy to prove the

Theorem 2. *The Legendre polynomial $P_n(x)$ has exactly n simple zeros in* $[-1, 1]$.

PROOF. The equation $P_n(x) = 0$ of degree n can have at most n roots. None of these can be multiple; for if x_1 were a double root, $P_n(x_1) = P_n'(x_1) = 0$ and the existence theorem of § 26 would require that $P_n(x) \equiv 0$. Suppose then that $P_n(x)$ has $m < n$ simple zeros $x_1, x_2, \ldots, x_m$ in $[-1, 1]$, and define

$$f_m(x) = (x - x_1)(x - x_2) \cdots (x - x_m), \qquad f_0(x) = 1;$$

then the integral in (4) is zero. This is manifestly impossible, however, since $f_m(1) > 0$, $P_n(1) = 1$, and at each zero $f_m(x)$ and $P_n(x)$ change sign together, so that $f_m(x) P_n(x) \geqq 0$ in $[-1, 1]$.

PROBLEMS

1. Show that the coefficient of x^n in $P_n(x)$ is $(2n)!/2^n n! \, n!$.

2. Use Problem 1 to find a_n in the Legendre expansions of $P'_{n+1}(x)$ and $xP_{n-1}(x)$. Hence show that

(a) $\displaystyle\int_{-1}^{1} P_n P'_{n+1} \, dx = 2,$ (b) $\displaystyle\int_{-1}^{1} xP_n P_{n-1} \, dx = \frac{2n}{4n^2 - 1}.$

3. Derive Legendre expansions for x^2, x^3, and x^4.

4. Prove that Parseval's equation for the Legendre expansion (1) is

$$\sum_{n=0}^{\infty} \frac{2}{2n + 1} a_n^2 = \int_{-1}^{1} f^2(x) \, dx.$$

[Cf. Prob. 116.9]

5. In the Legendre expansion (1) prove that $a_n/\sqrt{n} \to 0$ as $n \to \infty$.

6. Prove that

$$x^n = \frac{n!}{(2n + 1)!!} \left[(2n + 1)P_n + (2n - 3)\frac{2n + 1}{2} P_{n-2} \right.$$

$$\left. + (2n - 7)\frac{(2n + 1)(2n - 1)}{2 \cdot 4} P_{n-4} + \cdots \right]$$

with P_0 or P_1 in the last term.

122. CONFLUENT HYPERGEOMETRIC EQUATION

In the hg equation $\quad [\gamma - (\alpha + \beta + 1)t]\dot{y}$

$$t(1 - t)\ddot{y} + [\gamma - (\alpha + \beta + 1)t]\dot{y} - \alpha\beta y = 0,$$

change the independent variable to $x = \beta t$; then $\dot{y} = \beta y'$, $\ddot{y} = \beta^2 y''$; and, after dividing out β, we have

$$x\left(1 - \frac{x}{\beta}\right)y'' + \left(\gamma - x - \frac{\alpha + 1}{\beta}\right)y' - \alpha y = 0.$$

This equation has regular singular points at $x = 0$, β, and ∞; and if we let $\beta \to \infty$, it becomes

(1) $$xy'' + (\gamma - x)y' - \alpha y = 0.$$

The singularity at β has now coalesced with that at ∞, and this confluence of two singularities at ∞ produces an irregular singularity there (Prob. 10).

The change of variable $x = \beta t$ is simply made on the theta form of the hg equation

$$\vartheta(\vartheta + \gamma - 1)y - t(\vartheta + \alpha)(\vartheta + \beta)y = 0;$$

for $\dot{\vartheta} = \vartheta$, and we have

$$\vartheta(\vartheta + \gamma - 1)y - x(\vartheta + \alpha)\left(\frac{\vartheta}{\beta} + 1\right)y = 0.$$

When $\beta \to \infty$, this becomes

(2) $$\vartheta(\vartheta + \gamma - 1)y - x(\vartheta + \alpha)y = 0,$$

which is precisely the theta form of (1). Note that the *confluent hypergeometric equation* differs from the hg equation in lacking the factor $\vartheta + \beta$ in the second term. Like the hg equation it has a regular singular point at $x = 0$ with indices $0, 1 - \gamma$.

When γ is not an integer there are two independent series solutions *valid in the entire plane*, with the exception of $x = 0$ when $1 - \gamma < 0$; for deg $f = 2$, deg $g = 1$, and the power series converge for all x (§ 108). Index $\lambda_1 = 0$:

$$y_1 = \sum_{n=0}^{\infty} c_n x^n.$$

The recurrence relation is

$$n(n + \gamma - 1)c_n = (n + \alpha - 1)c_{n-1}$$

and has the solution

$$c_n = \frac{\alpha(\alpha + 1) \cdots (\alpha + n - 1)\, c_0}{\gamma(\gamma + 1) \cdots (\gamma + n - 1)\, n!}.$$

Hence with $c_0 = 1$,

(3) $$y_1 = F(\alpha; \gamma; x) = 1 + \sum_{n=1}^{\infty} \frac{\alpha(\alpha + 1) \cdots (\alpha + n - 1)}{\gamma(\gamma + 1) \cdots (\gamma + n - 1)} \frac{x^n}{n!}$$

where $F(\alpha; \gamma; x)$ is defined by the series on the right. Thus $F(0; \gamma; x) = 1$; and the series terminates if α is a negative integer. Moreover

(4) $$F(\alpha; \alpha; x) = \sum_{n=0}^{\infty} \frac{x^n}{n!} = e^x.$$

Index $\lambda_2 = 1 - \gamma$:

$$y_2 = x^{1-\gamma}u(x).$$

Substitute y_2 in (2), shift the power $x^{1-\gamma}$ and cancel it from the equation; then $u(x)$ satisfies

$$\vartheta(\vartheta + 1 - \gamma)u - x(\vartheta + \alpha + 1 - \gamma)u = 0,$$

which is also a confluent hg equation with parameters $\alpha_1 = \alpha - \gamma + 1$, $\gamma_1 = 2 - \gamma$. Thus

(5) $$y_2 = x^{1-\gamma}F(\alpha - \gamma + 1; 2 - \gamma; x).$$

When γ is an integer ≤ 0, the solution for the smaller index 0 involves $\log x$; then the series $F(\alpha; \gamma; x)$ does not exist, but the solution for the positive index $1 - \gamma$ is given by (5). Similarly, when γ is an integer ≥ 2, the series for y_2 does not exist, but y_1 is given by (3). In these cases a second solution may be found as in § 112.

An equation

$$(6) \qquad (\vartheta + a)(\vartheta + b)y - kx^m(\vartheta + c)y = 0$$

may be reduced to the standard form (2) by changing variables. The substitution $y = x^{-a}u$ gives

$$\vartheta(\vartheta + b - a)u - kx^m(\vartheta + c - a)u = 0. \qquad \text{(cf. § 115)}$$

Now put

$$mt = kx^m, \qquad \vartheta = m\dot{\vartheta}$$

to obtain

$$(7) \qquad \dot{\vartheta}\left(\dot{\vartheta} + \frac{b - a}{m}\right)u - t\left(\dot{\vartheta} + \frac{c - a}{m}\right)u = 0.$$

This is a confluent hg equation which may be solved for $u(t)$; a return to the original variables will give the solution $y(x)$ of (6).

Example 1. $2xy'' - (1 + 2x^2)y' - xy = 0.$

The theta form

$$\vartheta(2\vartheta - 3)y - x^2(2\vartheta + 1)y = 0$$

assumes the standard form (2) when

$$2t = x^2, \qquad \vartheta = 2\dot{\vartheta};$$

$$\dot{\vartheta}(\dot{\vartheta} - \tfrac{3}{4})y - t(\dot{\vartheta} + \tfrac{1}{4})y = 0.$$

The parameters are $\alpha = \tfrac{1}{4}$, $\gamma = \tfrac{1}{4}$ and

$$y_1 = F(\tfrac{1}{4}; \tfrac{1}{4}; t) = e^t = e^{x^2/2},$$

$$y_2 = t^{3/4}F(1; \tfrac{7}{4}; t)$$

$$= t^{3/4}\left[1 + \sum_{n=1}^{\infty} \frac{(4t)^n}{7 \cdot 11 \cdots (4n + 3)}\right], \qquad t = \frac{x^2}{2}.$$

Discarding a constant factor, we may take

$$y_2 = x^{3/2}\left[1 + \sum_{n=1}^{\infty} \frac{2^n}{7 \cdot 11 \cdots (4n + 3)} x^{2n}\right].$$

Example 2. $y'' + xy' + 3y = 0$

or $\qquad\qquad \vartheta(\vartheta - 1)y + x^2(\vartheta + 3)y = 0.$

This assumes the form (2) when

$$-2t = x^2, \qquad \vartheta = 2\dot\vartheta:$$
$$\vartheta(\dot\vartheta - \tfrac{1}{2})y - t(\dot\vartheta + \tfrac{3}{2})y = 0$$

with parameters $\alpha = \tfrac{3}{2}$, $\gamma = \tfrac{1}{2}$.

$$y_1 = F(\tfrac{3}{2}; \tfrac{1}{2}; t) = 1 + \sum_{n=1}^{\infty} \frac{2n + 1}{n!} t^n,$$

$$y_2 = t^{1/2} F(2; \tfrac{3}{2}; t) = t^{1/2}\left[1 + \sum_{n=1}^{\infty} \frac{n + 1}{(2n + 1)!!} (2t)^n\right].$$

In both solutions the 1 may be assimilated into the sum for $n = 0$. Reverting to x and discarding a constant factor in y_2,

$$y_1 = \sum_{n=0}^{\infty} (-1)^n \frac{2n + 1}{2^n n!} x^{2n},$$

$$y_2 = \sum_{n=0}^{\infty} (-1)^n \frac{n + 1}{(2n + 1)!!} x^{2n+1}.$$

Example 3. $xy'' - xy' + y = 0$.

The theta form

$$\vartheta(\vartheta - 1)y - x(\vartheta - 1) = 0$$

discloses the parameters $\alpha = -1$, $\gamma = 0$. The nonexistence of $F(-1; 0; x)$ shows that the solution for the index 0 involves $\log x$. For the index 1 we have

$$y_2 = xF(0; 2; x) = x,$$

an obvious solution of $(\vartheta - 1)y = 0$. A second solution is given by (28.8) with $u = x$:

$$v = x \int_1^x \frac{e^t}{t^2}\, dt.$$

If we replace e^t by its Maclaurin series and integrate term by term, we find

$$v = x \log x - 1 + \sum_{n=2}^{\infty} \frac{x^n}{(n - 1)n!} - Kx.$$

Since $u = x$, the term Kx may be omitted to obtain y_1 (cf. Prob. 112.6).

PROBLEMS

In Problems 1, 2, 3, deduce the given solutions.

1. $xy'' - xy' - y = 0$; $\qquad xe^x, \quad xe^x \displaystyle\int_1^x \frac{e^{-t}}{t^2}\, dt.$

2. $xy'' + (2 - x)y' - y = 0$; $\qquad x^{-1}, \quad x^{-1}e^x.$

3. $xy'' + (3 - x)y' - y = 0$; $\qquad x^{-2}e^x, \quad x^{-1} + x^{-2}.$

In the following problems reduce the equation to the theta form and find the non-log solutions.

4. $2xy'' + (1 - 2x)y' - y = 0$.

5. $xy'' - (x - 4)y' + 2y = 0$.

6. $y'' - xy' + y = 0$.

7. $x^2y'' + x(1 + x)y' - y = 0$.

8. $x^2y'' + x(1 - x)y' - (1 + 3x)y = 0$.

9. $y'' + 3xy' + 3y = 0$.

10. Show that equation (1) has an irregular singular point at ∞.

11. Show that the self-adjoint form of the confluent hg equation is

$$D(x^\gamma e^{-x}y') - \alpha x^{\gamma-1}e^{-x}y = 0.$$

123. LAGUERRE'S EQUATION

(1) $$xy'' + (1 - x)y' + ny = 0$$

has the theta form

(2) $$\vartheta^2 y - x(\vartheta - n)y = 0.$$

It is therefore a confluent hg equation with parameters $\alpha = -n$, $\gamma = 1$.

The singular point $x = 0$ is regular with equal indices $0, 0$. The power series solution is

(3) $$y_1 = F(-n; 1; x) = \sum_{k=0}^{\infty}(-1)^k\binom{n}{k}\frac{x^k}{k!}.$$

The second solution involves $\log x$ and may be found as in § 111.

When n is a positive integer, the series for y_1 terminates and defines the Laguerre polynomial $L_n(x)$ of degree n:*

(4) $$L_n(x) = F(-n; 1; x) = \sum_{k=0}^{\infty}(-1)^k\binom{n}{k}\frac{x^k}{k!}.$$

Thus

$$L_0(x) = 1 \qquad\qquad L_1(x) = 1 - x$$
$$L_2(x) = 1 - 2x + \tfrac{1}{2}x^2 \qquad L_3(x) = 1 - 3x + \tfrac{3}{2}x^2 - \tfrac{1}{6}x^3.$$

The Laguerre polynomials are orthonormal on the interval $0 \leq x < \infty$ with respect to the weight function $\rho(x) = e^{-x}$:

(5) $$\int_0^{\infty} e^{-x}L_m(x)L_n(x)\, dx = \begin{cases} 0, & m \neq n \\ 1, & m = n. \end{cases}$$

---

* $L_n(x)$ is sometimes defined as $n!\, F(-n; 1; x)$; then all coefficients are integers. The French mathematician Edmond Laguerre (1834–1886) is best known for his work in geometry and infinite series.

PROOF. Multiply equation (1) by the factor

$$\sigma = \frac{1}{x} \exp \int \frac{1 - x}{x} \, dx = \frac{1}{x} xe^{-x} = e^{-x} \tag{33.8}$$

that makes it self-adjoint:

(6) $$\qquad\qquad\qquad D\{xe^{-x}y'\} + ne^{-x}y = 0.$$

This is a singular Sturm-Liouville equation over $0 \leqq x < \infty$ with

$$p(x) = xe^{-x}, \qquad q(x) = 0, \qquad \rho(x) = e^{-x}, \qquad \lambda = n.$$

Since $p(x) = 0$ for $x = 0$ and $x = \infty$, no boundary conditions are needed. The eigenvalues for polynomial solutions are $\lambda = 0, 1, 2, \ldots$, and the corresponding eigenfunctions are the Laguerre polynomials $L_n(x)$. Theorem 117.1 now shows that they are orthogonal over the interval $0 \leqq x < \infty$ with the weight function e^{-x}.

The second equation of (5) may be deduced from the analog of Rodrigues' formula for $L_n(x)$:

(7) $$\qquad\qquad\qquad L_n(x) = \frac{1}{n!} e^x D^n(e^{-x}x^n),$$

or, on using the exponential shift,

(8) $$\qquad\qquad\qquad L_n(x) = \frac{1}{n!} (D - 1)^n x^n.$$

To prove (8) we show that it is equivalent to the defining equation (4) for $L_n(x)$; for

$$(D - 1)^n x^n = \sum_{k=0}^{n} (-1)^k \binom{n}{k} D^{n-k} x^n = \sum_{k=0}^{n} (-1)^k \binom{n}{k} \frac{n!}{k!} x^k.$$

Using (7), we now have

$$\int_0^\infty e^{-x} L_n{}^2(x) \, dx = \frac{1}{n!} \int_0^\infty L_n(x) D^n(e^{-x}x^n) \, dx.$$

Integrate by parts, putting

$$u = L_n(x) \qquad\qquad v' = \frac{1}{n!} D^n(e^{-x}x^n)$$

$$u' = L_n'(x) \qquad\qquad v = \frac{1}{n!} D^{n-1}(e^{-x}x^n);$$

then since uv is a polynomial times xe^{-x}, the integrated part is zero at both limits and

$$\int_0^\infty e^{-x}L_n{}^2(x)\,dx = -\frac{1}{n!}\int_0^\infty L_n{}'(x)D^{n-1}(e^{-x}x^n)\,dx$$

$$= (-1)^2\frac{1}{n!}\int_0^\infty L_n{}''(x)D^{n-2}(e^{-x}x^n)\,dx$$

$$= (-1)^n\frac{1}{n!}\int_0^\infty L_n^{(n)}(x)e^{-x}x^n\,dx.$$

Since the highest power in $L_n(x)$ is $(-1)^nx^n/n!$, then $L_t^{(n)}(x) = (-1)^n$ and

$$\int_0^\infty e^{-x}L_n{}^2(x)\,dx = \frac{1}{n!}\int_0^\infty e^{-x}x^n\,dx = \frac{n!}{n!} = 1;$$

for from

$$\pounds\{t^n\} = \int_0^\infty e^{-st}t^n\,dt = \frac{n!}{s^{n+1}}, \qquad \int_0^\infty e^{-t}t^n\,dt = n!.$$

To conform with the notation of § 99 we now write $L_t(z)$ instead of $L_n(x)$. We shall see (§ 133, Ex. 2) that $L_t(z)$ has the recurrence relation

(9) $$(t + 1)L_{t+1} - (2t + 1 - z)L_t + tL_{t-1} = 0.$$

From this we deduce the generating function

$$F(x, z) = \sum_{t=0}^\infty L_t(z)x^t$$

for $L_t(z)$. From Table 99a we have the following transforms:

$$(t + 1)L_{t+1} \sim F', \qquad tL_t \sim xF',$$

where the primes denote x-derivatives. The definition $L_{-1} = 0$ satisfies (9) when $t = 0$; hence

$$tL_{t-1} \sim x(xF)' = xF + x^2F'.$$

Equation (9) therefore transforms into

$$F' - 2xF' - (1 - z)F + xF + x^2F' = 0.$$

Thus

$$(1 - x)^2F' - (1 - x - z)F = 0,$$

$$\frac{F'}{F} = \frac{1}{1 - x} - \frac{z}{(1 - x)^2},$$

and on integration with respect to x we have

$$\log F(x, z) = -\log(1 - x) - \frac{z}{1 - x} + C(z).$$

When $x = 0$, $F(0, z) = L_0 = 1$ and $C(z) = z$; hence

$$\log F = \frac{-zx}{1 - x} - \log(1 - x)$$

$$F(x, z) = \frac{1}{1 - x} \exp \frac{-zx}{1 - x}, \qquad |x| < 1,$$

(10) $$\frac{1}{1 - x} \exp \frac{-zx}{1 - x} = \sum_{t=0}^{\infty} L_t(z)x^t.$$

Example. The Laplace transform of $L_n(t)$ is

(11) $$\pounds\{L_n(t)\} = \frac{(s - 1)^n}{s^{n+1}}.$$

$L_n(t)$ is the solution of Laguerre's equation

(1) $$ty'' + (1 - t)y' + ny = 0,$$

for which $y(0) = 1$. The equation itself shows that $y'(0) = -n$. Since

$$\pounds\{y'\} = sY - 1, \qquad \pounds\{y''\} = s^2 Y - s + n,$$

we may use Table B, III (p. 659) to transform equation (1):

$$-D(s^2 Y - s + n) + (1 + D)(sY - 1) + nY = 0$$

or

$$s(s - 1)Y' + (s - n - 1)Y = 0.$$

This separable equation has the solution

$$Y = \frac{c(s - 1)^n}{s^{n+1}}.$$

To find c we make use of (68.5): as $s \to \infty$, $sY \to y(0) = 1$; hence $c = 1$, and we obtain the transform given in (11).

Using V and VI of Table B, it is now easy to prove that

(12) $$\pounds\{e^{-at} L_n(a - b)t\} = \frac{(s + b)^n}{(s + a)^{n+1}}.$$

PROBLEMS

1. Prove that

$$\pounds\{L_n(at)\} = \frac{(s - a)^n}{s^{n+1}}$$

and show that the formula checks dimensionally when s and a have the dimension T^{-1}.

2. Deduce L_0, L_1 and L_2 from (10).

124. HERMITE'S EQUATION*

Hermite's polynomials $H_n(x)$ are orthogonal over the interval $-\infty < x < \infty$ with respect to the weight function $\rho(x) = e^{-x^2}$. Since $\rho'(x) = -2xe^{-x^2}$, $\rho(x)$ satisfies the differential equation

$$\rho'(x) + 2x\rho = 0.$$

By repeated differentiation we find

$$\rho'' + 2x\rho' + 2 = 0$$

$$\rho''' + 2x\rho'' + 4\rho' = 0$$

and, in general,

(1) $$\rho^{(n+1)} + 2x\rho^{(n)} + 2n\rho^{(n-1)} = 0.$$

Since

$$\rho' = -2x\rho, \qquad \rho'' = (4x^2 - 2)\rho,$$

we can use these equations and (1) to prove by induction that $D^n\rho$ is the product of $\rho = e^{-x^2}$ and a polynomial of degree n. We now define the *Hermite polynomials* $H_n(x)$ as

(2) $$H_n(x) = (-1)^n e^{x^2} D^n e^{-x^2}.$$

If we multiply (1) by $(-1)^{n+1}\rho^{-1}$ and use $H_n = (-1)^n \rho^{-1} D^n \rho$, we obtain the recurrence relation

(3) $$H_{n+1} - 2xH_n + 2nH_{n-1} = 0.$$

Moreover, on differentiating (2) we find

$$H_n' = 2xH_n + (-1)^n e^{x^2} D^{n+1} e^{-x^2} = 2xH_n - H_{n+1}$$

or

(4) $$H_{n+1} = 2xH_n - H_n'.$$

This equation enables us to compute H_{n+1} from H_n. Thus starting with $H_0 = 1$ we have

$$H_1 = 2x, \qquad H_2 = 4x^2 - 2, \qquad H_3 = 8x^3 - 12x,$$

$$H_4 = 16x^4 - 48x^2 + 12, \qquad H_5 = 32x^5 - 160x^3 + 120x, \dots,$$

the highest power in H_n being $2^n x^n$.

---

* The French mathematician Charles Hermite (1822–1901) is best known for his work in algebra and his proof (1881) of the transcendence of π.

A comparison of (3) and (4) shows that

$$(5) \qquad H_n{}' = 2nH_{n-1}.$$

If we differentiate equation (3), we have

$$H'_{n+1} - 2H_n - 2xH_n{}' + H_n{}'' = 0.$$

Therefore the polynomials $H_n(x)$ satisfy *Hermite's differential equation*

$$(6) \qquad y'' - 2xy' + 2ny = 0.$$

The theta form of this equation

$$(7) \qquad \vartheta(\vartheta - 1)y - 2x^2(\vartheta - n)y = 0$$

shows that the substitution

$$t = x^2, \qquad \vartheta = 2\dot{\vartheta}$$

converts it into the standard confluent hg equation

$$(8) \qquad \dot{\vartheta}(\dot{\vartheta} - \tfrac{1}{2})y - t\left(\dot{\vartheta} - \frac{n}{2}\right)y = 0$$

with parameters $\alpha = -n/2$, $\gamma = \tfrac{1}{2}$. Therefore it has the independent series solutions (§ 122)

$$(9) \qquad y_1 = F\left(\frac{n}{2}; \frac{1}{2}; x^2\right),$$

$$(10) \qquad y_2 = xF\left(\frac{1-n}{2}; \frac{3}{2}; x^2\right).$$

When $n = 2m$, an even integer, $y_1 = F(-m; \tfrac{1}{2}; x^2)$ is a polynomial of degree $2m$; and when $n = 2m + 1$, an odd integer, $y_2 = xF(-m; \tfrac{3}{2}; x^2)$ is a polynomial of degree $2m + 1$. Since $c_1 y_1$ and $c_2 y_2$ are the only polynomial solutions of Hermite's equation, the solutions $y_1(x)$ and $y_2(x)$ can only differ from the Hermite polynomials by a constant factor. For example,

$$F(0; \tfrac{1}{2}; x^2) = 1, \qquad\qquad xF(0; \tfrac{3}{2}; x^2) = x,$$

$$F(-1; \tfrac{1}{2}; x^2) = 1 - 2x^2, \qquad xF(-1; \tfrac{3}{2}; x^2) = x - \tfrac{2}{3}x^3.$$

When these polynomials are normalized so that their highest power is $2^n x^n$, they become the Hermite polynomials.

When equation (6) is multiplied by e^{-x^2} it becomes self-adjoint:

$$(11) \qquad D(e^{-x^2}y) + 2ne^{-x^2}y = 0.$$

This is a Sturm-Liouville equation over the interval $-\infty < x < \infty$ with

$$p(x) = e^{-x^2}, \qquad q(x) = 0, \qquad \rho(x) = e^{-x^2}, \qquad \lambda = 2n.$$

Since $p(x) = 0$ for $x = \pm\infty$, no boundary conditions are needed. The eigenvalues for polynomial solutions are $\lambda = 0, 1, 2, \ldots$, and the eigenfunctions are the Hermite polynomials $H_n(x)$. Theorem 117.1 now shows that they are orthogonal on the interval $-\infty < x < \infty$ with the weight function $\rho(x) = e^{-x^2}$:

$$(12) \qquad \int_{-\infty}^{\infty} e^{-x^2} H_m(x) H_n(x)\, dx = \begin{cases} 0, & m \neq n \\ 2^n n!\, \sqrt{\pi}, & m = n. \end{cases}$$

To obtain the last result, integrate

$$\int_{-\infty}^{\infty} e^{-x^2} H_n^{\,2}(x)\, dx = (-1)^n \int_{-\infty}^{\infty} H_n(x) D^n e^{-x^2}\, dx$$

by parts, putting

$$u = H_n \qquad v' = (-1)^n D^n e^{-x^2}$$
$$u' = H_n' \qquad v = (-1)^n D^{n-1} e^{-x^2};$$

then since uv is a polynomial times e^{-x^2}, the integrated part is zero at both limits and

$$\int_{-\infty}^{\infty} e^{-x^2} H_n^{\,2}(x)\, dx = (-1)^{n+1} \int_{-\infty}^{\infty} H_n'(x) D^{n-1} e^{-x^2}\, dx$$

$$= (-1)^{n+2} \int_{-\infty}^{\infty} H_n''(x) D^{n-2} e^{-x^2}\, dx$$

$$= (-1)^{2n} \int_{-\infty}^{\infty} H_n^{(n)}(x) e^{-x^2}\, dx.$$

Since the highest power in $H_n(x)$ is $2^n x^n$, $H_n^{(n)}(x) = 2^n n!$ and the last integral is

$$(2^n n!) 2 \int_0^{\infty} e^{-x^2}\, dx = 2^n n!\, \sqrt{\pi}\, {}^*$$

in agreement with (12).

From (3) we can obtain the generating function of $H_n(x)$ by the method of § 99. In harmony with the notation of § 99 we write $H_t(z)$ instead of $H_n(x)$; then (3) becomes

$$(3)' \qquad\qquad H_{t+1} - 2zH_t + 2tH_{t-1} = 0,$$

or, on division by $t!$,

$$\frac{H_{t+1}}{t!} - 2z\frac{H_t}{t!} + \frac{H_{t-1}}{(t-1)!} = 0.$$

---

* *Advanced Calculus*, p. 365, (3).

Writing $f_t(z) = H_t/t!$, we have the difference equation

(13) $$(t + 1)f_{t+1} - 2zf_t + 2f_{t-1} = 0.$$

Now let

$$F(x, z) = \sum_{t=0}^{\infty} f_t(z)x^t$$

be the generating function for $f_t(z)$. If we define $f_{-1} = 0$ (which satisfies (13) when $t = 0$, since $f_0 = 1$, $f_1 = 2z$) the Table 99 gives the following transforms:

$$(t + 1)f_{t+1} \sim F', \qquad f_t \sim F, \qquad f_{t-1} \sim xF.$$

Thus (13) becomes

$$F' - 2zF + 2xF = 0$$

where F' denotes an x-derivative and z a constant parameter; hence

$$\frac{F'}{F} = 2z - 2x, \qquad \log F = 2zx - x^2 + C.$$

When $x = 0$, $F(0, z) = f_0 = 1$, and $C = 0$; hence

$$F(x, z) = \exp(2zx - x^2),$$

(14) $$\exp(2zx - x^2) = \sum_{t=0}^{\infty} \frac{H_t(z)}{t!} x^t.$$

PROBLEMS

1. *Weber's polynomials* $W_n(x)$ are orthogonal on the interval $-\infty < x < \infty$ with respect to the weight function $\rho(x) = e^{-x^2/2}$.

Prove that $\rho(x)$ satisfies the differential equation

(i) $$\rho^{(n+1)} + x\rho^{(n)} + n\rho^{(n-1)} = 0,$$

and that $\rho^{(n)}(x)$ is the product of ρ and a polynomial of degree n. Define the Weber polynomials as

(ii) $$W_n(x) = (-1)^n \rho^{-1} D^n \rho, \qquad \rho = e^{-x^2/2},$$

and show that they satisfy the recurrence relations:

(iii) $$W_{n+1} - xW_n + nW_{n-1} = 0, \qquad n \geq 1,$$

(iv) $$W_{n+1} = xW_n - W_n',$$

(v) $$W_n' = nW_{n-1},$$

with $W_0 = 1$, $W_1 = x$.

Prove that $W_n(x)$ satisfies the equation

(vi) $$W_n'' - xW_n' + nW_n = 0$$

and thus is a solution of *Weber's equation* (Prob. 117.6)

(vii) $$y'' - xy' - \lambda y = 0$$

when $\lambda = -n$, an integer ≤ 0.

2. Reduce Weber's equation (vii) to a confluent hg equation having the solutions

$$y_1(\lambda) = 1 + \sum_{k=1}^{\infty} \frac{\lambda(\lambda + 2) \cdots (\lambda + 2k - 2)}{(2k)!} x^{2k},$$

$$y_2(\lambda) = x + \sum_{k=1}^{\infty} \frac{(\lambda + 1)(\lambda + 3) \cdots (\lambda + 2k - 1)}{(2k + 1)!} x^{2k+1}.$$

When $\lambda = 0, -1, -2, \ldots$, these are polynomials of even or odd degree; and when normalized to become *monic* (coefficient of highest power 1), they coincide with $W_n(x)$. Specifically, $W_0 = 1$, $W_1 = x$, and

$$W_{2m}(x) = (-1)^m (2m - 1)!! y_1(-2m),$$
$$W_{2m+1}(x) = (-1)^m (2m + 1)!! y_2(-2m - 1).$$

Compute W_2, W_3, W_4, W_5.

3. Reduce equation (vii) to the self-adjoint form and set up a S-L system over $(-\infty, \infty)$ with polynomial solutions for the eigenvalues $\lambda = 0, -1, -2, \ldots$. Show that the eigenfunctions $W_n(x)$ satisfy the orthogonality relations

(viii) $$\int_{-\infty}^{\infty} e^{-x^2/2} W_m(x) W_n(x) \, dx = \begin{cases} 0, & m \neq n \\ \sqrt{2\pi}\, n!, & m = n. \end{cases}$$

4. Write $W_n(x)$ as $W_t(z)$ to conform to the notation of § 99 and show that $f_t(z) = W_t(z)/t!$ satisfies the difference equation

$$(t + 1)f_{t+1} - zf_t + f_{t-1} = 0.$$

From this deduce the generating function of $f_t(z)$:

$$F(x, z) = \exp\left(zx - \frac{1}{2}x^2\right) = \sum_{t=0}^{\infty} \frac{W_t(z)}{t!} x^t.$$

5. If $\tau = e^{x^2/2}$, prove that

$$\tau^{(n+1)} = x\tau^{(n)} + n\tau^{(n-1)},$$

and hence that equation (vii) admits the solution $u_n = D^{n-1}\tau$ when $\lambda = n$, a positive integer. Define the polynomials

(ix) $$V_n(x) = \tau^{-1}D^n\tau, \qquad n \geq 1,$$

and show that they satisfy the recurrence relation $V_{n+1} = xV_n + nV_{n-1}$ with $V_0 = 1$. Compute $V_1, \ldots, V_5$ and compare with $W_1, \ldots, W_5$ in Problem 2.

6. Show that the polynomials $V_n(x)$ satisfy the differential equation

(x) $$y'' + xy' + (1 - \lambda)y = 0$$

when $\lambda = n$, a positive integer.

125. BESSEL'S EQUATION OF ORDER n

(1)
$$x^2 y'' + xy' + (x^2 - n^2)y = 0$$

has the theta form

(2)
$$(\vartheta^2 - n^2)y + x^2 y = 0;$$

$x = 0$ is a regular singular point with the indicial equation $\lambda^2 - n^2 = 0$. For any real n there is always a series solution

(3)
$$y_1 = \sum_{k=0}^{\infty} c_k x^{n+2k}$$

for the positive index n. Substituting (3) in (2), we find the recurrence relation
$$[(n + 2k)^2 - n^2]c_k + c_{k-1} = 0.$$

Hence
$$4k(n + k)c_k = -c_{k-1}$$
$$4(k - 1)(n + k - 1)c_{k-1} = -c_{k-2}$$
$$\cdot \quad \cdot \quad \cdot \quad \cdot \quad \cdot \quad \cdot \quad \cdot \quad \cdot \quad \cdot \quad \cdot \quad \cdot$$
$$4(1)(n + 1)c_1 = -c_0;$$

and when we multiply these k equations together, we find that
$$c_k = \frac{(-1)^k}{4^k k! \, (n + 1)(n + 2) \cdots (n + k)} c_0.$$

If we choose the arbitrary constant
$$c_0 = \frac{1}{2^n \Gamma(n + 1)},$$

successive applications of the functional equation $x\Gamma(x) = \Gamma(x + 1)$ show that
$$(n + k)(n + k - 1) \cdots (n + 1)\Gamma(n + 1) = \Gamma(n + k + 1).$$

With this value of c_k, (3) defines the *Bessel function of order* n:*

(4)
$$J_n(x) = \sum_{k=0}^{\infty} \frac{(-1)^k}{k! \, \Gamma(n + k + 1)} \left(\frac{x}{2}\right)^{n+2k}.$$

The series converges for all x except $x = 0$ when n is negative (§ 108, $\deg f = 2$, $\deg g = 0$).

---

* Friedrich Wilhelm Bessel (1784–1846), German astronomer and mathematician.

When n is a non-negative integer, $\Gamma(n + k + 1) = (n + k)!$. Thus for the important cases $n = 0$ and $n = 1$, we have

(5) $$J_0(x) = \sum_{k=0}^{\infty} \frac{(-1)^k}{k! \, k!} \left(\frac{x}{2}\right)^{2k}$$

$$= 1 - \frac{x^2}{2^2} + \frac{x^4}{2^2 \cdot 4^2} - \frac{x^6}{2^2 \cdot 4^2 \cdot 6^2} + \cdots,$$

(6) $$J_1(x) = \sum_{k=0}^{\infty} \frac{(-1)^k}{k! \, (k + 1)!} \left(\frac{x}{2}\right)^{2k+1}$$

$$= \frac{x}{2}\left[1 - \frac{x^2}{2 \cdot 4} + \frac{x^4}{2 \cdot 4^2 \cdot 6} - \frac{x^6}{2 \cdot 4^2 \cdot 6^2 \cdot 8} + \cdots\right].$$

$J_0(x)$ and $J_1(x)$ have an infinite number of simple zeros and oscillate in a way that suggests $\cos x$ and $\sin x$, but without periodicity (Fig. 125a). This rough analogy is reenforced by the relation $J_0'(x) = -J_1(x)$, which follows at once from the foregoing series.

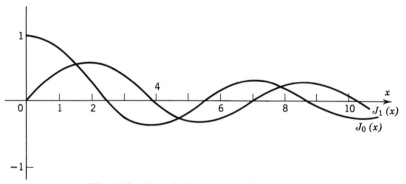

Fig. 125a Bessel functions $J_0(x)$ and $J_1(x)$.
$J_0(x) = 0$: $x = 2.405$, 5.520, 8.654, 11.792, ... ;
$J_1(x) = 0$: $x = 0$, 3.382, 7.016, 10.173, 13.324, ...

If n is not an integer, we obtain in the same way a solution for the negative index $-n$. Replacing n by $-n$ in (4), we have

(7) $$J_{-n}(x) = \sum_{k=0}^{\infty} \frac{(-1)^k}{k! \, \Gamma(-n + k + 1)} \left(\frac{x}{2}\right)^{-n+2k},$$

and the series converges for all $x \neq 0$. For non-integral n, $J_n(x)$ and $J_{-n}(x)$ are linearly independent solutions of (1) and the general solution is therefore

(8) $$y = AJ_n(x) + BJ_{-n}(x).$$

If n is an integer, we define

(9) $$J_{-n}(x) = \lim_{v \to n} J_{-v}(x).$$

Now as $v \to n$, $\Gamma(-v + k + 1) \to \infty$ for $k = 0, 1, \ldots, n - 1$ (§ 66) and the first n terms of the series (7) approach zero; hence

$$J_{-n}(x) = \sum_{k=n}^{\infty} \frac{(-1)^k}{k! \, (k - n)!} \left(\frac{x}{2}\right)^{-n+2k}.$$

The index change $k = n + j$ now gives

$$J_{-n}(x) = (-1)^n \sum_{j=0}^{\infty} \frac{(-1)^j}{j! \, (n + j)!} \left(\frac{x}{2}\right)^{n+2j}.$$

Since $(n + j)! = \Gamma(n + j + 1)$, a comparison with (4) shows that

(10) $$J_{-n}(x) = (-1)^n J_n(x), \qquad n = 1, 2, 3, \ldots,$$

for integral n, $J_{-n}(x)$ differs from $J_n(x)$ only in sign. A second independent solution may now be found by the procedure of § 111 ($n = 0$) or § 112. The cases $n = 0$ and $n = 1$ are dealt with in Example 111.1 and 112.2. These led to the Bessel functions $K_0(x)$ and $K_1(x)$ of the second kind.

If we put $A = \cos n\pi$, $B = -\csc n\pi$ in (8), we obtain the *Neumann function**

(11) $$Y_n(x) = \frac{\cos n\pi \, J_n(x) - J_{-n}(x)}{\sin nx},$$

which is a solution of (1) when n is not an integer. When n is an integer we see from (10) that $Y_n(x)$ assumes the indeterminate form $0/0$; but a solution linearly independent of $J_n(x)$ is given by the limiting function defined by

(12) $$Y_n(x) = \lim_{v \to n} Y_v(x) = \frac{1}{\pi} \left[\frac{\partial J_v(x)}{\partial v} - (-1)^n \frac{\partial J_{-v}(x)}{\partial v} \right]_{v=n}.$$

We omit the proof of this fact and also the general form of $Y_n(x)$†; but

(13) $$\frac{\pi}{2} Y_0(x) = \left(\log \frac{x}{2} + \gamma\right) J_0(x) - \sum_{k=1}^{\infty} \frac{(-1)^k \Omega_k}{k! \, k!} \left(\frac{x}{2}\right)^{2k},$$

where $\gamma = -\Gamma'(1) = 0.57731\ 56649 \cdots$ is Euler's constant. *Tables of*

---

* Carl Neumann (1832–1925), German mathematician and physicist.
† See Frank-von Mises, *Die Differentialgleichungen und Integralgleichungen der Mechanik und Physik*, vol. 1, p. 409, 1961, Dover, New York.

$Y_n(x)$ are given in ref. 9. Referring to Example 111.1 we see that

(14)
$$\frac{\pi}{2} Y_0(x) = (\gamma - \log 2)J_0(x) + K_0(x).$$

The Neumann function $Y_n(x)$ is also called a Bessel function of the second kind. The general solution of (1) for any real $n \geq 0$ may now be written

(15)
$$y = AJ_n(x) + BY_n(x).$$

$J_n(x)$ as defined by (4) is $(x/2)^n$ times a power series. This power series converges absolutely and uniformly in any finite interval* and defines a

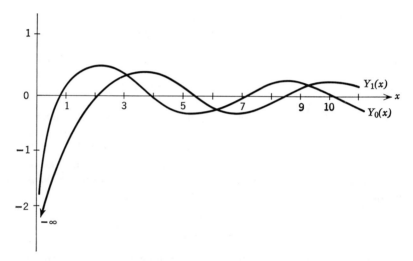

Fig. 125b Neumann functions $Y_0(x)$ and $Y_1(x)$.

continuous function. Thus $J_n(x)$ is everywhere continuous except for a singularity at the origin due to the factor x^n when $n < 0$. When $n = 0, 1, 2, \ldots$, the series for $J_n(x)$ is a power series that converges for all x and admits derivatives of all orders. When $n > 0$ but nonintegral, certain derivatives of $J_n(x)$ will cease to exist at $x = 0$. In any case,

> *The function $J_n(x)$ defined by (4) is a solution of Bessel's equation when $x \neq 0$ for every real n if we define $1/\Gamma(r) = 0$ when $r = 0$, $-1, -2, \ldots$.*

We omit the proof of this fact and also the general form of $Y_n(x)$.

The graphs of $J_0(x)$, $J_1(x)$ (Fig. 125a) and $Y_0(x)$, $Y_1(x)$ (Fig. 125b) show the character of these functions near the origin. It can be shown that as

---

* *Advanced Calculus*, § 180.

$n \to \infty$, $J_n(x)$ and $Y_n(x)$ have the asymptotic form†

(16) $$J_n(x) = \sqrt{\frac{2}{\pi x}} \cos\left(x - \frac{\pi}{4} - \frac{n\pi}{2}\right) + O(x^{-\frac{3}{2}})$$

(17) $$Y_n(x) = \sqrt{\frac{2}{\pi x}} \sin\left(x - \frac{\pi}{4} - \frac{n\pi}{2}\right) + O(x^{-\frac{3}{2}}).†$$

These formulas show that $J_n(x)$ and $Y_n(x)$ have an infinite number of positive zeros that for large x lie near

$$x_k = k\pi + \frac{n\pi}{2} - \frac{\pi}{4} \quad \text{and} \quad x_k = k\pi + \frac{n\pi}{2} + \frac{\pi}{4}$$

respectively. The general solution (15) shows that every solution of Bessel's equation has an infinite number of positive zeros. The distribution of the zeros of $J_n(x)$ is discussed in § 129.

   G. N. Watson's *Treatise* (ref. 18) is a standard work on Bessel functions.

126. RELATION OF BESSEL TO F-FUNCTIONS

   Just as the omission of the factor $\vartheta + \beta$ from the hg equation leads to the confluent hg equation, the omission of $\vartheta + \alpha$ from the latter leads to

(1) $$\vartheta(\vartheta + \gamma - 1)y - xy = 0,$$

or in D-form

(1)′ $$xy'' + \gamma y' - y = 0.$$

The usual procedure now gives two solutions of (1),

(3) $$y_1 = F(*; \gamma; x)$$

(4) $$y_2 = x^{1-\gamma}F(*; 2 - \gamma; x)$$

where we define

(5) $$F(*; \gamma; x) = 1 + \sum_{k=1}^{\infty} \frac{1}{\gamma(\gamma + 1) \cdots (\gamma + k - 1)} \frac{x^k}{k!},$$

the asterisk indicating the absence of a parameter in the numerator. Note the analogy of (5) with the definition of $F(\alpha; \gamma; x)$ given in § 122.

---

† G. Tolstov, ref. 16, chapter 8, § 9. Englewood-Cliffs, N.J. For the O notation see *Advanced Calculus*, p. 129; read $O(x^{-\frac{3}{2}})$ "terms of order $x^{-\frac{3}{2}}$."

Bessel's equation

(6) $$(\vartheta - n)(\vartheta + n)y + x^2 y = 0$$

may be reduced to the form (1) by a change of variables. First put $y = x^n u$, shift x^n to the left and cancel it:

$$\vartheta(\vartheta + 2n)u + x^2 u = 0.$$

Then put $x^2 = -4t$, $\vartheta = 2\dot{\vartheta}$ and divide the resulting equation by 4:

(7) $$\dot{\vartheta}(\dot{\vartheta} + n)u - tu = 0.$$

This equation has the form (1) with $\gamma = n + 1$. From (3) and (4) we have the two solutions

$$u_1 = F(*; n + 1; t), \qquad u_2 = t^{-n}F(*; -n + 1; t);$$

and on putting $y = x^n u$, $t = -x^2/4$, we have two solutions of Bessel's equation:

(8) $$y_1 = Ax^n F\left(*; n + 1; \frac{-x^2}{4}\right),$$

(9) $$y_2 = Bx^{-n} F\left(*; -n + 1; \frac{-x^2}{4}\right),$$

where A and B are arbitrary constants. When

$$A = 1/2^n \Gamma(n + 1), \qquad B = 1/2^{-n}\Gamma(-n + 1),$$

these become $J_n(x)$ and $J_{-n}(x)$, respectively. In particular,

(10) $$J_0(x) = F\left(*; 1; \frac{-x^2}{4}\right),$$

(11) $$J_1(x) = \frac{x}{2} F\left(*; 2; \frac{-x^2}{4}\right).$$

127. RELATIONS BETWEEN BESSEL FUNCTIONS

In this section we write J_n, Y_n for $J_n(x)$, $Y_n(x)$.

Theorem 1. *For any index n,*

(1) $$D(x^n J_n) = x^n J_{n-1},$$

(2) $$D(x^{-n} J_n) = -x^{-n} J_{n+1};$$

(3) $$D(x^n Y_n) = x^n Y_{n-1},$$

(4) $$D(x^{-n} Y_n) = -x^{-n} Y_{n+1}.$$

PROOF. From (125.4) we have

$$x^n J_n = \sum_{k=0}^{\infty} \frac{(-1)^k}{k!\,\Gamma(n+k+1)} \frac{x^{2n+2k}}{2^{n+2k}},$$

$$D(x^n J_n) = \sum_{k=0}^{\infty} \frac{(-1)^k}{k!\,\Gamma(n+k)} \frac{x^{2n+2k-1}}{2^{n+2k-1}}$$

$$= x^n \sum_{k=0}^{\infty} \frac{(-1)^k}{k!\,\Gamma(n+k)} \left(\frac{x}{2}\right)^{n-1+2k} = x^n J_{n-1}.$$

$$x^{-n} J_n = \sum_{k=0}^{\infty} \frac{(-1)^k}{k!\,\Gamma(n+k+1)} \frac{x^{2k}}{2^{n+2k}}.$$

$$D(x^{-n} J_n) = \sum_{k=1}^{\infty} \frac{(-1)^k}{(k-1)!\,\Gamma(n+k+1)} \frac{x^{2k-1}}{2^{n-1+2k}}$$

$$= \sum_{j=0}^{\infty} \frac{(-1)^{j+1}}{j!\,\Gamma(n+j+2)} \frac{x^{2j+1}}{2^{n+1+2j}} \qquad (j = k - 1)$$

$$= -x^{-n} \sum_{j=0}^{\infty} \frac{(-1)^j}{j!\,\Gamma(n+j+2)} \left(\frac{x}{2}\right)^{n+1+2j} = -x^{-n} J_{n+1}.$$

Thus (1) and (2) are established.

To prove (3), replace n by $-n$ in (2):

(2)′ $$D(x^n J_{-n}) = -x^n J_{-n+1}.$$

Multiply (1) by $\cot n\pi$, (2)′ by $-\csc n\pi$, and add: then

$$D\left\{x^n \frac{J_n \cos n\pi - J_{-n}}{\sin n\pi}\right\} = x^n \frac{J_{n-1} \cos n\pi + J_{-n+1}}{\sin n\pi}$$

if n is not an integer, or since

$$\cos n\pi = -\cos(n-1)\pi, \qquad \sin n\pi = -\sin(n-1)\pi,$$

(3) $$D(x^n Y_n) = x^n Y_{n-1} \qquad\qquad (125.11).$$

To prove (4), replace n by $-n$ in (1):

(1)′ $$D(x^{-n} J_{-n}) = x^{-n} J_{-n-1}.$$

Multiply (2) by $\cot n\pi$, (1)′ by $-\csc n\pi$, and add:

$$D\left\{x^{-n} \frac{J_n \cos n\pi - J_{-n}}{\sin n\pi}\right\} = -x^{-n} \frac{J_{n+1} \cos n\pi + J_{-n-1}}{\sin n\pi},$$

or since

$$\cos n\pi = -\cos(n+1)\pi, \qquad \sin n\pi = -\sin(n+1)\pi,$$

(4) $$D(x^{-n} Y_n) = -x^{-n} Y_{n+1}.$$

Thus (3) and (4) are proved when n is not an integer. By passing to the limit $n \to$ integer, they may also be proved for integral n.

When $n = 0$, (2) and (4) give

$$(5, 6) \qquad\qquad J_0' = -J_1, \qquad Y_0' = -Y_1.$$

On performing the differentiation in (1) and (2) we obtain the formulas

$$(7) \qquad\qquad x J_n' + n J_n = x J_{n-1}$$

$$(8) \qquad\qquad x J_n' - n J_n = -x J_{n+1}.$$

Adding and subtracting these now gives

$$(9) \qquad\qquad J_{n-1} - J_{n+1} = 2 J_n'$$

$$(10) \qquad\qquad J_{n-1} + J_{n+1} = \frac{2n}{x} J_n.$$

From (3) and (4) we obtain formulas of the same type for Y_n.

The integral forms of (1) and (2)

$$(1)' \qquad\qquad \int x^n J_{n-1} \, dx = x^n J_n + c,$$

$$(2)' \qquad\qquad \int x^{-n} J_{n+1} \, dx = -x^{-n} J_n + c,$$

are often used in computing the coefficients of Fourier-Bessel series (§ 131). For example,

$$(11) \qquad\qquad \int x J_0 \, dx = x J_1 + c \qquad [n = 1 \text{ in } (1)'],$$

$$(12) \qquad\qquad \int J_1 \, dx = -J_0 + c \qquad [n = 0 \text{ in } (2)'].$$

Note that the sum of the exponent of x and the index of J is odd in formulas (1)$'$ and (2)$'$. To evaluate an integral of the type $\int x^m J_n \, dx$ we resort to integration by parts and this yields another integral of this type in which $m + n$ has the same parity (see the reduction formulas in the following problems). In order that $\int x^m J_n \, dx$ be a *proper* integral, $m + n \geqq 0$ (why?). When this condition is fulfilled and $m + n$ is odd, the integral can be expressed in terms of Bessel functions with the eventual use of (1)$'$ and (2)$'$; but when $m + n$ is even, there will always be a residual integral $\int J_0 \, dx$. For this reason $\int J_0(t) \, dt$ and $\int Y_0(t) \, dt$ have been tabulated.*

---

* Lowan and Abramowitz, *Tables of Integrals of* $\displaystyle\int_0^x J_0(t) \, dt$ *and* $\displaystyle\int_0^x Y_0(t) \, dt$, J. Math. Phys., v. **22** (1943); pp. 3–12.

Example 1. Find $\int x^{-1} J_1 \, dx$. Integrate $\int x^{-2} \cdot x J_1 \, dx$ by parts:

$$u = x J_1 \qquad v' = x^{-2}$$

$$u' = x J_0 \qquad v = -x^{-1}; \qquad \int x^{-1} J_1 \, dx = -J_1 + \int J_0 \, dx.$$

Example 2. Find $\int x^2 J_0 \, dx$. Integrate $\int x \cdot x J_0 \, dx$ by parts:

$$u = x \qquad v' = x J_0$$

$$u' = 1 \qquad v = x J_1; \qquad \int x^2 J_0 \, dx = x^2 J_1 - \int x J_1 \, dx.$$

Integrate $\int x J_1 \, dx$ by parts:

$$u = x \qquad v' = J_1$$

$$u' = 1 \qquad v = -J_0; \qquad \int x J_1 \, dx = -x J_0 + \int J_0 \, dx.$$

Hence

$$\int x^2 J_0 \, dx = x^2 J_1 + x J_0 - \int J_0 \, dx.$$

Example 3. Find $\int J_3 \, dx$. Integrate $\int x^2 x^{-2} J_3 \, dx$ by parts:

$$u = x^2 \qquad v' = x^{-2} J_3$$

$$u' = 2x \qquad v = -x^{-2} J_2; \qquad \int J_3 \, dx = -J_2 + 2 \int x^{-1} J_2 \, dx.$$

From (2) the last integral is $-x^{-1} J_1$; hence

$$\int J_3 \, dx = -J_2 - 2x^{-1} J_1 + c.$$

Or we may use (9) with $n = 2$: $J_3 = J_1 - 2 J_2'$;

$$\int J_3 \, dx = \int J_1 \, dx - 2 J_2 = -J_0 - 2 J_2 + c.$$

Since $2x^{-1} J_1 = J_0 + J_2$ from (10), the results agree.

Example 4. The Laplace transform of $J_n(x)$ is

(12) $$\pounds\{J_n(t)\} = \frac{[\sqrt{1 + s^2} - s]^n}{\sqrt{1 + s^2}}, \qquad n = 0, 1, 2, \ldots.$$

First consider $J_0(t)$, the unique solution of Bessel's equation of zero order

(13) $$t y'' + y' + t y = 0$$

for which $y(0) = 1$, $y'(0) = 0$. Since

$$\pounds\{y'\} = s Y - 1, \qquad \pounds\{y''\} = s^2 Y - s,$$

we may use Table B, III, p. 659, to transform equation (13);

$$-D(s^2 Y - s) + sY - 1 - DY = 0$$

or

$$(s^2 + 1)Y' + sY = 0.$$

This separable equation has the solution

$$Y = c(1 + s^2)^{-\frac{1}{2}}.$$

To find c we make use of (68.5): as $s \to \infty$, $sY \to y(0) = 1$; hence $c = 1$ and

(14) $$£\{J_0(t)\} = (1 + s^2)^{-\frac{1}{2}}.$$

This is formula (12) for $n = 0$. We may verify this result by a backward transform of the series

$$(1 + s^2)^{-\frac{1}{2}} = \frac{1}{s}\left(1 + \frac{1}{s^2}\right)^{-\frac{1}{2}} = \sum_{k=0}^{\infty} \binom{-\frac{1}{2}}{k} \frac{1}{s^{2k+1}}$$

term by term; thus

$$\sum_{k=0}^{\infty} \binom{-\frac{1}{2}}{k} \frac{t^{2k}}{(2k)!} = \sum_{k=0}^{\infty} \frac{(-1)^k}{k!\,k!} \left(\frac{t}{2}\right)^{2k} = J_0(t).$$

The details in the last change are left to the reader. Moreover, from Table B, V, we have

(15) $$£\{J_0(at)\} = \frac{1}{a}\left(\frac{s^2}{a^2} + 1\right)^{-\frac{1}{2}} = (s^2 + a^2)^{-\frac{1}{2}}.$$

From (2) we have $J_1(t) = -J_0'(t)$; hence from Table B, I,

(16) $$£\{J_1(t)\} = -\left(\frac{s}{\sqrt{1 + s^2}} - 1\right) = \frac{\sqrt{1 + s^2} - s}{\sqrt{1 + s^2}}.$$

We can now use the relation

$$J_{n+1} = J_{n-1} - 2J_n'$$

to prove by induction the general formula (12). Assuming its truth for $n - 1$ and n, we have, since $J_n(0) = 0$,

$$£\{J_{n+1}\} = £\{J_{n-1}\} - 2s£\{J_n\} \qquad (n > 1)$$

$$= \frac{(\sqrt{1 + s^2} - s)^{n-1} - 2s(\sqrt{1 + s^2} - s)^n}{\sqrt{1 + s^2}}$$

$$= \frac{(\sqrt{1 + s^2} - s)^{n-1}(1 - 2s\sqrt{1 + s^2} + 2s^2)}{\sqrt{1 + s^2}}$$

$$= \frac{(\sqrt{1 + s^2} - s)^{n+1}}{\sqrt{1 + s^2}}.$$

PROBLEMS

Use formulas (1)′ and (2)′ to obtain the following integrals:

1. $\int x^3 J_0 \, dx = x_3 J_1 - 2x^2 J_2 + c.$

2. $\int x J_1 \, dx = \int J_0 \, dx - x J_0.$

3. $\int x^4 J_1 \, dx = x^4 J_2 - 2x^3 J_3 + c.$

4. $\int J_2 \, dx = \int J_0 \, dx - 2J_1.$

5. $\int x^{-2} J_2 \, dx = -\tfrac{1}{3} x^{-1} J_2 - \tfrac{1}{3} J_1 + \tfrac{1}{3} \int J_0 \, dx.$

6. $\int_0^1 x J_0(\lambda x) \, dx = J_1(\lambda)/\lambda.$

If $m + n \geq 0$, prove the following reduction formulas:

7. $(m > n)$: $\int x^m J_n \, dx = x^m J_{n+1} - (m - n - 1) \int x^{m-1} J_{n+1} \, dx.$

Apply to Problem 3.

8. $(m \leq n)$: $\int x^m J_n \, dx = -x^m J_{n-1} + (m + n - 1) \int x^{m-1} J_{n-1} \, dx.$

Apply to Problem 2.

9. $\int x^{-n} J_n \, dx = -\frac{x^{-n+1}}{2n - 1} J_n + \frac{1}{2n - 1} \int x^{-(n-1)} J_{n-1} \, dx.$

Apply to Problem 5.

10. Show that $\pounds\{J_1(t)/t\} = \sqrt{1 + s^2} - s.$

11. Prove that

$$\pounds\{J_n(at)\} = \frac{[\sqrt{a^2 + s^2} - s]^n}{a^n \sqrt{a^2 + s^2}}$$

and show that the formula checks dimensionally when s and a have the dimension T^{-1}.

128. BESSEL FUNCTIONS OF HALF-INTEGRAL ORDER

When $n = \tfrac{1}{2}$, the defining equation for $J_n(x)$ becomes

$$J_{1/2}(x) = \sum_{k=0}^{\infty} \frac{(-1)^k}{k! \, \Gamma(k + \tfrac{3}{2})} \left(\frac{x}{2}\right)^{2k+1/2}$$

$$= \sqrt{2/x} \sum_{k=0}^{\infty} \frac{(-1)^k}{k! \, (k + \tfrac{1}{2}) \cdots \tfrac{3}{2} \cdot \tfrac{1}{2}\Gamma(\tfrac{1}{2})} \frac{x^{2k+1}}{2^{2k+1}}$$

or since $\Gamma(\tfrac{1}{2}) = \sqrt{\pi}$, (66.8),

$$J_{1/2}(x) = \sqrt{2/\pi x} \sum_{k=0}^{\infty} \frac{(-1)^k x^{2k+1}}{(2 \cdot 4 \cdots 2k)(1 \cdot 3 \cdots 2k+1)}$$

$$= \sqrt{2/\pi x} \sum_{k=0}^{\infty} (-1)^k \frac{x^{2k+1}}{(2k+1)!},$$

that is,

(1) $$J_{1/2}(x) = \sqrt{\frac{2}{\pi x}} \sin x.$$

In similar fashion we find

(2) $$J_{-1/2}(x) = \sqrt{\frac{2}{\pi x}} \cos x.$$

Thus the general solution of Bessel's equation of order $\tfrac{1}{2}$ is

$$y = \frac{1}{\sqrt{x}} (A \sin x + B \cos x).$$

The recurrence relation

$$J_{n-1} + J_{n+1} = \frac{2n}{x} J_n$$

now enables us to compute the half-index functions $J_{p+1/2}(x)$ and $J_{-p-1/2}(x)$ when p is an integer. For example, when $n = \pm\tfrac{1}{2}$,

$$J_{-1/2} + J_{3/2} = \frac{1}{x} J_{1/2}, \qquad J_{3/2} + J_{1/2} = -\frac{1}{x} J_{-1/2},$$

give $J_{3/2}$ and $J_{-3/2}$ in Table 128:

Table 128   Bessel Functions of Half-integral Order

p	$\sqrt{\pi x/2}\, J_{p+1/2}(x)$	$\sqrt{\pi x/2}\, J_{-p-1/2}(x)$
0	$\sin x$	$\cos x$
1	$\dfrac{\sin x}{x} - \cos x$	$-\sin x - \dfrac{\cos x}{x}$
2	$\left(\dfrac{3}{x^2} - 1\right)\sin x - \dfrac{3}{x}\cos x$	$\dfrac{3}{x}\sin x + \left(\dfrac{3}{x^2} - 1\right)\cos x$
3	$\left(\dfrac{15}{x^3} - \dfrac{6}{x}\right)\sin x - \left(\dfrac{15}{x^2} - 1\right)\cos x$	$-\left(\dfrac{15}{x^2} - 1\right)\sin x - \left(\dfrac{15}{x^3} - \dfrac{6}{x}\right)\cos x$
$\sim$	$\sin\left(x - \dfrac{p}{2}\pi\right)$	$\cos\left(x + \dfrac{p}{2}\pi\right)$

The last row gives the asymptotic values which may be deduced from (125.16).

From the definition (125.8) for $Y_n(x)$ we have also

(3) $$Y_{p+\frac{1}{2}}(x) = (-1)^{p+1}J_{-p-\frac{1}{2}}(x)$$

(4) $$Y_{-p-\frac{1}{2}}(x) = (-1)^p J_{p+\frac{1}{2}}(x).$$

129. REDUCTION TO BESSEL'S EQUATION

The equation

(1) $$(\vartheta - a)(\vartheta - b)y + k^2 x^{2m} y = 0, \qquad b \geq a,$$

can be reduced to Bessel's equation by changing dependent and independent variables as follows:

1. Put $y = x^{(a+b)/2}u$; shift $x^{(a+b)/2}$ to the left and cancel it:

(2) $$\left(\vartheta + \frac{b-a}{2}\right)\left(\vartheta - \frac{b-a}{2}\right)u - k^2 x^{2m}u = 0.$$

2. Put $kx^m = mt$, $\vartheta = m\dot\vartheta$; then (2) becomes, after division by m^2,

(3) $$\left(\dot\vartheta + \frac{b-a}{2m}\right)\left(\dot\vartheta - \frac{b-a}{2m}\right)u + t^2 u = 0.$$

This is a Bessel equation of order $n = (b-a)/2m$ in u and t. Its general solution is

$$u = AJ_n(t) + BJ_{-n}(t) \quad \text{or} \quad AJ_n(t) + BY_n(t)$$

according as n is an integer or not. A return to the original variables gives the solution of (1).

Example 1. $x^2 y'' - 2xy' + (2 + x^2)y = 0.$ In the theta form,

$$(\vartheta - 1)(\vartheta - 2)y + x^2 y = 0,$$

$a = 1, b = 2$. The substitution $y = x^{\frac{3}{2}}u$ yields the Bessel equation of order $\frac{1}{2}$:

$$(\vartheta + \tfrac{1}{2})(\vartheta - \tfrac{1}{2})u + x^2 u = 0$$

and

$$u = c_1 J_{\frac{1}{2}}(x) + c_2 J_{-\frac{1}{2}}(x)$$
$$= \sqrt{2/\pi x}(c_1 \sin x + c_2 \cos x), \qquad (\S 128)$$
$$y = x(A \sin x + B \cos x).$$

Example 2. $xy'' + 2y' + 4y = 0.$ In the theta form

$$\vartheta(\vartheta + 1)y + 4xy = 0,$$

$a = 0, b = -1$. The substitution $y = x^{-\frac{1}{2}}u$ gives

$$(\vartheta - \tfrac{1}{2})(\vartheta + \tfrac{1}{2})u + 4xu = 0,$$

in which $k = 2$, $m = \frac{1}{2}$. With

$$2x^{\frac{1}{2}} = \tfrac{1}{2}t \quad \text{or} \quad t = 4x^{\frac{1}{2}}, \quad \vartheta = \tfrac{1}{2}\dot{\vartheta},$$

and we get the Bessel equation of order 1

$$(\dot{\vartheta} - 1)(\dot{\vartheta} + 1)u + t^2u = 0$$

whose solution is

$$u = AJ_1(t) + BY_1(t).$$

Hence the solution of the given equation is

$$y = \frac{1}{\sqrt{x}}[AJ_1(4\sqrt{x}) + BY_1(4\sqrt{x})].$$

PROBLEMS

Find the general solution in problems 1 to 7.
1. $x^2y'' + xy' + (x^2 - \tfrac{1}{4})y = 0$.
2. $x^2y'' + 3xy' + (1 + x)y = 0$.
3. $x^2y'' + (9x^3 - 20)y = 0$.
4. $y'' - xy = 0$
5. $y'' + k^2x^2y = 0$.
6. $y'' + 5y' + xy = 0$.
7. $y'' + k^2y = 0$; solve as a Bessel equation.
8. $xy'' + y = 0$; solve if $y(0) = 0$, $y'(0) = 1$.
9. Prove formula (128.2).
10. From (125.16) derive the asymptotic values given in the Table 128.
11. $x^2y'' + axy' + (b + k^2x^{2m})y = 0$.
Put in the theta form and show that the substitution $y = x^{(1-a)/2}u$, $t = kx^m/m$ reduces it to a Bessel equation in u and t.
12. $xD^2y + (1 + 2x)(D + 1)y = 0$.
Put $y = e^{-x}u$, use exponential shift, and solve as a Bessel equation.

130. ZEROS OF BESSEL FUNCTIONS

All Bessel functions have an infinite number of simple positive zeros. To prove this we need a comparison theorem due to Sturm.

Theorem 1. *Let* $u(x)$ *and* $v(x)$ *be nontrivial solutions of*

(1) $$u'' + f(x)u = 0,$$

(2) $$v'' + g(x)v = 0.$$

Let $u(x)$ *have consecutive zeros* α, β $(\alpha < \beta)$ *and* $f(x)$, $g(x)$ *be continuous functions in* $[\alpha, \beta]$ *such that* $f(x) \leqq g(x)$. *Then if*

1°. $f(x) \not\equiv g(x)$, $v(x)$ *will have a zero between* α *and* β;

2°. $f(x) \equiv g(x)$, $v(x)$ *will have just one zero between* α *and* β *if* $v(x) \neq Cu(x)$.

PROOF. Multiply (1) by $-v$, (2) by u and add; then

$$D(uv' - vu') + (g - f)uv = 0$$

and after integrating between α and β, we have

$$(3) \qquad v(\alpha)u'(\alpha) - v(\beta)u'(\beta) + \int_{\alpha}^{\beta}(g - f)uv \, dx = 0,$$

since $u(\alpha) = u(\beta) = 0$. The zeros α, β are simple, for if $u'(\alpha)$ or $u'(\beta) = 0$, $u \equiv 0$ by the existence theorem of § 26. Suppose now that $v(x)$ has *no* zeros between α and β; we may then assume that

$$u(x) > 0, \qquad v(x) > 0, \qquad \alpha < x < \beta,$$

for a function and its negative have the same zeros. Then

$$v(\alpha), v(\beta) \geqq 0, \qquad u'(\alpha) > 0, \qquad u'(\beta) < 0.$$

Case 1°. $f \not\equiv g$. Equation (3) is impossible because the first two terms are non-negative and the third is positive since $g - f \geqq 0$ and $uv \geqq 0$. This contradiction shows that $v(x)$ must vanish between α and β.

Case 2°. $f \equiv g$. Now $v(\alpha) > 0$, $v(\beta) > 0$, for $v(\alpha) = 0$ or $v(\beta) = 0$ would make the Wronskian $W(u, v) = 0$ and $v = Cu$ by Theorem 28.1, contrary to hypothesis. The first two terms in (3) are now positive and the third is zero so that the equation is again impossible. Hence $v(x)$ must vanish between α and β. Moreover $v(x)$ can vanish *only once*; for if $v(x)$ had two zeros between α and β, the foregoing proof would require $u(x)$ to vanish between them, and α and β would not be *consecutive* zeros of $u(x)$ (cf. Theorem 28.4).

Before applying the theorem to Bessel's equation

$$(4) \qquad (\vartheta^2 - n^2)y + x^2 y = 0,$$

we put $y = x^{-\frac{1}{2}}v$; then on shifting $x^{-\frac{1}{2}}$ we have

$$[(\vartheta - \tfrac{1}{2})^2 - n^2]v + x^2 v = \vartheta(\vartheta - 1)v + (x^2 + \tfrac{1}{4} - n^2)v = 0.$$

Since $\vartheta(\vartheta - 1)v = x^2 v''$, this yields the equation

$$(5) \qquad v'' + \left(1 - \frac{4n^2 - 1}{4x^2}\right)v = 0.$$

Since $y = J_n(x)$ is a solution of (4), $v = \sqrt{x}\,J_n(x)$ is a solution of (5) having the same zeros as $J_n(x)$. Now when x is sufficiently large, (5) differs but little from $v'' + v = 0$ whose general solution

$$v = A \cos x + B \sin x$$

has the period 2π. Therefore, for large x we may expect that $y = v/\sqrt{x}$ will behave about like a sinusoid damped with the factor $1/\sqrt{x}$; in particular, this suggests that $J_n(x)$ has an infinite number of simple zeros. We shall now *prove* this fact.

Theorem 2. $J_0(x)$ *has a simple zero in each interval of positive values of length π.*

PROOF. Take $a \leqq x \leqq a + \pi$ $(a > 0)$ as the interval. Now compare the equations having the solutions shown:

$$u'' + u = 0, \qquad\qquad u = \sin (x - a)$$

$$v'' + \left(1 + \frac{1}{4x^2}\right) v = 0, \qquad v = \sqrt{x} J_0 (x).$$

Since $1 < 1 + \tfrac{1}{4}x^{-2}$ in the interval and $\sin (x - a)$ has zeros at a and $a + \pi$, we conclude that $\sqrt{x} J_0(x)$, and hence $J_0(x)$, has a zero in the interval $a < x < a + \pi$ if $a > 0$. The proof does not apply to the interval $0 \leqq x \leqq \pi$ since $1 + \tfrac{1}{4}x^{-2}$ is infinite at $x = 0$; nevertheless $J_0(x)$ has a zero in this interval (Fig. 125a).

Theorem 3. *Between consecutive positive zeros of $J_n(x)$ there is a zero of $J_{n-1}(x)$ and $J_{n+1}(x)$.*

PROOF. Let $J_n(x)$ have consecutive positive zeros at α and β. Then since $x^n J_n(x)$ and $x^{-n} J_n(x)$ also have these zeros, Rolle's theorem shows that the derivatives

$$D(x^n J_n) = x^n J_{n-1}, \qquad D(x^{-n} J_n) = -x^{-n} J_{n+1} \qquad (127.1\text{--}2)$$

will vanish at least once between α and β. Thus $J_{n-1}(x)$ and $J_{n+1}(x)$ have at least one zero between α and β.

Theorem 4. *The positive zeros of $J_n(x)$ and $J_{n+1}(x)$ separate each other.*

PROOF. If α, β are consecutive zeros of $J_n(x)$, $J_{n+1}(x)$ vanishes at least once between α and β. Moreover $J_{n+1}(x)$ vanishes just once between α and β; for if it had two zeros, $J_n(x)$ would vanish between them by Theorem 3 and α and β would not be *consecutive* zeros of $J_n(x)$.

It now follows from these theorems that $J_0(x), J_1(x), J_2(x), \ldots$ all have an infinite number of positive zeros.

Theorem 5. *If α and β are consecutive zeros of $J_n(x)$ $(n > \tfrac{1}{2})$, then $\beta - \alpha > \pi$; and by taking α sufficiently large $\beta - \alpha - \pi$ can be made arbitrarily small.*

PROOF. Compare

$$u'' + \left(1 - \frac{4n^2 - 1}{4n^2}\right)u = 0, \qquad u = \sqrt{x}\,J_n(x);$$

$$v'' + v = 0, \qquad\qquad\qquad v = \sin(x - \alpha).$$

Since

$$1 - \frac{4n^2 - 1}{4n^2} < 1 \quad \text{when} \quad 4n^2 - 1 > 0 \quad \text{or} \quad n > \tfrac{1}{2},$$

v will have a zero between α and β; and since α and $\alpha + \pi$ are consecutive zeros of v, $\alpha + \pi < \beta$ or $\beta - \alpha > \pi$.

Now let $\varepsilon > 0$ be arbitrarily small and compare

$$u'' + \left(\frac{\pi}{\pi + \varepsilon}\right)^2 u = 0, \qquad u = \sin\frac{\pi}{\pi + \varepsilon}(x - \alpha),$$

$$v'' + \left(1 - \frac{4n^2 - 1}{4x^2}\right)v = 0, \qquad v = \sqrt{x}\,J_n(x).$$

Take x sufficiently large so that coef u < coef v. Since α and $\alpha + \pi + \varepsilon$ are consecutive zeros of u, the zero β of $J_n(x)$ which follows α will fall short of $\alpha + \pi + \varepsilon$, that is, $\beta - \alpha - \pi < \varepsilon$.

PROBLEMS

1. Show that no nontrivial solution of

$$u'' + f(x)u = 0, \qquad f(x) \leqq 0,$$

has more than one zero. [Compare with $v'' = 0$ which has $v = 1$ as solution.]

2. Show that every solution of

$$v'' + f(x)v = 0, \qquad f(x) \geqq k^2$$

vanishes at least once in every interval of length π/k. [Compare with $u'' + k^2u = 0$.]

3. (a) Show that every solution of

$$v'' + (1 + x^2)v = 0$$

has a zero between 0 and π.

(b) Show that every solution of the Riccati equation

$$y' + y^2 + x + 1 = 0$$

becomes infinite between 0 and π [cf. Theorem 18].

4. Show that the general solution of Bessel's equation of order $\pm\tfrac{1}{2}$ is $y = (A\cos x + B\sin x)/\sqrt{x}$. [Use (5).]

5. Prove the comparison theorem:

Theorem. *Let $u(x)$ and $v(x)$ be nontrivial solutions of*

$$D[p(x)u'(x)] + f(x)u(x) = 0,$$
$$D[p(x)v'(x)] + g(x)v(x) = 0,$$

where $p(x) > 0$, $f(x) \leqq g(x)$ and $p'(x)$, $f(x)$, $g(x)$ are continuous in the interval $[\alpha, \beta]$ determined by two consecutive zeros α, β of $u(x)$. Then if
  $1°.$ $f(x) \not\equiv g(x)$, $v(x)$ *will have a zero between α and β;*
  $2°$ $f(x) \equiv g(x)$, $v(x)$ *will have just one zero between α and β if $v(x) \neq Cu(x)$.*
[Prove that $D\{p(uv' - vu')\} + (g - f)uv = 0$.]

  6. Show that all solutions of the *Airy equation*, $y'' + xy = 0$, have an infinite number of positive zeros and at most one negative zero. [Compare with $y'' + y = 0$ when $x > 0$; with $y'' = 0$ when $x < 0$.] Sir George Bidwell Airy (1801–1892) was a British astronomer.

131. ORTHOGONALITY OF BESSEL FUNCTIONS

Let $y(t)$ be a solution of Bessel's equation

$$(1) \qquad\qquad (\vartheta^2 - n^2)y + t^2 y = 0, \qquad n \geqq 0.$$

Then if $t = \lambda x$, $\dot{\vartheta} = \vartheta$, and $y(\lambda x)$ is a solution of

$$(2) \qquad\qquad (\vartheta^2 - n^2)y + \lambda^2 x^2 y = 0.$$

Since $\vartheta^2 = xD(xD) = x^2 D^2 + xD$, (2) has the D-form

$$(3) \qquad\qquad x^2 y'' + xy' + (\lambda^2 x^2 - n^2)y = 0;$$

this is known as the *parametric form* of Bessel's equation.

  When (3) is multiplied by $\sigma = 1/x$ (§ 33.8), it becomes self-adjoint. The equation

$$(4) \qquad\qquad D(xy') + \left(\lambda^2 x - \frac{n^2}{x}\right)y = 0$$

with the end conditions of case $1°$ (§ 117) is a regular Sturm-Liouville system over any interval $0 < a \leqq x \leqq b$ with

$$p(x) = x, \qquad q(x) = -\frac{n^2}{x}, \qquad \rho(x) = x.$$

  Over the interval $[0, b]$ the Sturm-Liouville system composed of equation (4) and the end condition

$$y(\lambda b) = 0$$

is *singular*; for $p(x)$ vanishes and $q(x)$ becomes infinite at $x = 0$. Nevertheless, the equation, written

$$y'' + \frac{y'}{x} + \left(\lambda^2 \frac{n^2}{x^2}\right)y = 0$$

has a regular singular point at $x = 0$ and has the continuous solution $y = J_n(\lambda x)$ since $n \geqq 0$. The end condition is now

$$(5) \qquad\qquad J_n(\lambda b) = 0;$$

and since this equation has an infinite number of positive roots $x_1, x_2, \ldots,$ the zeros of $J_n(\lambda b)$ are $\lambda_1 = x_1/b$, $\lambda_2 = x_2/b$, $\ldots$. Since $p(0) = 0$, we are in case 4° of § 117. The eigenvalues are $\lambda_i{}^2$ and the corresponding eigenfunctions $J_n(\lambda_i x)$. Theorem 117.1* now states that the functions $J_n(\lambda_i x)$ form an orthogonal set over $[0, b]$ with respect to the weight function $\rho(x) = x$:

$$(6) \qquad\qquad \int_0^b x J_n(\lambda_i x) J_n(\lambda_j x)\, dx = 0, \qquad m \neq n.$$

Or we may say that the set $\{\sqrt{x}\, J_n(\lambda_i x)\}$ is orthogonal over $[0, b]$.

Example 1. When $n = \frac{1}{2}$, $b = \pi$, we have the orthogonal set

$$\sqrt{x} J_{1/2}(x) = \sqrt{2/\pi} \sin \lambda x \qquad\qquad (128.1)$$

over $[0, \pi]$. Equation (5) now reduces to $\sin \lambda\pi = 0$ and has the roots $1, 2, 3, \ldots$; the eigenvalues $1, 4, 9, \ldots$ now belong to the eigenfunctions $\sin x$ $\sin 2x$, $\sin 3x, \ldots$, which are orthogonal on $[0, \pi]$ (cf. Ex. 117.1).

To utilize the set $\{J_n(\lambda_i x)\}$ in forming the *Fourier-Bessel* series of a function, we must compute the integral (6) when $m = n$.

When equation (4) is multiplied by $2xy'$, it may be written

$$D(xy')^2 + (\lambda^2 x^2 - n^2)Dy^2 = 0,$$

or on integration between 0 and b,

$$(xy')^2 \Big|_0^b + \int_0^b (\lambda^2 x^2 - n^2)Dy^2\, dx = 0.$$

Integration by parts with $u = \lambda^2 x^2 - n^2$, $v' = Dy^2$ gives

$$(7) \qquad\qquad [(xy')^2 + (\lambda^2 x^2 - n^2)y^2]_0^b = 2\lambda^2 \int_0^b xy^2\, dx$$

in which $y = J_n(\lambda x)$. In the relation

$$t J_n{}'(t) = n J_n(t) - t J_{n+1}(t) \qquad\qquad (127.8)$$

put $t = \lambda x$; then since $t\, d/dt = x\, d/dx$,

$$x J_n{}'(\lambda x) = n J_n(\lambda x) - \lambda x J_{n+1}(\lambda x)$$

---

* The fact that $q(x) = -n^2/x$ has a pole at $x = 0$ does not invalidate the proof.

and the left member of (7) becomes

$$[\{nJ_n(\lambda x) - \lambda x J_{n+1}(\lambda x)\}^2 + (\lambda^2 x^2 - n^2)J_n{}^2(\lambda x)]_0^b$$
$$= [-2n\lambda x J_n(\lambda x)J_{n+1}(\lambda x) + \lambda^2 x^2\{J_{n-1}^2(\lambda x) + J_n{}^2(\lambda x)\}]_0^b.$$

When $\lambda = \lambda_i$, a root of (5), this expression reduces to $\lambda_i{}^2 b^2 J_{n+1}{}^2(\lambda_i b)$ and from (7) we have

(8) $$\int_0^b x J_n{}^2(\lambda_i x)\, dx = \frac{b^2}{2} J_{n+1}^2(\lambda_i b), \qquad n = 1, 2, \ldots .$$

Assume now that a function $f(x)$ can be expanded in a series

(9) $$f(x) = \sum_{j=1}^{\infty} c_j J_n(\lambda_i x).$$

The procedure of § 116, when valid, will determine the coefficients c_j. Multiply (9) by $x J_n(\lambda_i x)$ and integrate the series term by term from 0 to b. By virtue of equations (6) and (8) we then obtain the equation

(10) $$\int_0^b x f(x) J_n(\lambda_i x)\, dx = c_i \frac{b^2}{2} J_{n+1}^2(\lambda_i b),$$

which determines c_i. When $f(x)$ and $f'(x)$ are piecewise continuous on the interval $[0, b]$, the *Fourier-Bessel Series* (9), with c_i given by (10), actually converges to $\frac{1}{2}[f(x+) + f(x-)]$ at every point of the open interval $0 < x < b$. Compare this theorem (proof omitted) with the corresponding theorem for Fourier series stated in § 116.

Example 2. Fourier-Bessel series in $J_0(\lambda_i x)$ for $f(x) = 1$, $(0 < x < b)$ where $\lambda_i b = \beta_i$ are positive zeros of $J_0(x)$.

From (10) the coefficients c_i are given by

$$c_i \frac{b^2}{2} J_1{}^2(\beta_i) = \int_0^b x J_0(\lambda_i x)\, dx, \qquad t = \lambda_i x$$

$$= \frac{1}{\lambda_i{}^2} \int_0^{\lambda_i b} t J_0(t)\, dt$$

$$= \frac{1}{\lambda_i{}^2}\left[t J_1(t) \right]_0^{\lambda_i b} \qquad (127.1')$$

$$= \frac{b}{\lambda_i} J_1(\beta_i), \qquad (J_1(0) = 0);$$

$$c_i = \frac{2}{\beta_i J_1(\beta_i)}$$

Hence the Fourier-Bessel series for 1 is

$$1 = 2 \sum_{i=1}^{\infty} \frac{J_0(\lambda_i x)}{\beta_i J_1(\beta_i)}, \qquad 0 < x < b.$$

PROBLEMS

1. In formula (10) show that $J_{n+1}^2(\lambda_i b) = J_{n-1}^2(\lambda_i b)$. $[J_n(\lambda_i b) = 0]$
2. Show that the Fourier-Bessel series in $J_1(\lambda_i x)$ for $f(x) = x$ $(0 < x < b)$, where $\beta_i = \lambda_i b$ are the positive zeros of $J_1(x)$, is

$$x = 2b \sum_{i=1}^{\infty} \frac{J_1(\lambda_i x)}{\beta_i J_2(\beta_i)}. \qquad |J_2(\beta_i) = -J_0(\beta_i)|$$

In Problems 3 and 4, obtain the Fourier-Bessel series in $J_0(\lambda_i x)$ for the given functions, where $\beta_i = \lambda_i b$ are the positive zeros of $J_0(x)$.
3. $f(x) = x^2$ $(0 < x < b)$;

$$x^2 = 2b^2 \sum_{i=1}^{\infty} \frac{1}{\beta_i J_1(\beta_i)} \left(1 - \frac{4}{\beta_i^2}\right) J_0(\lambda_i x).$$

4. $f(x) = \begin{cases} k, & 0 < x < a \\ 0, & a < x < b; \end{cases}$

$$f(x) = \frac{2ak}{b} \sum_{i=1}^{\infty} \frac{J_1(\lambda_i a)}{\beta_i J_1^2(\beta_i)} J_0(\lambda_i x).$$

5. Show that the Fourier-Bessel series in $J_2(\lambda_i x)$ for $f(x) = x^2$ $(0 < x < b)$, where $\beta_i = \lambda_i b$ are the positive zeros of $J_2(x)$, is

$$x^2 = 2b^2 \sum_{i=1}^{\infty} \frac{J_2(\lambda_i x)}{\beta_i J_3(\beta_i)}.$$

From (127.10) show that $J_3(\beta_i) = -J_1(\beta_i)$.

132.   GENERATING FUNCTION FOR $J_n(x)$

In § 104 we obtained the generating function*

(1)
$$\exp \frac{1}{2} x\left(t - \frac{1}{t}\right) = \sum_{n=-\infty}^{\infty} J_n(x) t^n$$

by a heuristic derivation. We now proceed to *prove* (1) by multiplying the two absolutely convergent series

$$\exp \tfrac{1}{2} xt = \sum_{i=0}^{\infty} \frac{1}{i!}\left(\frac{xt}{2}\right)^i, \qquad \exp\left(\frac{-x}{2t}\right) = \sum_{j=0}^{\infty} \frac{1}{j!}\left(\frac{-xt}{2}\right)^j$$

to obtain the double series

(2)
$$\exp \tfrac{1}{2} x\left(t - \frac{1}{t}\right) = \sum_{i=0}^{\infty} \sum_{j=0}^{\infty} \frac{(-1)^j}{i! \, j!}\left(\frac{x}{2}\right)^{i+j} t^{i-j}.$$

---

* This is equation (104.7) with z, x, t, replaced by x, t, n.

Since this series is absolutely convergent, the terms may be added in any order. We shall sum the terms along the diagonals $i - j = n$ of the lattice (i, j) for $n = 0, 1, 2, \ldots$ (Fig. 132) and then sum j from 0 to ∞ along each diagonal; thus for all lattice points on and below the diagonal $n = 0$ we put $i = n + j$ and find

$$(3) \qquad \sum_{n=0}^{\infty} t^n \sum_{j=0}^{\infty} \frac{(-1)^j}{(n+j)!\, j!} \left(\frac{x}{2}\right)^{n+2j} = \sum_{n=0}^{\infty} J_n(x) t^n.$$

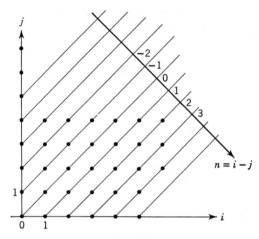

Fig. 132

We next sum along the diagonals $i - j = -n$ for $n = 1, 2, 3, \ldots$, and then sum i from 0 to ∞ along each diagonal. Note that i (not j) must be summed to include *all* the points on these upper diagonals. Thus putting $j = n + i$ we have

$$(4) \qquad \sum_{n=1}^{\infty} t^{-n}(-1)^n \sum_{i=1}^{\infty} \frac{(-1)^i}{i!\,(n+i)!} \left(\frac{x}{2}\right)^{n+2i} = \sum_{n=0}^{\infty} J_{-n}(x) t^{-n}$$

when we use formula (125.10) for $J_{-n}(x)$.

We have now summed over all lattice points (i, j), each point occurring just once. Thus when (3) and (4) are combined, equation (2) takes the form (1), which is now firmly established.

When $t = e^{i\theta}$,

$$\frac{1}{2} x \left(t - \frac{1}{t} \right) = ix \frac{e^{i\theta} - e^{-i\theta}}{2i} = ix \sin \theta$$

and (1) becomes

$$(5) \qquad e^{ix \sin \theta} = \sum_{n=-\infty}^{\infty} J_n(x) e^{in\theta}.$$

After equating the real and imaginary parts of both members we have

(6)
$$\cos (x \sin \theta) = \sum_{n=-\infty}^{\infty} J_n(x) \cos n\theta$$

(7)
$$\sin (x \sin \theta) = \sum_{n=-\infty}^{\infty} J_n(x) \sin n\theta.$$

Now since $J_{-n}(x) = (-1)^n J_n(x)$ and

$$\cos (-nx) = \cos nx, \qquad \sin (-nx) = -\sin nx,$$

all terms for odd n cancel in (6), and all terms for even n cancel in (7). Hence

(6)'
$$\cos (x \sin \theta) = J_0 + 2 \sum_{n=1}^{\infty} J_{2n}(x) \cos 2n\theta,$$

(7)'
$$\sin (x \sin \theta) = 2 \sum_{n=1}^{\infty} J_{2n-1}(x) \sin (2n - 1)\theta.$$

Equation (6)' shows that $J_{2n}(x)$ are the Fourier coefficients a_{2n} of $\frac{1}{2} \cos (x \sin \theta)$ regarded as a function of θ; and since this function is even, we have from (116.14)

(8)
$$J_{2n}(x) = \frac{1}{\pi} \int_0^\pi \cos (x \sin \theta) \cos 2n\theta \, d\theta.$$

Equation (7)' shows that $J_{2n-1}(x)$ are the Fourier coefficients b_{2n-1} of $\frac{1}{2} \sin (x \sin \theta)$ regarded as a function of θ; and since this function is odd, we have from (116.14)

(9)
$$J_{2n-1}(x) = \frac{1}{\pi} \int_0^\pi \sin (x \sin \theta) \sin (2n - 1)\theta \, d\theta.$$

From Bessel's inequality (116.10) we know that all Fourier coefficients $c_n \to 0$ as $n \to \infty$; hence

(10)
$$\lim_{n \to \infty} J_n(x) = 0.$$

We may also obtain an integral formula for $J_n(x)$ for any integral n. Multiply (6) by $\cos k\theta$, (7) by $\sin k\theta$, and add the resulting equations; then

$$\cos (x \sin \theta - k\theta) = \sum_{n=-\infty}^{\infty} J_n(x) \cos (n - k)\theta.$$

Now integrate both members from $\theta = 0$ to $\theta = \pi$; on the right

$$\int_0^\pi \cos (n - k)\theta \, d\theta = \begin{cases} 0, & n \neq k, \\ \pi, & n = k, \end{cases}$$

and we obtain the single term $\pi J_k(x)$; putting $k = n$ we have

(11)
$$J_n(x) = \frac{1}{\pi} \int_0^\pi \cos (x \sin \theta - n\theta) \, d\theta,$$

which is known as Bessel's integral form of $J_n(x)$. Since $|\cos \varphi| \leqq 1$, we have

(12) $|J_n(x)| \leqq 1$;

here the equal sign applies only when $n = 0$ and $x = 0$, namely $J_0(0) = 1$.

If we differentiate (11) k times we get

$$D^k J_n(x) = \frac{1}{\pi} \int_0^\pi \sin^k \theta \cos \left(x \sin \theta - n\theta + k\frac{\pi}{2} \right) d\theta,$$

so that also

(13) $|D^k J_n(x)| \leqq 1$, $k, n = 0, 1, 2, \ldots$.

Thus the Bessel functions have the same boundedness property as the sine and cosine.

On putting $\theta = 0$ in (6)′ we get the remarkable series

(14) $1 = J_0(x) + 2J_2(x) + 2J_4(x) - \cdots$;

and on putting $\theta = \pi/2$ in (6)′ and (7)′, we have

(15) $\cos x = J_0(x) - 2J_2(x) + 2J_4(x) - \cdots$,

(16) $\sin x = 2J_1(x) - 2J_3(x) + 2J_5(x) - \cdots$.

Since the functions $\frac{1}{2}\cos(x \sin \theta)$ and $\frac{1}{2}\sin(x \sin \theta)$ have the $J_n(x)$ of even and odd index for Fourier coefficients, and these functions and their derivatives are continuous in $(-\pi, \pi)$, we know that the series $\sum_{n=0}^{\infty} J_n(x)$ is absolutely convergent for every x.* Hence the series (14), (15), and (16) are absolutely convergent.

133. FUNCTIONS ber (x) AND bei (x)

The function $J_n(ax)$ is a solution of the equation

(1) $(\vartheta^2 - n^2)y + a^2x^2y = 0$.

When $a^2 = i^3 = -i$, the solution $J_n(i^{3/2}x)$ may be written

(2) $J_n(i^{3/2}x) = \text{ber}_n(x) + i \,\text{bei}_n(x)$,

where $\text{ber}_n(x)$ and $\text{bei}_n(x)$ are real series, the real and imaginary parts of $J_n(i^{3/2}x)$. In the most important case $n = 0$, these functions are written simply ber x and bei x. Now in the series

$$J_0(i^{3/2}x) = \sum_{k=0}^{\infty} (-1)^k \frac{i^{3k}}{k!\,k!} \left(\frac{x}{2}\right)^{2k}$$

---

* *Advanced Calculus*, § 228.

the real terms occur when $k = 2j$ is even, and the imaginary terms occur when $k = 2j + 1$ is odd. Since $(-1)^{2j} = 1$, $i^{6j} = (-1)^j$,

(3)
$$\text{ber } x = \sum_{j=0}^{\infty} \frac{(-1)^j}{(2j)!\,(2j)!} \left(\frac{x}{2}\right)^{4j}$$

$$= 1 - \frac{x^4}{2^2 4^2} + \frac{x^8}{2^2 4^2 6^2 8^2} - \cdots ;$$

and since $(-1)^{2j+1} = -1$, $i^{6j+3} = (-1)^j(-1)$,

(4)
$$\text{bei } x = \sum_{j=0}^{\infty} \frac{(-1)^j}{(2j + 1)!\,(2j + 1)!} \left(\frac{x}{2}\right)^{4j+2}$$

$$= \frac{x^2}{2^2} - \frac{x^6}{2^2 4^2 6^2} + \frac{x^{10}}{2^2 4^2 6^2 8^2 10^2} - \cdots .$$

Both functions are even and have an infinite number of positive zeros; but unlike the Bessel functions their graphs oscillate with increasing amplitude (Fig. 133).

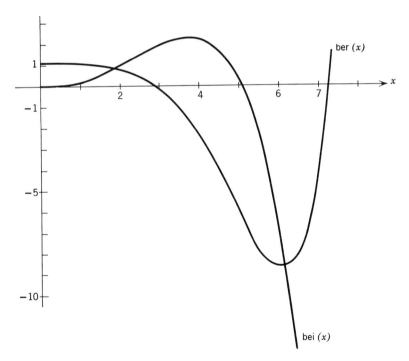

Fig. 133 Functions ber (x) and bei (x).

134. ORTHOGONAL POLYNOMIALS

Let $\{P_n(x)\}$ be any sequence of orthogonal polynomials of degree $n = 0, 1, 2, \ldots$ over $[a, b]$ with the weight function $\rho(x)$:

$$(1) \qquad \int_a^b \rho(x)P_i(x)P_j(x)\,dx = \begin{cases} 0, & i \neq j \\ h_i \neq 0, & i = j. \end{cases}$$

Theorem 1. *The polynomial $P_n(x)$ of degree n is orthogonal to all polynomials whose degree is less than n.*

PROOF. Let $Q(x)$ be a polynomial of degree $m < n$; then $Q(x)$ can be written as the linear combination

$$Q(x) = c_0 P_0 + c_1 P_1 + \cdots + c_m P_m.$$

First choose c_m so that $Q - c_m P_m$ has no term in x^m; then choose c_{m-1} so that $Q - c_m P_m - c_{m-1}P_{m-1}$ has no term in x^{m-1}; and proceed in this manner until c_0 is chosen so that $Q - c_m P_m - \cdots - c_1 P_1 - c_0 P_0 = 0$. Then

$$\int_a^b \rho Q P_n\,dx = \sum_{i=0}^m c_i \int_a^b \rho P_i P_n\,dx = 0,$$

since each integral on the right ($i < n$) is zero in view of (1). The constants c_i are precisely the Fourier constants

$$c_i = \frac{1}{h_i}\int_a^b \rho(x)Q(x)P_i(x)\,dx,$$

because these constants give the best polynomial approximation to $Q(x)$ in the sense of least squares (§ 116), and the best *is* $Q(x)$.

Theorem 2. *The polynomial $P_n(x)$ of degree n has exactly n simple zeros in $[a, b]$.*

PROOF. Let $P_n(x)$ change sign at m distinct points $x_1, x_2, \ldots, x_m$ in $[a, b]$. Then the polynomial

$$Q(x) = (x - x_1)(x - x_2) \cdots (x - x_m)$$

also changes sign at these points and hence $\rho(x)Q(x)P_n(x)$ never changes sign in $[a, b]$; hence

$$\int_a^b \rho(x)Q(x)P_n(x)\,dx \neq 0.$$

Now $Q(x)$ is of degree m; and if $m < n$, the foregoing integral is zero in view of Theorem 1; hence $m \geq n$. But $m > n$ is impossible since $P_n(x)$ can have at most n zeros; hence $m = n$.

Theorem 3. *If the polynomial $P_n(x)$ of the orthogonal set defined by (1) is*

$$(2) \qquad P_n(x) = a_n x^n + b_n x^{n-1} + \cdots, \qquad a_n \neq 0,$$

then three successive polynomials satisfy the recurrence relation

$$(3) \qquad xP_n = \frac{a_n}{a_{n+1}} P_{n+1} + \left(\frac{b_n}{a_n} - \frac{b_{n+1}}{a_{n+1}} \right) P_n + \frac{a_{n-1}}{a_n} \frac{h_n}{h_{n-1}} P_{n-1}.$$

PROOF. Express $xP_n(x)$ as a linear combination of $P_0, P_1, \ldots, P_{n+1}$:

$$(4) \qquad xP_n(x) = \sum_{k=0}^{n+1} c_{nk} P_k(x),$$

where the Fourier constants

$$(5) \qquad c_{nk} = \frac{1}{h_k} \int_a^b \rho(x) x P_n(x) P_k(x) \, dx.$$

Since $P_n(x)$ is orthogonal to all polynomials of degree less than n, $P_n(x)$ is orthogonal to $xP_k(x)$ when $k + 1 < n$, that is, when $k = 0, 1, \ldots, n - 2$. Hence $c_{nk} = 0$ for these values and (4) becomes

$$(6) \qquad xP_n = c_{n,n-1} P_{n-1} + c_{n,n} P_n + c_{n,n+1} P_{n+1}.$$

Equating the coefficients of x^{n+1} in (6) we have $a_n = c_{n,n+1} a_{n+1}$, whence

$$(7) \qquad c_{n,n+1} = \frac{a_n}{a_{n+1}}.$$

Equating the coefficients of x^n in (6), we see that

$$b_n = c_{n,n} a_n + c_{n,n+1} b_{n+1} = c_{nn} a_n + \frac{a_n}{a_{n+1}} b_{n+1},$$

$$(8) \qquad c_{n,n} = \frac{b_n}{a_n} - \frac{b_{n+1}}{a_{n+1}}.$$

Finally, from (5) we have $c_{nk} h_k = c_{kn} h_n$ so that

$$c_{n,n-1} h_{n-1} = c_{n-1,n} h_n = \frac{a_{n-1}}{a_n} h_n \qquad \text{from (7),}$$

$$(9) \qquad c_{n,n-1} = \frac{a_{n-1}}{a_n} \frac{h_n}{h_{n-1}}.$$

When the values in (7), (8), (9) are substituted in (6), we obtain the relation (3).

Example 1. **Legendre Polynomials** (§ 119).

$$P_n(x) = \frac{1}{n!\, 2^n}\, D^n(x^2 - 1)^n, \quad P_0(x) = 1; \quad h_n = \frac{2}{2n+1}.$$

Now

$$a_n = \frac{2n(2n - 1) \cdots (n + 1)}{n!\, 2^n}, \quad b_n = 0,$$

$$\frac{a_n}{a_{n+1}} = 2(n + 1)\frac{n + 1}{(2n + 2)(2n + 1)} = \frac{n + 1}{2n + 1};$$

$$\frac{a_{n-1}}{a_n} \cdot \frac{h_n}{h_{n-1}} = \frac{n}{2n - 1}\frac{2n - 1}{2n + 1} = \frac{n}{2n + 1}.$$

The recurrence relation (5) is therefore

$$xP_n = \frac{n + 1}{2n + 1}P_{n+1} + \frac{n}{2n + 1}P_{n-1},$$

or, as in (120.4),

$$(n + 1)P_{n+1} - (2n + 1)xP_n + nP_{n-1} = 0.$$

Example 2. **Laguerre Polynomials** (§ 123).

$$L_n(x) = \frac{1}{n!}\,(D - 1)^n x^n, \quad L_0(x) = 1; \quad h_n = 1.$$

Since $(D - 1)^n = (-1)^n + n(-1)^{n-1}D + \cdots$,

$$a_n = \frac{(-1)^n}{n!}, \quad b_n = \frac{(-1)^{n-1}n^2}{n!}; \quad \frac{b_n}{a_n} = -n^2;$$

$$\frac{a_n}{a_{n+1}} = -(n + 1), \quad \frac{b_n}{a_n} - \frac{b_{n+1}}{a_{n+1}} = (n + 1)^2 - n^2 = 2n + 1$$

and (5) becomes

$$xL_n = -(n + 1)L_{n+1} + (2n + 1)L_n - nL_{n-1},$$

or, as in (123.9),

$$(n + 1)L_{n+1} - (2n + 1 - x)L_n + nL_{n-1} = 0.$$

PROBLEMS

1. Deduce the recurrence relation for the Hermite polynomials (§ 124). $[a_n = 2^n, b_n = 0; h_n = 2^n n!\ \sqrt{\pi}\,]$.

2. Deduce the recurrence relation for the Chebyshev polynomials (118.7), if $T_0(x) = 1$ is not involved. $[a_n = 2^{n-1}, b_n = 0; h_n = \pi/2, n > 0]$.

3. Deduce the generating function

$$F(z, x) = \sum_{t=0}^{\infty} T_t(z)x^t = \frac{1 - x^2}{1 - 2zx + x^2}$$

for the Chebyshev polynomials from their recurrence relation given in (118.7).

135. EQUATIONS WITH 3-TERM RECURRENCE RELATIONS

If a differential equation cannot be put in the theta form of § 108, we can always resort to the more general method of § 107, which also gives the indices λ_1, λ_2. When the recurrence relation has three or more terms, no general method of solving it is known. Nevertheless at an ordinary or regular point there is always one series solution (107.3) and as many coefficients of this series can be found to ensure the desired accuracy. Of course, the series is not *known* until its general term is known, and only in exceptional cases will many-term recurrence relations lead to solutions in terms of well-known or tabulated functions. The following examples illustrate the procedure. When $\lambda_1 = \lambda_2$, one solution will always involve logarithms, and this is *usually* the case when $\lambda_1 - \lambda_2$ is an integer.

Example 1. $xy'' + (2 - x)y' - (1 + x)y = 0.$
Multiply by x and reduce to the theta form:

(i) $$\vartheta(\vartheta + 1)y - x(\vartheta + 1)y - x^2 y = 0.$$

The indicial equation is $\lambda(\lambda + 1) = 0$.
We first find a power series solution for the larger index $\lambda_1 = 0$ and assume

$$y' = \sum_{n=0}^{\infty} c_n x^n, \qquad c_0 = 1.$$

On substituting this series in (i) we obtain

$$\sum_{n=1}^{\infty} n(n + 1)c_n x^n - \sum_{n=0}^{\infty} (n + 1)c_n x^{n+1} - \sum_{n=0}^{\infty} c_n x^{n+2} = 0.$$

With the convention that $c_n = 0$ when $n < 0$, this can be written

$$\sum_{n-1}^{\infty} [n(n + 1)c_n - nc_{n-1} - c_{n-2}]x^n = 0$$

and yields the recurrence relation

(ii) $$n(n + 1)c_n = nc_n + c_{n-2}, \qquad n \geqq 1.$$

We now let $n = 1, 2, 3, \ldots$ and obtain

$$
\begin{aligned}
2c_1 &= c_0 + c_{-1} = 1, & c_1 &= \tfrac{1}{2} \\
6c_2 &= 2c_1 + c_0 = 2, & c_2 &= \tfrac{1}{3} \\
12c_3 &= 3c_2 + c_1 = \tfrac{3}{2}, & c_3 &= \tfrac{1}{8} \\
20c_4 &= 4c_3 + c_5 = \tfrac{5}{6}, & c_4 &= \tfrac{1}{24} \\
30c_5 &= 5c_4 + c_3 = \tfrac{1}{3}, & c_5 &= \tfrac{1}{90},
\end{aligned}
$$

and so on. Thus the series for y_1 begins

$$y_1 = 1 + \tfrac{1}{2}x + \tfrac{1}{3}x^2 + \tfrac{1}{8}x^3 + \tfrac{1}{24}x^4 + \tfrac{1}{90}x^5 + \cdots.$$

The recurrence relation (ii) admits a simple solution. Put $c_n = k_n/(n + 1)!$; then (ii) becomes

$$k_n = k_{n-1} + k_{n-2}$$

and from $c_0 = 1$, $c_1 = \frac{1}{2}$ we have the initial values $k_0 = 1$, $k_1 = 1$. The solution for k_n is the well-known *Fibonacci sequence* $\{k_n\} = 1, 1, 2, 3, 5, 8, 13, 21, \ldots$ (Ex. 91.3) and

$$y_1 = \sum_{n=0}^{\infty} k_n \frac{x^n}{(n + 1)!}.$$

For the smaller index $\lambda_2 = -1$, we assume

$$y_2 = \sum_{n=0}^{\infty} c_n x^{n-1}, \qquad c_0 = 1$$

and obtain the recurrence relation

(iii) $$(n - 1)nc_n = (n - 1)c_{n-1} + c_{n-2}, \qquad n \geq 1.$$

For $n = 1$ this gives $0 \cdot c_1 = 0$, so that c_1 is arbitrary. If we take $c_1 = 0$, we find

$$2c_2 = c_1 + c_0 = 1, \qquad c_2 = \tfrac{1}{2}$$
$$6c_3 = 2c_2 + c_1 = 1, \qquad c_3 = \tfrac{1}{6}$$
$$12c_4 = 3c_3 + c_2 = 1, \qquad c_4 = \tfrac{1}{12}$$
$$20c_5 = 4c_4 + c_3 = \tfrac{1}{2}, \qquad c_5 = \tfrac{1}{40}$$
$$30c_6 = 5c_5 + c_4 = \tfrac{5}{24}, \qquad c_6 = \tfrac{1}{144},$$

and so on. Thus the series for y_2 begins

$$y_2 = x^{-1} + \tfrac{1}{2}x + \tfrac{1}{6}x^2 + \tfrac{1}{12}x^3 + \tfrac{1}{40}x^4 + \tfrac{1}{144}x^5 + \cdots.$$

With $c_n = h_n/n!$, the recurrence relation (iii) again reduces to the Fibonacci equation

$$h_n = h_{n-1} + h_{n-2}$$

with $h_0 = 1$, $h_1 = 0$ whose solution is $\{h_n\} = 1, 0, 1, 1, 2, 3, 5, 8, \ldots$ and

$$y_2 = \sum_{n=0}^{\infty} h_n \frac{x^{n-1}}{n!}.$$

For an arbitrary choice of c_1 we would obtain the solution $y = y_2 + c_1 y_1$. If in the solution for $\lambda_2 = -1$, both $c_0 = B$ and $c_1 = A$ are arbitrary constants, we obtain the general solution of (i), namely $y = Ay_1 + By_2$, by the sole use of relation (iii). This, of course, is an exceptional occurrence.

Example 2. $xy'' + (2 - x)y' - (2 + x)y = 0$.

The theta form is

$$\vartheta(\vartheta + 1)y - x(\vartheta + 2)y - x^2 y = 0,$$

and the indicial equation is $\lambda(\lambda + 1) = 0$.

As before, we first find a power series solution for the larger index $\lambda_1 = 0$:

$$y_1 = \sum_{n=0}^{\infty} c_n x^n, \qquad c_0 = 1.$$

The recurrence relation is now

$$n(n + 1)c_n = (n + 1)c_{n-1} + c_{n-2}, \qquad n \geq 1.$$

and we find

$$2c_1 = 2c_0 + c_{-1} = 2, \qquad c_1 = 1$$
$$6c_2 = 3c_1 + c_0 = 4, \qquad c_2 = \tfrac{2}{3}$$
$$12c_3 = 4c_2 + c_1 = \tfrac{11}{3}, \qquad c_3 = \tfrac{11}{36}$$
$$20c_4 = 5c_3 + c_2 = \tfrac{79}{36}, \qquad c_4 = \tfrac{79}{720},$$

and so on; thus

$$y_1 = 1 + x + \tfrac{2}{3}x^2 + \tfrac{11}{30}x^3 + \tfrac{79}{720}x^4 + \cdots.$$

For the smaller index $\lambda_2 = -1$, assume

$$y_2 = \sum_{n=0}^{\infty} c_n x^{n-1}, \qquad c_0 = 1.$$

The recurrence relation

$$(n - 1)n c_n = n c_{n-1} + c_{n-2}, \qquad n \geq 1$$

now gives for $n = 1$, $0 \cdot c_1 = c_0 + c_{-1} = 1$ and cannot be satisfied. A second solution involves $\log x$, and may be found as in § 112 but with more tedious calculations.

Example 3. $xy'' + (2 - x)y' + (x - 1)y = 0.$

The theta form is

$$\vartheta(\vartheta + 1)y - x(\vartheta + 1)y + x^2 y = 0.$$

and the indicial equation is $\lambda(\lambda + 1) = 0$.

For the larger index $\lambda_1 = 0$, $y_1 = \sum_{n=0}^{\infty} c_n x^n$, and the recurrence relation is

$$n(n + 1)c_n = n c_{n-1} - c_{n-2}, \qquad n \geq 1.$$

With $c_0 = 1$ we find

$$2c_1 = c_0 - c_{-1} = 1, \qquad c_1 = \frac{1}{2}$$
$$6c_2 = 2c_1 - c_0 = 0, \qquad c_2 = 0$$
$$12c_3 = 3c_2 - c_1 = -\frac{1}{2}, \qquad c_3 = -\frac{1}{4!}$$
$$20c_4 = 4c_3 - c_2 = -\frac{1}{3!}, \qquad c_4 = -\frac{1}{5!}$$
$$30c_5 = 5c_4 - c_3 = 0, \qquad c_5 = 0$$
$$42c_6 = 6c_5 - c_4 = \frac{1}{5!}, \qquad c_6 = \frac{1}{7!}$$
$$56c_7 = 7c_6 - c_5 = \frac{1}{6!}, \qquad c_7 = \frac{1}{8!}$$
$$72c_8 = 8c_7 - c_6 = 0, \qquad c_8 = 0.$$

The law governing c_n is beginning to emerge and can be shown by induction to hold in general. Thus for y_1 we have the gap series

$$y_1 = 1 + \frac{x}{2!} - \frac{x^3}{4!} - \frac{x^4}{5!} + \frac{x^6}{7!} + \frac{x^7}{8!} - \frac{x^9}{10!} - \frac{x^{10}}{11!} + \cdots .$$

If we put $c_n = k_n/(n + 1)!$, the recurrence relation becomes

$$k_n = k_{n-1} - k_{n-2},$$

and from $c_0 = 1$, $c_1 = \frac{1}{2}$ we have $k_0 = k_1 = 1$. From § 91 we readily find (cf. Prob. 91.18)

$$k_n = \cos \frac{n\pi}{3} + \frac{1}{\sqrt{3}} \sin \frac{n\pi}{3} = \frac{\sin (n + 1)\pi/3}{\sin \pi/3}$$

from which we obtain the sequence

$$\{k_n\} = 1, 1, 0, -1, -1, 0; \ldots$$

of period 6. The values of $c_n = k_n/(n + 1)!$ are those given earlier.

For the smaller index $\lambda_2 = -1$, $y_2 = \sum_{n=0}^{\infty} c_n x^{n-1}$, and the recurrence relation is

$$n(n - 1)c_n = (n - 1)c_{n-1} - c_{n-2}.$$

With $c_0 = 1$ we have $0 \cdot c_1 = 0 \cdot c_0 + c_{-1} = 0$ so that c_1 is arbitrary. If we take $c_1 = 0$, we obtain the sequence

$$\{c_n\} = 1, 0, -\frac{1}{2!}, -\frac{1}{3!}, 0, \frac{1}{5!}, \frac{1}{6!}, 0, \ldots .$$

These values suggest the gap series

$$y_2 = x^{-1} - \frac{x}{2!} + \frac{x^2}{3!} + \frac{x^4}{5!} + \frac{x^5}{6!} - \frac{x^7}{8!} - \frac{x^8}{9!} + \cdots .$$

That this is correct is shown by putting $c_n = h_n/(n + 1)!$; then

$$h_n = h_{n-1} - h_{n-2}, \qquad h_0 = 1, \qquad h_1 = 0,$$

and we obtain the solution

$$\{h_n\} = 1; 0, 1, 1, 0, -1, -1; \ldots$$

which is also of period 6 after $h_0 = 1$.

If we choose $c_1 = 1$, we get the solution

$$y_3 = x^{-1} + 1 - \frac{x^2}{3!} - \frac{x^3}{4!} + \frac{x^5}{6!} + \frac{x^6}{7!} - \cdots = y_1 + y_2.$$

In this example, as in Example 1, we have solved the recurrence relation, but in general, this is rarely possible.

The solution

$$y_1 = \sum_{n=0}^{\infty} \frac{\sin (n + 1)\pi/3}{\sin \pi/3} \frac{x^n}{(n + 1)!} = \frac{2}{x\sqrt{3}} \sum_{n=2}^{\infty} \sin n\pi/3 \frac{x^n}{n!}$$

is readily expressed in closed form. For since

$$\sin \frac{n\pi}{3} = \frac{1}{2i}(\alpha^n - \alpha^{-n}), \qquad \alpha = e^{i\pi/3} = \frac{1}{2}(1 + i\sqrt{3}),$$

we have

$$y_1 = \frac{1}{ix\sqrt{3}} \sum_{n=0}^{\infty} \frac{(\alpha x)^n - (\alpha^{-1}x)^n}{n!}$$

$$= \frac{1}{ix\sqrt{3}} (e^{\alpha x} - e^{\alpha^{-1}x})$$

$$= \frac{1}{ix\sqrt{3}} e^{x/2}(e^{i\sqrt{3}x/2} - e^{-i\sqrt{3}x/2})$$

$$= \frac{1}{ix\sqrt{3}} e^{x/2}\, 2i \sin \frac{\sqrt{3}}{2} x$$

or

$$y_1 = e^{x/2} \frac{\sin \sqrt{3}x/2}{\sqrt{3}x/2}, \qquad x \neq 0.$$

Note that as $x \to 0$, $y_1 \to 1$ in agreement with the series for y_1.

We have also

$$xy_3 = D(xy_1), \qquad xy_2 = D(xy_1) - xy_1,$$

from which we find

$$y_2 = e^{x/2} \frac{\sin (\pi/3 - \sqrt{3}x/2)}{\sqrt{3}x/2}.$$

Example 4. $xy'' + (1 - 2x)y' + (x - 1)y = 0.$

The theta form

$$\vartheta^2 y - x(2\vartheta + 1)y + x^2 y = 0$$

shows that $\lambda_1 = \lambda_2 = 0$. The power series solution has the form

$$y_1 = \sum_{n=0}^{\infty} c_n x^n, \qquad c_0 = 1,$$

and yields the recurrence relation

$$n^2 c_n - (2n - 1)c_{n-1} + c_{n-2} = 0, \qquad n \geq 1.$$

If $k_n = nc_n - c_{n-1}$, this can be written

$$nk_n - k_{n-1} = 0, \qquad k_0 = 0.$$

Hence $k_n = 0$ and $nc_n - c_{n-1} = 0$, $c_0 = 1$. This recurrence relation has the solution $c_n = 1/n!$ and hence $y_1 = e^x$.

The formula (28.8) now gives $y_2 = e^x \log x$ as the second solution.

Example 5. Emden's Equation.

$$xy'' + y' + xy^n = 0.$$

If we attempt to find a power series solution of this nonlinear equation, as it stands, by the method of § 22, we find that the indeterminate form $0/0$ appears repeatedly.* This can be avoided by reducing it to the theta form

(i) $$\vartheta(\vartheta + 1)y + x^2 y^n = 0,$$

which discloses that it admits a series solution in even powers:

(ii) $$y = 1 + a_1 x^2 + a_2 x^4 + a_3 x^6 + \cdots.$$

Consider (i) when $n = 3$. The power y^3 is readily found to be

$$y^3 = 1 + 3a_1 x^2 + (3a_2 + 3a_1)x^4 + (3a_3 + 6a_1 a_2 + a_1{}^3)x^6 + \cdots;$$

and since $\vartheta(\vartheta + 1)x^n = n(n + 1)x^n$, we have after the substitution of (ii) in (i):

$$(2 \cdot 3a_1 + 1)x^2 + (4 \cdot 5a_2 + 3a_1)x^4 + (6 \cdot 7a_3 + 3a_2 + 3a_1{}^2)x^6$$
$$+ (8 \cdot 9a_4 + 3a_3 + 6a_1 a_2 + a_1{}^3)x^8 + \cdots = 0.$$

Since all coefficients must vanish, we have

$$a_1 = -\frac{1}{6}, \, a_2 = \frac{1}{40}, \, a_3 = -\frac{19}{5040}, \, a_4 = \frac{619}{1088640}, \ldots.$$

PROBLEMS

1. Check the first four terms of both solutions of Example 1.

2. Show that

$$4x(1 - x)y'' + 2(1 + x^2)y' - (1 + x)y = 0$$

has the theta form

$$2\vartheta(2\vartheta - 1)y - x(2\vartheta - 1)^2 y + x^2(2\vartheta - 1)y = 0.$$

For $\lambda_1 = 0$ and $\lambda_2 = \frac{1}{2}$, deduce the recurrence relations for $n \geq 2$:

$$2n(2n - 1)c_n - (2n - 3)^2 c_{n-1} + (2n - 5)c_{n-2} = 0,$$
$$n(2n + 1)c_n - 2(n - 1)^2 c_{n-1} + (n - 2)c_{n-2} = 0,$$

and obtain the solutions for $c_0 = 1$ in closed form.

3. From the theta form of

$$xy'' + (x + 1)xy' - (2x^2 - 2x + 1)y = 0,$$

find the indices $\lambda_1 = 1$, $\lambda_2 = -1$. First find y_1, then y_2, and check both series.

4. In Problem 3 find the solution y_1 for $\lambda_1 = 1$ by taking $c_0 = 0$, $c_2 = 1$ in the recurrence relation for $\lambda_2 = -1$.

5. Reduce to the theta form and find one solution of

$$x^2 y'' + x(3 + x)y' + (1 + x + x^2)y = 0.$$

6. Show that if the series

$$y = \sum_{n=0}^{\infty} b_n \frac{x^n}{n!} \quad \text{satisfies} \quad (1 - x)y'' + y = 0, \quad \text{then}$$

$$b_0 + b_2 = 0, \qquad b_{n+2} - nb_{n+1} + b_n = 0 \qquad (n \geq 1).$$

Obtain two solutions by taking $b_0 = 1$, $b_1 = 0$, and $b_0 = 0$, $b_1 = 1$.

---

* See Z. Kopal, ref. 11, p. 144.

CHAPTER 11

Mikusiński's Operational Calculus

136. THE CONVOLUTION RING

In a series of papers published in 1949 to 1956, the Polish mathematician Jan G. Mikusiński* developed an operational calculus that casts a new light on Laplace transform methods, in effect freeing them from considerations of convergence introduced by the improper integral $\int_0^\infty e^{-st}f(t)\,dt$ and bringing the essential theory into the realm of algebra. The rules for transforming derivatives given in § 68 presuppose properties of a function which in actual practice are not known in advance; for the function to be transformed is often the unknown solution of a differential or integral equation. Mikusiński accomplishes this change of climate by setting up a commutative *ring* in which the elements are the class $\mathscr{C}$ of continuous real- or complex-valued functions over the interval $0 \leqq t < \infty$, in which the operations are the addition and convolution (§ 70) of functions. Thus from the functions a and b we obtain by addition and convolution the functions $a + b$ and ab (the $a * b$ of § 70).

(A) $\qquad\qquad (a + b)(t) = a(t) + b(t),$

(M) $\qquad\qquad (ab)(t) = \int_0^t a(x)\, b(t - x)\, dx.$

Under these operations the set of functions forms a *commutative ring*, an algebraic system closed under two operations, addition and convolution, and satisfying the six postulates:

A_1: $\quad a + b = b + a$;

A_2: $\quad (a + b) + c = a + (b + c)$;

A_3: $\quad$ Given a, b, there exists an element x such that $a + x = b$;

M_1: $\quad ab = ba$;

M_2: $\quad (ab)c = a(bc)$;

D: $\quad a(b + c) = ab + ac$.

---

* The first papers (1949) of Mikusiński were, *Sur le calcul opératoire*, Časopis Pest. Mat. Fys. **74**, pp. 89–94; *Sur le fondaments du calcul opératoire*, Studia Math. **11**, pp. 41–70.

Postulates A_1 and A_2 express the commutative and associative laws for addition, A_3 denotes the feasibility of subtraction, M_1 and M_2 express the commutative and associative laws for convolution, and D states that convolution is distributive with respect to addition. That convolution is commutative and associative was proved in § 70, the latter by use of Lerch's theorem. A direct proof without reference to this theorem is as follows. Let

$$f(t) = \int_0^t a(x)b(t - x)\,dx, \qquad g(t) = \int_0^t b(u)c(t - u)\,du;$$

then M_2 states that $fc = ag$. Now

$$fc(t) = \int_0^t f(y)c(t - y)\,dy = \int_0^t \int_0^y a(x)b(y - x)c(t - y)\,dx\,dy$$

is the double integral over the triangle $0 \leq x \leq y \leq t$ in the xy-plane; and

$$ag(t) = \int_0^t a(t - v)g(v)\,dv = \int_0^t \int_0^v a(t - v)b(u)c(v - u)\,du\,dv$$

is the double integral over the triangle $0 \leq u \leq v \leq t$ in the uv-plane. The substitution

$$x = t - v, \qquad y - x = u \qquad (y = t + u - v,\ t - y = v - u)$$

whose Jacobian $\partial(x, y)/\partial(u, v) = 1$ now converts the first integral into the second.*

From the six postulates for a commutative ring we make two important deductions.

I. *There is a unique element "0" such that for any element b, $b + 0 = b$.*
PROOF. From A_3, there exists elements x and z such that

$$a + x = b, \qquad a + z = a.$$

Now by use of A_1 and A_2 we have

$$b + z = (a + x) + z = (x + a) + z = x + (a + z)$$
$$= x + a = a + x = b.$$

Thus adding z to any element leaves it unchanged; z is called the identity element for addition and written 0 (zero).

II. *For given a and b, the element x, such that $a + x = b$, is unique.*

---

* *Advanced Calculus*, p. 364, equation (2). Draw the two triangles and show that the substitution maps one on the other in a one-to-one fashion.

PROOF. Suppose that $a + x_1 = a + x_2$; By A_3 there exists an element a' such that $a' + a = 0$; hence

$$a' + (a + x_1) = a' + (a + x_2)$$
$$(a' + a) + x_1 = (a' + a) + x_2$$
$$0 + x_1 = 0 + x_2$$

and hence $x_1 = x_2$ from I.

The unique element x in $a + x = b$ is called the difference of a and b and written $b - a$. Thus not only is subtraction *feasible* (A_3) but also *unique*. For any a, the difference $a - a = 0$.

The unique element x satisfying $a + x = 0$ is written $-a$ and is called the *additive inverse* or simply the *negative* of a. Thus

$$a + (-a) = (-a) + a = 0$$

and it is easy to show that

$$a - b = a + (-b).$$

Thus subtraction is converted to addition.

If $\mathscr{F}$ is the field of complex numbers $(\alpha, \beta, \dots, \lambda, \mu, \dots)$ the functions of class $\mathscr{C}$ $(a, b, \dots, f, g, \dots)$ form a *vector space* over $\mathscr{F}$;* for they satisfy the following postulates pertaining to *scalar multiplication*:

S_1:　　$\lambda(ab) = (\lambda a)b$,　　　　$(\lambda\mu)a = \lambda(\mu a)$,

S_2:　　$\lambda(a + b) = \lambda a + \lambda b$,　　　$(\lambda + \mu)a = \lambda a + \mu a$.

It is essential to distinguish a function $\{f(t)\}$ over the interval $t \geq 0$ (represented, say, by its graph) from the value $f(t)$ of the function for a given t (a single point of the graph). We shall also write f for $\{f(t)\}$. We therefore use f or $\{f(t)\}$ to represent the complete function, whereas $f(t)$ denotes a function value. Thus $\{2\}$ denotes the constant function having the value 2 at all points t. The numerical product $\alpha\beta$ differs from the convolution $\{\alpha\}\{\beta\}$ of constant functions: for

$$\{\alpha\}\{\beta\} = \left\{\int_0^t \alpha\beta \, dt\right\} = \{\alpha\beta t\}.$$

The Heaviside unit function h (§ 71) has the value

(1)　　　　　　$h(t) = \begin{cases} 0, & t < 0, \\ 1, & t \geq 0. \end{cases}$

---

* L. Brand, *Vector Analysis*, § 88.

Hence $h = \{1\}$ when $t \geq 0$; moreover

(2)
$$h(t - a) = \begin{cases} 0, & t < a, \\ 1, & t \geq a. \end{cases}$$

For the convolution hf we have

(3)
$$hf(t) = \int_0^t f(x)h(t - x)\, dx = \int_0^t f(x)\, dx;$$

thus h is an integral operator in the convolution hf.

We denote the convolution of n functions f by f^n and its value by $f^n(t)$. Thus

$$h^2(t) = \int_0^t h(x)h(t - x)\, dx = \int_0^t dx = t,$$

$$h^3(t) = \int_0^t xh(t - x)\, dx = \int_0^t x\, dx = \frac{t^2}{2},$$

and by induction, for any positive integer n,

(4)
$$h^n(t) = \frac{t^{n-1}}{(n - 1)!}.$$

Passing from function values to the functions themselves, we have

(5)
$$\{1\}^n = h^n = \left\{ \frac{t^{n-1}}{(n - 1)!} \right\},$$

and hence

(6)
$$\{t^n\} = n!\, h^{n+1}.$$

Since $\{t\} = h^2$ we have also

(7)
$$\{t\}^n = h^{2n} = \left\{ \frac{t^{2n-1}}{(2n - 1)!} \right\}.$$

Obviously the function $\{t^n\}$ must not be confused with the n-fold convolution $\{t\}^n$.

Example 1. Since convolution is distributive and commutative,

$$\{t + 1\}\{t - 1\} = \{t\}^2 - \{t\}\{1\} + \{1\}\{t\} - \{1\}^2$$
$$= \{t\}^2 - \{1\}^2 = \left\{ \frac{t^3}{6} - t \right\}.$$

Example 2. From (5) we have

$$h^n f = \left\{ \frac{t^{n-1}}{(n - 1)!} \right\} \{f(t)\},$$

where $h^n f$ is the n-fold integral of f from 0 to t; hence

$$(6) \quad (h^n f)(t) = \frac{1}{(n-1)!} \int_0^t x^{n-1} f(t-x)\, dx = \frac{1}{(n-1)!} \int_0^t (t-x)^{n-1} f(x)\, dx.$$

This is Cauchy's formula for expressing an n-tuple integral as a simple integral.

PROBLEMS

Prove the following identities:

1. $\{\alpha\}^n = \alpha^n h^n.$

2. $\{e^{\alpha t}\}^n = \left\{ e^{\alpha t} \dfrac{t^{n-1}}{(n-1)!} \right\}.$

3. From $\{e^{i\alpha t}\}^2 = \{t e^{i\alpha t}\}$, deduce that

$$\{\cos \alpha t\}^2 - \{\sin \alpha t\}^2 = \{t \cos \alpha t\},$$
$$\{\sin \alpha t\}\{\cos \alpha t\} = \{\tfrac{1}{2} t \sin \alpha t\}.$$

4. $\{e^{\alpha t} f(t)\}\{e^{\alpha t} g(t)\} = \{e^{\alpha t} \cdot fg(t)\}.$

5. $\{tf(t)\}\{g(t)\} + \{tg(t)\}\{f(t)\} = \{t \cdot fg(t)\}.$

6. $\{t^n\}/\{t^m\} = \dfrac{n!}{m!} \left\{ \dfrac{t^{n-m-1}}{(n-m-1)!} \right\}, \quad m > n.$

7. $\dfrac{\{t\}^n}{\{t\}^m} = \left\{ \dfrac{t^{2n-2m-1}}{(2n-2m-1)!} \right\}, \quad m > n.$

8. Solve for the function f:

$$f^2 - f = \{t e^t\} - \{e^t\}.$$

9. Show that

$$h^n\{e^{\alpha t}\} = \left\{ \frac{e^{\alpha t}}{(n-1)!} \int_0^t x^{n-1} e^{-\alpha x}\, dx \right\}.$$

137. TITCHMARSH'S THEOREM

A famous theorem due to Titchmarsh* shows that the convolution ring has no divisors of zero; that is, there are no non-zero functions of class $\mathscr{C}$ whose convolution is $\{0\}$. We state this result as

Theorem 1. *If $f(t)$, $g(t)$ are functions of class $\mathscr{C}$, the convolution*

$$fg = \{0\} \quad implies \quad f = \{0\} \quad or \quad g = \{0\}.$$

An elementary proof due to Ryll-Nardzewski is given in chapter II of Mikusiński's *Operational Calculus*.† The complete proof is rather long.

---

* Titchmarsh, E. C., *The zeros of certain integral functions*, Proc. London Math. Soc. **25** (1926), pp. 283–302.

† Jan Mikusiński, ref. 12.

Erdélyi, ref. 5, § 2.2.

But the general case follows easily from the special case $f(t) = g(t)$. If $f(t)$ is of exponential order α, this special case is a consequence of the convolution theorem of § 70. For let $\pounds\{f(t)\} = F(s)$ and

$$\pounds\{f(t) * f(t)\} = [F(s)]^2 = 0, \qquad s > \alpha;$$

since $F(s)$ is continuous, $F(s) = 0$ when $s > \alpha$ and hence $f(t) = 0$, $t \geq 0$. Thus $f^2 = \{0\}$ implies $f = \{0\}$.

Assuming the truth of Theorem 1 when $f = g$, we now give Ryll-Nardzewski's proof when $f \neq g$. Let $fg = \{0\}$, that is

$$\int_0^t f(x)g(t-x)\,dx = 0, \qquad t \geq 0;$$

then also

$$\int_0^t xf(x)g(t-x)\,dx + \int_0^t f(x)(t-x)g(t-x)\,dx = t\int_0^t f(x)g(t-x)\,dx = 0.$$

If we define

$$f_n(t) = t^n f(t), \qquad g_n(t) = t^n g(t),$$

this equation may be written

$$f_1 g + f g_1 = \{0\}.$$

Therefore

$$fg_1(f_1 g + f g_1) = (fg)(f_1 g_1) + (fg_1)^2 = \{0\}$$

since convolution is commutative, associative, and distributive. Since $fg = \{0\}$ by hypothesis, $(fg_1)^2 = \{0\}$ and hence $fg_1 = \{0\}$ from the special case already proved. From $fg_1 = \{0\}$ we deduce in the same way $fg_2 = \{0\}$; and thus, in general, $fg_n = \{0\}$, or

$$(1) \qquad \int_0^t f(t-x)x^n g(x)\,dx = 0, \qquad n = 1, 2, 3, \ldots .$$

We now appeal to the

Moment Theorem. *If the function $u(x)$ is continuous in the interval $[0, a]$ and*

$$(2) \qquad \int_0^a x^n u(x)\,dx = 0, \qquad n = 0, 1, 2, \ldots ,$$

then $u(x) = 0$ in $[0, a]$.

PROOF. From the Weierstrass' Approximation Theorem* there exists a

---

* *Advanced Calculus*, p. 529, Theorem 2. The integral in (2) is called the *nth moment* of $u(x)$ over $[0, a]$.

polynomial $P(x)$ such that

$$|u(x) - P(x)| < \varepsilon \quad \text{in} \quad [0, a]$$

for any positive ε arbitrarily small. Hence

$$\int_0^a u^2(x)\, dx = \int_0^a u(x)[u(x) - P(x)]\, dx \leq \varepsilon \int_0^a |u(x)|\, dx$$

since $P(x)$ is a sum of terms in x^0, x^1, x^2, ... Since the right member may be made arbitrarily small, the integral on the left is zero and hence $u(x) = 0$.

This moment theorem applied to equation (1) shows that

(3) $$f(t - x)g(x) = 0, \qquad 0 \leq x \leq t < \infty.$$

If $g(x) = 0$ there is nothing to prove. Suppose, then, that there is a value x_0 for which $g(x_0) \neq 0$; then (3) requires that $f(t - x_0) = 0$ for all $t \geq x_0$, that is, $f(x) = 0$ for all $x \geq 0$. Thus Theorem 1 is proved for continuous functions of exponential order.

138. CONVOLUTION QUOTIENT FIELD

The absence of divisors of zero in the convolution ring whose elements a, b, ... are continuous functions of class $\mathscr{C}$ (§ 136) enables us to extend this ring into a field Q whose elements are ordered pairs (a, b) with $b \neq \{0\}$ and which has the equivalence relation*

(1) $$(a, b) = (c, d) \quad \text{iff} \quad ad = bc.$$

This is a true equivalence relation; for it is

(i) reflexive: $(a, b) = (a, b)$;
(ii) symmetric: $(a, b) = (c, d)$ implies $(c, d) = (a, b)$;
(iii) transitive: $(a, b) = (c, d), (c, d) = (e, f)$ imply $(a, b) = (e, f)$.

The commutative law M_1 proves (i) and (ii). From M_1, M_2, and D we deduce (iii): for if

$$ad = bc \quad \text{and} \quad cf = de, \qquad b, d, f \neq \{0\},$$

we have

$$(ad)f = (bc)f = b(cf) = b(de),$$

$$d(af - be) = \{0\}, \qquad af - be = \{0\}$$

from Titchmarsh's theorem and hence $(a, b) = (e, f)$ from (1).

---

* *Advanced Calculus*, page 1. The postulates for a field are given on page 4.

The equivalence relation (1) shows that for any $f \neq \{0\}$ belonging to $\mathscr{C}$.

(2) $(a, b) = (af, bf)$.

We denote by a/b the class of all ordered pairs equivalent to (a, b). The addition and multiplication of such equivalence classes is defined in the same way as for rational fractions, namely

(3)
$$\frac{a}{b} + \frac{c}{d} = \frac{ad + bc}{bd},$$

(4)
$$\frac{a}{b}\frac{c}{d} = \frac{ac}{bd}.$$

Since $b, d \neq \{0\}$, $bd \neq \{0\}$ by Titchmarsh's theorem, thus the sum (3) and product (4) are members of $\mathscr{C}$. These definitions give the same sum and product irrespective of which member of the equivalence class is chosen to represent a/b and c/d. Thus if

$$\frac{a}{b} = \frac{a'}{b'} \quad (ab' = ba'), \qquad \frac{c}{d} = \frac{c'}{d'} \quad (cd' = dc'),$$

then

$$\frac{a'}{b'} + \frac{c'}{d'} = \frac{a}{b} + \frac{c}{d}, \qquad \frac{a'}{b'}\frac{c'}{d'} = \frac{a}{b}\frac{c}{d}.$$

To prove the first we must show that

$$(a'd' + b'c')bd = b'd'(ad + bc);$$

in fact, the left member

$$ba' \cdot d'd + dc' \cdot b'b = ab' \cdot d'd + cd' \cdot b'b,$$

which equals the right member. Similarly,

$$a'c' \cdot bd = ba' \cdot dc' = ab' \cdot cd' = b'd' \cdot ac,$$

establishes the second.

We can now pass from the field of ordered pairs (a, b) to the field of convolution quotients a/b (in which $b \neq \{0\}$) with the equivalence relation

(5)
$$\frac{a}{b} = \frac{c}{d} \quad \text{iff} \quad ad = bc.$$

From the properties of convolution it is easy to show that the convolution quotients x/y, $y \neq \{0\}$, satisfy all the postulates of a field. With addition and multiplication defined by (3) and (4), the convolution quotients form the following:

1. A commutative group under addition with $\{0\}/f$, $f \neq \{0\}$, as *zero* element.

2. With zero omitted, a commutative group under convolution with $f/f, f \neq \{0\}$, as *unit* element.

3. Convolution is distributive with respect to addition.*

The proofs depend on the properties of convolution. For zero and the unit element we have

(6)
$$\frac{\{0\}}{f} + \frac{a}{b} = \frac{\{0\}b + fa}{fb} = \frac{fa}{fb} = \frac{a}{b},$$

(7)
$$\frac{fa}{fb} = \frac{fa}{fb} = \frac{a}{b}.$$

Moreover, the product of any element by zero is zero; for

(8)
$$\frac{\{0\}}{f}\frac{a}{b} = \frac{\{0\}a}{fb} = \frac{\{0\}}{fb} = \frac{\{0\}}{f}.$$

If we take $f = h = \{1\}$, the zero and unit elements become $\{0\}/h$, $\{1\}/h$. As for the distributive law,

$$\frac{p}{q}\left(\frac{a}{b} + \frac{c}{d}\right) = \frac{p(ad + bc)}{qbd} = \frac{pad}{qbd} + \frac{pbc}{qbd} = \frac{pa}{qb} + \frac{pc}{qd}.$$

Division by any non-zero element of Q is always possible and unique:

(9)
$$\frac{a}{b} \Big/ \frac{c}{d} = \frac{ad}{bc}, \qquad b, d \neq \{0\};$$

for ad/bc is a solution of

$$\frac{c}{d}\frac{x}{y} = \frac{a}{b}; \qquad \text{and if} \qquad \frac{c}{d}\frac{x'}{y'} = \frac{a}{b}$$

we must have $x/y = x'/y'$ (why?).

The convolution quotient of two functions of class $\mathscr{C}$ may be another function of $\mathscr{C}$; thus

$$\frac{\{t^3\}}{\{t\}} = \{6t\} \quad \text{for} \quad 6\int_0^t x(t - x)\,dx = 6\left[\frac{tx^2}{2} - \frac{x^3}{3}\right]_0^t = t^3.$$

However, the convolution quotient a/b of two functions of class $\mathscr{C}$ may not be a function at all. For example, $\{1\}/f$ is not a function g, for the equation

$$\{1\} = fg = \left\{\int_0^t f(x)\,g(t - x)\,dx\right\}$$

---

* Cf. *Advanced Calculus*, § 2.

cannot be satisfied by any integrable function g; for when $t = 0$ the convolution integral is zero whereas the function $\{1\}$ has the value 1. In particular, $\{1\}/\{1\}$ is not a function; but since from, (73.4),

$$\delta(t) * f(t) = f(t), \qquad \text{or} \qquad \delta f = f,$$

we see that the Dirac symbol $\delta(0) = \delta$ is the unit multiplicative element:

$$(10) \qquad \delta = \frac{f}{f} = \frac{\{1\}}{h}.$$

We now denote the operator $\delta(t - a)$ of §73 by δ_a, and $\delta(t)$ is simply written δ. Mikusiński's notation still has certain unresolved difficulties. Since the *function f* has the *values f(t)*, the values of the function

$$h\{e^t\} = \left\{ \int_0^t e^t \, dt \right\} = \{e^t - 1\}$$

should be written

$$h\{e^t\}(t) = e^t - 1,$$

an awkward and easily misunderstood notation.

Since the convolution quotients a/b of functions of class $\mathscr{C}$ are sometimes functions and sometimes entities of a different character, convolution quotients constitute a generalization of the function concept. Mikusiński, who first developed this algebra, calls the elements a/b *operators*. We shall adopt this term and henceforth call δ the *Dirac operator*. Thus functions form a special class of operators; and if α is a real or complex number, the operator $\{\alpha\}/h$ behaves in addition and convolution just as numbers in addition and multiplication; for

$$(11) \qquad \frac{\{\alpha\}}{h} + \frac{\{\beta\}}{h} = \frac{\{\alpha\} + \{\beta\}}{h} = \frac{\{\alpha + \beta\}}{h},$$

$$(12) \qquad \frac{\{\alpha\}}{h} \frac{\{\beta\}}{h} = \frac{\{\alpha\}\{\beta\}}{h^2} = \frac{\{\alpha\beta t\}}{h^2} = \frac{h\{\alpha\beta\}}{h^2} = \frac{\{\alpha\beta\}}{h},$$

where we have used (136.3) to replace $\{\alpha\beta t\}$ by $h\{\alpha\beta\}$. Mikusiński calls $\{\alpha\}/h$ a *numerical operator* and denotes it by the *number* α. Then (11) and (12) become numerical identities $\alpha + \beta = \alpha + \beta$, $\alpha\beta = \alpha\beta$; moreover, the product

$$\alpha \frac{a}{b} = \frac{\{\alpha\}}{h} \frac{a}{b} = \frac{\left\{ \int_0^t \alpha a(x) \, dx \right\}}{hb} = \frac{h(\alpha a)}{hb} = \frac{\alpha a}{b}.$$

Thus if we *define*

$$(13) \qquad \alpha \frac{a}{b} = \frac{\alpha a}{b},$$

numerical operators may be replaced by their corresponding numbers.

If $a/b = a'/b'$, that is, $ab' = ba'$, we have

$$\alpha \frac{a}{b} = \frac{\alpha a}{b} = \frac{\alpha a b'}{bb'} = \frac{\alpha b a'}{bb'} = \frac{\alpha a'}{b'} = \alpha \frac{a'}{b'},$$

showing that (13) is truly a relation between equivalence classes.

The zero element, written as $\{0\}/h$, is the numerical operator 0; hence (6) and (8) can be written

(14)
$$0 + \frac{a}{b} = \frac{a}{b}, \qquad 0\frac{a}{b} = 0.$$

Since $\{1\} = h$, the Dirac operator $\delta = \{1\}/h$ is the numerical operator 1; and from (13)

(15)
$$1\frac{a}{b} = \frac{a}{b}.$$

In brief, the zero and unit elements in the algebra of convolution quotients are the numerical operators 0 and 1 and may be written as such. Note, however, that $\alpha = \{\alpha\}$ when and only when $\alpha = 0$.

The entire foregoing development is analogous to the extension of the commutative ring of integers (which has no divisors of zero) into the field of rational fractions. Rational fractions also represent equivalence classes; they are added and multiplied in accordance with (3) and (4) and have (5) as their equivalence relation. The zero and unit elements are $0/n$ and $1/n$ where n is any non-zero integer. The fractions $n/1$ behave just as integers in addition and multiplication and may be written simply as n. Thus the rational fractions extend the number system but include the integers from which they were derived. The integers 0 and 1 are still identity elements in the field of rational numbers. The convolution ring, however, whose elements are functions of class $\mathscr{C}$ has $\{0\}$ as zero element *but no multiplicative unit.* When extended into the field Q of convolution, quotients $\{0\}/h$, $\{1\}/h$ are the zero and unit elements, whereas zero is the same as before, and Q has acquired a unit element, lacking in the ring from which Q was derived. This essential difference is due to the fact that the ring of integers already has a unit element, whereas the convolution ring of functions has none. The unit element in Q is the Dirac operator— which is thus legitimized as a member of the field Q.

The field Q of operators a/b contains numerical operators $\{\alpha\}/h$, continuous and discontinuous functions, the integral operator h, and, as we shall see, the differential operator $s = 1/h$, as well as other operators. That these diverse entities may be handled from the same point of view and with common rules of operation is an important virtue of Mikusiński's operational calculus.

Example 1. If $a/b = f$, $a = bf$, and if the functions have Laplace transforms, $A = BF$; thus

$$\frac{a}{b} = \pounds^{-1}\left\{\frac{A(s)}{B(s)}\right\} = \{f(t)\}$$

if $f(t)$ exists. For example,

$$\frac{\{t^2\}}{\{t\}} = \pounds^{-1}\left\{\frac{2/s^3}{1/s^2}\right\} = \pounds^{-1}\left\{\frac{2}{s}\right\} = \{2\}.$$

Example 2. The reciprocal $1/f$ of a function is not a function g. For the equation $1 = fg$ cannot be true since 1 is the Dirac operator and fg is a function.

PROBLEMS

Verify the following identities:

1. $\dfrac{\{\sin t\}}{\{\cos t\}} = h = \dfrac{\{\sinh t\}}{\{\cosh t\}}.$

2. $\dfrac{\{te^t\}}{\{e^t\}\{e^t\}} = 1.$

3. $\dfrac{\{\sin t\}}{\{t \sin t\}} = 2\{\cos t\}.$

4. $\dfrac{\{\sin t - t \cos t\}}{\{\sin t\}} = 2\{\sin t\}.$

5. $\dfrac{\{t^4\}}{\{t^2\}} = 12\{t\}.$

139. THE OPERATOR $s = 1/h$

The basic property of the operator $s = 1/h$ is expressed in the following theorem.

Theorem 1. *If $f'(t)$ is continuous for all $t \geqq 0$, then*

(1) $$f' = sf - f(0)$$

where $f(0)$ is a number.

PROOF. Since h is the integral operator, the equation

$$\left\{\int_0^t f'(t)\, dt\right\} = \{f(t)\} - \{f(0)\}$$

may be written

$$hf' = f - \{f(0)\}.$$

Hence

$$f' = \frac{f}{h} - \frac{\{f(0)\}}{h} = sf - f(0)$$

where $\{f(0)\}/h$ is the number $f(0)$.

When $f(0) = 0$, $sf = f'$ and s is the differential operator $D = d/dt$. Thus

$$s\{t\} = \{1\} = h, \qquad s\{\sin t\} = \{\cos t\};$$

but

$$s\{e^t\} = \{e^t\} + 1, \qquad s\{\cos t\} = -\{\sin t\} + 1.$$

Theorem 2. *If $f''(t)$ is continuous for all $t \geq 0$, then*

(2) $$f'' = s^2 f - sf(0) - f'(0)$$

where $f(0)$ and $f'(0)$ are numbers.

PROOF. Since $f'(t)$ is also continuous, we have from (1)

$$f'' = sf' - f'(0) = s[sf - f(0)] - f'(0).$$

If $f^{(n)}$ is continuous (or merely exists) in the interval $0 \leq t < \infty$, then $f(t)$ and its derivatives up to order $n - 1$ are also continuous in this interval. We can now give an inductive proof of

Theorem 3. *If $f^{(n)}(t)$ is continuous for all $t \geq 0$, then*

(3) $$f^{(n)} = s^n f - s^{n-1} f(0) - s^{n-2} f'(0) - \cdots - f^{(n-1)}(0)$$

where $f(0), f'(0), \ldots, f^{(n-1)}(0)$ are numbers.

When a function $f(t)$ and its first $n - 1$ derivatives vanish when $t = 0$, $s^n f = f^{(n)}$; then s^n is the operator of n-fold differentiation.

As an example of this theorem, let $f = \{t^n\}$; then

$$f^{(n)} = n! \{1\} = n! \, h = \frac{n!}{s} \quad \text{and} \quad f(0) = f'(0) = \cdots = f^{(n-1)}(0) = 0;$$

hence $n!/s = s^n \{t^n\}$ or

(4) $$\{t^n\} = \frac{n!}{s^{n+1}}$$

in agreement with (136.4). Note that $\{1\} = 1/s$, and the important special cases:

(5) $$\{t\} = \frac{1}{s^2},$$

(6) $$\{t^2\} = \frac{2}{s^3}.$$

When $f = \{e^{\alpha t}\}$, where α is a complex number, we have from (1),

$$\alpha\{e^{\alpha t}\} = s\{e^{\alpha t}\} - 1,$$

(7)
$$\{e^{\alpha t}\} = \frac{1}{s - \alpha}.$$

We compute powers by convolution:

$$\frac{1}{(s - \alpha)^2} = \{e^{\alpha t}\}\{e^{\alpha t}\} = \left\{\int_0^t e^{\alpha(t-x)}e^{\alpha x}\, dx\right\} = \{te^{\alpha t}\},$$

$$\frac{1}{(s - \alpha)^3} = \{e^{\alpha t}\}\{te^{\alpha t}\} = \left\{\int_0^t e^{\alpha(t-x)}xe^{\alpha x}\, dx\right\} = \left\{\frac{t^2}{2!}\, e^{\alpha t}\right\},$$

and by induction

(8)
$$\left\{\frac{t^n}{n!}\, e^{\alpha t}\right\} = \frac{1}{(s - \alpha)^{n+1}}.$$

When $\alpha = 0$, this reduces to (4).

If we replace α by $-\alpha + i\beta$ (α, β real), we have from (7)

$$\{e^{-\alpha t}e^{i\beta t}\} = \frac{1}{s + \alpha - i\beta} = \frac{s + \alpha + i\beta}{(s + \alpha)^2 + \beta^2}.$$

The real and imaginary parts of this equation give

(9)
$$\{e^{-\alpha t} \cos \beta t\} = \frac{s + \alpha}{(s + \alpha)^2 + \beta^2},$$

(10)
$$\{e^{-\alpha t} \sin \beta t\} = \frac{\beta}{(s + \alpha)^2 + \beta^2}.$$

When $\alpha = 0$, these become

(11)(12)
$$\{\cos \beta t\} = \frac{s}{s^2 + \beta^2}, \qquad \{\sin \beta t\} = \frac{\beta}{s^2 + \beta^2}.$$

From (10) we compute powers of $[(s + \alpha)^2 + \beta^2]^{-1}$ by convolution:

$$[(s + \alpha)^2 + \beta^2]^{-2} = \frac{1}{\beta^2}\{e^{-\alpha t} \sin \beta t\}\{e^{-\alpha t} \sin \beta t\}.$$

The convolution equals (Prob. 70.6)

$$\{e^{-\alpha t}(\sin \beta t) * (\sin \beta t)\} = \frac{1}{2}\left\{e^{-\alpha t}\left(\frac{1}{\beta} \sin \beta t - t \cos \beta t\right)\right\}$$

so that

(13)
$$\frac{1}{[(s + \alpha)^2 + \beta^2]^2} = \frac{1}{2\beta^2}\left\{e^{-\alpha t}\left(\frac{1}{\beta} \sin \beta t - t \cos \beta t\right)\right\}.$$

When $\alpha = 0$, this becomes

(14) $$\frac{1}{(s^2 + \beta^2)^2} = \frac{1}{2\beta^2}\left\{\frac{1}{\beta}\sin\beta t - t\cos\beta t\right\}.$$

Since this function vanishes when $t = 0$, we have, on applying $s = D$,

(15) $$\frac{s}{(s^2 + \beta^2)^2} = \frac{1}{2\beta}\{t\sin\beta t\}.$$

Again, by applying $s = D$ to (15), in which $f(0) = 0$, we have

(16) $$\frac{s^2}{(s^2 + \beta^2)^2} = \frac{1}{2\beta}\{\sin\beta t + \beta t\cos\beta t\}.$$

Observe that formulas (4) to (16) agree with Laplace transforms in Table A, § 67; but now s is an *operator* and derivations are not concerned with the evaluation of the Laplace integral or with convergence questions connected therewith.

The formulas (1), (2), (3) for transforming derivatives also agree with their counterparts in § 68 when $\mathcal{L}\{f(t)\}$ is replaced by $f(t)$. We shall generalize them in § 141 so that they apply to integrable functions that have only a finite number of discontinuities in any finite interval.

Example 1. We may evaluate the operator $1/s^2(s^2 + \alpha^2)$ by resolving it into partial fractions and using (5) and (12):

$$\frac{1}{s^2(s^2 + \alpha^2)} = \frac{1}{\alpha^2}\left[\frac{1}{s^2} - \frac{1}{s^2 + \alpha^2}\right] = \frac{1}{\alpha^2}\left\{t - \frac{1}{\alpha}\sin\alpha t\right\}.$$

Or we may interpret $1/s = h$ as the integral operator and integrate

$$1/(s^2 + a^2) = \{(\sin\alpha t)/\alpha\}$$

twice:

(17) $$\frac{1}{s(s^2 + \alpha^2)} = \frac{1}{\alpha}\left\{\int_0^t \sin\alpha t\, dt\right\} = \frac{1}{\alpha^2}\{1 - \cos\alpha t\},$$

(18) $$\frac{1}{s^2(s^2 + \alpha^2)} = \frac{1}{\alpha^2}\left\{\int_0^t (1 - \cos\alpha t)\, dt\right\} = \frac{1}{\alpha^2}\left\{t - \frac{1}{\alpha}\sin\alpha t\right\}.$$

Example 2. To show the care needed in matters of notation, we compute the convolution quotients:

$$\frac{\{t\}}{\{t + 1\}} = \frac{1/s^2}{(1/s^2) + (1/s)} = \frac{1}{1 + s} = \{e^{-t}\},$$

$$\frac{\{t\}}{\{t\} + 1} = \frac{1/s^2}{(1/s^2) + 1} = \frac{1}{1 + s^2} = \{\sin t\}.$$

Here both quotients are functions. Consider, however,

$$\frac{\{e^{-t}\}}{\{e^{-t}+1\}} = \frac{\dfrac{1}{s+1}}{\dfrac{1}{s+1}+\dfrac{1}{s}} = \frac{s}{2s+1}$$

$$= \frac{1}{2}\frac{2s+1-1}{2s+1} = \frac{1}{2} - \frac{1}{4s+2} = \frac{1}{2} - \frac{1}{4}\{e^{-t/2}\},$$

$$\frac{\{e^{-t}\}}{\{e^{t}\}+1} = \frac{\dfrac{1}{s+1}}{\dfrac{1}{s+1}+1} = \frac{1}{s+2} = \{e^{-2t}\};$$

the latter is a function, the former is not, for $\frac{1}{2}$ is a number and not the function $\{\frac{1}{2}\}$.

PROBLEMS

1. Carry through the induction to establish formula (8).

2. Use (9) and (10) to show that

$$\frac{\kappa s + \lambda}{(s+\alpha)^2 + \beta^2} = \left\{ e^{-\alpha t}\left(\kappa \cos \beta t + \frac{\lambda - \alpha\kappa}{\beta} \sin \beta t \right) \right\}.$$

Establish the following equations:

3. $\dfrac{s}{s^2 - \beta^2} = \{\cosh \beta t\}, \qquad \dfrac{\beta}{s^2 - \beta^2} = \{\sinh \beta t\}.$

4. $\dfrac{s^2 + 1}{s + 1} \{e^{-t} \sin t\} = \{e^{-t}(2 - \cos t - 2 \sin t)\}.$

5. $\{t \cos \beta t\} = \dfrac{s^2 - \beta^2}{(s^2 + \beta^2)^2}.$

6. $\dfrac{3s}{s^3 - 1} = \left\{ e^t + e^{-t/2}\left(\sqrt{3} \sin \dfrac{\sqrt{3}}{2}t - \cos \dfrac{\sqrt{3}}{2}t \right) \right\}.$

7. $\dfrac{3s^2}{s^3 - 1} = \left\{ e^t + 2e^{-t/2} \cos \dfrac{\sqrt{3}}{2}t \right\}$ [Use Prob. 6].

140. LINEAR DIFFERENTIAL EQUATIONS

Since the transforms of functions and their derivatives in terms of the *operator s* agree with their Laplace transforms in terms of the *variable s*, the operational solution of linear differential equations with constant coefficients is formally the same as the method of Laplace transforms.

Example 1. Consider the equation of Example 69.4;

$$y' + 2y + \int_0^t y \, dt = \sin t, \qquad y(0) = 1.$$

From § 139 we have

$$y' = sy - 1, \qquad \int_\alpha^t y \, dt = hy = \frac{y}{s},$$

and the equation becomes

$$sy - 1 + 2y + \frac{y}{s} = \frac{1}{s^2 + 1}.$$

Just as in § 69, we see that

$$y = \frac{s(s + 2)}{(s + 1)^2(s^2 + 1)} = \frac{1}{s + 1} - \frac{\frac{3}{2}}{(s + 1)^2} + \frac{\frac{1}{2}}{s^2 + 1},$$

$$y(t) = e^{-t} - \tfrac{3}{2}te^{-t} + \tfrac{1}{2} \sin t.$$

Example 2. $x' - x = (2t - 1)e^{t^2}$, $x(0) = 2$. This problem was given by Mikusiński* to illustrate the applicability of his calculus when the Laplace transform of the input function does not exist. We have, in fact,

$$sx - 2 - x = \{(2t - 1)e^{t^2}\} = f,$$

$$x = \frac{2}{s - 1} + \frac{1}{s - 1}f = \{2e^t\} + \{e^t\}f.$$

The convolution $\{e^t\}f$ is

$$\int_0^t e^{t-u}(2u - 1)e^{u^2} \, du = e^t \int_0^t e^{u^2-u}(2u - 1) \, du$$

$$= e^t(e^{t^2-t} - 1) = e^{t^2} - e^t;$$

hence

$$x(t) = 2e^t + e^{t^2} - e^t = e^{t^2} + e^t.$$

The classical solution of § 16 confirms this result (Problem 16.8).

Example 3. $x'' + x = t$, $x(0) = x(\pi/2) = 0$. Assume for the moment that $x'(0) = \lambda$; then the equation becomes

$$s^2x - \lambda + x = \frac{1}{s^2},$$

(i) $$x = \frac{\lambda}{s^2 + 1} + \frac{1}{s^2(s^2 + 1)} = \{\lambda \sin t + t - \sin t\}$$

on using the result of (139.18). The boundary condition $x(\pi/2) = 0$ now gives

$$0 = \lambda + \tfrac{1}{2}\pi - 1, \qquad \lambda = 1 - \tfrac{1}{2}\pi,$$

and

$$x(t) = t - \tfrac{1}{2}\pi \sin t.$$

---

* Ref. 12, p. 42, Ex. 1.

If the boundary conditions were $x(0) = x(\pi) = 0$, there would be no solution, for from (i),

$$x(\pi) = \lambda \sin \pi + \pi - \sin \pi = \pi.$$

141. THE OPERATOR h^{λ}

In § 136 we obtained the n-fold convolution

$$h^n = \left\{ \frac{t^{n-1}}{(n-1)!} \right\} = \left\{ \frac{t^{n-1}}{\Gamma(n)} \right\}$$

for positive integral n. We now generalize this result by defining

(1) $$h^{\lambda} = \left\{ \frac{t^{\lambda-1}}{\Gamma(\lambda)} \right\}, \qquad \lambda > 0$$

for any positive λ. This definition conforms to the functional equation for powers,

(2) $$h^{\alpha} h^{\beta} = h^{\alpha+\beta};$$

for, on using (1), the convolution $h^{\alpha} h^{\beta}$ is

$$\frac{1}{\Gamma(\alpha)\Gamma(\beta)} \int_0^t x^{\alpha-1}(t-x)^{\beta-1}\,dx = \frac{t^{\alpha+\beta-1}}{\Gamma(\alpha)\Gamma(\beta)} \int_0^1 y^{\alpha-1}(1-y)^{\beta-1}\,dy$$

on making the change of variable

$$x = ty, \qquad dx = t\,dy.$$

The last integral is Euler's beta function $B(\alpha, \beta)$; hence from (66.18) we see that

$$h^{\alpha} h^{\beta} = \left\{ \frac{B(\alpha, \beta)}{\Gamma(\alpha)\Gamma(\beta)} t^{\alpha+\beta-1} \right\} = \left\{ \frac{t^{\alpha+\beta-1}}{\Gamma(\alpha+\beta)} \right\} = h^{\alpha+\beta}.$$

The formula for positive integral n

$$\frac{1}{(s-\gamma)^n} = \left\{ \frac{t^{n-1}}{(n-1)!} e^{\gamma t} \right\} \qquad (139.8)$$

is generalized in the same way by defining

(3) $$\frac{1}{(s-\gamma)^{\lambda}} = \left\{ \frac{t^{\lambda-1}}{\Gamma(\lambda)} e^{\gamma t} \right\}, \qquad \lambda > 0;$$

and we can show as before that this definition implies that

(4) $$(s-\gamma)^{-\alpha}(s-\gamma)^{-\beta} = (s-\gamma)^{-\alpha-\beta}.$$

142. DISCONTINUOUS FUNCTIONS

We shall say that a real or complex valued function $\{f(t)\}$ belongs to class $\mathcal{K}$:

1° If it has at most a finite number of discontinuities in any finite interval $0 \leq t \leq t_1$.

2° If f becomes infinite at some discontinuity its improper Riemann integral over $[0, t_1]$ is finite.

Examples

The Heaviside function $h(t - a)$ belongs to class $\mathcal{K}$, for its only singularity is a finite jump at $t = a$. The integral

$$\int_0^{t_1} h(t - a)\, dt = (t_1 - a)h(t_1 - a).$$

The square wave $f_1(t)$ of Table C, p. 660 belongs to class $\mathcal{K}$, for it has only a finite number of unit jumps in $[0, t_1]$. The integral

$$\int_0^{t_1} f_1(t)\, dt = af_2(t_1) \qquad \text{(Table C).}$$

The function $t^{-\lambda}$ $(0 < \lambda < 1)$ is also a member of class $\mathcal{K}$; although $t^{-\lambda} \to \infty$ as $t \to 0+$, the improper integral

$$\int_0^{t_1} t^{-\lambda}\, dt = \frac{t_1^{1-\lambda}}{1 - \lambda}$$

is finite.

Two functions f, g of class $\mathcal{K}$ are said to be equal $(f = g)$ when and only when

(1) $$\int_0^t f(u)\, du = \int_0^t g(u)\, du \quad \text{or} \quad hf = hg.$$

Differentiating this equation we have $f(t) = g(t)$ at every point t where *both* $f(t)$ and $g(t)$ are continuous. Conversely, if $f(t) = g(t)$ at all such points, $hf = hg$ and $f = g$ in the sense just defined. Thus for functions of class $\mathcal{C}$ or $\mathcal{K}$, $f = g$ means that $f(t) = g(t)$ at all points where both functions are continuous.

Any function f of class $\mathcal{K}$ is a convolution quotient of two functions of class $\mathcal{C}$, because

(2) $$a = \int_0^t f(x)\, dx = hf$$

is a continuous function which has the derivative $a'(t) = f(t)$ at all points t where $f(t)$ is continuous.* At such points,

$$(3) \qquad\qquad f = sa = \frac{a}{h} = \frac{a}{\{1\}}.$$

If f and g are members of class $\mathscr{K}$ and $hf = a$, $hg = b$, we define

$$f + g = \frac{a}{h} + \frac{b}{h}, \qquad fg = \frac{a}{h}\frac{b}{h}.$$

Both $f + g$ and fg are again members of class $\mathscr{K}$;† moreover, convolution between functions of class $\mathscr{K}$ is commutative, associative, and distributive with respect to addition.

We can now generalize Theorem 139.1 as follows:

Theorem 1. *If the continuous function f has a derivative f' of class $\mathscr{K}$,*

$$(4) \qquad\qquad f' = sf - f(0),$$

where $f(0)$ is a number.

PROOF. Integrating between the discontinuities of f', we have

$$\left\{ \int_0^t f'(x)\, dx \right\} = \{f(t)\} - \{f(0)\}$$

since f is continuous; thus

$$hf' = f - \{f(0)\}.$$

Multiply this equation by $s = 1/h$; then noting that $\{f(0)\}/h = f(0)$, a number, we obtain (4).

The requirement that f be continuous is essential; for if both f and f' belong to class $\mathscr{K}$, the last equation, on which our proof rests, would have a continuous left member hf' but a discontinuous right member.

Theorem 2. *If the function f has a continuous derivative f' and a second derivative of class $\mathscr{K}$, then*

$$(5) \qquad\qquad f'' = s^2 f - sf(0) - f'(0).$$

PROOF. The continuity of f' implies the continuity of f; hence from Theorem 1

$$f'' = sf' - f'(0) = s[sf - f(0)] - f'(0).$$

Theorem 3. *If the function f has a continuous derivative $f^{(n-1)}$ of order $n - 1$, and an nth derivative $f^{(n)}$ of class $\mathscr{K}$, then*

$$(6) \qquad f^{(n)} = s^n f - s^{n-1}f(0) - s^{n-2}f'(0) - \cdots - f^{(n-1)}(0).$$

---

* *Advanced Calculus*, § 119.
† Cf. Mikusiński, ref. 12, pp. 108–109.

PROOF. Since $f^{(n-1)}$ is continuous, so also are $f^{(n-2)}, \ldots, f', f$. Applying Theorem 1 to $f^{(n-1)}, f^{(n-2)}, \ldots, f$ yields equation (6).

Equation (6) may be used to change a differential equation of order n

(7) $$P(D)x = f,$$

where P is a polynomial of degree n and f is a discontinuous function of class $\mathscr{K}$, into the operational equation

$$P(s)x + Q(s) = f$$

where $Q(s)$ is a polynomial whose degree is at most $n - 1$ and whose coefficients depend on the initial values $x(0), x'(0), \ldots, x^{(n-1)}(0)$. Then

$$x = -\frac{Q(s)}{P(s)} + \frac{1}{P(s)} f.$$

Here $-Q/P$ and $1/P$ may be decomposed into real partial fractions whose denominators are powers of linear or quadratic functions. When these rational operators in s are expressed as functions of t (§ 139), say

$$-\frac{Q(s)}{P(s)} = \{a(t)\}, \qquad \frac{1}{P(s)} = \{b(t)\},$$

then

(8) $$x = a + bf$$

where the convolution

$$bf = \int_0^t b(u) f(t - u)\, du \quad \text{or} \quad \int_0^t b(t - u) f(u)\, du.$$

By virtue of the general equation (6) which requires the continuity of all derivatives of order $<n$, the unique solution (8) of equation (7) will be of class $\mathscr{C}^{n-1}$ and will satisfy (8) at all points where f is continuous (cf § 75).

Example 1. Consider the equation of § 75,

(i) $$x'' + x = f_1(t), \qquad x(0) = 1,$$

where $f_1(t)$ is the square wave of Table C, p. 660, with $a = \pi$. The operational form of (i) is

$$s^2 x - s + x = f_1,$$

whence

$$x = \frac{s}{s^2 + 1} + \frac{1}{s^2 + 1} f_1$$

$$= \{\cos t\} + \{\sin t\}\{f_1(t)\}.$$

The value of $f_1(t)$ in $j\pi < t < (j + 1)\pi$ is $(-1)^j$; hence when t lies in the interval

$n\pi < t < (n + 1)\pi$, x has the *value*

$$x_n(t) = \cos t + \sum_{j=0}^{n-1}(-1)^j\int_{j\pi}^{(j+1)\pi}\sin(t-u)\,du + (-1)^n\int_{n\pi}^{t}\sin(t-u)\,du.$$

Now

$$(-1)^j\int_{j\pi}^{(j+1)\pi}\sin(t-u)\,du = (-1)^j\cos(t-u)\Big|_{u=j\pi}^{u=(j+1)\pi}$$

$$= (-1)^j[\cos t\cos(j+1)\pi - \cos t\cos j\pi]$$

$$= (-1)^{2j+1}(\cos t + \cos t)$$

$$= -2\cos t;$$

$$(-1)^n\int_{n\pi}^{t}\sin(t-u)\,du = (-1)^n\cos(t-u)\Big|_{u=n\pi}^{u=t}$$

$$= (-1)^n[1 - \cos(t-n\pi)]$$

$$= (-1)^n[1 - \cos t\cos n\pi]$$

$$= (-1)^n - \cos t,$$

for $\cos n\pi = (-1)^n$. Since the sum in $x_n(t)$ is $-2n\cos t$,

$$x_n(t) = \cos t - 2n\cos t + (-1)^n - \cos t$$

$$= (-1)^n - 2n\cos t$$

in agreement with the Laplace solution of this problem in § 75.

Example 2. We apply Mikusiński's calculus to the problem of Example 75.1:

$$x' + 4x + 3hx = f_1, \qquad x(0) = 0,$$

where f_1 is the square wave of Table C, p. 660, with $a = 1$. In terms of operators,

$$\left(s + 4 + \frac{3}{s}\right)x = f_1,$$

and

$$x = \frac{s}{(s+1)(s+3)}f_1 = \left(\frac{\frac{3}{2}}{s+3} - \frac{\frac{1}{2}}{s+1}\right)f_1,$$

where the right member is the convolution

$$x(t) = \{\tfrac{3}{2}e^{-3t} - \tfrac{1}{2}e^{-t}\}\{f_1(t)\}$$

$$= \frac{3}{2}\int_0^t e^{-3(t-u)}f_1(u)\,du - \frac{1}{2}\int_0^t e^{-(t-u)}f_1(u)\,du.$$

In the interval $j < t < j + 1$, $f_1(u) = (-1)^j$, and the integrals become

$$\tfrac{3}{2}(-1)^j e^{-3t}\int_j^{j+1}e^{3u}\,du = \tfrac{1}{2}(-1)^j(e^3 - 1)e^{-3t}e^{3j},$$

$$\tfrac{1}{2}(-1)^j e^{-t}\int_j^{j+1}e^u\,du = \tfrac{1}{2}(-1)^j(e - 1)e^{-t}e^j.$$

Hence, when t lies in the interval $n < t < n + 1$, $x(t)$ equals

$$x_n(t) = \tfrac{1}{2}(e^3 - 1)e^{-3t}\sum_{j=0}^{n-1}(-1)^j e^{3j} - \tfrac{1}{2}(e - 1)e^{-t}\sum_{j=0}^{n-1}(-1)^j e^j$$

$$+ \tfrac{3}{2}(-1)^n e^{-3t}\int_n^t e^{3u}\,du - \tfrac{1}{2}(-1)^n e^{-t}\int_n^t e^u\,du.$$

Since the foregoing sums are respectively

$$\frac{1 - (-1)^n e^{3n}}{1 + e^3}, \qquad \frac{1 - (-1)^n e^n}{1 + e},$$

$$x_n(t) = \frac{1}{2}\frac{e^3 - 1}{e^3 + 1}e^{-3t}[1 - (-1)^n e^{3n}] - \frac{1}{2}\frac{e - 1}{e + 1}e^{-t}[1 - (-1)^n e^n]$$

$$+ \frac{1}{2}(-1)^n[1 - e^{-3(t-n)}] - \frac{1}{2}(-1)^n[1 - e^{-(t-n)}].$$

The transient term is obviously

$$\operatorname{Tr} x(t) = \frac{1}{2}\frac{e^3 - 1}{e^3 + 1}e^{-3t} - \frac{1}{2}\frac{e - 1}{e + 1}e^{-t}.$$

The remaining terms give the steady-state solution; with $\tau = t - n$, this reduces to

$$\xi_n(\tau) = \frac{(-1)^n}{2}\left[\left(\frac{e - 1}{e + 1} + 1\right)e^{-\tau} - \left(\frac{e^3 - 1}{e^3 + 1} + 1\right)e^{-3\tau}\right]$$

$$= (-1)^n\left[\frac{e}{e + 1}e^{-\tau} - \frac{e^3}{e^3 + 1}e^{-3\tau}\right],$$

a continuous wave of period 2. These results agree with § 75.

143. THE SHIFT OPERATOR h_α

We next obtain an operator that serves to generate important functions of class $\mathscr{K}$. Its effect is stated in

Theorem 1. *The operator*

(1) $$h_\alpha = s\{h(t - \alpha)\}$$

shifts the graph of any function acted on a distance α along the positive t-axis and cuts it off to the left of $t = \alpha$.

PROOF. We have from the definition of convolution

$$h_\alpha f = s\{h(t - \alpha)\}\{f(t)\} = s\left\{\int_0^t h(t - x - \alpha)f(x)\,dx\right\}$$

where

$$h(t - x - \alpha) = \begin{cases} 1 \\ 0 \end{cases} \quad \text{when} \quad \begin{array}{l} x \leq t - \alpha \\ x > t - \alpha \end{array};$$

hence

$$h_\alpha f(t) = \begin{cases} s \displaystyle\int_0^{t-\alpha} f(x)\,dx = f(t-\alpha), & t \geqq \alpha, \\ 0, & t < \alpha; \end{cases}$$

that is,

(2) $$h_\alpha f = \{h(t-\alpha)f(t-\alpha)\}.$$

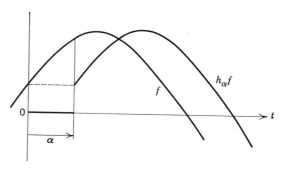

Fig. 143   Shift and cutoff operator h_α.

This is the symbolic statement of the theorem, which is illustrated in Fig. 143.

We term h_α the *shift* (and cutoff) *operator*. Note that

$$h_0 = 1 \ (not \ \{1\}),$$

for

$$h_0 = s\{h(t)\} = h' + h(0) = 0 + 1 = 1.$$

Moreover, from (1)

(3) $$\{h(t-\alpha)\} = \frac{h_\alpha}{s}.$$

The succession of shifts α, β is equivalent to the single shift $\alpha + \beta$; hence

(4) $$h_\alpha h_\beta = h_{\alpha+\beta}.$$

and

(5) $$h_\alpha h_\beta\{h(t)\} = \{h(t-\alpha-\beta)\}.$$

We can use the shift operator to compute convolutions with $h(t-\alpha)$. Thus (Prob. 71.9)

$$\{h(t-\alpha)\}\{f(t)\} = \frac{h_\alpha}{s} f = h_\alpha \left\{ \int_0^t f(x)\,dx \right\},$$

and, after using (2),

(6) $$\{h(t-\alpha)\}\{f(t)\} = \left\{ h(t-\alpha) \int_0^{t-\alpha} f(x)\,dx \right\}.$$

We can now give a neat solution of Problem 71.10:

$$\{h(t-\alpha)\}\{h(t-\beta)\} = \frac{h_\alpha}{s}\frac{h_\beta}{s} = h_\alpha h_\beta \frac{1}{s^2} = h_{\alpha+\beta}\{t\}$$

and hence from (2)

(7) $$\{h(t-\alpha)\}\{h(t-\beta)\} = \{(t-a-\beta)h(t-\alpha-\beta)\}.$$

Example 1. The operational form of the problem of Example 71.4

$$y'' + y = h(t-\pi) - h(t-2\pi), \qquad y(0) = y'(0) = 0,$$

is

$$s^2 y + y = \frac{h_\pi}{s} - \frac{h_{2\pi}}{s}.$$

Hence

$$y = (h_\pi - h_{2\pi})\frac{1}{s(s^2+1)}$$

$$= (h_\pi - h_{2\pi})\left(\frac{1}{s} - \frac{s}{s^2+1}\right)$$

$$= (h_\pi - h_{2\pi})\{1 - \cos t\},$$

or, after using (2),

$$y(t) = h(t-\pi)[1 - \cos(t-\pi)] - h(t-2\pi)[1 - \cos(t-2\pi)]$$
$$= h(t-\pi)(\cos t + 1) + h(t-2\pi)(\cos t - 1)$$

in agreement with Example 71.4.

Example 2. The equation of Example 71.5

$$y' + 3y + \int_0^t y(\tau)\,d\tau = h(t-1) - h(t-2), \qquad y(0) = 1$$

has the operational form

$$sy - 1 + 3y + \frac{2}{s}y = \frac{h_1}{s} - \frac{h_2}{s}.$$

Solving for y, we have

$$y = \frac{s}{(s+1)(s+2)} + \frac{h_1 - h_2}{(s+1)(s+2)}$$

$$= \left(\frac{2}{s+2} - \frac{1}{s+1}\right) + (h_1 - h_2)\left(\frac{1}{s+1} - \frac{1}{s+2}\right)$$

$$= \{2e^{-2t} - e^{-t}\} + (h_1 - h_2)\{e^{-t} - e^{-2t}\},$$

$$y(t) = 2e^{-2t} - e^{-t} + h(t-1)[e^{-(t-1)} - e^{-2(t-1)}]$$
$$- h(t-2)[e^{-(t-2)} - e^{-2(t-2)}]$$

after making use of (2). This coincides with our previous solution.

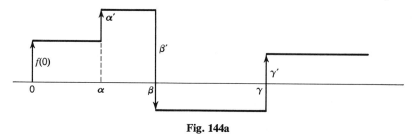

Fig. 144a

144. STEP FUNCTIONS

The graph of a step function f consists of a series of horizontal segments with vertical jumps α', β', ..., at the points $t = \alpha$, β, ... (Fig. 144a). The function may now be expressed as a sum of Heaviside functions with the jumps as coefficients:

$$(1) \qquad f(t) = f(0)h(t) + \alpha'h(t - \alpha) + \beta'h(t - \beta) + \cdots .$$

We now introduce shift operators through the formula

$$h(t - \alpha) = \frac{h_\alpha}{s} \qquad\qquad (143.3)$$

and write

$$(2) \qquad f = \frac{1}{s}(\{f(0)\} + \alpha'h_\alpha + \beta'h_\beta + \cdots).$$

If f is continuous but has a discontinuous derivative f' of the form (2), we have $sf = f' - f(0)$ from (142.4) and hence

$$(3) \qquad f = \frac{1}{s}[f' - f(0)].$$

Example 1. The graph of Fig. 144b corresponds to the operator

$$g = \frac{1}{s}(1 - h_\alpha - h_\beta + h_{\alpha+\beta})$$

or since $h_{\alpha+\beta} = h_\alpha h_\beta$,

$$g = \frac{1}{s}(1 - h_\alpha)(1 - h_\beta).$$

Example 2. The continuous function f whose graph is Fig. 144c has a derivative $f' = g$ whose graph is 144b. Since $f(0) = 0$, equation (3) gives

$$f = \frac{g}{s} = \frac{1}{s^2}(1 - h_\alpha)(1 - h_\beta).$$

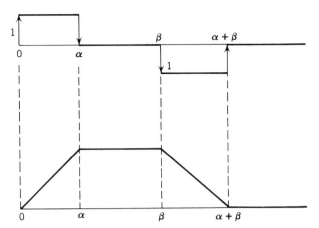

Fig. 144b, c

Example 3. One element of the square wave (Fig. 144*d*) is

$$\frac{1}{s}(1 - 2h_a + h_{2a}) = \frac{1}{s}(1 - h_a)^2.$$

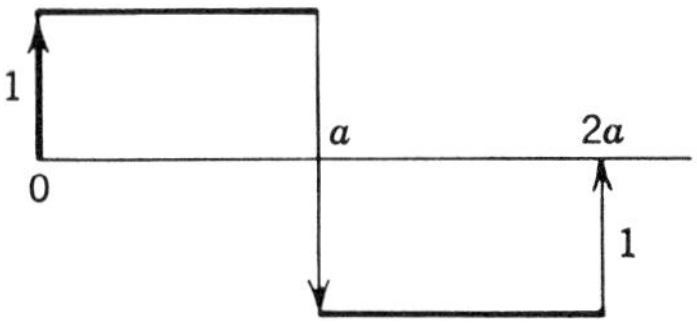

Example 4. The sawtooth function f and its derivative f' have graphs shown in Fig. 144*e*. Since

$$f' = (1 - 2h_1 + 2h_3 - h_4)/s,$$
$$f = (1 - 2h_1 + 2h_3 - h_4)/s^2$$
$$= (1 - 2h_1 + 2h_3 - h_4)\{t\}$$
$$= \{t - 2(t - 1)h(t - 1) + 2(t - 3)h(t - 3) - (t - 4)h(t - 4)\}$$

Fig. 144d

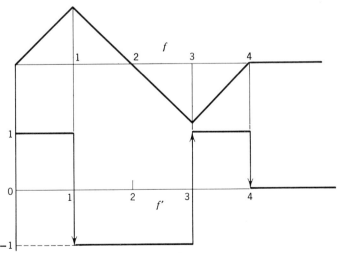

Fig. 144e

PROBLEMS

Express the functions given by the graphs in terms of translation operators.
1. Fig. 144*f*.

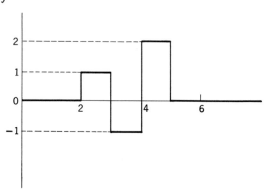

Fig. 144f

2. Fig. 144*g*.

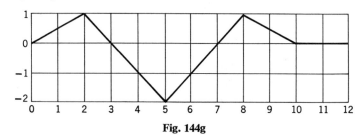

Fig. 144g

3. Show that $(1 + h_\pi)\{\sin t\}$ represents one arch of the sine curve; $(1 - h_\pi^2)\{\sin t\}$ two arches; and $(1 + h_\pi)^2\{\sin t\}$ two rectified arches.

4. Obtain the following operators for the functions in Table C, p. 660.

$$f_1 = \frac{1}{s}(1 - 2h_a + 2h_{2a} - 2h_{3a} + \cdots);$$

$$f_2 = \frac{f_1}{as};$$

$$f_3 = \frac{1}{s}(1 - h_a + h_{2a} - h_{3a} + \cdots);$$

$$f_4 = \frac{1}{as^2} - \frac{1}{s}(1 + h_a + h_{2a} + h_{3a} + \cdots);$$

$$f_5 = \frac{b}{s^2 + b^2}(1 + 2h_{\pi/b} + 2h_{2\pi/b} + \cdots).$$

145. INTEGRAL EQUATIONS OF THE CONVOLUTION TYPE

If the unknown function y satisfies the integral equation of the *first kind*

(1) $$\int_0^t k(t-u)y(u)\,du = f(t)$$

or of the *second kind*

(2) $$y(t) + \int_0^t k(t-u)y(u)\,du = f(t),$$

we may find y as a convolution quotient, for the integral is the convolution ky. Hence from

(1)′ $$ky = f, \qquad y = \frac{f}{k};$$

(2)′ $$y + ky = f, \qquad y = \frac{f}{1+k}.$$

If the *kernel* k and the given function f belong to class $\mathcal{K}$, the solution $f/(1+k)$ of (2)′ will also belong to class $\mathcal{K}$; but the solution f/k of (1)′ need not be a function even when k and f are both members of class $\mathcal{C}$.*

Example 1. The integral equation of the first kind

$$\int_0^t \cos(t-u)y(u)\,du = \alpha \sin t + \beta t$$

may be written

$$\frac{s}{s^2+1}\,y = \frac{\alpha}{s^2+1} + \frac{\beta}{s^2}.$$

Hence the solution is

$$y = \frac{\alpha+\beta}{s} + \frac{\beta}{s^3} = \{\alpha + \beta + \beta t^2\},$$

a continuous function for all values of α and β.

Example 2. The integral equation

$$\int_0^t \sin(t-u)y(u)\,du = \alpha \sin t + \beta t$$

or

$$\frac{1}{s^2+1}\,y = \frac{\alpha}{s^2+1} + \frac{\beta}{s^2}$$

---

* Cf. Erdélyi, ref. 5, § 3.4.

has the solution $y = \alpha + \beta + \beta/s^2$ or

$$y = \alpha + \beta + \{\beta t\},$$

a number plus a function. This is not a function for any values of $\alpha, \beta \neq 0$; the equation admits no function as solution.

Example 3. Abel's Integral Equation.

$$\int_0^t (t - u)^{-k} y'(u) \, du = f(t), \qquad 0 < k < 1.$$

From the equation $\{t^{-k}\} y' = f$ we have

$$y' = sy - y(0) = \frac{f}{\{t^{-k}\}} = \frac{f}{\Gamma(1 - k)h^{1-k}}. \tag{141.1}$$

Multiplying by $h = 1/s$, we have

$$y = \frac{f h^k}{\Gamma(1 - k)} + \frac{y(0)}{s}$$

$$= \frac{f\{t^{k-1}\}}{\Gamma(1 - k)\Gamma(k)} + \{y(0)\}$$

$$= \frac{\sin k\pi}{\pi} f\{t^{k-1}\} + \{y(0)\}, \tag{66.13}$$

$$y(t) = \frac{\sin k\pi}{\pi} \int_0^t f(u)(t - u)^{k-1} \, du + y(0).$$

Example 4. $\displaystyle\int_0^t J_0(t - u)y(u) \, du = t.$

If we assume that

$$J_0(t) = \frac{1}{\sqrt{1 + s^2}},$$

the Laplace transform given in (127.14), the operational equation is

$$\frac{y}{\sqrt{1 + s^2}} = \frac{1}{s^2},$$

$$y = \frac{\sqrt{1 + s^2}}{s^2} = \frac{1 + s^2}{s^2 \sqrt{1 + s^2}} = \frac{1}{s^2 \sqrt{1 + s^2}} + \frac{1}{\sqrt{1 + s^2}}$$

$$= h^2\{J_0(t)\} + \{J_0(t)\}.$$

Since h is the integral operator, the first term is

$$\int_0^t du \int_0^u J_0(x) \, dx = t \int_0^t J_0(x) \, dx - \int_0^t u J_0(u) \, du$$

after integrating by parts; hence from (127.11)

$$y(t) = t \int_0^t J_0(x) \, dx - t J_1(t) + J_0(t).$$

Example 5. The integral equation of the second kind

$$y(t) = \cos t - 2 \int_0^t \cos (t - u) y(u) \, du$$

implies $y(0) = 1$. We have

$$y = \frac{s}{s^2 + 1} - \frac{2s}{s^2 + 1} y,$$

$$y = \frac{s}{(s + 1)^2} = \frac{1}{s + 1} - \frac{1}{(s + 1)^2},$$

$$y(t) = (1 - t)e^{-t}, \qquad y(0) = 1.$$

Example 6. $y(t) + \displaystyle\int_0^t y(t - u) y(u) \, du = (1 + t)e^{-t}$

implies $y(0) = 1$. We have

$$y + y^2 = \{e^{-t}\} + \{te^{-t}\} = \{e^{-t}\} + \{e^{-t}\}^2 \qquad \text{(Prob.70.2)}$$

so that if $x = \{e^{-t}\}$,

$$y + y^2 = x + x^2 \quad \text{or} \quad (y - x)(y + x + 1) = 0.$$

Hence from Titchmarsh's theorem $y = x$ or $-(x + 1)$; but only

$$y(t) = e^{-t} \quad \text{satisfies} \quad y(0) = 1.$$

PROBLEMS

Solve the following integral equations:

1. $y(t) = t + a \displaystyle\int_0^t y(u) \, du$.

2. $y(t) = \cos t + \displaystyle\int_0^t y(u) e^{-(t-u)} \, du$.

3. $y'(t) = a - a^2 \displaystyle\int_0^t y(u) \, du, \qquad y(0) = 0$.

4. $y(t) = e^t - 4t + \displaystyle\int_0^t (3 - 2t + 2x) y(x) \, dx$.

5. $y(t) = \cos 2t + 6 \displaystyle\int_0^t \sin 2(t - u) y(u) \, du$.

6. $\displaystyle\int_0^t e^{-t+u} y(u) \, du = 1 + te^{-t}$.

Show that $y(t) = \delta(t) + 1 + e^{-t}$ and verify this solution using the sifting property of $\delta(t)$.

146. CONVOLUTION RING OF SEQUENCES

In applying operational methods to the solution of difference equations, Mikusiński used a method which, in his words, "is not connected in any essential way with the operational calculus."* But an operational calculus in which the elements are sequences may be constructed which closely parallels the calculus of Mikusiński. This was first done by Josef Eliás.† We shall, however, present a different calculus of sequences in which they are expressed in terms of a shift operator by formulas which are the operational equivalents of the generating functions given in § 99.

To solve difference equations by an operational calculus‡ analogous to that of Mikusiński, we now form a commutative ring in which the elements are real or complex valued sequences, and the operations are addition and convolution defined as follows. Let a and b be sequences defined over the set $t = 0, 1, 2, \ldots$. Then their sum $a + b$ and convolution ab are defined by

(1) $$(a + b)(t) = a(t) + b(t)$$

(2) $$(ab)(t) = \sum_{x=0}^{\infty} a(x)b(t - x).$$

The *convolution* of sequences defined by (2) is their well-known *Cauchy product*. For example, if the sequences are

$$a = \{1, 1, 1, \ldots\}, \qquad b = \{1, 2, 3, 4, \ldots\},$$
$$a + b = \{1 + 1, 1 + 2, 1 + 3, \ldots\} = \{2, 3, 4, \ldots\},$$
$$ab = \{1, 2 + 1, 3 + 2 + 1, \ldots\} = \{1, 3, 5, \ldots\}.$$

Under the operations of addition and convolution, the sequences form a commutative ring satisfying the six postulates of § 136:

A_1: $a + b = b + a$;

A_2: $(a + b) + c = a + (b + c)$;

A_3:   Given a, b, there exists a sequence x such that $a + x = b$;

M_1: $ab = ba$;

M_2: $(ab)c + a(bc)$;

D: $a(b + c) = ab + ac$.

---

* Mikusiński, ref. 12, p. 164, § 12.

† Josef Eliás, *O Operátorovej Metóde Riesenia Diferenčyyeh Revnik*, Matematicke-Fyzikálny Casopis, Sav. VIII. 4, 1958. See also D. H. Moore, "*Convolution Products and Quotients*" etc., Am. Math. Monthly, **69**, no. 2, 1962.

‡ Louis Brand, *A Division Algebra for Sequences and Its Associated Operational Calculus*, Am. Math. Monthly, **71**, no. 7, 1964.

All follow readily from definitions (1) and (2). As to the associative law M_2, the proof of § 136 can be modified so that it almost applies verbatim. Let

$$f(t) = \sum_{x=0}^{t} a(x)b(t - x), \qquad g(t) = \sum_{u=0}^{t} b(u)c(t - u);$$

then M_2 states that $fc = ag$. Now

$$fc(t) = \sum_{y=0}^{t} f(y)c(t - y) = \sum_{y=0}^{t} \sum_{x=0}^{y} a(x)b(y - x)c(t - y)$$

is the double sum over the lattice points included by the 45° right triangle $0 \leq x \leq y \leq t$ in the xy-plane; and

$$ag(t) = \sum_{v=0}^{t} a(t - v)g(v) = \sum_{v=0}^{t} \sum_{u=0}^{v} a(t - v)b(u)c(v - u)$$

is the double sum over the lattice points included by the triangle $0 \leq u \leq v \leq t$ in the uv-plane. The substitution

$$x = t - v, \quad y - x = u \qquad (t - y = v - u)$$

now converts the first sum into the second, for it maps the triangle T_1 bounded by the lines $x = y, y = t, x = 0$ on the triangle T_2 bounded by the lines $u = 0, u = v, v = t$, and the lattice points of T_1 on those of T_2. Draw the figure.

The identity element for addition (x of A_3) is the zero sequence

(3) $$0 = \{0, 0, 0, \ldots\}.$$

The sequence

(4) $$1 = \{1, 0, 0, \ldots\}$$

is the identity for convolution. Its existence is not required by the six postulates for a commutative ring and, in fact, it is lacking in the ring of functions considered in § 136.

We now show that this ring has no divisors of zero.

Theorem. *The convolution of two sequences is zero when and only when one of the sequences is zero.*

PROOF. Let $c = ab = 0$. If $a = 0$ there is nothing to prove. Therefore let $a(n) \neq 0$ be the first non-zero element of z. Then

$$c(n) = \sum_{x=0}^{n} a(x)b(n - x) = a(n)b(0) = 0, \qquad b(0) = 0,$$

$$c(n + 1) = \sum_{x=0}^{n+1} a(x)b(n + 1 - x) = a(n)b(1) = 0, \qquad b(1) = 0;$$

and in general, by induction, $b(t) \equiv 0$.

147. QUOTIENT FIELD OF SEQUENCES

The absence of divisors of zero in the convolution ring whose elements $a, b, \ldots$ are sequences enables us to extend this ring into a field Q whose elements are ordered pairs (a, b) with $b \neq 0$, and having the equivalence relation

(1) $(a, b) = (c, d)$ iff $ad = bc.$

This relation shows that for any sequence $f \neq 0$

(2) $(a, b) = (af, bf).$

We denote by a/b the class of all ordered pairs equivalent to (a, b). The addition and convolution of such equivalence classes is defined as in § 138:

(3) $$\frac{a}{b} + \frac{c}{d} = \frac{ad + bc}{bd}, \qquad b, d \neq 0;$$

(4) $$\frac{a}{b}\frac{c}{d} = \frac{ac}{bd}, \qquad b, d \neq 0.$$

That these definitions give the same sum and product, irrespective of which member of the equivalence class is chosen to represent a/b and c/d, is proved as before (§ 138).

We can now pass from the field of ordered pairs (a, b) to the field of convolution quotients a/b ($b \neq 0$) with the equivalence relation

(5) $$\frac{a}{b} = \frac{c}{d} \quad \text{if} \quad ad = bc.$$

The zero and unit elements are now

(6) $$\frac{0}{f} = 0, \qquad \frac{f}{f} = 1, \qquad f \neq 0$$

where f is any non-zero sequence.

Division by any non-zero elements of Q is always possible and unique:

(7) $$\frac{a/b}{c/d} = \frac{ac}{bd}, \qquad b, d \neq 0.$$

But a convolution quotient of sequences need not be a sequence; for example, if

(8) $$s = \{0, 1, 0, 0, \ldots\},$$

$1/s$ is not a sequence a; for $sa(0) = 0$, whereas $1(0) = 1$. In fact, if f is any sequence whose first term is zero, $1/f$ is not a sequence.

The sequences

(9)
$$k = \{k, 0, 0, \ldots\}$$

are isomorphic with the *numbers* k; for

$$k_1 + k_2 = \{k_1 + k_2, 0, 0, \ldots\}, \qquad k_1 k_2 = \{k_1 k_2, 0, 0, \ldots\}.$$

Moreover, ka is the sequence obtained by multiplying each element of a by k; and

(10)
$$k\frac{a}{b} = \frac{k}{1}\frac{a}{b} = \frac{ka}{b}.$$

We shall call all elements of the quotient field Q *operators*; these include numbers (numerical operators), sequences, and new entities such as $1/s$. *All* elements of Q conform to the rules of operation given in (3) and (4).

148. SHIFT OPERATOR

The sequence

(1)
$$s = \{0, 1, 0, \ldots\}$$

is called the *shift operator* because of the convolution

(2)
$$sf = \{0, f(0), f(1), \ldots\},$$

in which each term of f is shifted one place to the right. Obviously, $s^2 = \{0, 0, 1, 0, \ldots\}$ and, in general,

(2)
$$s^n = \{\underbrace{0, 0, \ldots,}_{n} 0, 1, 0, 0, \ldots\}.$$

The operator s^n applied to any sequence f shifts all its terms n places to the right and fills the first n places with zeros; we may say it is a *right shift and cutoff operator*.

Any sequence f may be written as an infinite series

(3)
$$\{f(t)\} = \sum_{t=0}^{\infty} f(t)s^t = F(s).$$

The question of convergence is not germane to this notation, for (3) merely states that the term $f(n)$ of the sequence occupies the same place as the 1 in s^n. With this notation,

(4)
$$\{k^t f(t)\} = \sum_{t=0}^{\infty} k^t f(t)s^t = \sum_{t=0}^{\infty} f(t)(ks)^t = F(ks).$$

Moreover,

$$\{tf(t)\} = \sum_{t=0}^{\infty} tf(t)s^t = s\sum_{t=0}^{\infty} f(t)ts^{t-1},$$

or since the last sum is the formal derivative of the series $F(s)$ in (3),

(5) $$\{tf(t)\} = s\,\frac{dF}{ds}.$$

In formulas (4) and (5), $F(s)$ is a simple power series in s. They also hold when $F(s) = A(s)/B(s)$ is the quotient of such power series; for if

$$\{f(t)\} = \frac{\{a(t)\}}{\{b(t)\}} = \frac{A(s)}{B(s)} = F(s),$$

we have the convolution

$$\sum_{x=0}^{t} f(x)b(t-x) = a(t).$$

The identity

$$\sum_{x=0}^{t} k^x f(x)k^{t-x}b(t-x) = k^t a(t)$$

or

$$\{k^t f(t)\}\{k^t b(t)\} = \{k^t a(t)\}$$

implies

$$\{k^t f(t)\} = \frac{\{k^t a(t)\}}{\{k^t b(t)\}} = \frac{A(ks)}{B(ks)},$$

or since $A/B = F$,

(IV) $$\{k^t f(t)\} = F(ks).$$

Moreover, the identity

$$\sum_{x=0}^{t} xf(x)b(t-x) + \sum_{x=0}^{t} f(x)(t-x)b(t-x) = ta(t),$$

or

$$\{tf(t)\}\{b(t)\} + \{f(t)\}\{tb(t)\} = \{ta(t)\},$$

implies

$$\{tf(t)\} = \frac{\{ta(t)\}}{\{b(t)\}} - \{f(t)\}\frac{\{tb(t)\}}{\{b(t)\}}$$

$$= \frac{sA'}{B} - \frac{A}{B}\frac{sB'}{B} = s\,\frac{BA' - AB'}{B^2}$$

where the last fraction is the formal derivative of $A/B = F$. Thus we again have

(V) $$\{tf(t)\} = s\,\frac{dF}{ds}.$$

In the following articles we shall refer to these important formulas as (IV) and (V).

149. SUM OPERATOR

The sequence $\{1\}$, consisting entirely of 1's is written

(1) $$\sigma = \{1, 1, 1, \ldots\}$$

and called the *sum operator*; for the convolution

(2) $$\sigma f = \{f_0, f_0 + f_1, f_0 + f_1 + f_2, \ldots\} = \left\{\sum_{x=0}^{t} f(x)\right\}$$

where $f_n = f(n)$. Since

$$\sigma\{1, -1, 0, 0, \ldots\} = \{1, 0, 0, \ldots\} = 1,$$

(3) $$\frac{1}{\sigma} = \{1, -1, 0, 0, \ldots\} = 1 - s$$

and

(4) $$\{1\} = \sigma = (1 - s)^{-1}.$$

From (IV) we also have

(5) $$\{k^t\} = \{k^t \cdot 1\} = (1 - ks)^{-1}.$$

If ϑ denotes the operator sD ($D = d/ds$), formula (V) becomes

(V) $$\{tf(t)\} = \vartheta F(s).$$

We now apply ϑ to (4) to obtain

(6) $$\{t\} = \vartheta\{1\} = s(1 - s)^{-2},$$

(7) $$\{t^2\} = \vartheta\{t\} = s(s + 1)(1 - s)^{-3},$$

(8) $$\{t^3\} = \vartheta\{t^2\} = s(s^2 + 4s + 1)(1 - s)^{-4};$$

and, in general,

(9) $$\{t^n\} = \vartheta^n\{1\} = \vartheta^n(1 - s)^{-1}.$$

Moreover, from (IV)

(10) $$\{t^n k^t\} = \vartheta^n(1 - ks)^{-1}$$

and, in particular, from (6)

(11) $$\{tk^t\} = ks(1 - ks)^{-2}.$$

With $k = e^{i\alpha}$ (α real), (5) becomes

$$\{e^{i\alpha t}\} = \frac{1}{1 - se^{i\alpha}} = \frac{1 - se^{-i\alpha}}{1 - 2s\cos\alpha + s^2};$$

hence on taking real and imaginary parts, we see that

$$(12) \qquad \{\cos \alpha t\} = \frac{1 - s \cos \alpha}{1 - 2s \cos \alpha + s^2},$$

$$(13) \qquad \{\sin \alpha t\} = \frac{s \sin \alpha}{1 - 2s \cos \alpha + s^2}.$$

In particular, when $\alpha = \pi/2$,

$$(14) \qquad \left\{\cos \frac{\pi}{2} t\right\} = \frac{1}{1 + s^2},$$

$$(15) \qquad \left\{\sin \frac{\pi}{2} t\right\} = \frac{s}{1 + s^2}.$$

Applying (V) to these formulas we have

$$(16) \qquad \left\{t \cos \frac{\pi}{2} t\right\} = \frac{-2s^2}{(1 + s^2)^2},$$

$$(17) \qquad \left\{t \sin \frac{\pi}{2} t\right\} = \frac{s(1 - s^2)}{(1 + s^2)^2},$$

and hence

$$(18) \qquad \left\{\frac{t + 2}{2} \cos \frac{\pi}{2} t\right\} = \frac{1}{(1 + s^2)^2},$$

$$(19) \qquad \left\{\frac{t + 1}{2} \sin \frac{\pi}{2} t\right\} = \frac{s}{(1 + s^2)^2}.$$

If the sequences in equations (10) to (17) are multiplied by k^t, formula (IV) states that s must be replaced by ks on the right; thus

$$(20) \qquad \{k^t \cos \alpha t\} = \frac{ks \sin \alpha}{1 - 2ks \cos \alpha + k^2 s^2},$$

$$(21) \qquad \{k^t \sin \alpha t\} = \frac{ks \sin \alpha}{1 - 2ks \cos \alpha + k^2 s^2}.$$

We next compute the powers of σ from the Fundamental Theorem of the sum calculus:

$$\sum_{x=0}^{t} f(x) = \Delta^{-1} f(x) \Big|_{x=0}^{x=t+1}.$$

Remembering that

$$\Delta^{-1}(x + c)^{(n)} = \frac{(x + c)^{(n+1)}}{(n + 1)!}, \qquad (78.9)$$

we have

(22)
$$\sigma^2 = \sigma\{1\} = \left\{\sum_{x=0}^{t} 1\right\} = \{t + 1\},$$

(23)
$$\sigma^3 = \sigma\{t + 1\} = \left\{\sum_{x=0}^{t} (x + 1)\right\} = \left\{\frac{1}{2!}(t + 2)^{(2)}\right\},$$

and by induction

(24)
$$\sigma^{n+1} = \left\{\frac{1}{n!}(t + n)^{(n)}\right\}.$$

Since $\sigma = (1 - s)^{-1}$, this may be written

(25)
$$\{(t + n)^{(n)}\} = \frac{n!}{(1 - s)^{n+1}}.$$

If we apply the shift operator s^n to this equation, the left member becomes

$$\{0, 0, \ldots, 0, n^{(n)}, (1 + n)^n, \ldots\} = \{t^{(n)}\};$$

hence

(26)
$$\{t^{(n)}\} = \frac{n!\, s^n}{(1 - s)^{n+1}}.$$

When $n = 0$ and 1, this agrees with (4) and (6)

$F(s)$ is the generating function of the sequence $\{f(t)\}$ if

$$\sum_{t=0}^{\infty} f(t)s^t = F(s) \tag{§ 99}.$$

From this we have *formally*

(IV)′
$$\sum_{t=0}^{\infty} k^t f(t)s^t = F(ks),$$

and by formal differentiation

(V)′
$$\sum_{t=0}^{\infty} tf(t)s^t = sF'(s).$$

Thus $F(ks)$ is the generating function of $\{k^t f(t)\}$ and $sF'(s)$ the generating function of $\{tf(t)\}$. Formulas IV and V are operational analogs of these results, but without any reference to convergence. Moreover,

(4)′
$$\sum_{t=0}^{\infty} s^t = (1 - s)^{-1}$$

shows that $(1 - s)^{-1}$ is the generating function of the sequence $\{1\}$. Now all the formulas of this article were deduced from (4) with the aid of (IV) and (V); consequently,

The functions of s in the foregoing equations are generating functions for the corresponding sequences.

Table 99 of generating functions may therefore be used to find the operational expression for a sequence $\{f(t)\}$ by replacing x by s, the shift operator.

If the sequence $\{f(t)\}$ has the property

$$f(t + p) = f(t), \qquad t = 0, 1, 2, \ldots,$$

it is said to have the period p. Recalling the effect of the shift operator s^p (148.2), we have

$$(1 - s^p)\{f(t)\} = \{f(0), f(1), \ldots, f(p - 1); 0, 0, \ldots\}$$

or, in view of (148.3),

$$(1 - s^p)\{f(t)\} = \sum_{t=0}^{p-1} f(t)s^t.$$

Therefore the operational form of a sequence of period p is

(27) $$\{f(t)\} = \frac{\sum\limits_{t=0}^{p-1} f(t)s^t}{1 - s^p}.$$

This is the analog of the Laplace transform of a periodic function given in equation (71.8).

For example, if $f(t) = \frac{1}{2}\{1 + (-1)^t\}$, $p = 2$ and a period is $(1, 0)$; hence

(28) $$\left\{\frac{1 + (-1)^t}{2}\right\} = \frac{1}{1 - s^2}.$$

Moreover, (14) and (15) are direct consequences of (27); thus for $\left\{\cos\dfrac{\pi}{2}t\right\}$, $p = 4$ and a period is $(1, 0, -1, 0)$; hence

$$\cos\frac{\pi}{2}t = \frac{1 - s^2}{1 - s^4} = \frac{1}{1 + s^2}.$$

PROBLEMS

Prove the following:

1. $\dfrac{s^3}{(s^2 + 1)^2} = \left\{\dfrac{1 - t}{2}\sin\dfrac{\pi}{2}t\right\}.$

2. $\dfrac{1}{s^3 + 1} = \dfrac{1}{3}\left\{(-1)^t + 2\cos\dfrac{\pi}{6}t\right\}.$

3. $\dfrac{1}{1 - 2s\cos\alpha + s^2} = \left\{\dfrac{\sin\alpha(t + 1)}{\sin\alpha}\right\}.$

4. $\dfrac{1}{1 - s + s^2} = \left\{\dfrac{2\sin\frac{1}{3}\pi(t + 1)}{\sqrt{3}}\right\}.$

5. $\dfrac{1}{1 + s + s^2} = \left\{\dfrac{2\sin\frac{2}{3}\pi(t + 1)}{\sqrt{3}}\right\}.$

6. If $\{f(t)\}$ has the period $(1, 1, 0, -1, -1, 0)$,

$$\{f(t)\} = \frac{1}{1 - s + s^2}.$$

150. DIFFERENCE EQUATIONS

To solve linear difference equations we express the sequences $\{y(t + 1)\}$, $\{y(t + 2)\}, \ldots$ in terms of $\{y(t)\}$. Since

$$\{y(t)\} = y(0)\{1, 0, 0, \ldots\} + \{0, y(1), y(2), \ldots\}$$
$$= y(0) + s\{y(1), y(2), \ldots\}$$
$$= y(0) + s\{y(t + 1)\},$$

we have

(I) $$s\{y(t + 1)\} = \{y(t)\} - y(0)$$

where $y(0)$ is a number. Therefore,

$$s\{y(t + 2)\} = \{y(t + 1)\} - y(1);$$

multiplying by s and using (I) gives

(II) $$s^2\{y(t + 2)\} = \{y(t)\} - y(0) - sy(1).$$

Now we can use an induction proof to obtain

(III) $$s^n\{y(t + n)\} = y - y_0 - sy_1 - \cdots - s^{n-1}y_{n-1},$$

where $y = \{y(t)\}$ and $y_n = y(n)$.

To solve a difference equation of order n with constant coefficients,

(1) $$a_0y(t + n) + a_1y(t + n - 1) + \cdots + a_ny(t) = f(t),$$

multiply by s^n and use formulas of type III to put the left member in the form

$$(a_0 + a_1s + \cdots + a_ns^n)y + G(s)$$

where $G(s)$ is a polynomial of degree $n - 1$ at most, and whose coefficients depend on the first n terms of the sequence y: $y(0), y(1), \ldots, y(n - 1)$. These n values are the *initial conditions*. Use the formulas of § 149 (or the table of generating functions, Table 99, with $x = s$) to express $\{f(t)\} = F(s)$, and solve the transformed equation for y:

(2) $$y = \frac{s^nF(s) - G(s)}{a_0 + a_1s + \cdots + a_ns^n}.$$

Decompose the fraction into partial fractions and use the formulas of § 149 to interpret them as functions of t. Note that the roots of the equation

$$a_0 + a_1s \cdots + a_ns^n = 0$$

are the reciprocals of the roots of the *characteristic equation* (§ 89)

$$a_0r^n + a_1r^{n-1} + \cdots + a_n = 0.$$

The method is illustrated in the following examples in which we use the concise notation $y(n) = y_n$. Then I and II become

(I) $$s\{y(t + 1)\} = y - y_0,$$

(II) $$s^2\{y(t + 2)\} = y - y_0 - sy_1.$$

The formulas cited refer to § 149.

Example 1. $y(t + 2) - 3y(t + 1) + 2y(t) = 1$, $y_0 = 1$, $y_1 = 0$.
Multiply by s^2; then

$$(y - 1) - 3s(y - 1) + 2s^2y = \frac{s^2}{1 - s}, \tag{4}$$

$$(1 - 3s + 2s^2)y = 1 - 3s + \frac{s^2}{1 - s},$$

$$(1 - s)(1 - 2s)y = \frac{(1 - 2s)^2}{1 - s},$$

$$y = \frac{1 - 2s}{(1 - s)^2} = \frac{1}{(1 - s)^2} - 2\frac{s}{(1 - s)^2};$$

$$y(t) = (t + 1) - 2t = 1 - t$$

using (25) and (26).

Example 2. $y(t + 2) + 8y(t + 1) - 9y(t) = 2^t$, $y_0 = y_1 = 0$.

$$(1 + 8s - 9s^2)y = \frac{s^2}{1 - 2s}, \tag{5}$$

$$y = \frac{s^2}{(1 - 2s)(1 - s)(1 + 9s)}$$

$$= \frac{\frac{1}{11}}{1 - 2s} - \frac{\frac{1}{10}}{1 - s} + \frac{\frac{1}{110}}{1 + 9s};$$

$$y(t) = \tfrac{1}{11} 2^t - \tfrac{1}{10} + \tfrac{1}{110}(-9)^t$$

using (5), (4), and (5).

Example 3. $y(t + 3) - y(t + 2) - y(t + 1) + y(t) = 0$, $y_0 = 0$, $y_1 = 1$, $y_2 = 2$.
Multiply by s^3; then

$$(y - s - 2s^2) - s(y - s) - s^2y + s^3y = 0,$$

$$(1 - s - s^2 + s^3)y = s^2 + s,$$

$$(1 + s)(1 - s)^2y = s(s + 1).$$

$$y = \frac{s}{(1 - s)^2}, \qquad y(t) = t. \tag{6}$$

Example 4. $y(t + 2) + y(t) = \cos \frac{\pi}{2} t$, $y_0 = 1, y_1 = 2$.

$$(y - 1 - 2s) + s^2 y = \frac{s^2}{1 + s^2} \tag{14}$$

$$(1 + s^2)y = 1 + 2s + \frac{s^2}{1 + s^2},$$

$$y = \frac{1 + 2s}{1 + s^2} + \frac{s^2}{(1 + s^2)^2} = \frac{2 + 2s}{1 + s^2} - \frac{1}{(1 + s^2)^2};$$

$$y(t) = \left(2 \cos \frac{\pi}{2} t + 2 \sin \frac{\pi}{2} t\right) - \frac{t + 2}{2} \cos \frac{\pi}{2} t,$$

using (14), (15), and (18); hence

$$y(t) = \frac{2 - t}{2} \cos \frac{\pi}{2} t + 2 \sin \frac{\pi}{2} t.$$

Example 5. $y(t + 2) - 2y(t + 1) + 2y(t) = 0$, $y_0 = 0, y_1 = 3$.

$$(y - 3s) - 2sy + 2s^2 y = 0,$$

$$y = \frac{3s}{1 - 2s + 2s^2}.$$

Compare this with (21); then since

$$r = \sqrt{2}; \quad k \cos \alpha = k, \sin \alpha = 1, \quad \alpha = \pi/4,$$

$$y(t) = 3 \cdot 2^{t/2} \sin \frac{\pi}{4} t.$$

The initial conditions are satisfied; as a further check we have $y_2 = 2y_1 = 6$ from the equation, which agrees with $y_2 = 3 \cdot 2 \sin \pi/2$.

Example 6. $y(t + 2) + y(t) = \frac{1}{2}[1 + (-1)^t]$, $y_0 = 0, y_1 = 1$.

$$(y - s) + s^2 y = \frac{s^2}{2}\left(\frac{1}{1 - s} + \frac{1}{1 + s}\right) = \frac{s^2}{1 - s^2},$$

$$(1 + s^2)y = s + \frac{s^2}{1 - s^2} = \frac{s + s^2 - s^3}{1 - s^2},$$

$$y = \frac{s + s^2 - s^3}{(1 - s)(1 + s)(1 + s^2)}$$

$$= \frac{\frac{1}{4}}{1 - s} + \frac{\frac{1}{4}}{1 + s} + \frac{s - \frac{1}{2}}{1 + s^2};$$

$$y(t) = \frac{1}{4} + \frac{1}{4}(-1)^t + \sin \frac{\pi}{2} t - \frac{1}{2} \cos \frac{\pi}{2} t,$$

using (4), (5), (15), and (14). The initial conditions are satisfied; as a further check we have $y_2 = 1$ from the equation, which agrees with the solution.

PROBLEMS

1. Apply (I) to $y(t) = 1$ and k^t to obtain (4) and (5).
2. Apply (I) to $y(t) = t$ to obtain (6).

3. Apply (II) to $\cos \dfrac{\pi}{2} t$ to obtain (14).

4. Apply (II) to $\sin \dfrac{\pi}{2} t$ to obtain (15).

5. Given (25), deduce (26) by applying (III) to $y(t) = t^{(n)}$.
Solve the following difference equations:

6. $y(t + 2) + y(t) = \sin \dfrac{\pi}{2} t, \qquad y_0 = 1, y_1 = 0.$

7. $y(t + 2) - y(t) = 2^t, \qquad y_0 = 1, y_1 = 0.$
8. $y(t + 3) + y(t) = 0, \qquad y_0 = 1, y_1 = y_2 = 0.$
9. $y(t + 2) - 4y(t + 1) + 8y(t) = 0, \qquad y_0 = 0, y_1 = 1.$
10. $y(t + 2) - 4y(t) = 3 + 2t, \qquad y_0 = 1, y_1 = 0.$

11. $y(t + 2) + y(t) = \sin \dfrac{\pi}{2} t, \qquad y_0 = 0, y_1 = 1.$

12. $y(t + 2) + y(t) = \cos \dfrac{\pi}{2} t, \qquad y_0 = 1, y_1 = 0.$

13. $\Delta^2 y(t) + y(t) = \sin \dfrac{\pi}{2} t, \qquad y_0 = 1, y_1 = 0.$

14. $\Delta y(t) + 3y(t) + 2 \displaystyle\sum_{x=0}^{t} y(x) = (-1)^t, \qquad y_0 = 1.$

[See example 2 of the article cited in footnote ‡ of § 146.]

CHAPTER 12

Existence and Uniqueness Theorems

151. INITIAL VALUE PROBLEMS

In many practical problems the solution of a differential equation is required that satisfies certain initial conditions. For a first-order equation such an *initial* value problem is

(1) $$\frac{dy}{dx} = f(x, y), \qquad y(a) = b.$$

Consider, now, the equation

$$xy' - y + 1 = 0$$

in turn with the initial conditions:

(a) $y(0) = 0$; (b) $y(1) = 1$; (c) $y(0) = 1$.

In problem (a) there is *no solution;* for when $x = 0, y = 1$. In problem (b) there is just *one solution*, $y = 1$. In problem (c) there are an infinite number of solutions $y = 1 + cx$, one for each value of c.

This diverse behavior leads to two essential problems:

1. When does an initial value problem have a solution?
2. When does an initial value problem have just *one* solution?

These questions of the existence and unicity of solutions in an initial value problem shall be our next concern.

For the initial value problem (1) the facts are simple and are stated at once.

1. Existence Theorem. *If $f(x, y)$ is continuous at all points of the closed rectangle*

$$\mathscr{R}: \ |x - a| \leqq A, \qquad |y - b| \leqq B$$

and therefore bounded, say

$$|f(x, y)| \leqq M \text{ in } \mathscr{R},*$$

---

* A continuous function in a closed region is bounded; *Advanced Calculus*, § 75, Theorem 3.

then the initial value problem (1) *has at least one solution valid in an interval at least as large as*

$$|x - a| \leq \min\left(A, \frac{B}{M}\right).$$

Min $(A, B/M)$ means the smaller of the numbers A and B/M; but the solution may be (and usually is) valid in a larger interval as in the following example. This theorem, essentially due to Cauchy, has been refined by the Italian mathematician Peano. For the proof see Kamke, E., ref. 30, §§ 33–35.

2. Uniqueness Theorem. *If* $f(x, y)$ *and* $\partial f/\partial y$ *are continuous in the closed rectangle*

$$\mathscr{R}: \ |x - a| \leq A, \qquad |y - b| \leq B,$$

and therefore bounded, say

$$|f(x, y)| \leq M, \qquad |\partial f/\partial y| \leq M' \text{ in } \mathscr{R},$$

then the initial value problem (1) *has a unique solution valid in the interval*

$$|x - a| \leq \min(A, B/M).$$

We shall prove this theorem and show that the unique solution is the limit function in the Picard approximation process considered in the next article. This is based on the following

3. Equivalence Theorem. *In any region in which* $f(x, y)$ *is continuous, any solution of the initial value problem*

$$(1) \qquad\qquad \frac{dy}{dx} = f(x, y), \qquad y(a) = b,$$

is also a solution of the integral equation

$$(2) \qquad\qquad y(x) = b + \int_a^x f(t, y)\, dt,$$

and conversely.

PROOF. Any solution $y(x)$ of (1) converts (1) into an identity in x which on integration yields

$$y(x) - y(a) = \int_a^x f(t, y)\, dt.$$

Conversely, if $y(x)$ is any solution of (2), $y(a) = b$ and

$$\frac{dy}{dx} = f(x, y)$$

since $f(x, y)$ is continuous.*

---

* *Advanced Calculus*, § 119, Theorem 2.

Example.   In the initial value problem

$$(1 - x^2)y' = y, \qquad y(0) = 1,$$

$a = 0, b = 1$, and both

$$f(x, y) = \frac{y}{1 - x^2}, \qquad \frac{\partial f}{\partial y} = \frac{1}{1 - x^2}$$

are continuous in the rectangle

$$\mathscr{R}: \qquad |x| \leqq \sqrt{1 - \alpha} = A, \qquad |y - 1| \leqq B,$$

where $0 < \alpha < 1$ and B is arbitrarily large; hence

$$M = \frac{B + 1}{\alpha}, \qquad \frac{B}{M} = \frac{B}{B + 1} \alpha \simeq \alpha.$$

Thus if $\alpha = 0.64$, $A = \sqrt{0.36} = 0.60$, and the theorem guarantees a unique solution in the interval $|x| \leqq 0.6$.

The explicit solution, found by separation of variables, is

$$y = \frac{1}{\sqrt{1 - x^2}}$$

and is actually valid in the open interval $|x| < 1$. Since the given equation is linear, this interval of validity follows from Theorem 16.3.

PROBLEMS

Discuss the existence and unicity of solutions of the following initial value problems in the light of existence and unicity theorems and give solution curves when they exist.

1. $yy' + x = 0.$

    (a) $y(0) = 0$; (b) $y(0) = 1$; (c) $y(0) = -1$; (d) $y(1) = 0.$

2. $y' = 2\sqrt{y}.$

    (a) $y(1) = 1$; (b) $y(1) = 0.$

3. $x^2y' = y^2.$

    (a) $y(0) = 0$; (b) $y(0) = 1$; (c) $y(1) = 1$; (d) $y(1) = \frac{1}{2}.$

4. $y' = 3y^{2/3}, \quad y(1) = 0.$

5. $xy' + y = 0.$

    (a) $y(0) = 1$; (b) $y(1) = 1.$

6. $(1 - x^2)y' = 1 - y^2.$

    (a) $y(1) = 1$; (b) $y(a) = a$ $(a \neq \pm 1)$; (c) $y(0) = 1$; (d) $\lim_{x \to \infty} y = 0.$

7. $(2x - y)y' + (x + 2y) = 0, \qquad y(0) = 0.$

8. $(2x + y)y' = x + 2y, \quad y(1) = 1.$

152. PICARD'S ITERATION PROCESS

As a first approximation to the solution of the initial value problem

$$(1) \qquad\qquad y' = f(x, y), \qquad y(a) = b,$$

we choose $y_0(x)$ as any integrable function, preferably so that $y_0(a) = b$. Unless other information is available, a good choice is $y_0(x) = b$, a constant function. The successive approximations are now found by integrating the equation

$$y'_{n+1} = f(x, y_n), \qquad y_n(a) = b;$$

hence

$$(2) \qquad\qquad y_{n+1}(x) = b + \int_a^x f(t, y_n(t))\, dt.$$

When the integrals exist, this recursion formula determines a sequence of functions

$$y_0(x), y_1(x), y_2(x), \ldots,$$

and when $f(x, y)$ satisfies certain general conditions,

$$(3) \qquad\qquad \lim_{n \to \infty} y_n(x) = y(x),$$

the unique solution of problem (1).

We shall illustrate the process by solving the linear equation

$$(4) \qquad\qquad \frac{dy}{dx} = x + y, \qquad y(0) = 1,$$

whose solution (§ 16) is

$$(5) \qquad\qquad y = 2e^x - x - 1.$$

With $y_0 = 1$, we find in turn

$$y_1 = 1 + \int_0^x (t + 1)\, dt = 1 + x + \frac{x^2}{2},$$

$$y_2 = 1 + \int_0^x \left(1 + 2t + \frac{t^2}{2}\right) dt = 1 + x + x^2 + \frac{x^3}{6},$$

$$y_3 = 1 + \int_0^x \left(1 + 2t + t^2 + \frac{t^3}{6}\right) dt = 1 + x + x^2 + \frac{x^3}{3} + \frac{x^4}{24},$$

$$y_4 = 1 + \int_0^x \left(1 + 2t + t^2 + \frac{t^3}{3} + \frac{t^4}{24}\right) dt = 1 + x + x^2 + \frac{x^3}{3} + \frac{x^4}{12} + \frac{x^5}{120},$$

and, in general,

$$y_n = 1 + x + 2\left[\frac{x^2}{2!} + \frac{x^3}{3!} + \cdots + \frac{x^n}{n!}\right] + \frac{x^{n+1}}{(n+1)!}.$$

As $n \to \infty$, the quantity in brackets converges to $e^x - 1 - x$ and

$$y_n \to 1 + x + 2(e^x - 1 - x) + 0 = 2e^x - 1 - x,$$

which agrees with the foregoing solution in (5).

With the initial choice $y_0 = e^x$,

$$y_1 = 1 + \int_0^x (t + e^t)\, dt = \frac{x^2}{2} + e^x,$$

$$y_2 = 1 + \int_0^x \left(t + \frac{t^2}{2} + e^t\right) dt = \frac{x^2}{2} + \frac{x^3}{6} + e^x,$$

and, in general,

$$y_n = \frac{x}{2!} + \frac{x^3}{3!} + \cdots + \frac{x^{n+1}}{(n+1)!} + e^x,$$

so that

$$y_n \to (e^x - 1 - x) + e^x = 2e^x - 1 - x,$$

the same solution as before.

Finally, if we make the lucky guess $y_0 = 2e^x - 1 - x$, we find

$$y_1 = 1 + \int_0^x (2e^t - 1)\, dt = 1 + 2(e^x - 1) - x = y_0$$

which ends the iteration and shows that y_0 is a solution.

PROBLEMS

1. Solve the problem (3) in the text with (a) $y_0 = 1 + x$, (b) $y_0 = \cos x$.

2. Solve by iteration:
$$y' = xy, \qquad y(0) = 1.$$

3. Use iteration on Example 22.1 with $y_0 = 0$, stopping at y_5. Compare with the series given in Example 22.1.

4. Use iteration on Example 22.2 with $y_0 = 1$, stopping at y_5. Compare with the series given in Example 22.2.

5. Solve the Riccati equation
$$y' = 1 - y^2 + x^2, \qquad y(0) = 0$$

with (a) $y_0 = 0$, (b) $y_0 = -x$.

6. $(y + 2x)y' = x + 2y$, $y(0) = 0$. Solve by iteration when (a) $y_0 = 0$; (b) $y_0 = x$; (c) $y_0 = -x$. Explain.

7. If in solving equation (1) by iteration we find $y_{n+1} = y_n$, show that the solution is $y = y_n(x)$.

8. Solve by iteration and compare with the exact solution:

$$y' - xy = 1, \qquad y(0) = 0.$$

153. EXISTENCE THEOREM

To prove an existence theorem by means of Picard's iteration process we shall impose a *Lipschitz condition** on $f(x, y)$:

If (x, y) and $(x, \bar{y})$ are any two points of a region $\mathscr{R}$ having the same x, there exists a constant L (the *Lipschitz constant*) such that

(L) $$|f(x, y) - f(x, \bar{y})| \leq L\,|y - \bar{y}|.$$

If $\partial f/\partial y$ is continuous in $\mathscr{R}$ and therefore bounded, say

$$\left|\frac{\partial f}{\partial y}\right| \leq L,$$

then $f(x, y)$ satisfies a Lipschitz condition with the constant L. For from the mean-value theorem†

$$f(x, y) - f(x, \bar{y}) = (y - \bar{y})f_y(x, \eta),$$

where η lies between y and $\bar{y}$, and on taking absolute values we obtain the inequality (L). A Lipschitz condition is therefore a weaker requirement than the continuity of $\partial f/\partial y$.

Picard's Theorem (Existence and Uniqueness). *Let $f(x, y)$ be continuous in the closed rectangle*

$$\mathscr{R}: \qquad |x - a| \leq A, \qquad |y - b| \leq B,$$

and therefore bounded in $\mathscr{R}$, say

$$|f(x, y)| \leq M,$$

and also satisfy a Lipschitz condition there:

(L) $$|f(x, y) - f(x, \bar{y})| \leq L\,|y - \bar{y}|.$$

Then the initial value problem

(1) $$\frac{dy}{dx} = f(x, y), \qquad y(a) = b,$$

-----

* First stated by Rudolph Lipschitz in 1876.
† *Advanced Calculus*, § 57.

has a unique solution, the limit function $y(x)$ of the Picard approximations

(P) $$y_n(x) = b + \int_a^x f(t, y_{n-1}(t))\, dt, \qquad n = 1, 2, \ldots .$$

This solution is valid in the interval

$$|x - a| \leq h = \min\left(A, \frac{B}{M}\right).$$

and $y'(x)$ is continuous there.

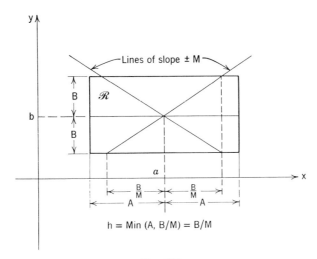

Fig. 153

PROOF. Although $y_0(x)$ may be any integrable function, we shall take $y_0 = b$. Then from (P)

(2) $$|y_1 - b| \leq \int_a^x |f(t, b)|\, dt \leq \int_a^x M\, dt = M(x - a),$$

where $a < x \leq A$; hence

$$|y_1 - b| \leq B \quad \text{if} \quad x - a \leq \frac{B}{M}.$$

With this new restriction on x, namely $x - a \leq h$ (the smaller of A and B/M: Fig. 153),

$$|y_2 - b| \leq \int_a^x |f(t, y_1)|\, dt \leq \int_a^x M\, dt = M(x - a),$$

and since $x - a \leq B/M$,

$$|y_2 - b| \leq B \quad \text{if} \quad x - a \leq h.$$

A simple induction now shows that, in general,

(3) $$|y_n - b| \leq B \quad \text{if} \quad x - a \leq h.$$

From now on we restrict x to the interval $x - a \leq h$; then from (P) and (L), valid because of (3),

(4) $$|y_{n+1} - y_n| \leq L \int_a^x |y_n - y_{n-1}| \, dt.$$

In particular, we have from (2)

$$|y_2 - y_1| \leq L \int_a^x |y_1 - b| \, dt \leq ML \int_a^x (t - a) \, dt = \frac{ML}{2}(x - a)^2,$$

$$|y_3 - y_2| \leq L \int_a^x |y_2 - y_1| \, dt \leq \frac{ML^2}{2} \int_a^x (t - a)^2 \, dt = \frac{ML^2}{3!}(x - a)^3,$$

and in general, since $x - a \leq h$,

(5) $$|y_n - y_{n-1}| \leq \frac{ML^{n-1}}{n!}(x - a)^n \leq \frac{M}{L}\frac{L^n h^n}{n!}.$$

Thus the terms of the telescopic series

(6) $$y_0 + \sum_{n=1}^{\infty} [y_n(x) - y_{n-1}(x)]$$

have absolute values which do not exceed the corresponding terms of the convergent series of positive constants,

$$b + \frac{M}{L} \sum_{n=1}^{\infty} \frac{L^n h^n}{n!} = b + \frac{M}{L}(e^{Lh} - 1).$$

The series (3) is therefore absolutely and uniformly convergent in the interval $x - a \leq h$ by the Weierstrass test,* and its partial sums

$$y_0 = b, y_1(x), y_2(x), \ldots$$

converge to a continuous function $y(x)$ in this interval.

From (P) and (L) we have also

$$y'_{n+1}(x) - y_n'(x) = f(x, y_n) - f(x, y_{n-1}),$$

$$|y'_{n+1} - y_n'| \leq L|y_n - y_{n-1}| \leq M\frac{L^n h^n}{n!}.$$

---

* Weierstrass' "M-test": The series of functions $\sum_{k=0}^{\infty} u_k(x)$ converges absolutely and uniformly in the interval $a \leq x \leq b$ if

$$|u_k(x)| \leq M_k \quad \text{in} \quad [a, b]$$

where $\sum_{k=0}^{\infty} M_k$ is a convergent series of positive constants. Cf. *Advanced Calculus*, § 179, § 180.

in view of (5); hence the series

(7) $$\sum_{n=1}^{\infty} [y_n'(x) - y_{n-1}'(x)],$$

obtained by differentiating series (6) term by term, is also absolutely and uniformly convergent and converges to the continuous function $y'(x)$.*
Now let $n \to \infty$ in the equation

$$y_n'(x) = f[x, y_{n-1}(x)]$$

obtained by differentiating (P); then

$$y_n'(x) \to y'(x), \qquad y_{n-1}(x) \to y(x), \qquad f(x, y_{n-1}) \to f(x, y)$$

since $f(x, y)$ is continuous, and we have

$$\frac{dy}{dx} = f(x, y).$$

Moreover $y_n(a) = b$ yields $y(a) = b$, so that $y(x)$ is a solution of the initial value problem (1) in the interval $0 \leq x - a \leq h$.

The change of variable

(8) $$a - t = x - a \quad \text{or} \quad t = 2a - x$$

converts (1) into the problem

(6) $$\frac{dy}{dt} = -f(2a - t, y), \qquad y(a) = b.$$

The foregoing argument proves that (6) has a solution in the interval $0 \leq t - a \leq h$; hence (1) has a solution in the interval $0 \leq a - x \leq h$ in which x lies to the left of a. The solution $y(x)$ is therefore valid in the interval $|x - a| \leq h$.

Another way of achieving this wider interval is to allow x to lie on either side of a in the integrals used in the proof. Then the preceding inequalities will still hold when $x - a$ is replaced by $|x - a|$.

Finally, we note that *any integrable function* $y_0(x)$ may be used to start the iteration. Such a function is bounded, and the proof is carried through as before by showing that the series $\sum_{n=2}^{\infty} [y_n(x) - y_{n-1}(x)]$ is uniformly convergent. Since the limit function $y(x)$ is independent of the choice of $y_n(x)$, we might suspect that $y(x)$ is the *only* solution of the problem. That this is indeed the case is shown in the next section.

---

* *Advanced Calculus*, § 182.

154. UNIQUENESS THEOREM

The existence theorem just proved states that the solution $y(x)$ obtained is unique. We give two proofs of this fact.

First Proof

Replace the initial value problem by the equivalent integral equation (§ 151):

$$(1) \qquad y(x) = b + \int_0^x f(t, y) \, dt.$$

If (1) has a second solution $\bar{y}(x)$, we have

$$y(x) - \bar{y}(x) = \int_0^x [f(t, y) - f(t, \bar{y})] \, dt,$$

$$(2) \qquad |y - \bar{y}| \leq \int_0^x |f(t, y) - f(t, \bar{y})| \, dt \leq L \int_0^x |y - \bar{y}| \, dt$$

after using (L). Since $y(x) - \bar{y}(x)$ is continuous and therefore bounded in the interval $|x - a| \leq h$, say $|y - \bar{y}| < N$, then

$$|y - \bar{y}| \leq LN \int_0^x dt = LN(x - a).$$

Using this value in (2) we find

$$|y - \bar{y}| \leq NL^2 \frac{(x - a)^2}{2}.$$

Putting *this* in (2) we find

$$|y - \bar{y}| \leq NL^3 \frac{(x - a)^3}{3!},$$

and by repetition of this process,

$$|y - \bar{y}| \leq NL^n \frac{(x - a)^n}{n!} \leq NL^n \frac{h^n}{n!}.$$

The last expression, however, is the general term of the *convergent* series for $N(e^{Lh} - 1)$ and therefore approaches zero as $n \to \infty$,* hence $\bar{y} = y$.

Second Proof

The basic idea is now quite different from that in the foregoing proof and will prove useful in subsequent theorems.

Consider the non-negative function

$$\varphi(x) = [y(x) - \bar{y}(x)]^2, \qquad \varphi(a) = 0.$$

---

* *Advanced Calculus*, p. 45.

Now
$$\varphi'(x) = 2(y - \bar{y})(y' - \bar{y}')$$
$$= 2(y - \bar{y})[f(x, y) - f(x, \bar{y})]$$
$$\leqq 2 |y - \bar{y}| |f(x, y) - f(x, \bar{y})|$$
$$\leqq 2L |y - \bar{y}|^2,$$

so that
$$\varphi'(x) - 2L\varphi(x) \leqq 0.$$

The positive multiplier e^{-2Lx} (§ 16) converts the left member into

$$\frac{d}{dx} [e^{-2Lx}\varphi(x)] \leqq 0,$$

so that $e^{-2Lx}\varphi(x)$ cannot increase as x increases. Therefore if $x > a$

$$e^{-2Lx}\varphi(x) \leqq e^{-2La}\varphi(a)$$

or since $\varphi(a) = 0$, $e^{-2Lx} > 0$,

$$\varphi(x) = (y - \bar{y})^2 \leqq 0.$$

But $(y - \bar{y})^2 \geqq 0$; hence $y - \bar{y} = 0$ when $0 \leqq x - a \leqq h$. The change of variable (152.8) shows that $y = \bar{y}$ also for negative values of $x - a$ such that $|x - a| \leqq h$.

The uniqueness theorem can be proved when (L) is replaced by the weaker condition of Nagumo

(N) $|x - a| |f(x, y) - f(x, \bar{y})| \leqq |y - \bar{y}|.$

For the proof see Kamke, ref. 30, § 54. Here it is also shown that a Lipschitz condition implies (N) in a suitable rectangle about (a, b).

The argument used in the second proof may also be used to prove the

Continuity Theorem. *Under the provisions of the existence theorem and for fixed a and x, the solution of the initial value problem in which $y(a) = b$ is a continuous function of b.*

PROOF. Write the solution $y(x, b)$ to show its dependence on b and define

$$\varphi(x) = [y(x, b) - y(x, \bar{b})]^2,$$

in which b and $\bar{b}$ are given arbitrary, but fixed, values and x is variable. Since $y(x, b)$ and $y(x, \bar{b})$ both satisfy $y' = f(x, y)$, we can show just as before that when $x > a$,

$$e^{-2Lx}\varphi(x) \leqq e^{-2La}\varphi(a),$$

or, on taking positive square roots,

$$|y(x, b) - y(x, \bar{b})| = e^{L(x-a)} |b - \bar{b}| \leqq e^{Lh} |b - \bar{b}|.$$

Thus if $\delta = \varepsilon e^{-Lh}$,

$$|y(x, b) - y(x, \overline{b})| < \varepsilon \qquad \text{when } |b - \overline{b}| < \delta.$$

Example 1. In the problem

$$y' = 3y^{2/3}, \qquad y(a) = 0,$$

$y^{2/3}$ is continuous in any region

$$\mathscr{R}: \qquad |x - a| \leqq A, \qquad |y - 0| \leqq B,$$

but cannot satisfy a Lipschitz condition

$$3(y^{2/3} - \bar{y}^{2/3}) \leqq L(y - \bar{y}) \qquad \text{in } \mathscr{R}.$$

For

$$\varphi(y, \bar{y}) = \frac{y^{2/3} - \bar{y}^{2/3}}{y - \bar{y}} \leqq \frac{L}{3}$$

contradicts the fact that $\varphi(y, \bar{y})$ is not bounded in any neighborhood of $y = 0$; for example, $\varphi(8\varepsilon^3, \varepsilon^3) = \frac{3}{7}\varepsilon^{-1}$.

The problem not only has the solutions

$$y = 0 \quad \text{and} \quad y = (x - a)^3$$

but an infinity of others; for if $c > a$, then

$$y = \begin{cases} 0, & x < c \\ (x - c)^3, & x \geqq c, \end{cases}$$

is also a solution. All of these solutions are of class $\mathscr{C}'$.

Example 2. $xy' - 2y = 2$.

All solutions of this linear equation (§ 16) have the form $y = Cx^2 - 1$. The curves of this one-parameter family are not the only integral curves, for these include all curves of the two-parameter family

$$y = c_1 x^2 - 1 \quad (x \leqq 0), \qquad y = c_2 x^2 - 1 \quad (x \geqq 0).$$

These curves are all tangent to the line $y = -1$ at the point $(0, -1)$; they consist of

(i) any two half-parabolas ($c_1, c_2 \neq 0$);
(ii) a half-parabola and half-line ($c_1 \neq 0, c_2 = 0$ or $c_1 = 0, c_2 \neq 0$);
(iii) the entire line $y = -1$ ($c_1 = c_2 = 0$).

In accordance with the theorem, through any point (a, b) of a region $\mathscr{R}$ in which $x \neq 0$ (and hence $2(y + 1)/x$ is continuous), there passes one and only one of the foregoing integral curves *which lies entirely in $\mathscr{R}$*, namely, a part of the parabola $a^2(y + 1) = (b + 1)x^2$ or line $y = -1$ (when $b = -1$).

The theorem fails to apply at a point $(0, b)$ where both $f(x, y)$ and f_y are singular. Indeed no integral curve passes through $(0, b)$ if $b \neq -1$, and an infinite number if $b = -1$.

PROBLEMS

1. Find all solutions of
$$y' = 2\sqrt{|y|}, \qquad y(a) = 0.$$

2. Show that xy satisfies a Lipschitz condition in any finite region
$$|x - a| \leq A, \qquad |y - b| \leq B.$$

Hence find the unique solution of
$$y' = xy, \qquad y(a) = b.$$

3. For the problem in the example show that
$$y(x) = \begin{cases} (x - a)^3, & x < a \\ 0, & a \leq x \leq c \\ (x - c)^3, & x > c \end{cases}$$

is a solution of class $\mathscr{C}'$.

155. COMPARISON THEOREM

Let $y(x)$ and $z(x)$ be solutions of the initial value problems with the same initial condition:
$$\begin{aligned} y' &= f(x, y) & y(a) &= b, \\ z' &= g(x, z) & z(a) &= b. \end{aligned}$$

If $f(x, y) \leq g(x, y)$ in a given region and f and g satisfy a Lipschitz condition, then for any $x_1 > a$ either

1° $y(x_1) < z(x_1)$, *or*

2° $y(x) \equiv z(x)$ for $a \leq x \leq x_1$.

PROOF. The initial value problems admit unique and continuous solutions $y(x)$, $z(x)$ such that $y(a) = z(a)$. If at some point $c > a$, $y(c) > z(c)$, let x_0 be the greatest x in the interval $[a, c]$ such that $y(x) \leq z(x)$; then $y(x_0) = z(x_0)$ and $y(x) > z(x)$ in the interval $x_0 < x \leq c$. Define $\varphi(x) = y(x) - z(x)$; then in $x_0 < x \leq c$ we have
$$\begin{aligned} \varphi'(x) &= f(x, y) - g(x, z) \\ &\leq g(x, y) - g(x, z) \\ &\leq |g(x, y) - g(x, z)|. \end{aligned}$$

Then if L is the Lipschitz constant for g, we have
$$\varphi'(x) \leq L|y - z| = L(y - z) = L\varphi(x)$$

or $$\varphi'(x) - L\varphi(x) \leqq 0.$$

The positive multiplier e^{-Lx} converts the left member into an exact derivative (§ 16):

$$e^{-Lx}(\varphi' - L\varphi) = \frac{d}{dx}[e^{-Lx}\varphi(x)] \leqq 0.$$

Hence $e^{-Lx}\varphi(x)$ cannot increase in the interval $x_0 < x \leqq c$, and

$$e^{-Lc}\varphi(c) \leqq e^{-Lx_0}\varphi(x_0) = 0.$$

Since $e^{-Lc} > 0$, $\varphi(c) = y(c) - z(c) \leqq 0$ which denies our assumption that $y(c) - z(c) > 0$. Hence at all points $x \geqq 0$, $y(x) \leqq z(x)$.

Now $y(a) = z(a)$; unless $y(x) \equiv z(x)$, there is some x_0 for which

$$y(x_0) < z(x_0) \qquad \text{or} \qquad \varphi(x_0) < 0.$$

As before we find that

$$\varphi'(x) \leqq |g(x, y) - g(x, z)| = L\,|y - z|,$$

but now $|y - z| = z - y$, so that

$$\varphi'(x) \leqq L(z - y) = -L\varphi(x)$$

or $$\varphi'(x) + L\varphi(x) \leqq 0.$$

We now use the multiplier e^{Lx} to obtain

$$e^{Lx}(\varphi' + L\varphi) = \frac{d}{dx}[e^{Lx}\varphi(x)] \leqq 0.$$

Hence $e^{Lx}\varphi(x)$ cannot increase and for any $x > x_0$,

$$e^{Lx}\varphi(x) \leqq e^{Lx_0}\varphi(x_0) < 0.$$

Thus $\varphi(x) < 0$ and

$$y(x) < z(x) \quad \text{for all} \quad x > x_0.$$

Consequently, if $y(x_1) = z(x_1)$ at any point x_1, $y(x) = z(x)$ over the entire interval $a \leqq x \leqq x_1$.

156. TWO EQUATIONS OF THE FIRST ORDER

Existence Theorem. *Let $f(x, y, z)$ and $g(x, y, z)$ be continuous in the closed region*

$$\mathscr{R}: \qquad |x - a| \leqq A, \qquad |y - b| \leqq B, \qquad |z - c| \leqq C,$$

and therefore bounded, say

$$|\varphi(x, y, z)| \leqq M, \qquad \varphi = f \quad \text{or} \quad g,$$

and also satisfy a Lipschitz condition

(L) $\qquad |\varphi(x, y, z) - \varphi(x, \bar{y}, \bar{z})| \leq L_1 |y - \bar{y}| + L_2 |z - \bar{z}|.$

Then the initial value problem

(1)
$$\begin{cases} \dfrac{dy}{dx} = f(x, y, z), & y(a) = b \\[2mm] \dfrac{dz}{dx} = g(x, y, z), & z(a) = c \end{cases}$$

has a unique solution, the limit functions $y(x)$, $z(x)$ *of the Picard approximations*

(P)
$$\begin{cases} y_n(x) = b + \displaystyle\int_a^x f(t, y_{n-1}, z_{n-1}) \, dt, \\[2mm] z_n(x) = c + \displaystyle\int_a^x g(t, y_{n-1}, z_{n-1}) \, dt, \end{cases} \qquad n = 1, 2, \dots.$$

This solution is of class $\mathscr{C}'$ and is valid in an interval at least as large as

$$|x - a| \leq h = \min\left(A, \frac{B}{M}, \frac{C}{M}\right).$$

PROOF. The argument is very similar to that given in § 153, and parallel results bear the same numbers. Although $y_0(x)$ and $z_0(x)$ may be any integrable functions, we shall take $y_0 = b$, $z_0 = c$. Then from (P) we find that

(2)
$$\left.\begin{aligned} |y_1 - b| &\leq \int_a^x |f(t, b, c)| \, dt \\ |z_1 - c| &\leq \int_a^x |g(t, b, c)| \, dt \end{aligned}\right\} \leq M(x - a),$$

where $a < x \leq A$; hence

$$|y_1 - b| \leq B \quad \text{if} \quad x - a \leq \frac{B}{M},$$

$$|z_1 - c| \leq C \quad \text{if} \quad x - a \leq \frac{C}{M}.$$

With this new restriction on x, namely $x - a \leq h$, we can show by induction that

(3)
$$\begin{aligned} |y_n - b| &\leq B \\ |z_n - c| &\leq C \end{aligned} \quad \text{if} \quad x - a \leq h.$$

From now on we restrict x to the interval $x - a \leq h$; then from (P)

and (L), valid because of (3),

(4)
$$\left.\begin{array}{l}|y_{n+1} - y_n| \\ |z_{n+1} - z_n|\end{array}\right\} \leqq L_1 \int_a^x |y_n - y_{n-1}|\, dt + L_2 \int_a^x |z_n - z_{n-1}|\, dt.$$

In particular, we have from (2)

$$\left.\begin{array}{l}|y_2 - y_1| \\ |z_2 - z_1|\end{array}\right\} \leqq L_1 \int_a^x |y_1 - b|\, dt + L_2 \int_a^x |z_1 - c|\, dt \leqq M(L_1 + L_2)(x - a).$$

Using these results in (4), we now find

$$\left.\begin{array}{l}|y_3 - y_2| \\ |z_3 - z_2|\end{array}\right\} \leqq M(L_1 + L_2)^2 \frac{(x - a)^2}{2!},$$

and, in general,

(5)
$$\left.\begin{array}{l}|y_{n+1} - y_n| \\ |z_{n+1} - z_n|\end{array}\right\} \leqq M(L_1 + L_2)^{n-1} \frac{h^n}{n!}.$$

Thus the terms of the telescopic series

(6)
$$y_0 + \sum_{n=1}^{\infty} [y_n(x) - y_{n-1}(x)], \qquad z_0 + \sum_{n=1}^{\infty} [z_n(x) - z_{n-1}(x)]$$

have absolute values which do not exceed the terms of a convergent series of positive constants. The partial sums of these series, $y_n(x)$ and $z_n(x)$, therefore converge absolutely and uniformly in the interval $x - a \leqq h$ to continuous functions $y(x)$ and $z(x)$.

As in § 153 we can now show that the series

(7)
$$\sum_{n=1}^{\infty} [y_n'(x) - y_{n-1}'(x)], \qquad \sum_{n=1}^{\infty} [z_n'(x) - z_{n-1}'(x)],$$

obtained by differentiating the series in (6) term by term, are also absolutely and uniformly convergent and converge to the continuous functions $y'(x)$, $z'(x)$.

On differentiating (P) we find the equations

$$y_n' = f(x, y_{n-1}, z_{n-1}), \qquad z_n' = g(x, y_{n-1}, z_{n-1}).$$

Now let $n \to \infty$; then in view of the continuity of the functions f and g, we have

$$y' = f(x, y, z), \qquad z' = g(x, y, z).$$

Moreover, $y_n(a) = b$, $z_n(a) = c$ yield $y(a) = b$, $z(a) = c$, so that $y(x)$ and $z(x)$ form a solution of the initial value problem (1).

The proof of the unicity of this solution may be given as follows:
(i) by a method analogous to the first proof of § 154; or
(ii) by the method of the second proof of § 154 if

$$\varphi(x) = |y(x) - \bar{y}(x)|^2\, |z(x) - \bar{z}(x)|^2.$$

We then find that
$$\varphi'(x) \leqq 2(L_1 + L_2)\varphi(x).$$

The Lipschitz condition will be fulfilled whenever $f(x, y, z)$ and $g(x, y, z)$ have continuous partial derivatives with respect to both y and z; for from the mean-value theorem* for functions of y and z, namely
$$\varphi(x, y, z) - \varphi(x, \bar{y}, \bar{z}) = (y - \bar{y})\varphi_y(x, \eta, \zeta) + (z - \bar{z})\varphi_z(x, \eta, \zeta)$$

where η lies between y and $\bar{y}$, and ζ lies between z and $\bar{z}$. Hence if $|\varphi_y| \leqq L_1$, $|\varphi_z| \leqq L_2$ in $\mathcal{R}$, the condition (L) is fulfilled.

PROBLEMS

Solve by the Picard process and compare with the exact solution:

1. $\dfrac{dy}{dx} = z, \quad \dfrac{dz}{dx} = y$: $y(0) = 1$, $z(0) = 0$.

2. $\dfrac{dy}{dx} - z = x, \quad \dfrac{dz}{dx} - y = x$:

(a) $y(0) = z(0) = -1$; (b) $y(0) = 1$, $z(0) = -1$.

3. If the initial conditions in Problem 2 are $y(a) = z(a) = b$, prove that $y(x) = z(x)$ without solving the system.

4. $\dfrac{dx}{dt} + y = 0, \quad \dfrac{dy}{dt} - x = 1$: $x(0) = y(0) = 0$.

5. $\dfrac{dx}{dt} + y = t, \quad \dfrac{dy}{dt} + x = 1$: $x(0) = 1$, $y(0) = -1$.

6. Give the unicity proof along the lines of the first proof of §153.
7. Supply the details of the second unicity proof.

157. LINEAR SYSTEMS

When the functions f and g in (156.1) are *linear* in y and z,
$$f(x, y, z) = p_1(x)y + q_1(x)z + r_1(x),$$
$$g(x, y, z) = p_2(x)y + q_2(x)z + r_2(x),$$

we can specify a precise interval in which the solution is valid. Let the coefficient functions p_i, q_i, r_i be continuous in the open interval $A < x < B$ and let I denote a slightly smaller closed interval
$$I: \qquad A + \varepsilon = x_1 \leqq x \leqq x_2 = B - \varepsilon.$$

---
* *Advanced Calculus*, § 90.

Then p_i, q_i, r_i are bounded in I: and if

$$|p_i(x)| \leqq L_1, \qquad |q_i(x)| \leqq L_2 \qquad (i = 1, 2),$$

both f and g satisfy the Lipschitz condition

(L) $\qquad |\varphi(x, y, z) - \varphi(x, \bar{y}, \bar{z})| \leqq L_1 |y - \bar{y}| + L_2 |z - \bar{z}|$

in the region

$$x \quad \text{in} \quad I: \ -\infty < y, z < \infty.$$

Return now to the proof in § 156 when f and g have the foregoing values. If a is any interior point of I, we may deduce the inequality (4) when $a < x \leqq x_2$ since (L) is valid for all y and z. We can then prove (5) with h replaced by $x_2 - a$.

When x lies to the left of a and $x_1 \leqq x < a$, (4) still holds if we integrate *from x to a.* In the following inequalities replace $x - a$ by $a - x$; then (5) holds with h replaced by $a - x_1$.

The convergence and unicity proofs are then the same as before and we obtain a solution valid over the entire closed interval I and indeed over the open interval $A < x < B$. This favorable result is due to the linearity of f and g and the consequent fact that (L) holds for all y and z, so that further restrictions on x are not necessary.

Theorem. *In the initial value problem*

$$\frac{dy}{dx} = p_1(x)y + q_1(x)z + r_1(x), \qquad y(a) = b,$$

$$\frac{dz}{dx} = p_2(x)y + q_2(x)z + r_2(x), \qquad z(a) = c,$$

let the coefficient functions be continuous in the open interval $A < x < B$ which contains point a. Then there is a unique solution $y(x)$, $z(x)$ which is valid over $A < x < B$, and this solution is of class $\mathscr{C}'$.

Note that the solution of a linear system can only have singular points at the *fixed* points where the coefficient functions are singular. Nonlinear systems have "*movable*" and usually unpredictable singularities. For example, the nonlinear system

$$y' = z, \qquad y(0) = b,$$
$$z' = 2y^3, \qquad z(0) = b^2,$$

has the solution

$$y = \frac{b}{1 - bx}, \qquad z = \frac{b^2}{(1 - bx)^2}$$

with a singularity at $x = 1/b$ which varies with the initial conditions.

PROBLEMS

1. Show that the linear system

$$y' = \frac{z}{4x^2}, \qquad z' = -y: \; y(1) = z(1) = 0$$

has unique solutions over the open intervals $-\infty < x < 0$, $0 < x < \infty$, and find them.

2. Verify the solution of the nonlinear system given in the text.

3. Solve by the Picard process up to y_3 and z_3:

$$y' = z, \qquad z' = 2y^3: \qquad y(0) = z(0) = 1.$$

Compare with the exact solution given in the book when $b = 1$.

4. Solve the equations in Problem 3 by the Picard process when $y(0) = z(0) = 0$.

158. EQUATION OF SECOND ORDER

The initial value problem of the second order

(1) $$y'' = f(x, y, y'), \qquad y(a) = b, \qquad y'(a) = c$$

is equivalent to the first order problem with two equations

(2) $$\begin{aligned} y' &= z & y(a) &= b, \\ z' &= f(x, y, z) & z(a) &= c. \end{aligned}$$

Since z obviously satisfies a Lipschitz condition (with $L = 1$), the theorem of § 156 yields the following

Existence Theorem. *Let $f(x, y, y')$ be continuous in the closed region*

$$\mathscr{R}: |x - a| \leq A, \qquad |y - b| \leq B, \qquad |y' - c| \leq C,$$

so that

$$|f(x, y, y')| \leq M \quad \text{in} \quad \mathscr{R},$$

and also satisfy a Lipschitz condition

$$|f(x, y, y') - f(x, \bar{y}, \bar{y}')| \leq L_1 |y - \bar{y}| + L_2 |y' - \bar{y}'|.$$

Then the initial value problem (1) *has a unique solution $y(x)$ of class $\mathscr{C}''$ which is valid in the interval*

$$|x - a| = h = \min\left(A, \frac{B}{M}, \frac{C}{M}\right).$$

If the partial derivatives $\partial f/\partial y$ and $\partial f/\partial y'$ are continuous in the closed region $\mathscr{R}$ they are bounded in $\mathscr{R}$:

$$|\partial f/\partial y| \leq L_1, \qquad |\partial f/\partial y'| \leq L_2.$$

From the mean-value theorem for functions of two variables we can conclude as in § 154 that the condition (L) is fulfilled with the foregoing constants.

The solution of the initial value problem (1) is

$$y(x) = \lim y_n(x)$$

where $y_n(x)$ is obtained by applying the Picard process to the system (2).

Example. $y'' + xy'^2 = 0$.
Here $f(x, y, y') = -xy'^2$ and $\partial f/\partial y = 0$, $\partial f/\partial y' = -2xy'$ are everywhere continuous in the 3-space of x, y, y'. Hence all initial value problems are uniquely soluble at least in the interval specified by the theorem. Thus the equation with the following initial conditions has the solution given:

(a) $y(0) = 1$, $y'(0) = 0$: $y = 1$;

(b) $y(0) = 0$, $y'(0) = 2$: $y = 2 \tan^{-1} x$;

(c) $y(0) = 0$, $y'(0) = -2$: $y = \log \dfrac{|1 - x|}{1 + x}$;

(d) $y(1) = 0$, $y'(1) = 2$; $y = 2 - \dfrac{2}{x}$.

PROBLEMS

Solve the following by the Picard process and compare with the exact solution:

1. $y'' = 2xy'$: $y(0) = 0$, $y'(0) = 1$.

2. $y'' = x + y$: $y(0) = 1$, $y'(0) = 0$.

3. $y'' = 1 - (y')^2$: $y(0) = y'(0) = 0$.

159. LINEAR EQUATION OF THE SECOND ORDER

We are now in position to prove the existence and uniqueness theorem stated in § 27, with the notation altered to conform with § 158.

Existence Theorem. *In the initial value problem*

$$y'' + P(x)y' + Q(x)y = R(x), \qquad y(a) = b, \qquad y'(a) = c,$$

in which b, c are any pair of real numbers, let the functions P(x), Q(x), R(x), be continuous in the open interval $A < x < B$ which contains the point a. Then there is a unique solution y(x) which is valid over $A < x < B$, and this solution is of class $\mathcal{C}''$.

PROOF. Problem (1) is equivalent to the linear system

$$y' = z, \qquad\qquad y(a) = b,$$
$$z' = -P(x)z - Q(x)y + R(x), \qquad z(a) = c.$$

From Theorem 156 this system has a unique solution $y(x)$, $z(x)$ of class $\mathscr{C}'$ valid over $A < x < B$. But since $y'' = z'$ and z' is continuous, $y(x)$ is of class $\mathscr{C}''$.

Our theorem applies to the Sturm-Liouville problem

(1)
$$D[p(x)y'] + [q(x) + \lambda\rho(x)]y = 0,$$
$$y(a) = b, \qquad y'(a) = c$$

where the functions p, p', q, ρ are continuous and $p(x)$, $\rho(x)$ positive in the closed interval $A \leq x \leq B$ and λ is a real parameter limited to a closed interval $\lambda_1 \leq \lambda \leq \lambda_2$. For $p(x) > 0$ ensures that

$$P(x) = \frac{p'}{p}, \qquad Q(x) = \frac{q + \lambda\rho}{p}$$

are continuous in $A < x < B$. It can *also* be shown that the functions $y_n(x, \lambda)$ in the Picard process converge uniformly for each λ to a unique solution $y(x, \lambda)$ or class $\mathscr{C}''$ in x and analytic in λ—that is, $y(x, \lambda)$ has continuous partial derivatives of *all* orders with respect to λ.

It is possible that the solution is valid over a larger interval than one in which $P(x)$, $Q(x)$, $R(x)$ are continuous. Consider, for example, the equation

$$y'' - \frac{y'}{x} + x^2 y = 0.$$

Here $P = 1/x$ is discontinuous at the origin, so that the interval specified by the theorem may be $0 < x < \infty$ or $-\infty < x < 0$. Nevertheless, all solutions of this equation are given by

$$y = C_1 \sin (\tfrac{1}{2}x^2 + C_2),$$

and have no singularities whatever. In either one of the foregoing intervals, an initial value problem will have a unique solution, but in an interval that contains the origin this is no longer the case. Thus the problem with

$$y(0) = 0, \qquad y'(x) = 0, \qquad -\infty < x < \infty,$$

has the 1-parameter family of solutions

$$y = C_1 \sin \tfrac{1}{2}x^2,$$

besides the null solution ($C_1 = 0$). But in the interval $0 < x < \infty$, the problem with

$$y(a) = 0, \qquad y'(a) = 0, \qquad 0 < a < \infty,$$

has the unique solution $y = 0$. Let the reader show that here C_1 must be zero.

PROBLEMS

1. Solve the problem

$$y'' - \frac{y'}{x} + \lambda^2 x^2 y = 0, \qquad y(0) = 0, \qquad y(\sqrt{\pi}) = 0.$$

2. Solve the problem

$$xy'' + y' + \frac{1}{x}y = 0, \qquad y(1) = 0, \qquad y'(1) = 1$$

on the intervals
(a) $0 < x < \infty$; (b) $-\infty < x < 0.$

160. PRÜFER EQUATIONS

To compare the solutions of two self-adjoint equations of the type

(1) $$D[p(x)y'] + q(x)y = 0, \qquad p(x) > 0,$$

we replace (1) by the first-order system

$$p(x)y' = z, \qquad z' = -q(x)y$$

and then introduce polar coordinates in the zy-plane:

(2) $$z = py' = r\cos\theta, \qquad y = r\sin\theta.$$

The new dependent variables, the *amplitude* $r(x)$ and *phase* $\theta(x)$, are determined by

(3) $$r^2 = z^2 + y^2 = (py')^2 + y^2, \qquad r > 0,$$

(4) $$\tan\theta = \frac{y}{z} = \frac{y}{py'}.$$

Evidently $r = 0$ is equivalent to $y = 0$, $y' = 0$ and yields the trivial solution $y \equiv 0$. This line of attack, due to the German mathematician Heinz Prüfer,* affords an elegant way of locating the zeros of a solution $y(x)$ and greatly simplifies the proof of the famous *oscillation theorem* which shows the character of the solutions of (1) when certain boundary conditions are imposed.

We now differentiate (3) and (4) with respect to x to obtain a pair of first-order equations equivalent to (1).

---

* *Mathematische Annalen*, Bd. 95 (1926).

From (3) we have

$$rr' = yy' + py'(py')'$$
$$= yy' + py'(-qy)$$
$$= yy'(1 - pq).$$

Equations (2) now give

$$pyy' = r^2 \sin \theta \cos \theta,$$

so that

(5)
$$\frac{r'}{r} = \left(\frac{1}{p} - q\right) \sin \theta \cos \theta, \qquad r > 0.$$

From (4) we have

$$\sec^2 \theta \, \theta' = \frac{y'}{py'} - \frac{y(py')'}{p^2 y'^2} \qquad (py' = z)$$

$$= \frac{1}{p} + \frac{qy^2}{p^2 y'^2} \qquad (z' = -qy)$$

$$= \frac{1}{p} + q \tan^2 \theta,$$

and hence

(6)
$$\theta' = \frac{1}{p} \cos^2 \theta + q \sin^2 \theta.$$

When $p(x) > 0$ and $p(x)$, $q(x)$ are continuous in $[a, b]$,

$$f(x, \theta) = \frac{1}{p} \cos^2 \theta + q \sin^2 \theta, \qquad \frac{\partial f}{\partial \theta} = \left(q - \frac{1}{p}\right) \sin 2\theta$$

are also continuous and $f(x, \theta)$ satisfies a Lipschitz condition whose constant L is an upper bound of $q - 1/p$. Thus (6) admits a unique solution $\theta(x)$ of class $\mathscr{C}'$ when an initial value $\theta(a) = \alpha$ is specified. When $\theta(x)$ is known, $r(x)$ may be found from (5) by a quadrature:

(7)
$$r(x) = K \exp \left\{ \int_a^x \left[\frac{1}{p(t)} - q(t)\right] \sin \theta(t) \cos \theta(t) \, dt \right\}.$$

Since

(8)
$$y(x) = r(x) \sin \theta(x),$$

a change in $K = r(a)$ merely multiplies $y(x)$ by a factor. Since $r(x) > 0$, the zeros of $y(x)$ are the points where $\sin \theta(x) = 0$, the roots of

(9)
$$\theta(x) = n\pi, \qquad n = 0, \pm 1, \pm 2, \ldots .$$

In a finite interval, a nontrivial solution can have but a finite number of zeros. If there were an infinite number they would have a cluster point ξ

and we could select from them a sequence $x_1, x_2, \ldots$ for which $x_n \to \xi$;[*] then

$$y(\xi) = \lim y(x_n) = 0,$$

$$y'(\xi) = \lim \frac{y(x_n) - y(\xi)}{x_n - \xi} = 0,$$

and the corresponding solution would be $y(x) \equiv 0$.

If $\theta(x)$ is a solution of (6), so is $\theta(x) + n\pi$ for integral n. It therefore suffices to consider solutions of (6) determined by

$$(10) \qquad\qquad \theta(a) = \alpha, \qquad 0 \le \alpha < \pi.$$

If x_0 is a zero of $\theta(x)$,

$$(11) \qquad\qquad \theta(x_0) = 0, \qquad \theta'(x_0) = \frac{1}{p(x_0)} > 0.$$

Thus if $\alpha > 0$, the curve $\theta = \theta(x)$ never crosses the x-axis because it would have to decrease at the point of crossing. If $\alpha = 0$, the curve crosses the x-axis at $x = a$ and never again. Consequently,

$$(12) \qquad\qquad \theta(x) > 0, \qquad a < x \le b.$$

The Prüfer equation (6) in the phase variable is now our source of information concerning solutions $y = r(x) \sin \theta(x)$ of (1). We shall consider the *regular* boundary value problem of § 117 with equation (1) and the conditions

$$(13) \qquad \begin{aligned} \cos \alpha \, y(a) - p(a) \sin \alpha \, y'(a) &= 0, \\ \cos \beta \, y(b) - p(b) \sin \beta \, y'(b) &= 0. \end{aligned}$$

These agree with (117.4) and (117.5) if we choose

$$p(a) \tan \alpha = -\frac{A'}{A}, \qquad 0 \le \alpha < \pi,$$

$$p(b) \tan \beta = -\frac{B'}{B}, \qquad 0 < \beta \ (\mathrm{mod}\ \pi).\dagger$$

If we now put

$$y = r \sin \theta, \qquad py' = r \cos \theta,$$

equations (13) reduce to

$$r(a) \sin [\theta(a) - \alpha] = 0,$$
$$r(b) \sin [\theta(b) - \beta] = 0.$$

---

[*] *Advanced Calculus*, p. 541.
$\dagger$ If $A = 0$, $\alpha = \frac{1}{2}\pi$; if $B = 0$, $\beta = \frac{1}{2}\pi$ (mod π).

or since $r(x) \neq 0$,

(14)
$$\theta(a) = \alpha, \qquad 0 \leq \alpha < \pi,$$
$$\theta(b) = \beta, \qquad 0 < \beta \pmod{\pi}.$$

In particular, the conditions
$$y(a) = 0, \qquad y(b) = 0$$
imply

(15)
$$\theta(a) = 0, \qquad \theta(b) = n\pi \qquad \text{integral } n.$$

When $q(x) < 0$ in $[a, b]$, this problem has no solution; for from (6) $\theta'(a) = \dfrac{1}{p(a)} > 0$, θ will increase but can never attain π, since at $\pi/2$, $\theta' = q(\pi/2) < 0$ and θ decreases.

We proceed to study cases where solutions do exist.

161. STURM'S SEPARATION THEOREM

Consider the two Prüfer equations

$$\theta_1' = \frac{1}{p_1} \cos^2 \theta + q_1 \sin^2 \theta = f(x, \theta), \qquad \theta_1(a) = \alpha,$$

$$\theta_2' = \frac{1}{p_2} \cos^2 \theta + q_2 \sin^2 \theta = g(x, \theta), \qquad \theta_2(a) = \alpha,$$

in the interval $a \leq x \leq b$ when

(1)
$$p_1(x) \geq p_2(x) > 0, \qquad q_2(x) \geq q_1(x);$$

and

(2)
$$[(p_1(x), q_1(x)] \neq [p_2(x), q_2(x)]$$

over any subinterval $a \leq x < c$ of $[a, b]$. The comparison theorem of § 155 then asserts that

(3)
$$\theta_2(x) > \theta_1(x), \qquad a < x \leq b.$$

Condition (2) serves to give the strict inequality (3). We can now prove the following

Separation Theorem. *If $y_1(x)$ and $y_2(x)$ are any nontrivial solutions of*

$$D[p_1(x)y_1'] + q_1(x)y_1 = 0,$$

$$D[p_2(x)y_2'] + q_2(x)y_2 = 0$$

under conditions (1) *and* (2), *then between any consecutive zeros of* $y_1(x)$ *there will be at least one zero of* $y_2(x)$.

PROOF. Let $y_1(x)$ have consecutive zeros at $x = \alpha$ and $x = \beta$; then

$$\theta_1(\alpha) = n\pi, \qquad \theta_1(\beta) = (n + 1)\pi$$

since $\theta(x)$ *increases* in passing through its zeros. We can now assume that $\theta_2(\alpha) - \theta_1(\alpha) < \pi$, for changing θ_2 by a multiple of π leaves $y_2(x)$ unchanged; hence

$$\theta_2(\alpha) < (n + 1)\pi,$$

and from (3), $\theta_2(\beta) > \theta_1(\beta)$, or

$$\theta_2(\beta) > (n + 1)\pi.$$

Since $\theta_2(x)$ is continuous, it must assume the value $(n + 1)\pi$ at some point ξ between α and β and $y_2(\xi) = 0$.

Corollary. *If* $y_1(x)$ *has exactly n zeros in any subinterval* $[a, k]$ *of* $[a, b]$, *then* $y_2(x)$ *will have at least n zeros in* $[a, k]$.

PROOF. Let $y_1(x)$ have the n zeros $x_1, x_2, \ldots, x_n$ in $[a, k]$; then $y_2(x)$ will have at least $n - 1$ zeros between them. Since $\theta_1(a) = \theta_2(a)$ and $\theta_2(x) > \theta_1(x)$ when $x > a$, $\theta_2(x)$ will assume the value π before $\theta_1(x)$; hence $y_2(x)$ will have a zero between a and x_1. Thus $y_2(x)$ has at least n zeros in $[a, k]$.

162. OSCILLATION THEOREM

Consider the differential equation

(1) $$D[p(x)y'] + [q(x) + \lambda r(x)]y = 0$$

with a real parameter λ; and let

$$p(x), r(x) > 0, \qquad p(x), q(x), r(x) \in \mathscr{C} \quad \text{in} \quad [a, b].$$

The corresponding Prüfer equation in θ is

(2) $$\theta' = \frac{1}{p} \cos^2 \theta + [q(x) + \lambda r(x)] \sin^2 \theta.$$

We consider solutions $\theta(x, \lambda)$ of (2) with the same initial condition

$$\theta(a, \lambda) = \alpha, \qquad 0 \leqq \alpha < \pi.$$

Then from (160.12),

$$\theta(x, \lambda) > 0, \qquad a \leqq x < b.$$

Lemma 1. $\lim\limits_{\lambda \downarrow -\infty} \theta(b, \lambda) = 0.$

PROOF. Suppose that $\theta(b, \lambda) \geq \beta > 0$ for a sequence $\lambda_n \downarrow -\infty$. Choose numbers α' and β so that

$$\alpha < \alpha' < \pi, \qquad 0 < \beta < \alpha'.$$

The slope of the line joining (a, α'), (b, β) is $(\beta - \alpha')/(b - a)$. By giving λ_0 a suitable negative value we can make

$$(3) \qquad \theta' = \frac{1}{p} \cos^2 \theta + (q + \lambda r) \sin^2 \theta < \frac{\beta - \alpha'}{b - a}$$

for all $\lambda \leq \lambda_0$ when the curve $y = \theta(x)$ lies in the strip

$$0 < \beta \leq \theta(x) \leq \alpha' < \pi, \qquad a \leq x \leq b.$$

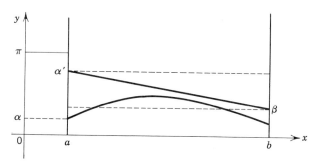

Fig. 162a

This is possible, for $\theta(x)$ is bounded away from 0 and π, $r(x) > 0$ and $1/p(x)$ is bounded in $[a, b]$. All curves

$$y = \theta(x, \lambda), \qquad \lambda \leq \lambda_0, \qquad a \leq x \leq b,$$

start under the line $\alpha'\beta$ (Fig. 162a) since $\theta(a, \lambda) = \alpha < \alpha'$. Moreover, the curves cannot cross the line at a point $x > a$, for at a crossing point their slope $\theta'(x)$ cannot be less than the slope of the line as required by (3). Hence the curves $y = \theta(x, \lambda)$ lie *under* the line $\alpha'\beta$ in the interval $[a, b]$. In particular, $\theta(b, \lambda) < \beta$ for all $\lambda \leq \lambda_0$ and since this holds for any $\beta > 0$ and $\theta(b, \lambda) > 0$, we conclude that $\lim \theta(b, \lambda) = 0$ as $\lambda \downarrow -\infty$.

Lemma 2. $\lim_{\lambda \uparrow +\infty} \theta(b, \lambda) = \infty$.

PROOF. From (2) we have

$$\theta' = \frac{1}{p} + \left(q - \frac{1}{p} + \lambda r \right) \sin^2 \theta.$$

Choose $\lambda_1 > 0$ so that

$$q(x) - \frac{1}{p(x)} + \lambda r(x) > 0 \qquad \text{when } \lambda \geq \lambda_1;$$

then

$$\theta'(x) \geqq \frac{1}{p(x)} \geqq \min \frac{1}{p(x)} = m.$$

Choose β so that the slope of the line joining (a, α), (b, β),

$$\frac{\beta - \alpha}{b - a} \geqq m,$$

and cut the line $\alpha\beta$ at points P_k by lines $y = k\pi$ $(k = 0, 1, 2, \ldots)$ parallel to the x-axis (Fig. 162b). We shall now construct a staircase joining (a, α) and (b, β) whose slope for any x is less than the corresponding slope θ' of the curve $y = \theta(x, \lambda)$ when λ is suitably large. First draw treads of slope $\frac{1}{2}m$ through each point P_k extending from $y = k\pi - \varepsilon$ to $y = k\pi + \varepsilon$. Join the ends of these treads by risers to form a staircase as shown, making suitable adjustments at (a, α) and (b, β). By choosing ε small enough, the slope of each riser will be less than some positive number;

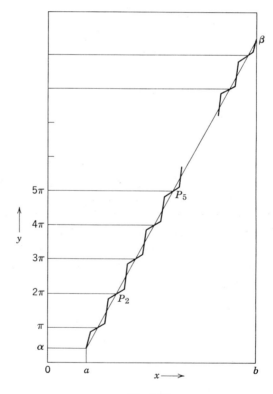

Fig. 162b

this is essential, for the following argument would not apply if the slope of the risers were infinite or negative.

Above each riser the slope of the curve

$$\theta' \geq \frac{1}{p} + \left(q - \frac{1}{p} + \lambda r \right) \sin^2 \varepsilon;$$

for as θ varies from $k\pi + \varepsilon$ to $(k+1)\pi - \varepsilon$, $\sin^2 \theta \geq \sin^2 \varepsilon$. By choosing λ large enough, say $\lambda \geq \lambda_2$, θ' will exceed the slope on each riser. Let $\lambda_0 = \max(\lambda_1, \lambda_2)$; then when $\lambda \geq \lambda_0$, the slope $\theta'(x)$ of the curve will exceed the slope $\frac{1}{2}m$ of the tread and also the slope of the riser for the same x. The proof given in Lemma 1 now shows that the curve $y = \theta(x, \lambda)$ lies *above* each staircase segment when $\lambda \geq \lambda_0$, and this applies no matter how high the point (b, β) is chosen. Hence $\lim \theta(b, \lambda) = +\infty$ as $\lambda \uparrow \infty$.

Return now to the problem of solving the Prüfer equation (2) with the boundary conditions (159.14):

(4) $\theta(a, \lambda) = \alpha, \qquad 0 \leq \alpha < \pi,$

(5) $\theta(b, \lambda) = \beta, \qquad 0 < \beta \qquad (\mod \pi).$

For every λ, the initial value problem (2)–(4) has a unique solution $\theta(x, \lambda)$. Since $r(x) > 0$, $q(x) + \lambda r(x)$ is an increasing function of λ. Sturm's comparison theorem (§ 160) shows that if $\lambda_2 > \lambda_1$,

$$\theta(x, \lambda_2) > \theta(x, \beta_1), \qquad a < x \leq b.$$

Moreover, it can be shown that $\theta(x, \lambda)$ increases *continuously* with λ. Thus as λ increases from $-\infty$ to $+\infty$, $\theta(b, \lambda)$ increases from 0 to ∞ and assumes every positive value just once. If $\beta < \pi$, $\theta(b, \lambda)$ assumes the values

$$\beta(\mod \pi) = \beta, \beta + \pi, \beta + 2\pi, \dots, \beta + n\pi, \dots$$

when $\lambda = \lambda_0 < \lambda_1 < \lambda_2 < \dots < \lambda_n < \dots,$

and for the entire sequence $\{\lambda_n\}$ the solutions $\theta(x, \lambda_n)$ fulfill the boundary condition (5).

Oscillation Theorem. *The regular Sturm-Liouville system*

$$D[p(x)y'] + [q(x) + \lambda r(x)]y = 0,$$
$$Ay(a) + A'y'(a) = 0, \qquad (A, A') \neq (0, 0),$$
$$By(b) + B'y'(b) = 0, \qquad (B, B') \neq (0, 0),$$

where $p(x), r(x) > 0$ and $p(x), q(x), r(x) \in \mathscr{C}$ in $[a, b]$,

has an infinite number of eigenvalues

$$\lambda_0 < \lambda_1 < \lambda_2 < \dots \uparrow \infty$$

for each of which the system has a solution $Cy(x, \lambda_n)$ determined except for a constant factor, and $y(x, \lambda_n)$ has exactly n simple zeros in $[a, b]$.

PROOF. The solution of the Sturm-Liouville system reduces to the solution of the boundary value problem formed by the Prüfer equation (2) and the boundary conditions (4), (5). Then $r(x)$ is found by a quadrature and

(6) $y(x, \lambda) = r(z) \sin \theta(x, \lambda).$

As shown earlier, the Prüfer problem has solutions for the sequence of *eigenvalues*
$$\lambda_0 < \lambda_1 < \lambda_2 < \cdots \uparrow \infty.$$

Each eigenvalue λ_n yields an *eigenfunction* $y_n(x) = y(x, \lambda_n)$ given by (6). Thus the Sturm-Liouville problem has a countable infinity of solutions $y_n(x)$ that correspond to a sequence of eigenvalues that increase to ∞ by virtue of Lemma 2. The eigenfunction $y_n(x)$ has zeros only when $\sin \theta_n(x) = 0$, that is, when

$$\theta_n(x) = \theta(x, \lambda_n) = \pi, 2\pi, 3\pi, \ldots, n\pi,$$

for these are the only multiples of π included in the range

$$\theta_n(a) = \alpha < \pi \quad \text{to} \quad \theta_n(b) = \beta + n\pi < (n + 1)\pi.$$

Moreover, $\theta_n(x)$ increases when $x = k\pi$ so that $\theta_n(x)$ assumes each value $k\pi$ just once. Thus $y_n(x)$ has exactly n simple zeros between a and b; in particular $y_0(x)$, which corresponds to the eigenvalue λ_0 for which $\theta(b, \lambda_0) = \beta < \pi$, has none.

Example. The Prüfer equations are excellent for disclosing the facts, but must not be regarded as affording a practical method of solving Sturm-Liouville systems. Thus
$$y'' + \lambda y = 0, \qquad y(0) = 0,$$
has the solution

$$y(x, \lambda) = \begin{cases} C \sin \sqrt{\lambda}\, x, & \lambda > 0, \\ Cx, & \lambda = 0, \\ C \sinh \sqrt{-\lambda}\, x, & \lambda < 0. \end{cases}$$

The corresponding Prüfer equation (2)
$$\theta' = \cos^2 \theta + \lambda \sin^2 \theta, \qquad \theta(0) = 0$$
has the unique solution given by $\tan \theta = y/y'$,

$$\theta(x, \lambda) = \begin{cases} \tan^{-1}\left(\dfrac{1}{\sqrt{\lambda}} \tan \sqrt{\lambda}\, x\right), & \lambda > 0, \\ \tan^{-1} x, & \lambda = 0, \\ \tan^{-1}\left(\dfrac{1}{\sqrt{-\lambda}} \tanh \sqrt{-\lambda}\, x\right), & \lambda < 0. \end{cases}$$

The multivalued function $\tan^{-1}$ must be chosen so that θ is a positive function which steadily increases with λ from
$$\theta(x, -\infty) = 0 \quad \text{to} \quad \theta(x, \infty) = \infty$$
for any fixed $x > 0$.

When the boundary condition $y(\pi) = 0$ is imposed, we obtain the eigenvalues $\lambda_n = n^2$ ($n = 1, 2, 3, \ldots$) and the eigenfunctions $y_n(x) = C \sin nx$ (Ex. 117.1).

CHAPTER 13

Interpolation and Numerical Quadrature

163. INTERPOLATION

For many practical purposes a function $f(x)$ over an interval can be replaced by a more tractable function $F(x)$ if $|f(x) - F(x)|$ is small enough over the interval. This process is called *interpolation*. When a function, such as $\log x$ or $\sin x$, is given for equally spaced values of x, intermediate values are usually computed by *linear interpolation*. Thus if $f(a)$ and $f(b)$ are given, linear interpolation gives the intermediate values

$$y = f(a) + \frac{f(b) - f(a)}{b - a}(x - a);$$

a line replaces the curve $y = f(x)$.

The interpolating function $F(x)$ is often taken as a polynomial

$$F(x) = a_0 x^n + a_1 x^{n-1} + \cdots + a_n.$$

The graph of $y = F(x)$ is a *straight line* when $n = 1$, a *parabola* with axis vertical when $n = 2$, and, in general, it is called a *parabola of degree n*. Interpolation of this type is called *parabolic* and is of great importance in practice. When

$$|f(x) - F(x)| < \varepsilon \quad \text{or} \quad |f'(x) - F'(x)| < \varepsilon$$

and ε is sufficiently small, we may use $F(x)$ instead of $f(x)$ in computing integrals or even derivatives when due caution is observed. The function

$$f(x) - F(x) = R(x)$$

is called the *error* function, and the upper bound of $|R(x)|$ indicates the accuracy of the interpolation process.

A formula for $f(x)$ is not needed for interpolation if the values of $f(t)$ are tabulated at equal or unequal intervals. Such "empirical functions" are of great importance as they represent the experimental data in many problems in physics and engineering. But if $f(x)$ is known only from tabular values, a general statement concerning the limits of error cannot be made because $f(x)$ may depart widely from $F(x)$ between its tabular values.

591

For example, $f(x) = x \sin 1/x$, has the value zero when

$$x = \frac{1}{10\pi}, \frac{1}{9\pi}, \ldots, \frac{1}{2\pi}, \frac{1}{\pi},$$

but $F(x) = 0$ does not represent $f(x)$ even roughly and gives no clue to its variation.

164. LAGRANGE'S INTERPOLATION FORMULA

A function $f(x)$ takes on the values $f(x_i) = y_i$ at the $n + 1$ points $x_0, x_1, \ldots, x_n$. There is just one polynomial $F(x)$ of degree $\leq n$ which takes on these values y_i at the points x_i. To find it, consider the polynomial

(1) $$P(x) = (x - x_0)(x - x_1) \cdots (x - x_n)$$

and form from it $n + 1$ polynomials $P_i(x)$ of degree n by omitting the factor $x - x_i$; thus

$$P_i(x) = (x - x_0) \cdots (x - x_{i-1}) * (x - x_{i+1}) \cdots (x - x_n),$$

the asterisk showing the factor omitted. Since

(2) $$\frac{P_i(x_j)}{P_i(x_i)} = \delta_{ij} = \begin{cases} 0, & j \neq i, \\ 1, & j = i, \end{cases} \qquad \text{(cf. § 116)}$$

the polynomial† of degree $\leq n$,

(3) $$F_n(x) = \frac{P_0(x)}{P_0(x_0)} y_0 + \frac{P_1(x)}{P_1(x_1)} y_1 + \cdots + \frac{P_n(x)}{P_n(x_n)} y_n$$

assumes the value y_i when $x = x_i$:

(4) $$F_n(x_i) = \frac{P_i(x_i)}{P_i(x_i)} y_i = y_i.$$

Moreover, $F_n(x)$ is the only polynomial of degree $\leq n$ having this property; for if $G(x)$ were another, the polynomial $F_n(x) - G(x)$ of degree $\leq n$ would have the $n + 1$ zeros $x_0, x_1, \ldots, x_n$, an impossibility unless $F_n(x) - G(x) \equiv 0$.

In general, $y = F_n(x)$ is a parabola of degree n. It passes through the $n + 1$ points

$$(x_0, y_0), (x_1, y_1), \ldots, (x_n, y_n)$$

---

† The degree may be $<n$ if the terms in x^n cancel.

of the curve $y = f(x)$. To estimate the error

$$R_n(x) = f(x) - F_n(x),$$

we first prove the

Lemma. *If $\varphi(x)$ has $n + 1$ zeros $x_0 < x_1 < \cdots < x_n$ and $\varphi(x)$ is of class $\mathscr{C}^n$ in the interval $[x_0, x_n]$, there is an interior point ξ such that*

$$\varphi^{(n)}(\xi) = 0, \qquad x_0 < \xi < x_n.$$

PROOF. By Rolle's theorem $\varphi'(x)$ vanishes at n points lying between the successive zeros of $\varphi(x)$. Hence $\varphi''(x)$ vanishes at $n - 1$ points lying between the successive zeros of $\varphi'(x)$. Continuing this argument we find that $\varphi^{(n)}(x)$ vanishes at a point ξ lying between two zeros of $\varphi^{(n-1)}(x)$.

An estimate of the error is now given by the

Theorem. *If $f(x)$ is of class $\mathscr{C}^{n+1}$.*

(5)
$$f(x) - F_n(x) = \frac{f^{(n+1)}(\xi)}{(n + 1)!} P(x),$$

where $P(x) = (x - x_0)(x - x_1) \cdots (x - x_n)$ and ξ lies between the greatest and least of x_0, x_n, x.

PROOF. Choose an $x \neq x_0, x_1, \ldots, x_n$ and construct the function

$$\varphi(t) = \begin{vmatrix} f(x) - F_n(x) & P(x) \\ f(t) - F_n(t) & P(t) \end{vmatrix}$$

where $P(x)$ is given by (1). Since $\varphi(t)$ has $n + 2$ zeros,

$$t = x, x_0, x, \ldots, x_n,$$

we have from the lemma

$$\varphi^{n+1}(\xi) = 0, \qquad \xi \text{ in } (x_0, x_n, x).$$

Now $F_n(t)$ is a polynomial of degree $\leqq n$, and $P(t)$ a monic polynomial of degree $n + 1$; hence

$$F_n^{(n+1)}(t) = 0, \qquad P^{(n+1)}(t) = (n + 1)!$$

and

$$\varphi^{(n+1)}(t) = \begin{vmatrix} f(x) - F_n(x) & P(x) \\ f^{(n+1)}(t) & (n + 1)! \end{vmatrix}.$$

When $t = \xi$, we obtain (5) for any $x \neq x_j$; and when $x = x_j$, (5) reduces to $0 = 0$.

Equation (3) is the Lagrange interpolation formula. The Lagrangian coefficients

$$(6) \qquad L_i(x) = \frac{P_i(x)}{P_i(x_i)}$$

depend only on the abscissas $x_0, x_1, \ldots, x_n$, and once computed can be used with any set of ordinates y_i.* To check them, apply (3) to the line $y = 1$; then

$$(7) \qquad 1 = \frac{P_0(x)}{P_0(x_0)} + \frac{P_1(x)}{P_1(x_1)} + \cdots + \frac{P_n(x)}{P_n(x_n)},$$

for (5) shows that the error function is zero.

Lagrange's formula shows that there is just one parabola $y = F_n(x)$ of degree n that can be drawn through the $n + 1$ points (x_i, y_i). The polynomial $F_n(x)$ is not necessarily a good approximation to $f(x)$ and may even fail to converge to $f(x)$ as $h \to 0$.

Example. To find a parabola which passes through the three points

$$(-h, y_0), \qquad (0, y_1), \qquad (h, y_2),$$

we form from

$$P(x) = (x + h)(x - 0)(x - h)$$

the Lagrange polynomial

$$F_2(x) = \frac{(x - 0)(x - h)}{(-h - 0)(-h - h)} y_0 + \frac{(x + h)(x - h)}{(0 + h)(0 - h)} y_1 + \frac{(x + h)(x - 0)}{(h + h)(h - 0)} y_2$$

or

$$(8) \quad F_2(x) = \frac{x^2 - hx}{2h^2} y_0 - \frac{x^2 - h^2}{h^2} y_1 + \frac{x^2 + hx}{2h^2} y_2.$$

Note that the sum of the coefficients is 1.

PROBLEMS

1. Show that the polynomial for which

$$y(x_1) = y_1, \quad y'(x_1) = y_1', \quad y(x_2) = y_2,$$

is

$$F(x) = \frac{x - x_2}{x_1 - x_2} \left[\left(1 - \frac{x - x_1}{x_1 - x_2} \right) y_1 + (x - x_1) y_1' \right] + \left(\frac{x - x_1}{x_2 - x_1} \right)^2 y_2.$$

2. Find the Lagrange coefficients when $x_0 = -2$, $x_1 = -1$, $x_2 = 0$, $x_3 = 1$, $x_4 = 2$ and check by using (6).

3. Find $F_2(x)$ for the function $(1 + x^2)^{-1}$ when $x_0 = -h$, $x_1 = 0$, $x_2 = h$. [cf. Example.]

---

* Cf. *Tables of Lagrangian Interpolation Coefficients*, National Bureau of Standards, Columbia University Press, New York, 1944.

4. Find the cubic polynomial $f(x)$ for which $f(0) = 1$, $f(1) = 2$, $f(2) = 7$, $f(3) = 19$.

5. If $f(x_i) = y_i$ $(i = 0, 1, \ldots, n)$, define the function of t

$$\begin{vmatrix} f(x) & x^{n+1} & x^n & \cdots & x & 1 \\ y_0 & x_0^{n+1} & x_0^n & \cdots & x_0 & 1 \\ \cdot & \cdot & \cdot & \cdots & \cdot & \cdot \\ y_n & x_n^{n+1} & x_n^n & \cdots & x_n & 1 \\ f(t) & t^{n+1} & t^n & \cdots & t & 1 \end{vmatrix} = \varphi(t).$$

Show that

$$\varphi^{(n+1)}(\xi) = 0, \qquad \xi \text{ in } (x_0, x_n, x),$$

solve this equation for $f(x)$, and obtain Lagrange's formula with remainder (Peano).

165. FACTORIAL POWERS

When $\Delta x = h$, instead of $\Delta x = 1$ as in Chapters 8 and 9, we define the integral factorial powers as

(1)
$$\begin{cases} x^{(n)} = x(x - h)(x - 2h) \cdots (x - nh + h) \\ x^{(0)} = 1 \\ x^{(-n)} = \dfrac{1}{(x + h)(x + 2h) \cdots (x + nh)}. \end{cases}$$

When $\Delta x = h$, we define the *forward difference operator* Δ by

(2) $$\Delta f(x) = f(x + h) - f(x).$$

If x and h are regarded as having the dimension 1, $x^{(n)}$ and $x^{(-n)}$ have the dimensions n and $-n$. Then since the operation Δ leaves dimensions unchanged*, our previous formula $\Delta x^{(n)} = nx^{(n-1)}$ (§ 78) now becomes

(3) $$\Delta x^{(n)} = hnx^{(n-1)}.$$

Repetitions of Δ give

$$\Delta^2 x^{(n)} = h^2 n(n - 1)x^{(n-2)}, \ldots ,$$

(4) $$\Delta^n x^{(n)} = h^n n!$$

(5) $$\Delta^m x^{(n)} = 0, \qquad m > n.$$

If we replace x by $-x$, we also have the formula

(6) $$(-1)^n(-x)^{(n)} = x(x + h)(x + 2h) \cdots (x + nh - h)$$

for products of n factors in which $h, 2h, \ldots$ are added.

---

* In contrast to the operator D which reduces dimensions by 1. The unit to which these dimensions apply is arbitrary; cf. § 20.

The formula (78.13) which expresses a polynomial in factorial powers now becomes

$$(7) \qquad f(x) = \sum_{j=0}^{n} \frac{\Delta^j f(0)}{j!\, h^j}\, x^{(j)}.$$

If $a_0 x^n$ is the term of highest degree in $f(x)$, we have from (4) and (5)

$$(8) \qquad \Delta^n f(x) = a_0 h^n n!,$$

$$(9) \qquad \Delta^m f(x) = 0, \qquad m > n.$$

The nth difference of a polynomial of degree n is constant and all higher differences are zero.

A consequence of (3) is that the *antidifference*

$$(10) \qquad \Delta^{-1} x^{(n)} = \frac{x^{(n+1)}}{h(n+1)} + \omega, \qquad n \neq -1.$$

where ω is any function of period h.

The foregoing formulas apply whenever $\Delta x = h$.

PROBLEMS

1. Prove directly that

$$(x + b)^{(n)} = hn(x + b)^{(n-1)}.$$

2. Express $f(x) = 2 + 3x + x^3$ in terms of factorial powers. When $h = 1$, check with the result given in § 78.

3. Prove that when $h = 1$,

$$\Delta^n \frac{1}{x} = \Delta^n (x - 1)^{(-1)} = \frac{(-1)^n\, n!}{x(x + 1)\cdots(x + n)}.$$

What is the corresponding formula for any value of h?

166. DIFFERENCE OPERATORS

The *forward* Δ, *backward* ∇, and *central* δ *difference operators* are defined by the equations

$$(\Delta) \qquad \Delta f(x) = f(x + h) - f(x),$$

$$(\nabla) \qquad \nabla f(x) = f(x) - f(x - h),$$

$$(\delta) \qquad \delta f(x) = f(x + \tfrac{1}{2}h) - f(x - \tfrac{1}{2}h).$$

In view of (Δ) we have

$$\nabla f(x) = \Delta f(x - h),$$
$$\delta f(x) = \Delta f(x - \tfrac{1}{2}h).$$

If r is a real number, the operator E^r is defined by

(E) $$E^r f(x) = f(x + rh).$$ (cf. § 89)

We then find that

$$E^r E^s = E^{r+s}, \qquad EE^{-1} = E^{-1}E = E^0 = 1,$$

so that the laws of exponents are valid.

All difference operators may be expressed in terms of E, for from the definitions above and (1), (2), we have

(1) $$\Delta = E - 1 = E\nabla,$$

(2) $$\nabla = 1 - E^{-1} = E^{-1}\Delta,$$

(3) $$\delta = E^{\frac{1}{2}} - E^{-\frac{1}{2}} = E^{-\frac{1}{2}}\Delta = E^{\frac{1}{2}}\nabla.$$

Some of these symbols may seem redundant, but all the operators are in current use and serve a definite purpose.

Iteration of these operators yields the equations

(4) $$\Delta^2 = E^2 - 2E + 1,$$

(5) $$\nabla^2 = 1 - 2E^{-1} + E^{-2},$$

(6) $$\delta^2 = E - 2 + E^{-1} = E^{-1}\Delta^2 = E\nabla^2.$$

Higher differences may be computed by use of the binomial theorem; for any positive integer n

(7) $$\Delta^n = (E - 1)^n = \sum_{j=0}^{n}(-1)^j \binom{n}{j} E^{n-j},$$

(8) $$\nabla^n = E^{-n}\Delta^n = \sum_{j=0}^{n}(-1)^j \binom{n}{j} E^{-j},$$

(9) $$\delta^n = E^{-n/2}\Delta^n = \sum_{j=0}^{n}(-1)^j \binom{n}{j} E^{n/2-j}.$$

All of the foregoing operators are linear and commute with each other. Note that Δ and ∇ are not inverse operators, but that

(10) $$\Delta\nabla = \nabla\Delta = \delta^2.$$

As usual, the inverse operators Δ^{-1} and ∇^{-1} are defined by

$$\Delta\Delta^{-1} = 1, \qquad \nabla\nabla^{-1} = 1.$$

Note, however, that $\Delta^{-1}\Delta \neq 1$, $\nabla^{-1}\nabla \neq 1$ owing to the addition of an arbitrary periodic; but, as stated above, $E^{-1}E = 1$.

From (1) and (2) we have the relations connecting Δ and ∇:

$$(11)(12) \qquad \nabla = \frac{\Delta}{1 + \Delta}, \qquad \Delta = \frac{\nabla}{1 - \nabla}.$$

Finally, we define the *central mean operator*

$$(13) \qquad \mu = \tfrac{1}{2}(E^{\frac{1}{2}} + E^{-\frac{1}{2}})$$

and note that

$$(14) \qquad \mu\delta = \tfrac{1}{2}(E - E^{-1}) = \tfrac{1}{2}(\Delta + \nabla).$$

Example. The central difference

$$\delta^6 y_3 = \sum_{j=0}^{6} (-1)^j \binom{6}{j} E^{3-j} y_3 \qquad \text{from (9),}$$

$$= y_6 - 6y_5 + 15y_4 - 20y_3 + 15y_2 - 6y_1 + y_0,$$

a result needed in deducing Weddle's rule for numerical integration.

PROBLEMS

Prove the following operational identities:

1. $\delta^2 = \Delta - \nabla$.

2. $\mu^2 = 1 + \tfrac{1}{4}\delta^2$.

3. $\delta^2 = \Delta^2 E^{-1} = \nabla^2 E$.

4. Construct a difference table for $f(x) = x^4$ and verify that

$$\delta^2 f(0) = 2, \qquad \delta^4 f(0) = 24.$$

167. DIFFERENCE FORMULAS

Let $f(x)$ be a function whose values

$$y_j = f(x_0 + jh)$$

are tabulated for equally spaced values of x ($\Delta x = h$). We can then form a staggered *difference table* (or *lozenge diagram*) as shown in Table 167a. This is a difference table for the function

$$f(x) = x^3 - 3x^2 + 2x + 2 = x^{(3)} + 2.$$

Table 167a

Differences ($h = 1$)

x	$f(x)$	1	2	3	4	
-4	-118					
		60				
-3	-58		-24			
		36		6		
-2	-22		-18		0	Path 2 $(2, 6, -12, 6, 0)$
		18		6		
-1	-4		-12		0	
		6		6		
0	2		-6		0	
		0		6		
1	2		0		0	
		0		6		
2	2		6		0	Path 1 $(2, 0, 0, 6, 0)$
		6		6		
3	8		12			
		18				
4	26					

Values of x increasing downward are in the x-column, corresponding values of y in the y-column. *The entries in the difference columns are found by subtracting the number above it in the preceding column from the number below.* Then starting at $f(x)$, its

> *forward* differences Δ^j lie on *downward* diagonals;
> *backward* differences ∇^j lie on *upward* diagonals;
> *central* differences δ^j lie on *horizontals*.

Thus

$$\Delta f(0) = 0, \qquad \Delta^2 f(0) = 0, \qquad \Delta^3 f(0) = 6;$$

$$\nabla f(0) = 6, \qquad \nabla^2 f(0) = -12, \qquad \nabla^3 f(0) = 6.$$

For any *tabulated* x only *even* central differences appear in the table; thus

$$\delta^2 f(0) = -6, \qquad \delta^4 f(0) = 0.$$

The other horizontals contain odd central differences for nontabulated halfway values of x. For this reason most formulas involving central differences usually involve those of even order.

Evidently, if n values of $f(x)$ are tabulated, such a table will contain $n - 1$ differences of order 1, $n - 2$ of order 2, and so on, ending with a single difference of order $n - 1$. In Table 167a differences of order 4 to 8 are all zero.

We shall now compute $f(x_0 \pm nh)$ in terms of forward or backward differences for a given x_0 and a positive integer n.

Newton's Forward Difference Formula*

From (166.1) we have $E = 1 + \Delta$; hence

$$f(x_0 + nh) = E^n f(x_0) = (1 + \Delta)^n f(x_0).$$

On expanding $(1 + \Delta)^n$ by the binomial theorem,

$$N_1 \qquad f(x_0 + nh) = f(x_0) + \sum_{j=0}^{n} \binom{n}{j} \Delta^j f(x)$$

where the binomial coefficient

$$(1) \qquad \binom{n}{j} = \frac{n(n-1)\cdots(n-j+1)}{n!}.$$

The series ends after $n + 1$ terms. To use this formula, a difference table with entries for $x_0, x_0 + h, \ldots, x_0 + nh$ is needed. Thus N_1 is used to interpolate between tabulated values or to extrapolate $f(x)$ beyond x_n.

Newton's Backward Difference Formula

From (166.2) we have $E = (1 - \nabla)^{-1}$; hence

$$f(x_0 + nh) = E^n f(x_0) = (1 - \nabla)^{-n} f(x_0).$$

On expanding $(1 - \nabla)^{-n}$ we have

$$N_2 \qquad f(x_0 + nh) = f(x_0) + \sum_{j=1}^{\infty} (-1)^j \binom{-n}{j} \nabla^j f(x_0),$$

an infinite series in which

$$(2) \qquad (-1)^j \binom{-n}{j} = \frac{n(n+1)\cdots(n+j-1)}{j!}.$$

If $f(x)$ is a polynomial of degree n, the series will end after $n + 1$ terms since $\nabla^j f(x) = 0$ when $j > n$. To use N_2 a difference table with entries for $x_0, x_0 - h, \ldots, x_0 - nh$ is needed for the backward differences. Thus N_2 is ideal for extrapolation beyond x_0.

---

* Actually discovered by James Gregory (1638–1675), a Scotch mathematician, in 1670.

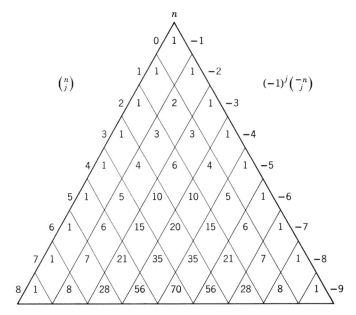

Table 167b   Fermat's Triangle

The binomial coefficients (1) and (2) that occur in N_1 and N_2 may be read off from Fermat's triangle which is constructed from $\binom{0}{n} = 1$ by using the relation

$$\binom{n+1}{j} = \binom{n}{j-1} + \binom{n}{j}, \qquad j = 1, 2, 3, \ldots,$$

to get any row from the row above. The numbers

(1) $\qquad\qquad\qquad \binom{n}{j}$ lie in *rows* to the right of n,

(2) $\qquad\qquad (-1)^j \binom{-n}{j}$ lie in *diagonals* below $-n$.

Note the symmetry and sum relations:

(3) $$\binom{n}{j} = \frac{n!}{j!\,(n-j)!} = \binom{n}{n-j},$$

(4) $$\binom{n}{0} + \binom{n}{1} + \cdots + \binom{n}{n} = 2^n.$$

Formulas N_1 and N_2 apply when advancing to larger values of x. In going backward to smaller values of x,

$$f(x_0 - nh) = E^{-n}f(0) = (1 - \nabla)^n f(x_0),$$

so that we have the finite series

$$N_3 \qquad f(x_0 - nh) = f(x_0) + \sum_{j=1}^{n} (-1)^j \binom{n}{j} \nabla^j f(x_0).$$

Finally, we state without proof *Everett's formula*,* which uses even central differences:

$$E \quad f(x_0 + nh) = \left[n + \binom{n+1}{3} \delta^2 + \binom{n+2}{5} \delta^4 + \cdots \right] f(x_0 + h)$$

$$+ \left[1 - n + \binom{2-n}{3} \delta^2 + \binom{3-n}{5} \delta^4 + \cdots \right] f(x_0).$$

Example 1. We use Table 167a to compute $f(5)$ from N_1 and N_2; then $f(-5)$ from N_3.

Path 1. Use N_1 with $x_0 = 0$, $n = 5$: since

$$\binom{5}{j} = 1, 5, 10, 10, 5, 1 \qquad \text{(Table 167b)};$$

$$f(5) = 1(2) + 5(0) + 10(0) + 10(6) = 62.$$

Path 2. Use N_2 with $x_0 = 0$, $n = 5$; since

$$(-1)^j \binom{-5}{j} = 1, 5, 15, 35, \ldots \qquad \text{(Table 167b)};$$

$$f(5) = 1(2) + 5(6) + 15(-12) + 35(6) = 62.$$

Path 3. Use N_3 with $x_0 = 0$, $n = 5$; since

$$(-1)^j \binom{5}{j} = 1, -5, 10, -10, 5, -1;$$

$$f(-5) = 1(2) - 5(6) + 10(-12) - 10(6) = -208.$$

All these results are exact since $f(x) = x^{(3)} + 2$ is a polynomial.

---

* Whittaker and Robinson, *A Short Course in Interpolation*, Van Nostrand, 1924, § 25.

Example 2. From the following difference table for log x, find log 3.5.

Table 167c

x	$\log x$	1	2	3	4
3.0	0.09861				
		0.06454			
3.2	0.16315		-0.00391		
		0.06063		0.00043	
3.4	0.22378		-0.00348		-0.00003
		0.05715		0.00040	
3.6	0.28093		-0.00308		
		0.05407			
3.8	0.33500				

We use N_3 with $x_0 = 3.8$, $n = \frac{3}{2}$; then

$$\log 3.5 = \left[1 - \binom{\frac{3}{2}}{1}\nabla + \binom{\frac{3}{2}}{2}\nabla^2 - \binom{\frac{3}{2}}{3}\nabla^3 + \binom{\frac{3}{2}}{4}\nabla^4\right]\log 3.8.$$

Since the binomial coefficients are

$$\tfrac{3}{2}, \quad \tfrac{1}{2}(\tfrac{3}{2})(\tfrac{1}{2}) = \tfrac{3}{8}, \quad \tfrac{1}{3}(\tfrac{3}{8})(-\tfrac{1}{2}) = -\tfrac{1}{16}, \quad \tfrac{1}{4}(-\tfrac{1}{16})(-\tfrac{3}{2}) = \tfrac{3}{128};$$

$$\log 3.5 = 0.33500 - \tfrac{3}{2}(0.05407) - \tfrac{3}{8}(0.00308) + \tfrac{1}{16}(0.00040)$$

$$= 0.33500 - 0.08111 - 0.00116 + 0.00003$$

$$= 0.33503 - 0.08227 = 0.25276$$

which is correct to five places.

Example 3. Table 167d is a difference table for e^x with $h = 0.2$.

Table 167d

x	e^x	Δ	Δ^2	Δ^3	Δ^4	Δ^5
0	1.000					
		0.2214				
.2	1.2214		0.0490			
		0.2704		0.0109		
.4	1.4918		0.0599		0.0023	
		0.3303		0.0132		0.0008
.6	1.8221		0.0731		0.0031	
		0.4034		0.0163		
.8	2.2255		0.0894			
		0.4928				
1.0	2.7183					

First we extrapolate for $e^{1.2}$ with N_1 and the forward differences of e^0. With $n = 6$,

$$\binom{6}{j} = 1, 6, 15, 20, 15, 6, 1 \qquad \text{(Table 167b)};$$

$$e^{1.2} = 1 + 6(1.2214) + 15(0.0490) + 20(0.0109) + 15(0.0023) + 6(0.0008)$$

$$= 1 + 1.3284 + 0.7350 + 0.2180 + 0.0345 + 0.0048$$

$$= 3.3207.$$

We next extrapolate for $e^{1.2}$ with N_2 and the backward differences of e^1. Since $n = -1$, all coefficients are 1 (Table 167b);

$$e^{1.2} = 2.7183 + 0.4928 + 0.0894 + 0.0163 + 0.0031 + 0.0008$$

$$= 3.3207.$$

Lastly, we use Everett's formula with $x_0 = 0.4$, $x = 1.2 = 0.4 + 4h$, and the central differences for $e^{0.4}$ and $e^{0.6}$:

$$e^{1.2} = \left[4 + \binom{5}{3}\delta^2 + \binom{6}{5}\delta^4 \right] e^{0.6} + \left[-3 + \binom{-2}{3}\delta^2 + \binom{-1}{3}\delta^4 \right] e^{0.4}$$

$$= 4(1.8221) + 10(0.0731) + 6(0.0031) - 3(1.4918) - 4(0.0599) - 0.0023$$

$$= 3.3207.$$

All results agree but the correct value is $e^{1.2} = 3.3201$.

PROBLEMS

1. Explain why the coefficients (2) may be obtained from the Fermat triangle.

2. Form a 6-decimal difference table for $f(x) = \sqrt{x}$ from $x = 1$ to $x = 1.25$ with $h = 0.05$.
(a) With $x_0 = 1$, use N_1 to find $\sqrt{1.125}$;
(b) With $x_0 = 1.25$, use N_3 to find $\sqrt{1.125}$.

3. From the table :

x	$\operatorname{erf} x = \dfrac{2}{\sqrt{\pi}} \displaystyle\int_0^x e^{-t^2}\, dt$
0.0	0.00000
0.1	0.11246
0.2	0.22270
0.3	0.32863
0.4	0.42839
0.5	0.52050

compute $\operatorname{erf} 0.25$ and $\operatorname{erf} 0.55$.

4. In Example 3, compute $e^{0.5}$ (a) using N_1; (b) using N_3.

168. NEWTON'S FORWARD INTERPOLATION FORMULA

In Newton's forward formula N_1, n is an integer. If we regard x as varying continuously forward from x_0, then

$$x = x_0 + sh, \qquad s \geq 0.$$

If we replace n by s in N_1, we obtain the interpolating polynomial

N_f
$$F_n(x) = f_0 + \sum_{j=1}^{n} \binom{s}{j} \Delta^j f_0,$$

or since

$$\binom{s}{j} = \frac{s(s-1) \cdots (s-j+1)}{j!} = \frac{(x-x_0)^{(j)}}{j! \, h^j},$$

N_f
$$F_n(x) = f_0 + \sum_{j=1}^{n} \frac{(x-x_0)^{(j)}}{j! \, h^j} \Delta^j f_0.$$

The forward differences $\Delta^j f_0$ lie on the *downward diagonal* from $f_0 = f(x_0)$ in the difference table based on the $n + 1$ values $f_0, f_1, \ldots, f_n$

at the equally spaced $x_0, x_1, \ldots, x_n$.

When $x = x_k$ $(s = k)$,

$$F_n(x_k) = f_0 + \sum_{j=1}^{k} \binom{k}{j} \Delta^j f_0$$

$$= (1 + \Delta)^k f_0 = E^k f_0 = f_k;$$

thus the polynomial $F_n(x)$ assumes the $n + 1$ values

$$f_0, f_1, \ldots, f_n \quad \text{at } x = x_0, x_1, \ldots, x_n.$$

It is Newton's solution of the problem whose Lagrangian solution was given in § 164; and since there is only *one* solution, the Lagrange and Newton polynomials differ only in form. The former is a sum of $n + 1$ polynomials of degree n, the latter a sum of $n + 1$ polynomials of degrees $0, 1, \ldots, n$.

For values of $x \neq x_k$, $f(x)$ is given by $F_n(x)$ plus the Lagrange remainder (164.5):

(1) $$f(x) = F_n(x) + \frac{f^{(n+1)}(\xi)}{(n+1)!}(x - x_0)(x - x_1) \cdots (x - x_n),$$

where ξ lies between the greatest and least of x_0, x_n, x. When $x = x_0 + sh$, the remainder takes the form

(2) $$R_n = \frac{h^{n+1}}{(n+1)!} f^{(n+1)}(\xi) s(s-1) \cdots (s-n);$$

and if

$$\max |f^{(n+1)}(x)| = M, \qquad \max |s^{(n)}| = N,$$

we have

(3) $$|R_n| \leqq \frac{h^{n+1}}{(n+1)!} MN.$$

In using tables, linear or parabolic interpolation is commonly applied.

Linear Interpolation between x_0 and x_1.

Let $x = x_0 + \theta h$ $(0 < \theta < 1)$; then $s = \theta$ and from $F_1(x)$ and (1),

(4) $$f(x) = f_0 + \theta \, \Delta f_0 + R_1.$$

Since $\max |s^2 - s| = \frac{1}{4}$ $(0 < s < 1)$,

(5) $$R_1 \leqq \frac{h^2}{8} \max |f''(x)|, \qquad x_0 < x < x_1.$$

Parabolic Interpolation between x_0 and x_2.

If x lies between x_0 and x_1, let $x = x_0 + \theta h$ $(0 < \theta < 1)$; then $s = \theta$ and from $F_2(x)$ and (1),

(6) $$f(x) = f_0 + \theta \, \Delta f_0 - \tfrac{1}{2}\theta(1 - \theta) \, \Delta^2 f_0 + R_2.$$

Since $\max |s(s-1)(s-2)| = \frac{2}{9}\sqrt{3}$ $(0 < s < 2)$,

(7) $$|R_2| \leqq \frac{h^3}{9\sqrt{3}} |\max f'''(x)|.$$

If x lies between x_1 and x_2, then

$$x = x_1 + \theta h, \qquad x = x_0 + (1 + \theta)h, \qquad s = 1 + \theta,$$

and from (1),

$$f(x) = f_0 + (1 + \theta) \, \Delta f_0 + \tfrac{1}{2}(1 + \theta)\theta \, \Delta^2 f_0 + R_2,$$

or since

$$\tfrac{1}{2}\theta\,\Delta^2 f_0 = \tfrac{1}{2}\theta(f_2 - 2f_1 + f_0),$$

$$F_2(x) = (f_0 + \Delta f_0) + \theta(f_1 - f_0 + \tfrac{1}{2}f_2 - f_1 + \tfrac{1}{2}f_0) + \tfrac{1}{2}\theta^2\Delta^2 f_0,$$

(8) $$f(x) = f_1 + \tfrac{1}{2}\theta(f_2 - f_0) + \tfrac{1}{2}\theta^2\,\Delta^2 f_0 + R_2.$$

Example 1. To illustrate parabolic interpolation, consider the values of the Bessel function $J_0(x)$:

x	J_0	ΔJ_0	$\Delta^2 J_0$
1.00	0.7652		
		−0.0941	
1.20	0.6711		−0.0101
		−0.1042	
1.40	0.5669		

To find $J_0(1.10)$, use (6) with $h = 0.2$, $\theta = \tfrac{1}{2}$:

$$J_0(1.10) = 0.7652 - \tfrac{1}{2}(0.0941) + \tfrac{1}{8}(0.0101) = 0.7195.$$

To find $J_0(1.30)$, use (8) with $h = 0.2$, $\theta = \tfrac{1}{2}$:

$$J_0(1.30) = 0.6711 - \tfrac{1}{4}(0.1983) - \tfrac{1}{8}(0.0101) = 0.6200.$$

Both results are correct to 0.0001. Since $|J_0'''(x)| < 1$ (132.13), (7) shows that the error is less than $\dfrac{0.008}{9}\,3 = 0.0005$.

Example 2. In Example 164 we found the parabola $y = F_2(x)$ through the points

$$(-h, y_0), \ (0, y_1), \ (h, y_2)$$

by the Lagrange formula. We shall now find $F_2(x)$ by Newton's formula N_f. Since $x - x_0 = x + h$, we have

$$F_2(x) = y_0 + \frac{x+h}{h}\,\Delta y_0 + \frac{(x+h)^{(2)}}{2!\,h^2}\,\Delta^2 y_0$$

$$= y_0 + \frac{x+h}{h}\,(y_1 - y_0) + \frac{(x+h)x}{2h^2}\,(y_2 - 2y_1 + y_0).$$

This agrees with our former result.

PROBLEMS

1. Given $J_1(1.0) = 0.4401, J_1(1.2) = 0.4983, J_1(1.4) = 0.5419$, compute $J_1(1.1)$ and $J_1(1.3)$ by parabolic interpolation.

2. What is the interpolating polynomial for $f(x) = x^2 + \sin \pi x$ through $(0, 0)$, $(1, 1)$, $(2, 4)$? What is the error when $x = \tfrac{1}{2}$?

3. Show that the parabola through (x_0, y_0), (x_1, y_1), (x_2, y_2) has the equation

$$\begin{vmatrix} y & 1 & x & x^2 \\ y_0 & 1 & x_0 & x_0{}^2 \\ y_1 & 1 & x_1 & x_1{}^2 \\ y_2 & 1 & x_2 & x_2{}^2 \end{vmatrix} = 0.$$

4. Show that the parabola through (x_1, y_1), (x_2, y_2) and whose slope at x_1 is $y'(x_1) = y_1'$ has the equation

$$\begin{vmatrix} y & 1 & x & x^2 \\ y_1 & 1 & x_1 & x_1{}^2 \\ y_2 & 1 & x_2 & x_2{}^2 \\ y_1' & 0 & 1 & 2x_1 \end{vmatrix} = 0.$$

5. Show that the parabola for which $y(0) = y_0$, $y'(0) = y_0'$, $y''(0) = y_0''$, has the equation

$$\begin{vmatrix} y & 1 & x & x^2 \\ y_0 & 1 & 0 & 0 \\ y_0' & 0 & 1 & 0 \\ y_0'' & 0 & 0 & 1 \end{vmatrix} = 0.$$

6. When $n = 3$, show that

$$|P_3(x)| = |(x^2 - \tfrac{1}{2}h^2)(x^2 - \tfrac{9}{2}h^2)| \leq \tfrac{9}{16}h^4.$$

$$|R_3(x)| \leq \frac{3h^4}{128} \max |f^{iv}(x)|.$$

7. Use N_f to express $f(x) = x^3 + 3x + 2$ in factorial powers. [Take $x_0 = 1$, $h = 1$.]

8. Find the largest value of h (radians) that will ensure 5-place accuracy in a table of $\sin x$.

169. NEWTON'S BACKWARD INTERPOLATION FORMULA

If a difference table is based on the $n + 1$ values $f_0, f_{-1}, f_{-2}, \ldots, f_{-n}$, we can use Newton's backward formula

$$N_2 \qquad f(x_0 + nh) = f_0 + \sum_{j=0}^{\infty} (-1)^j \binom{-n}{j} \nabla^j f_0$$

to obtain an interpolating polynomial that assumes these values at x_0, $x_{-1}, \ldots, x_{-n}$ by writing

$$x = x_0 + sh,$$

replacing n by s and stopping the summation at $j = n$:

N_b
$$B_n(x) = f_0 + \sum_{j=0}^{n}(-1)^j \binom{-s}{j}\nabla^j f_0$$

or since

$$(-1)^j \binom{-s}{j} = (-1)^j \frac{(x_0 - x)^{(j)}}{j!\,h^j}$$
$$= \frac{(x - x_0)(x - x_0 + h)\cdots[x - x_0 + (n-1)h]}{j!\,h^j},$$

N_b
$$B_n(x) = f_0 + \sum_{j=1}^{n}(-1)^j \frac{(x_0 - x)^{(j)}}{j!\,h^j}\nabla^j f_0.$$

The backward differences $\nabla^j f_0$ lie on the upward diagonal from f_0 in the difference table based on the $n + 1$ values $f_{-n}, \ldots, f_{-1}, f_0$ at the equally spaced values $x_{-n}, \ldots, x_{-1}, x_0$:

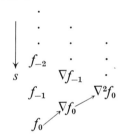

When $x = x_{-k}$ $(s = -k)$,

$$B_n(x_{-k}) = f_0 + \sum_{j=0}^{k}(-1)^j \binom{k}{j}\nabla^j f_0 \qquad \left[\binom{k}{j} = 0, j > k\right]$$
$$= (1 - \nabla)^k f_0 = E^{-k}f_0 = f_{-k};$$

thus the polynomial $B_n(x)$ assumes the $n + 1$ values

$$f_0, f_{-1}, \ldots, f_{-n} \quad \text{at} \quad x_0, x_{-1}, \ldots, x_{-n}.$$

Hence $B_n(x)$ is the same as the corresponding Lagrange polynomial. When x is not one of these points, $f(x)$ is given by $B_n(x)$ plus the Lagrange remainder (164.5):

(1) $$f(x) = B_n(x) + \frac{f^{(n+1)}(\xi)}{(n + 1)!}(x - x_0)(x - x_{-1})\cdots(x - x_{-n})$$

where ξ lies between the greatest and least of x_{-n}, x_0, x. If we put $x = x_0 + sh$,

$$x - x_{-k} = sh - (-kh) = h(s + k)$$

and the remainder takes the form

$$(2) \qquad R_n = \frac{h^{n+1}}{(n+1)!} f^{(n+1)}(\xi) s(s+1) \cdots (s+n).$$

Newton's backward formula N_f is used to *extrapolate* values $f_1, f_2, \ldots$ beyond those in the difference table. It is especially useful in advancing the solution of a differential equation to higher values of x.

Example 1. From the following table for natural logarithms we shall extrapolate for log 4.0 using N_b.

x	$\log x$	∇^1	∇^2	∇^3	∇^4
3	1.09861				
		0.06454			
3.2	1.16315		−0.00391		
		0.06063		0.00043	
3.4	1.22378		−0.00348		−0.00003
		0.05715		0.00040	
3.6	1.28093		−0.00308		
		0.05407			
$x_0 = 3.8$	1.33500				

Since the coefficients $(-1)^j \binom{-1}{j} = 1$,

$$\log 4 = \log x_1 = \log x_0 + \sum_{j=0}^{4} \nabla^j \log x_0$$

$$= 1.33500 + 0.05407 - 0.00308 + 0.00040 - 0.00003$$

$$= 1.38947 - 0.00311 = 1.38636.$$

The correct value is 1.38629.

170. NEWTON-COTES QUADRATURE

The fundamental theorem of the calculus

$$\int_a^b f(x)\, dx = D^{-1} f(x) \Big|_a^b$$

gives the definite integral of $f(x)$ when an antiderivative $D^{-1}f(x)$ is known. But in many cases, even for comparatively simple functions such as $\sqrt{1 + x^3}$, $1/\log x$, $\sin x^2$, e^{-x^2}, the antiderivative cannot be expressed by means of a *finite* number of elementary functions. We may then replace $f(x)$ by an interpolating polynomial $F_n(x)$ which may be integrated exactly and thus obtain an approximation to the required integral.

In geometrical terms we replace the curve $y = f(x)$ by the parabola of degree n, $y = F_n(x)$, through $n + 1$ points of the curve

$$(x_0, y_0), (x_1, y_1), \ldots, (x_n, y_n).$$

In § 164 we found

$$F_n(x) = L_0(x)y_0 + L_1(x)y_1 + \cdots + L_n(x)y_n.$$

The Lagrangian coefficients

$$L_i(x) = \frac{P_i(x)}{P_i(x_i)}, \qquad P_i(x) = (x - x_0) \cdots (*_i) \cdots (x - x_n)$$

where $(* i)$ means that the factor $x - x_i$ is lacking. The $L_i(x)$ depend only on the abscissas $x_0 < x_1 < \cdots < x_n$ relative to any origin. When they are known for a given set x_i, we may compute $\int_a^b f(x)\, dx$ approximately by replacing $f(x)$ by $F_n(x)$:

$$\int_a^b f(x)\, dx \simeq \sum_{i=0}^n y_i \int_a^b L_i(x) dx, \qquad y_i = f(x_i).$$

When $n + 1$ points x_i are equidistant,

$$\Delta x_i = h, \qquad b - a = nh,$$

we make the change of variable

$$x = a + ht, \qquad dx = h\, dt = \frac{b - a}{n}\, dt, \qquad x_i = a + hi;$$

then

(1)
$$\int_a^b L_i(x)\, dx = (b - a)C_{ni}$$

where C_{ni} is the *Cotes number*† defined by

(2)
$$C_{ni} = \frac{1}{n} \int_0^n \frac{(t - 0)(t - 1) \cdots (*i) \cdots (t - n)}{(i - 0)(i - 1) \cdots (*) \cdots (i - n)}\, dt.$$

Thus if $y = f(x)$, we have the general formula for equidistant spacing h,

(3)
$$\int_a^b f(x)\, dx \simeq (b - a) \sum_{i=0}^n C_{ni}y_i, \qquad n = \frac{b - a}{h}.$$

When $f(x) = 1$, (3) gives

(4)
$$\sum_{i=0}^n C_{ni} = 1;$$

---

† Roger Cotes, *Harmonia Mensarum*, 1722.

and the substitution $t = n - \tau$ in (2) shows that

(5) $$C_{n,n-i} = C_{ni}.$$

For $n = 1$, we have

$$C_{10} = \int_0^1 \frac{t-1}{0-1}\, dt = \frac{1}{2}, \qquad C_{11} = \frac{1}{2}.$$

For $n = 2$,

$$C_{20} = \frac{1}{2} \int_0^2 \frac{(t-1)(t-2)}{(0-1)(0-2)}\, dt = \frac{1}{6}, \qquad C_{22} = \frac{1}{6}, \qquad C_{21} = \frac{4}{6}.$$

For $n = 3$,

$$C_{30} = \frac{1}{3} \int_0^3 \frac{(t-1)(t-2)(t-3)}{(0-1)(0-2)(0-3)}\, dt = \frac{1}{8}, \qquad C_{33} = \frac{1}{8};$$

hence $C_{31} = C_{32} = \frac{3}{8}$ from (4).

Table 170a gives Cotes numbers C_{ni} for $n = 1$ to $n = 6$. Cotes numbers are not always positive; some are negative for $n = 8$ and $n = 10$.

Table 170a Cotes Numbers: $n + 1$ Points

n \\ i	0	1	2	3	4	5	6	Denom-inator	$b - a$	Error
1	1	1						2	h	$-\dfrac{h^3}{12} f''(\xi)$
2	1	4	1					6	$2h$	$-\dfrac{h^5}{90} f^{iv}(\xi)$
3	1	3	3	1				8	$3h$	$-\dfrac{3h^5}{80} f^{iv}(\xi)$
4	7	32	12	32	7			90	$4h$	$-\dfrac{8h^7}{945} f^{vi}(\xi)$
5	19	75	50	50	75	19		288	$5h$	$-\dfrac{275h^7}{12096} f^{vi}(\xi)$
6	41	216	27	272	27	216	41	840	$6h$	$-\dfrac{9h^9}{1400} f^{viii}(\xi)$

If n is even, the error in (3) for both n and $n + 1$ is of order h^{n+3}; thus formulas for even n are simpler and nearly as accurate as those for $n + 1$.

The case $n = 1$, $b - a = h$ yields the *Trapezoid Rule:*

(6) $$\int_0^h f(x)\, dx = \frac{1}{2} h[f(0) + f(h)] - \frac{h^3}{12} f''(\xi), \qquad 0 < \xi < h.$$

To find the error, given

$$E(h) = \int_0^h f(x)\, dx - \tfrac{1}{2} h[f(0) + f(h)],$$

we assume that $f(x) \in \mathscr{C}''$; then

$$E'(h) = \tfrac{1}{2}[f(h) - f(0)] - \tfrac{1}{2} h f'(h)$$
$$E''(h) = -\tfrac{1}{2} h f''(h).$$

Since $E(0) = E'(0) = 0$, the function

$$\varphi(t) = \begin{vmatrix} E(h) & h^3 \\ E(t) & t^3 \end{vmatrix}$$

has the properties $\varphi(0) = \varphi'(0) = 0$ and $\varphi(h) = 0$. Now Rolle's theorem*
gives successively

$$\varphi'(\xi_1) = 0, \qquad \varphi''(\xi) = 0, \qquad 0 < \xi < \xi_1 < h;$$

and

$$\varphi''(\xi) = \begin{vmatrix} E(h) & h^3 \\ -\tfrac{1}{2}\xi f''(\xi) & 6\xi \end{vmatrix} = 0$$

yields the value of $E(h)$ in (6).

The case $n = 2$, $b - a = 2h$ yields the important *Simpson's Rule:*

(7) $$\int_{-h}^h f(x)\, dx = \frac{h}{3}[f(-h) + 4f(0) + f(h)] - \frac{h^5}{90} f^{\text{iv}}(\xi),$$

in which the error

$$E(h) = \int_{-h}^h f(x)\, dx - \frac{h}{3}[f(-h) + 4f(0) + f(h)].$$

---

* *Advanced Calculus*, § 55.

To verify the error term in (7) we assume that $f(x) \in \mathscr{C}^4$ in $[-h, h]$; then since

$$\frac{d}{dh} \int_{-h}^{h} f(x) \, dx = f(h) - f(-h)(-1) = f(h) + f(-h),$$

$$E'(h) = \frac{2}{3} [f(h) + f(-h) - 2f(0)] - \frac{h}{3} [f'(h) - f'(-h)],$$

$$E''(h) = \frac{1}{3} [f'(h) - f'(-h)] - \frac{h}{3} [f''(h) + f''(-h)],$$

$$E'''(h) = -\frac{h}{3} [f'''(h) - f'''(-h)].$$

Since $E(0) = E'(0) = E''(0) = E'''(0) = 0$, the function

$$\varphi(t) = \begin{vmatrix} E(h) & h^5 \\ E(t) & t^5 \end{vmatrix}$$

has the properties $\varphi(0) = \varphi'(0) = \varphi''(0) = \varphi'''(0) = 0$ and $\varphi(h) = 0$. Now Rolle's theorem gives, successively,

$$\varphi'(\xi_1) = 0, \qquad \varphi''(\xi_2) = 0, \qquad \varphi'''(\xi) = 0, \qquad 0 < \xi_3 < \xi_2 < \xi_1 < h,$$

and from

$$\varphi'''(\xi_3) = \begin{vmatrix} E(h) & h^5 \\ -\dfrac{\xi_3}{3} [f'''(\xi_3) - f'''(-\xi_3)] & 60\xi_3^2 \end{vmatrix} = 0$$

we have

$$E(h) = -\frac{h^5}{90} \frac{f'''(\xi_3) - f'''(-\xi_3)}{2\xi_3} = -\frac{h^5}{90} f^{iv}(\xi), \qquad -\xi_3 < \xi < \xi_3,$$

on applying the mean-value theorem.* As to ξ we only know that it lies within the interval of integration: $-h < \xi < h$. If $f^{iv}(x)$ does not change sign in this interval, the *sign* of the error is known; and if $|f^{iv}(x)| \leq M$, the error cannot exceed $Mh^5/90$ in absolute value.

When $f(x)$ is a polynomial of degree <4, $f^{iv}(x) = 0$; hence Simpson's rule is *exact* when $f(x)$ is a cubic polynomial.

In general, the accuracy is improved by taking the ordinates close together. Thus in computing $\int_a^b f(x) \, dx$ we may divide $b - a$ into an even number $2n$ of equal subintervals h, apply Simpson's rule to n sub-intervals of length $2h$ and add the results. If the ordinates are written y_0,

---

* *Advanced Calculus*, § 57.

$y_1, \ldots, y_{2n}$, we obtain in this way *Simpson's composite rule:*

(8)
$$\int_a^b f(x)\, dx = \frac{h}{3}\, [y_0 + y_{2n} + 2(y_2 + y_4 + \cdots + 2y_{2n-2})$$

$$+ 4(y_1 + y_3 + \cdots + y_{2n-1})] - \frac{nh^5}{90} f^{iv}(\xi)$$

where $h = (b - a)/2n$ and $a < \xi < b$.

The continuity of $f^{iv}(x)$ requires that

$$\frac{1}{n}\, [f^{iv}(\xi_1) + \cdots + f^{iv}(\xi_n)] = f(\xi), \qquad a < \xi < b.$$

If we divide $b - a$ into n equal subintervals of length h, we can compute $\int_a^b f(x)\, dx$ by applying the trapezoid rule in each subinterval and adding the results. This gives the *composite trapezoid rule:*

(9)
$$\int_a^b f(x)\, dx = h[\tfrac{1}{2}y_0 + y_1 + \cdots + y_{n-1} + \tfrac{1}{2}y_n] - \frac{nh^2}{12} f'''(\xi),$$

where $h = (b - a)/n$ and $a < \xi < b$.

The Newton-Cotes quadrature for $n = 6$, namely (see Table 170a)

(10)
$$\int_{x_0}^{x_6} f(x)\, dx \simeq \frac{6h}{840}\, [41y_0 + 216y_1 + 27y_2$$

$$+ 272y_3 + 27y_4 + 216y_5 + 41y_6],$$

is very accurate but its coefficients are not simple. To remedy this we add to the right member the small quantity (Ex. 166)

$$\frac{6h}{840}\, \delta^6 y_3 = \frac{6h}{840}\, [y_0 - 6y_1 + 15y_2 - 20y_3 + 15y_4 - 6y_5 + y_6]$$

and obtain

$$\int_{x_0}^{x_6} f(x)\, dx \simeq \frac{6h}{840}\, [42y_0 + 210y_1 + 42y_2 + 252y_3 + 42y_4 + 210y_5 + 42y_6].$$

When the fractions are reduced, this becomes *Weddle's rule:*

(11)
$$\int_{x_0}^{x_6} f(x)\, dx \simeq \frac{6h}{20}\, [y_0 + 5y_1 + y_2 + 6y_3 + y_4 + 5y_5 + y_6].$$

It has the advantage of simple coefficients but is less accurate than (9) and has a complex error term.

The error in any Newton-Cotes quadrature may be derived from the error (164.5) in Lagrangian interpolation

$$R_n(x) = \frac{f^{(n+1)}(\xi)}{(n+1)!}(x - x_0)(x - x_1) \cdots (x - x_n), \quad x_0 < \xi < x_n.$$

The quadrature error is therefore

$$E_n = \frac{1}{(n+1)!} \int_{x_0}^{x_n} f^{(n+1)}(\xi)(x - x_0)(x - x_1) \cdots (x - x_n) \, dx$$

or on putting $x = x_0 + th$, $x_j = x_0 + jh$,

$$(12) \quad E_n = \frac{h^{n+2}}{(n+1)!} \int_0^n f^{(n+1)}(\tau) t(t - 1) \cdots (t - n) \, dt, \qquad 0 < \tau < n.$$

We cannot use the second mean-value theorem* to shift some value of $f^{(n+1)}(\tau)$ outside the integral sign. Nevertheless it can be shown† that this is permissible when n is odd:

$$(13) \quad E_{n(\text{odd})} = \frac{h^{n+2} f^{(n+1)}(\xi)}{(n+1)!} \int_0^n t(t - 1) \cdots (t - n) \, dt, \qquad x_0 < \xi < x_n.$$

But when n is even, the formula becomes

$$(14) \quad E_{n(\text{even})} = \frac{h^{n+3} f^{(n+2)}(\xi)}{(n+2)!} \int_0^n (t - \tfrac{1}{2}n)t(t - 1) \cdots (t - n) \, dt$$

$$x_0 < \xi < x_n.$$

Thus for $n = 1$ and $n = 2$

$$E_1 = \frac{h^3 f''(\xi)}{2!} \int_0^1 t(t - 1) \, dt = -\frac{h^3}{12} f''(\xi);$$

$$E_2 = \frac{h^5 f^{\text{iv}}(\xi)}{4!} \int_0^2 t(t - 1)^2(t - 2) \, dt, \qquad t = u + 1$$

$$= \frac{h^5 f^{\text{iv}}(\xi)}{24} 2 \int_0^1 (u^2 - 1)u^2 \, du = -\frac{h^5}{90} f^{\text{iv}}(\xi).$$

Example. Compute $\int_0^{2.4} J_0(x) \, dx$ by Simpson's composite rule.

---

* *Advanced Calculus*, p. 266, (121.2).
† Cf. Kopal, ref. 11, p. 400 ff.

Table 170b

x	0	0.4	0.8	1.2	1.6	2.0	2.4
$J_0(x)$	1	0.9604	0.8463	0.6711	0.4554	0.2239	0.0025
coef.	1	4	2	4	2	4	1

$$\int_0^{2.4} J_0(x)\, dx = \frac{0.4}{3}\,[1.0025 + 4(1.8554) + 2(1.3017)]$$

$$= \frac{4}{30}\,11.0275 = 1.4703.$$

Since $|J_0^{iv}(x)| < 1$, this result may be too large by an amount $\leqq 3(0.4)^5/90 = 0.0003$. It is correct, however, to the fourth place.

PROBLEMS

1. Compute the Cotes numbers for $n = 4$.

2. A cubic parabola passes through the points $(1, 2)$, $(3, 5)$, $(5, 11)$; find the area under the curve from $x = 1$ to $x = 5$.

3. Compute $\operatorname{erf}(0.1) = \dfrac{2}{\sqrt{\pi}} \displaystyle\int_0^{.1} e^{-x^2}\, dx$ using (8) with $h = 0.01$. [Obtain values of e^{-x^2} from a Table, e.g., ref. 4.]

4. Use (8) and (9) to compute

$$\log 2 = \int_1^2 \frac{dx}{x} \qquad \text{with } h = 0.1$$

and compare actual and estimated errors.

5. Use (8) and (9) to compute

$$\frac{\pi}{2} = \int_0^1 \frac{dx}{1 + x^2} \qquad \text{with } h = 0.1$$

and compare actual and estimated errors.

6. Use Simpson's rule to compute

$$\int_1^{2.4} J_1(x)\, dx \qquad \text{with } h = 0.4$$

and check with (127.12).

7. Deduce the $\frac{3}{8}$-rule with error term E_3:

(15) $$\int_0^{3h} f(x)\, dx = \frac{3}{8}\, h(y_0 + 3y_1 + 3y_2 + y_3) - \frac{3}{80}\, hf^{5(iv)}(\xi).$$

8. Show that the error in quadrature (10) is

$$E_6 = -\frac{9h^9}{1400} f^{\text{vii}}(\xi).$$

9. In the error formula (14) when n is even ($n = 2m$), show that the integral becomes

$$2 \int_0^m u^2(u^2 - 1^2)(u^2 - 2^2) \cdots (u^2 - m^2) \, du$$

after putting $t = u + m$.

171. OPEN-END QUADRATURE

Approximate quadrature formulas which lack the terminal values of the function integrated are called *open end*. Such formulas play an important part in predicting values in the numerical integration of differential equations.

We begin with the very simple formula

$$\int_{-h}^h f(x) \, dx = 2hf(0) + E(h),$$

in which the approximating curve is a horizontal line $y = f(0)$ through the central point $[0, f(0)]$. The error in this crude approximation is

$$E(h) = \int_{-h}^h f(x) \, dx - 2hf(0), \qquad E(0) = 0$$

and

$$E'(h) = f(h) + f(-h) - 2f(0), \qquad E'(0) = 0,$$
$$E''(h) = f'(h) - f'(-h), \qquad E''(0) = 0.$$

We now form the function

$$\varphi(t) = \begin{vmatrix} E(h) & h^3 \\ E(t) & t^3 \end{vmatrix},$$

for which $\varphi(0) = \varphi'(0) = 0$ and $\varphi(h) = 0$. Hence from Rolle's theorem,

$$\varphi'(\xi_1) = 0, \qquad \varphi''(\xi_2) = 0, \qquad 0 < \xi_2 < \xi_1 < h.$$

Since

$$\varphi''(t) = \begin{vmatrix} E(h) & h^3 \\ f'(t) - f'(-t) & 6t \end{vmatrix},$$

$\varphi''(\xi_2) = 0$ gives

$$E(h) = \frac{h^3}{3} \frac{f'(\xi_2) - f'(-\xi_2)}{2\xi_2} = \frac{h^3}{3} f''(\xi), \qquad -h < \xi < h.$$

We thus have the open-end formula

(1)
$$\int_{-h}^{h} f(x)\,dx = 2hf(0) + \frac{h^3}{3} f''(\xi).$$

Contrast this formula with the trapezoid rule (170.6)

(2)
$$\int_{0}^{h} f(x)\,dx = \tfrac{1}{2}h[f(0) + f(h)] - \frac{h^3}{12} f''(\xi),$$

which contains both terminal values. If $f''(x)$ does not change sign, the errors in (1) and (2) have opposite signs and the closed formula is about four times as accurate.

We next derive an open-end formula for $\int_{-2h}^{2h} f(x)\,dx$ by using the interpolating polynomial through $(-h, y_1)$, $(0, y_2)$, (h, y_3):

$$F(x) = \frac{1}{2h^2} [(x^2 - hx)y_1 - 2(x^2 - h^2)y_2 + (x^2 + hx)y_3].$$

We may integrate this between $-2h$ and $2h$ by dropping the terms in x (which add nothing to the integral) and doubling the integral from 0 to $2h$:

$$\frac{1}{h^2} \int_{0}^{2h} [(y_1 - 2y_2 + y_3)x^2 + 2h^2 y_2]\,dx = \frac{4h}{3}(2y_1 - y_2 + 2y_3).$$

This gives the open-end formula

(3)
$$\int_{-2h}^{2h} f(x)\,dx = \frac{4}{3} h[2f(-h) - f(0) + 2f(h)] + \frac{14}{45} h^5 f^{iv}(\xi).$$

The errors in open-end quadratures may be computed from formulas (12) and (13) of the preceding article provided the limits are taken as -1 and $n + 1$. Thus the error in (3) is

$$E_2 = \frac{h^5 f^{iv}(\xi)}{4!} \int_{-1}^{3} t(t - 1)^2(t - 2)\,dt,$$

or, when we put $t = u + 1$,

$$E_2 = \frac{h^5 f^{iv}(\xi)}{4!} 2\int_{0}^{2} (u^2 - 1)u^2\,du = \frac{14h^5}{45} f^{iv}(\xi).$$

Open-end quadratures are used as *predictors*, closed-end quadratures as *correctors* in the numerical solution of differential equations. Hamming's method (§ 179) uses (1) and (2), Milne's method (§ 180) uses (3) and Simpson's rule (170.7).

PROBLEMS

Deduce the open-end quadratures:

1. $\displaystyle\int_0^{3h} f(x)\,dx = \frac{3h}{2}(y_1 + y_2) + \frac{3h^3}{4}f''(\xi).$

Take the origin at $3h/2$ and use the interpolating polynomial through $(-h/2, y_1)$, $(h/2, y_2)$.

2. $\displaystyle\int_0^{5h} f(x)\,dx = \frac{5h}{24}(11y_1 + y_2 + y_3 + 11y_4) + \frac{95h^3}{4}f^{(\mathrm{iv})}(\xi).$

Take the origin at $5h/2$ and use the interpolating polynomial through $(-3h/2, y_1)$ and $(3h/2, y_2)$.

172. CENTRAL DIFFERENCE QUADRATURE

To obtain quadrature formulas in terms of central differences, we use the symbolic method. Since $E = e^{hD}$,

(1) $\qquad \delta = E^{\frac{1}{2}} - E^{\frac{1}{2}} = e^{hD/2} - e^{-hD/2} = 2\sinh\dfrac{hD}{2}.$

From this we find

$$hD = 2\sinh^{-1}\frac{\delta}{2} = \delta - \frac{1}{24}\delta^3 + \frac{3}{640}\delta^5 - \frac{5}{7168}\delta^7 + \cdots\ ;$$

and on inverting this series

(2) $\qquad \dfrac{1}{hD} = \delta^{-1}\left[1 + \dfrac{1}{24}\delta^2 - \dfrac{17}{5760}\delta^4 + \dfrac{367}{967680}\delta^6 - \cdots\right].$

Now

$$\frac{1}{h}\int_{a-h/2}^{a+h/2} f(x)\,dx = \delta\left[\frac{1}{h}\,D^{-1}f(a)\right]$$

and hence

(3) $\qquad \dfrac{1}{h}\displaystyle\int_{a-h/2}^{a+h/2} f(x)\,dx = \left[1 + \dfrac{1}{24}\delta^2 - \dfrac{17}{5760}\delta^4 + \cdots\right]f(a).$

Note also that the central mean operator

(4) $\qquad \mu = \frac{1}{2}(E^{\frac{1}{2}} + E^{-\frac{1}{2}}) = \cosh\dfrac{hD}{2} = \sqrt{1 + \delta^2/4} \qquad (166.13).$

Central differences of even order are found from a staggered difference table. Referring to Table 167a for $f(x) = x^3 - 3x^2 + 2x + 2$, the entries under

$$\Delta^1 y \text{ are differences } \delta \text{ for } x = -\tfrac{7}{2} \text{ to } \tfrac{7}{2};$$
$$\Delta^2 y \text{ are differences } \delta^2 \text{ for } x = -3 \text{ to } 3;$$
$$\Delta^4 y \text{ are differences } \delta^4 \text{ for } x = -2 \text{ to } 2.$$

Although the differences $\Delta^j f(a)$ and $\nabla^j f(a)$ lie on downward and upward diagonals from $f(a)$, the central differences $\delta^{2j} f(a)$ lie on *horizontal lines* from $f(a)$. Thus in Table 167.1

$$\delta^2 f(-2) = -18, \qquad \delta^2 f(0) = -6, \qquad \delta^4 f(0) = 0,$$

and differences of odd order only appear for intermediate half-values of x. From (166.3), $\delta = \Delta E^{-\frac{1}{2}} = \nabla E^{\frac{1}{2}}$; hence

$$\delta^{2n} f(a) = \Delta^{2n} E^{-n} f(a) = \Delta^{2n} f(a - nh),$$
$$\delta^{2n} f(a) = \nabla^{2n} E^{n} f(a) = \nabla^{2n} f(a + nh).$$

Thus from a single difference table with staggered entries we can read forward and backward differences on the diagonals and central differences of even order on the horizontals.

We next compute an integral from a to $a + h$. Since $E - 1 = \delta E^{\frac{1}{2}}$ from (1), we have

$$\frac{1}{h} \int_a^{a+h} f(x)\, dx = (E - 1)\frac{1}{hD} f(a) = \left(\delta \frac{1}{hD}\right) f\left(a + \frac{h}{2}\right),$$

where δ/hD is the bracketed series in (2). This formula, however, involves central differences not in the table. We modify it, therefore, by writing

$$\frac{1}{h} \int_a^{a+h} f(x)\, dx = \frac{1}{\mu}\left(\frac{\delta}{hD}\right)\mu f\left(a + \frac{h}{2}\right) = \frac{1}{\mu}\left(\frac{\delta}{hD}\right)\frac{f(a) + f(a + h)}{2}.$$

From (4)

$$\frac{1}{\mu} = \left(1 + \frac{\delta^2}{4}\right)^{-\frac{1}{2}} = 1 - \frac{1}{8}\delta^2 + \frac{3}{128}\delta^4 - \cdots,$$

and from the product of this series and the series in (2), we have

(5) $\quad \dfrac{1}{h} \displaystyle\int_a^{a+h} f(x)\, dx = \left[1 - \frac{1}{12}\delta^2 + \frac{11}{720}\delta^4 - \cdots\right]\frac{f(a) + f(a + h)}{2}.$

Example 1. If $f(x) = x^3 - 3x^2 + 2x + 2$, we have from Table 167a and formula (3) with $a = 2$, $h = 1$:

$$\int_{3/2}^{5/2} f(x)\, dx = \left[1 + \frac{1}{24}\delta^2\right] f(2) = 2 + \frac{6}{24} = 2\tfrac{1}{4},$$

the exact result.

Example 2. Compute $\int_3^4 \log x \, dx$ from (5). From the difference table,

Table 172

x	$\log x$	Δ	Δ^2	Δ^3	Δ^4	Δ^5
1	0.0000					
		0.6931				
2	0.6931		−0.2876			
		0.4055		0.1698		
→3	1.0986		−0.1178		−0.1166	
		0.2877		0.032		0.0873
→4	1.3863		−0.0646		−0.0293	
		0.2231		0.0239		
5	1.6094		−0.0407			
		0.1824				
6	1.7918					

$$\int_3^4 \log x \, dx = \frac{1}{2}\left[2.4849 + \frac{1}{12} 0.1824 - \frac{11}{720} 0.1459 \right]$$

$$= 1.2425 + 0.0076 - 0.0011 = 1.2491.$$

The correct value is

$$\int_3^4 \log x \, dx = x(\log x - 1) \Big|_3^4 = 4 \log 4 - 3 \log 3 - 1 = 1.2494.$$

PROBLEMS

1. Show that $\mu\delta = \sinh hD$.
2. Invert the series for $2 \sinh \frac{1}{2}\delta$.
3. Show that

$$\mu = \sqrt{1 + \frac{\delta^2}{4}} = 1 + \frac{\delta^2}{8} - \frac{\delta^4}{128} + \frac{\delta^6}{1024} - \cdots.$$

4. Derive the formula

(6) $$\frac{1}{2h}\int_{a-h}^{a+h} f(x) \, dx = \mu\delta\frac{D^{-1}}{h} f(a) = \left[1 + \frac{1}{6}\delta^2 - \frac{1}{180}\delta^4 + \cdots \right] f(a).$$

5. Compute $\int_0^1 x^4 \, dx$ using formula (5).

6. Compute $\int_{-1}^1 x^4 \, dx$ using formula (6).

7. Using Table 167a, compute $\int_2^3 f(x) \, dx$ using formula (5). Check for accuracy.

8. Form a difference table for $f(x) = 1/(x + 4)$ from $x = -3$ to 3. Verify that $\delta^2 f(0) = \delta^4 f(0) = \frac{1}{30}$ and compute $\int_{-\frac{1}{2}}^{\frac{1}{2}} dx/(x + 4)$:

(a) by integration,
(b) by Simpson's rule,
(c) by formula (3).

173. GREGORY'S QUADRATURE

To find an integration formula in terms of differences, we seek an expression for the operator D^{-1} in terms of Δ or ∇.

Since Taylor's series for $f(x + h)$ can be written

$$Ef(x) = f(x + h) = \sum_{j=0}^{\infty} \frac{h^j D^j}{j!} f(x) = e^{hD} f(x),$$

we have the relations

(1) $$E = e^{hD} = 1 + \Delta,$$

(2) $$hD = \log (1 + \Delta),$$

and since $\Delta = \nabla/(1 - \nabla)$ from (166.12),

(3) $$hD = -\log (1 - \nabla).$$

Recall now the series, valid when $|x| < 1$:

$$f(x) = \frac{\log (1 + x)}{x} = 1 - \frac{1}{2}x + \frac{1}{3}x^2 - \frac{1}{4}x^3 + \cdots$$

$$f(-x) = \frac{-\log (1 - x)}{x} = 1 + \frac{1}{2}x + \frac{1}{3}x_2 + \frac{1}{4}x^3 + \cdots,$$

where $f(0)$ is defined as 1, the limit as $x \to 0$. If

$$\frac{1}{f(x)} = 1 + b_1 x + b_2 x^2 + \cdots,$$

the coefficients b_i satisfy the relation*

(4) $$\sum_{j=0}^{n}(-1)^j \frac{b_j}{n + 1 - j} = 0.$$

When $n = 1, 2, 3, \ldots$ we have

$$\tfrac{1}{2} - b_1 = 0, \qquad \tfrac{1}{3} - \tfrac{1}{2}b_1 + b_2 = 0, \qquad \tfrac{1}{4} - \tfrac{1}{3}b_1 + \tfrac{1}{2}b_2 - \tfrac{1}{3}b_3 = 0,$$

---

* *Advanced Calculus*, § 212.

and so forth, and we obtain, successively,

$$b_1 = \tfrac{1}{2}, \qquad b_2 = -\tfrac{1}{12}, \qquad b_3 = \tfrac{1}{24}, \qquad b_4 = -\tfrac{19}{720}, \qquad b_5 = \tfrac{3}{160}, \ldots .$$

Thus we have

$$\frac{x}{\log(1+x)} = 1 + \frac{1}{2}x - \frac{1}{12}x^2 + \frac{1}{24}x^3 - \frac{19}{720}x^4 + \frac{3}{160}x^5 - \cdots,$$

$$\frac{x}{-\log(1-x)} = 1 - \frac{1}{2}x - \frac{1}{12}x^2 - \frac{1}{24}x^3 - \frac{19}{720}x^4 - \frac{3}{160}x^5 - \cdots.$$

We now embark on a voyage of discovery, putting $x = \Delta$ in the first series, and $x = \nabla$ in the second. Then from (2) and (3), we see that

$$(5) \qquad \frac{\Delta}{hD} = 1 + \frac{1}{2}\Delta - \frac{1}{12}\Delta^2 + \frac{1}{24}\Delta^3 - \frac{19}{720}\Delta^4 + \frac{3}{160}\Delta^5 - \cdots,$$

$$(6) \qquad \frac{\nabla}{hD} = 1 - \frac{1}{2}\nabla - \frac{1}{12}\nabla^2 - \frac{1}{24}\nabla^3 - \frac{19}{720}\nabla^4 - \frac{3}{160}\nabla^5 - \cdots.$$

Now consider the integral

$$\frac{1}{h}\int_a^{a+h} f(x)\,dx = \Delta\,\frac{1}{hD}f(a) = \nabla\,\frac{1}{hD}f(a+h).$$

Since the operators Δ/hD and ∇/hD are given by (5) and (6), we have the basic equations for one-step quadrature:

$$(7) \quad \frac{1}{h}\int_a^{a+h} f(x)\,dx$$

$$= \left[1 + \frac{1}{2}\Delta - \frac{1}{12}\Delta^2 + \frac{1}{24}\Delta^3 - \frac{19}{720}\Delta^4 + \frac{3}{160}\Delta^5 - \cdots\right]f(a),$$

$$(8) \quad \frac{1}{h}\int_a^{a+h} f(x)\,dx$$

$$= \left[1 - \frac{1}{2}\nabla - \frac{1}{12}\nabla^2 - \frac{1}{24}\nabla^3 - \frac{19}{720}\nabla^4 - \frac{3}{160}\nabla^5 - \cdots\right]f(a+h).$$

We may convert (8) into an operation on $f(a)$ by replacing $f(a+h)$ by

$$Ef(a) = (1 - \nabla)^{-1}f(a) = [1 + \nabla + \nabla^2 + \cdots]f(a)$$

and forming the Cauchy product of the series. In the product the coefficients are the partial sums of the coefficients in (8):

$$1, \quad 1 - \tfrac{1}{2} = \tfrac{1}{2}, \quad \tfrac{1}{2} - \tfrac{1}{12} = \tfrac{5}{12}, \quad \tfrac{5}{12} - \tfrac{1}{24} = \tfrac{3}{8}, \ldots ,$$

and we obtain the *open* quadrature

(9)
$$\frac{1}{h}\int_a^{a+h} f(x)\,dx$$
$$= \left[1 + \frac{1}{2}\nabla + \frac{5}{12}\nabla^2 + \frac{3}{8}\nabla^3 + \frac{251}{720}\nabla^4 + \frac{95}{288}\nabla^5 + \cdots\right]f(a),$$

a formula which depends on $f(a)$ and its backward differences. We shall see that (9) is used as a *predictor*, and (8) as a *corrector* in Adam's method of solving differential equations (§ 182). When $f(x)$ is a polynomial of degree n, these series end with the term in Δ^n or ∇^n (§ 165) and the formulas are exact.

When $f(x)$ is not a polynomial, the series may be truncated for an approximate quadrature. The error is then obtained by replacing $\Delta^n f(a)$ in (7), or $\nabla^n f(a+h)$ in (8), by $h^n f^n(\xi)$ in the first non-zero term omitted, and ξ lies in the interval prescribed by the terms retained.* Thus from (7),

$$\frac{1}{h}\int_a^h f(x)\,dx = \left(1 + \frac{1}{2}\Delta\right)f(a) - \frac{h^2}{12}f''(\xi),$$

or by writing $f(a) = f_0, f(a+h) = f_1$, we see that

(7)′
$$\int_a^h f(x)\,dx = \frac{h}{2}(f_0 + f_1) - \frac{h^3}{12}f''(\xi), \qquad a < \xi < h.$$

This is the trapezoid rule (170.6). If we include the second difference, (7) yields

$$\frac{1}{h}\int_a^h f(x)\,dx = \left(1 + \frac{1}{2}\Delta - \frac{1}{12}\Delta^2\right)f(a) + \frac{h^3}{24}f'''(\xi),$$

or, after the differences are evaluated,

(7)″
$$\int_a^h f(x)\,dx = \frac{h}{12}(5f_0 + 8f_1 - f_2) + \frac{h^4}{24}f'''(\xi), \qquad a < \xi < a + 2h.$$

This is also a well-known quadrature.

We shall next derive the *n*-step quadrature

$$\frac{1}{h}\int_a^{a+nh} f(x)\,dx = (E^n - 1)\frac{1}{hD}f(a) = \frac{E^n - 1}{E - 1}\frac{\Delta}{hD}f(a),$$

where

$$\frac{\Delta}{hD}f(a) = \frac{\nabla}{hD}f(a+h)$$

---

* Cf. Hildebrand, ref. 8, § 5.4.

is given by the series in (7) or (8). Using (8) yields a more practical formula since the backward differences involved are included in a difference table for $f(x)$ from $x = a$ to $x = a + nh$. We proceed to deduce this by writing $f(a + nh) = f_n$ and

$$\frac{1}{h} \int_a^{a+nh} f(x)\, dx = \frac{E^n - 1}{E - 1}\left[1 - \frac{1}{2}\nabla - \frac{1}{12}\nabla^2 - \frac{1}{24}\nabla^3 - \cdots\right] Ef(a).$$

For the first term we put

$$\frac{E^n - 1}{E - 1} E = E + E^2 + \cdots + E^n$$

and obtain

$$(E + E^2 + \cdots + E^n)f_0 = f_1 + f_2 + \cdots + f_n.$$

In the remaining terms put $\nabla E/\Delta = 1$; we then have

$$-\tfrac{1}{2}(E^n - 1)f_0 = -\tfrac{1}{2}(f_n - f_0),$$

$$-\tfrac{1}{12}(E^n - 1)\nabla f_0 = -\tfrac{1}{12}(\nabla f_n - \nabla f_0),$$

$$-\tfrac{1}{24}(E^n - 1)\nabla^2 f_0 = -\tfrac{1}{24}(\nabla^2 f_n - \nabla^2 f_0),$$

and so on. The final result is therefore

$$(10) \quad \frac{1}{h}\int_a^{a+nh} f(x)\, dx = T_n - \frac{1}{12}[\nabla f_n - \nabla f_0] - \frac{1}{24}[\nabla^2 f_n - \nabla^2 f_0]$$

$$- \frac{19}{720}\nabla^3 f_n - \nabla^3 f_0] - \frac{3}{160}[\nabla^4 f_n - \nabla^4 f_0] - \cdots,$$

where

$$hT_n = h[\tfrac{1}{2}f_0 + f_1 + f_2 + \cdots + f_{n-1} + \tfrac{1}{2}f_n]$$

is the approximate quadrature effected by the composite trapezoid rule (170.9) and the remaining terms constitute the error. This result is known as *Gregory's backward formula*. Its truncation error is rather complex.

We now test these heuristic formulas. Referring to Table 173 we see that (7), (8), and (9) all check. As to (10) we have

$$\int_0^3 x^3\, dx = T_3 - \tfrac{1}{12}[\nabla f_3 - \nabla f_0] - \tfrac{1}{24}[\nabla^2 f_3 - \nabla^2 f_2] - \cdots$$

$$= (0 + 1 + 8 + \tfrac{27}{2}) - \tfrac{1}{12}(19 - 1) - \tfrac{1}{24}(12 + 6)$$

$$= \tfrac{36}{4} + \tfrac{54}{4} - \tfrac{6}{4} - \tfrac{3}{4} = \tfrac{81}{4},$$

by using backward differences for $f_3 = 27$ and $f_0 = 0$.

Table 173

x^3	Δ	Δ^2	Δ^3	Δ^4	$(h=1)$
-27					
	19				
-8		-12		0	
	7		6		
-1		-6		0	
	1		6		
0		0		0	
	1		6		
1		6		0	
	7		6		
8		12		0	
	19		6		
27		18		0	
	37		6		
64		24			
	61		6		
125		30			

$$(9)\quad \int_0^1 x^3\,dx = 0 + \tfrac{1}{2}(1) + \tfrac{5}{12}(-6) + \tfrac{3}{8}(6)$$
$$= \tfrac{1}{2} - \tfrac{5}{2} + \tfrac{9}{4} = \tfrac{1}{4}$$

$$(8)\quad \int_0^1 x^3\,dx = 1 - \tfrac{1}{2}(1) - \tfrac{1}{12}(0) - \tfrac{1}{24}(6)$$
$$= 1 - \tfrac{1}{2} - \tfrac{1}{4} = \tfrac{1}{4}$$

$$(7)\quad \int_0^1 x^3\,dx = 0 + \tfrac{1}{2}(1) - \tfrac{1}{12}(6) + \tfrac{1}{24}(6)$$
$$= \tfrac{1}{2} - \tfrac{1}{2} + \tfrac{1}{4} = \tfrac{1}{4}$$

We conclude with the simple two-step quadrature

$$(11)\quad \frac{1}{h}\int_a^{a+2h} f(x)\,dx = \left[2 + \frac{1}{3}\nabla^2 + \frac{1}{3}\nabla^3 + \frac{29}{90}\nabla^4 + \cdots\right]f(a+h).$$

The integral is derived from (8):

$$(E^2 - 1)\frac{1}{hD}f(a) = (E + 1)\frac{\Delta}{hD}f(a) = [1 + (1 - \nabla)^{-1}]\frac{\nabla}{hD}f(a+h)$$

$$= [2 + \nabla + \nabla^2 + \nabla^3 + \cdots]$$
$$\times [1 - \tfrac{1}{2}\nabla - \tfrac{1}{12}\nabla^2 - \tfrac{1}{24}\nabla^3 - \cdots]f(a+h)$$
$$= [2 + \tfrac{1}{3}\nabla^2 + \tfrac{1}{3}\nabla^3 + \tfrac{29}{90}\nabla^4 + \tfrac{14}{45}\nabla^5 + \cdots]f(a+h).$$

Example. To show the power of the operational method in discovering formulas, we shall obtain the *Euler transform* of the series

$$\sum_{j=0}^{\infty}(-1)^j f_j = (1 - E + E^2 - E^3 + \cdots)f_0 = (1 + E)^{-1}f_0.$$

Since $1 + E = 2 + \Delta = 2(1 + \tfrac{1}{2}\Delta)$, we have

$$(1 + E)^{-1} = \tfrac{1}{2}(1 + \tfrac{1}{2}\Delta)^{-1} = \tfrac{1}{2}\sum_{j=0}^{\infty}\frac{(-1)^j}{2^j}\Delta^j f_0;$$

$$(12)\qquad \sum_{j=0}^{\infty}(-1)^j f_j = \tfrac{1}{2}\sum_{j=0}^{\infty}\frac{(-1)^j}{2^j}\Delta^j f_0.$$

If the series on the left converges, the series on the right converges rapidly and to the same sum; this was first proved by L. D. Ames, an American mathematician in 1901.* Euler's transformation also assigns a "sum" to certain alternating series. Thus the Newton series (in factorial powers)

$$\sum_{j=0}^{\infty} \frac{x^{(j)}}{j!} = 2^x \quad \text{when } x > -1, \quad \text{diverges when } x \leq -1.$$

Thus when $x = -2$ it becomes $\sum_{j=0}^{\infty}(-1)^j(j+1) = 1 - 2 + 3 - 4 + \cdots$, but its Euler transform is the *finite* series $\frac{1}{2} - \frac{1}{4}$ whose sum $\frac{1}{4} = 2^{-2}$.

Euler's transformation may be used to compute the sum of a slowly converging series such as

$$\sum_{j=0}^{\infty} \frac{(-1)^j}{j+1} = \log 2 = 0.69314\ 71806 \ldots .$$

To accelerate its convergence we sum a few terms at the outset and then apply (12) to the "tail" where the differences are smaller. Thus if we sum nine terms,

$$\log 2 = S_9 - (\tfrac{1}{10} - \tfrac{1}{11} + \tfrac{1}{12} - \cdots),$$

where $S_9 = 0.7456348$, $f_0 = \frac{1}{10}$ and

$$\Delta^n \tfrac{1}{10} = \frac{(-1)^n\, n!}{10 \cdot 11 \cdots (10+n)} \qquad \text{(Prob. 165.3)},$$

and if we stop at the fifth difference, we obtain $\log 2$ correct to six decimals. Use of the original series would require a million terms to attain this accuracy.

PROBLEMS

1. Compute $\int_0^4 x^3 \, dx$ using (10).

2. From (8) deduce *Gregory's forward formula*:

(13) $$\frac{1}{h} \int_a^{a+nh} f(x) \, dx = T_n - \tfrac{1}{12}[\Delta f_n - \Delta f_0] + \tfrac{1}{24}[\Delta^2 f_n - \Delta^2 f_0]$$
$$- \tfrac{19}{720}[\Delta^3 f_n - \Delta^3 f_0] + \tfrac{3}{160}[\Delta^4 f_n - \Delta^4 f_0] - \cdots .$$

3. Use (13) to compute $\int_0^3 x^3 \, dx$ and $\int_0^4 x^3 \, dx$.

4. Obtain the more general Euler transform:

$$\sum_{j=0}^{\infty} q^j f_j = (1+p)\sum_{j=0}^{\infty} p^k \Delta^k f_0, \qquad p = \frac{q}{1-q}.$$

5. Show that

(14) $$b_j = \frac{1}{j!} \int_0^1 x^{(j)} \, dx, \qquad h = 1$$

satisfies the recurrence relation (4).

---

* For the proof see Knopp, ref. 10, § 144. The Δ in this proof is $-\Delta$ of current usage.

6. Show that

(15) $$\frac{1}{h}\int_a^{a+2h} f(x)\,dx = [2 - 2\nabla + \tfrac{1}{3}\nabla^2 - \tfrac{1}{90}\nabla^4 + \cdots]f(a + 2h)$$

$$= S_2 - \tfrac{1}{90}\nabla^4 f^{\text{iv}}(\xi), \qquad a < \xi < a + 2h,$$

where hS_2 is Simpson's quadrature. [Put $f(a + h) = E^{-1}f(a + 2h) = (1 - \nabla)$ $f(a + 2h)$ in (11).]

7. Obtain the formula

(16) $$\sum_{j=0}^{\infty}(-1)^j f_j = \tfrac{1}{2}[f_0 - \tfrac{1}{2}f_0' + \tfrac{1}{24}f_0''' - \tfrac{1}{240}f_0^{\text{v}} + \cdots]$$

by expanding $(1 + E)^{-1} = (1 + e^D)^{-1}$, $h = 1$.

8. Apply (16) to compute $\log 2 = S_9 - [\tfrac{1}{10} - \tfrac{1}{11} + \tfrac{1}{12} - \cdots]$ with $S_9 = 0.7456348$.

9. Show that both (12) and (16) give

$$\sum_{j=0}^{\infty}\frac{(-3)^j}{j!} = \sum_{j=0}^{\infty}(-1)^j\frac{(j + 2)^{(2)}}{2} = 2^{-3}.$$

174. GAUSS-LEGENDRE QUADRATURE

The Cotes equal interval quadrature with $n + 1$ points $x_0, x_1, \ldots, x_n$ is exact for polynomials of degree n. Simpson's rule ($n = 2$) gave an even better result since it is exact for cubic polynomials. A further improvement in this direction was made by Gauss *by choosing $x_0, x_1, \ldots, x_n$ as the roots of the Legendre polynomial $P_{n+1}(x)$*; the resulting quadrature is then exact for all polynomials of degree $2n + 1(!)$ whose graphs pass through the given $n + 1$ points (x_i, y_i).

First, recall from Theorem 121.2 that $P_{n+1}(x)$ has $n + 1$ simple zeros in $[-1, 1]$ and that for any polynomial $Q(x)$ of degree $\leq n$,

(1) $$\int_{-1}^{1} Q(x)P_{n+1}(x)\,dx = 0 \qquad (121.4).$$

Let $F_n(x)$ be the Lagrange interpolation polynomial for the $n + 1$ zeros x_i of $P_{n+1}(x)$; then

(2) $$\int_{-1}^{1} F_n(x)\,dx = \sum_{i=0}^{n} y_i \int_{-1}^{1} L_i(x)\,dx$$

is exact for all polynomials of degree $\leq n$. Now let $f(x)$ be a polynomial of degree $2n + 1$ which passes through the same $n + 1$ points (x_i, y_i) as $F_n(x)$. Divide $f(x)$ by $P_{n+1}(x)$ to find a quotient $Q(x)$ and remainder $G(x)$,

$$f(x) = Q(x)P_{n+1}(x) + G(x),$$

where both $Q(x)$ and $G(x)$ are of degree $\leq n$. Then since the x_i are the zeros of $P_{n+1}(x)$, $f(x_i) = G(x_i) = y_i$. Moreover, from (1), we see that

$$(3) \qquad \int_{-1}^{1} f(x)\, dx = \int_{-1}^{1} G(x)\, dx = \int_{-1}^{1} F_n(x)\, dx;$$

for $G(x) \equiv F_n(x)$ since both polynomials of degree $\leq n$ pass through the same $n + 1$ points. Since (2) is exact for $F_n(x)$, (3) is exact for $f(x)$.

The error in Gaussian quadrature with the zeros of $P_n(x)$ has been shown to be*

$$(4) \qquad E_n = \frac{2^{2n+1}(n!)^4}{(2n + 1)[(2n)!]^3} f^{(2n)}(\xi), \qquad -1 < \xi < 1.$$

To apply this quadrature to $\displaystyle\int_a^b \varphi(t)\, dt$, we make the change of variable

$$2t = (b - a)x + a + b, \qquad 2\, dt = (b - a)\, dx;$$

then if $\varphi(t) = f(x)$, we see that

$$\int_a^b \varphi(t)\, dt = \frac{b - a}{2} \int_{-1}^{1} f(x)\, dx.$$

Example 1. The zeros of the Legendre polynomial

$$P_2(x) = \tfrac{1}{3}(3x^2 - 1) \quad \text{are} \quad -\sigma,\ \sigma = \frac{\sqrt{3}}{3}.$$

The coefficients of the interpolating polynomial (164.6) are therefore

$$\frac{x - \sigma}{-2\sigma} = -\frac{\sqrt{3}}{2}(x - \sigma) \qquad \frac{x + \sigma}{2\sigma} = \frac{\sqrt{3}}{2}(x + \sigma).$$

Then the interpolating polynomial is

$$F_1(x) = -\frac{\sqrt{3}}{2}(x - \sigma)y_0 + \frac{\sqrt{3}}{2}(x + \sigma)y_1$$

and

$$\int_{-1}^{1} F_1(x)\, dx = \sigma\sqrt{3}\, y_0 + \sigma\sqrt{3}\, y_1 = y_0 + y_1.$$

Thus if $y = f(x)$, we have the remarkable formula

$$(5) \qquad \int_{-1}^{1} f(x)\, dx = f(-\sigma) + f(\sigma) + \tfrac{1}{135} f^{\mathrm{iv}}(\xi).$$

where $\sigma = \sqrt{3}/3$ and the error is given by (4) when $n = 2$.

---

* Kopal, ref. 11, p. 373.

Example 2. The zeros of the Legendre polynomial

$$P_3(x) = \tfrac{1}{2}(5x^3 - 3x) \quad \text{are} \quad -\omega, 0, \omega = \sqrt{\tfrac{3}{5}}.$$

The coefficients of the interpolating polynomial (164.6) are now

$$\frac{x(x - \omega)}{-\omega(-2\omega)} = \frac{5}{6}(x^2 - \omega x), \qquad \frac{(x + \omega)(x - \omega)}{\omega(-\omega)} = -\frac{5}{3}\left(x^2 - \frac{3}{5}\right),$$

$$\frac{(x + \omega)x}{(2\omega)\omega} = \frac{5}{6}(x^2 + \omega x).$$

The interpolating polynomial is therefore

$$F_2(x) = \tfrac{5}{6}(x^2 - \omega x)y_0 - (\tfrac{5}{3}x^2 - 1)y_1 + \tfrac{5}{6}(x^2 + \omega x)y_2$$

and

$$\int_{-1}^{1} F_2(x)\, dx = 2[\tfrac{5}{18}y_0 + \tfrac{4}{9}y_1 + \tfrac{5}{18}y_2].$$

Thus if $y = f(x)$,

(6)
$$\int_{-1}^{1} f(x)\, dx = \frac{1}{9}[5f(-\omega) + 8f(0) + 5f(\omega)] + \frac{f^{\mathrm{vi}}(\xi)}{15750}$$

where $\omega = \sqrt{\tfrac{3}{5}}$ and the error is given by (4) when $n = 3$.

175. THE EULER-MACLAURIN SUM FORMULA

To find a summation formula in terms of differences we seek an expression for the operator Δ^{-1}. This can be found from

$$\Delta^{-1} = \frac{1}{E - 1} = \frac{1}{e^{hD} - 1} = \frac{1}{h}\frac{hD}{e^{hD} - 1}D^{-1}.$$

Recalling from § 79 the symbolic expansion $t/(e^t - 1) = e^{Bt}$, we may write

(1)
$$\Delta^{-1} = \frac{1}{h}e^{hBD}D^{-1},$$

and on expanding the exponential, we have

(2)
$$\Delta^{-1} = \frac{1}{h}D^{-1} + \sum_{j=1}^{\infty}\frac{B_j h^{j-1}}{j!}D^{j-1}.$$

Since $B_1 = -\tfrac{1}{2}, B_2 = \tfrac{1}{6}, B_4 = -\tfrac{1}{30}, B_6 = \tfrac{1}{42}, B_8 = -\tfrac{1}{30}, \ldots,$

(3)
$$\Delta^{-1} = \frac{1}{h}D^{-1} - \frac{1}{2} + \frac{h}{6}\frac{D}{2!} - \frac{h^3}{30}\frac{D^3}{4!} + \frac{h^5}{42}\frac{D^5}{6!} - \cdots.$$

First, multiply by Δ and apply the operator

$$\frac{1}{h} \Delta D^{-1} = 1 + \tfrac{1}{2}\Delta - \frac{h}{12} \Delta D + \frac{h^3}{720} \Delta D^3 - \frac{h^5}{30240} \Delta D^5 + \cdots$$

to $f(a)$; we then obtain the formula

$$(4) \quad \frac{1}{h} \int_a^{a+h} f(x)\, dx = \frac{1}{2}[f(a+h) + f(a)] - \frac{h}{12}[f'(a+h) - f'(a)]$$

$$+ \frac{h^3}{720}[f'''(a+h) - f'''(a)] - \frac{h^5}{30240}[f^{\vee}(a+h) - f^{\vee}(a)] + \cdots.$$

When $f(x)$ is a polynomial, the series terminates and gives an exact result. When the series is truncated after the term in f', and $b = a + h$, we obtain the quadrature

$$(5) \quad \int_a^{a+h} f(x)\, dx = \frac{h}{2}[f(b) + f(a)] - \frac{h^2}{12}[f'(b) - f'(a)] + \frac{h^5}{720} f^{iv}(\xi).$$

The error $E(h)$, given in (5), may be verified as in § 169. Regarding h as a variable,

$$E'(h) = f(b) - \tfrac{1}{2}[f(b) + f(a)] - \frac{h}{2}f'(b) + \frac{h}{6}[f'(b) - f'(a)] + \frac{h^2}{12}f''(b)$$

or

$$E'(h) = \frac{1}{2}[f(b) - f(a)] - \frac{h}{3}f'(b) - \frac{h}{6}f'(a) + \frac{h^2}{12}f''(b),$$

$$E''(h) = \frac{1}{6}[f'(b) - f'(a)] - \frac{h}{6}f''(b) + \frac{h^2}{12}f'''(b),$$

$$E'''(h) = \frac{h^2}{12}f^{iv}(b) = \frac{h^2}{12}f^{iv}(a + h).$$

Form the function

$$\varphi(t) = \begin{vmatrix} E(h) & h^5 \\ E(t) & t^5 \end{vmatrix}$$

and note that $\varphi(0) = \varphi'(0) = \varphi''(0) = 0$ and $\varphi(h) = 0$. Then from Rolle's theorem we have, successively,

$$\varphi'(\xi_1) = \varphi''(\xi_2) = \varphi'''(\xi_3) = 0, \qquad 0 < \xi_3 < \xi_2 < \xi_1 < h,$$

and hence

$$\varphi'''(\xi_3) = \begin{vmatrix} E(h) & h^5 \\ \dfrac{\xi_3{}^2}{12} f^{iv}(a + \xi_3) & 60\xi_3{}^2 \end{vmatrix} = 0,$$

$$E(h) = \frac{h^5}{720} f^{iv}(\xi), \qquad a < \xi < b.$$

Second, multiply (3) by

$$(1 + E + E^2 + \cdots + E^{n-1})\Delta = E^n - 1$$

and apply this operator to $f(a)$. The left member is then the sum of n terms

$$(1 + E + \cdots + E^{n-1})f(a) = \sum_{x=a}^{b-h} f(x)$$

where $b = a + nh$, and

$$(6) \quad \sum_{x=a}^{b-h} f(x) = \frac{1}{h} \int_a^b f(x)\, dx - \frac{1}{2} [f(b) - f(a)] + \frac{h}{12} [f'(b) - f'(a)]$$

$$- \frac{h^3}{720} [f'''(b) - f'''(a)] + \frac{h^5}{30240} [f^{v}(b) - f^{v}(a)] - \cdots .$$

This is the famous *Euler-Maclaurin sum formula.* On adding $f(b)$ to both sides, it assumes the form

$$(7) \quad \sum_{x=a}^{b} f(x) = \frac{1}{h} \int_a^b f(x)\, dx + \frac{1}{2} [f(b) + f(a)]$$

$$+ \sum_{j=1}^{\infty} \frac{B_{2j}}{(2j)!} h^{2j-1} [f^{(2j-1)}(b) - f^{(2j-1)}(a)],$$

in which we have restored the Bernoulli numbers. For a rigorous treatment of this series see Knopp.* When $f(x)$ is a polynomial, the series terminates and gives exact results. For example, if $f(x) = x^2$, $a = 0$, $h = 1$, $b = n$, we find

$$\sum_{x=0}^{n} x^2 = \int_0^n x^2\, dx + \frac{n^2}{2} + \frac{\frac{1}{6}}{2!} 2n = \frac{1}{6} n(n + 1)(2n + 1).$$

In general, for an analytic $f(x)$, the series usually diverges since the Bernoulli numbers B_j increase rapidly and become infinite as $j \to \infty$. Nevertheless, the series can be used for computation since in many cases it can be shown that the *trucation error is less in absolute value and has the same sign as the*

_____

* Knopp, ref. 10, §§ 64, 65.

first term neglected. This is always so when the differences $f^{2k+1}(b) - f^{2k+1}(a)$ maintain the same sign; for since the Bernoulli numbers alternate in sign, the series will be alternating and the usual estimate for its remainder* remains valid. Thus, if we stop at a term where the estimated error is within tolerance, the series can be summed to this point even if it diverges. This is an instance of an *asymptotic series;* for a precise definition of such series see Knopp, ref. 10, § 65.

Example 1. Euler's Series.

$$1 + \frac{1}{2^2} + \frac{1}{3^2} + \cdots = \frac{\pi^2}{6}.$$

To reach terms in (7) that decrease rapidly, we add the first nine terms:

$$
\begin{aligned}
&1.00000\ 00000 \\
&0.25000\ 00000 \\
&0.11111\ 11111 \\
&0.06250\ 00000 \\
&0.04000\ 00000 \\
&0.02777\ 77776 \\
&0.02040\ 81633 \\
&0.01562\ 50000 \\
&0.01234\ 56790 \\
\hline
&1.53976\ 77310 = \sum_{x=1}^{9} x^{-2}.
\end{aligned}
$$

To sum the "tail," put $f(x) = (10 + x)^{-2}$ in (7); since

$$f'(x) = -2!\,(10 + x)^{-3}, \qquad f'''(x) = -4!\,(10 + x)^{-5},$$

$$\sum_{x=0}^{\infty} f(x) = \int_0^{\infty} f(x)\,dx + \tfrac{1}{2}f(0) - \tfrac{1}{12}f'(0) + \tfrac{1}{720}f'''(0) - \cdots$$

$$= 10^{-1} + \tfrac{1}{2}\,10^{-2} + \tfrac{1}{6}10^{-3} - \tfrac{1}{30}10^{-5} + \cdots$$

$$= 0.10516\ 667 - 0.00000\ 033$$

$$= 0.10516\ 634.$$

Therefore,

$$\sum_{x=1}^{\infty} x^{-2} = 1.53976\ 773 + 0.10516\ 634$$

$$= 1.64493\ 407.$$

Since the first term neglected is $0.00000\ 00024$, this result should be accurate to the last figure—which it is, since $\pi^2/6 = 1.64493\ 40668 \cdots$.

Example 2. Euler's constant.

$$\gamma = \lim_{n \to \infty} \left[1 + \frac{1}{2} + \frac{1}{3} + \cdots + \frac{1}{n} - \log n \right] = 0.57721\ 56649.$$

Using the plan of Example 1 we first compute

$$S_9 = 1 + \tfrac{1}{2} + \tfrac{1}{3} + \cdots + \tfrac{1}{9} = 2.82896\ 82540.$$

---

* *Advanced Calculus,* § 34.

With $f(x) = 1/x$, we have from (7)

$$\sum_{x=1}^{n} \frac{1}{x} = S_9 + \int_{10}^{n} \frac{dx}{x} + \frac{1}{2}\left[\frac{1}{10} + \frac{1}{n}\right] + \frac{B_2}{2!}\left[\frac{1}{10^2} - \frac{1}{n^2}\right]$$

$$+ \frac{B_4 \, 3!}{4!}\left[\frac{1}{10^4} - \frac{1}{n^4}\right] + \frac{B_6 5!}{6!}\left[\frac{1}{10^6} - \frac{1}{n^6}\right] + \cdots$$

$$\lim_{n\to\infty}\left[1 + \frac{1}{2} + \cdots + \frac{1}{n} - \log n\right] = S_9 - \log 10 + \frac{1}{2}10^{-1} + \frac{1}{12}10^{-2}$$

$$- \frac{1}{120}10^{-4} + \frac{1}{252}10^{-6} - \frac{1}{240}10^{-8} + \cdots,$$

$$= 2.82896\ 92540 - 2.30358\ 50930$$
$$+ 0.05000\ 00000$$
$$+ 0.00083\ 33333 - 0.00000\ 08333$$
$$+ 0.00000\ 00040$$
$$= 2.87980\ 15913 - 2.30258\ 59263$$
$$= 0.57721\ 56650.$$

Since the first neglected term $= 10^{-10}/2.4$, this result agrees with γ as required by theory.

PROBLEMS

1. Use (7) to verify $\sum_{x=0}^{10} x^5 = 220825$.

2. Use the procedure of Example 1 to compute $\sum_{1}^{\infty} x^{-3}$ to eight decimal places. No simple expression for this sum is known.

3. Show that (7) may be written

$$(8)\qquad \int_{x_0}^{x_m} f(x)\,dx = hT_n - \sum_{j=1}^{\infty}\frac{B_{2j}}{(2j)!}h^{2j}[f_n^{(2j-1)} - f_0^{(2j-1)}]$$

where hT_n is the trapezoidal quadrature (170.9) and the sum, when truncated, represents a correction.

4. With $f(x) = y'(x)$ in (8), deduce that

$$(9)\qquad y_{n+1} = y_n + \frac{1}{2}h(y'_{n+1} + y_n') - \frac{h^2}{12}(y''_{n+1} - y_n'') + \frac{h}{720}y^{\mathrm{v}}(\xi),$$

where

$$x_{n+1} = x_n + h \quad \text{and} \quad x_n < \xi < x_{n+1}.$$

Verify (9) when $y = x^4$ and $h = 1$.

5. With $f(x) = \log x$, $a = 1$, $b = n$, (7) becomes

$$(10)\qquad \log n! \sim (n + \tfrac{1}{2})\log n - n + 1 + \sum_{j=1}^{\infty}\frac{B_{2j}}{(2j-1)(2j)}\left(\frac{1}{n^{2j-1}} - 1\right).$$

This leads to *Stirling's formula:*

$$(11)\qquad n! = \sqrt{2\pi n}\ n^n \exp(-n + \theta/12n), \qquad 0 < \theta < 1,$$

a very useful result when n is large. Thus $\log n!$ shows that $1000!$ is a number with 2508 digits which begin with 402 (Knopp).

CHAPTER 14

Numerical Solutions

176. INTRODUCTION

We first consider the initial value problem

(1) $$\frac{dy}{dx} = f(x, y), \qquad y(x_0) = y_0.$$

In problems that arise in practice, it is often impossible or impracticable to obtain the solution of (1) in closed form. In such cases we may resort to power series expansions (§ 22) or Picard iterations (§ 132) to obtain an approximate solution. But both methods have their drawbacks when $f(x, y)$ is not a simple function. The method of Taylor series needs the derivatives $y^{(n)}(x_0)$; these must be computed from (1) by successive differentiation, and the formulas involved may become very complex after a few steps. The Picard process involves repeated integrations and these may soon become very cumbersome. The way out of these difficulties is to employ numerical methods. Many such methods, of varying degrees of simplicity and accuracy, have been developed, but all depend on one basic idea, namely

(2) $$y(b) = y(a) + \int_a^b y' \, dx,$$

and replacing the integral by some approximate quadrature that depends on certain known values of y' in the interval $a \leq x < b$. We thus advance from $y(a)$ to $y(b)$.

The end product of a numerical solution of (1) is a table of values of y, usually for equally spaced values of x, say of mesh h. Using the notation

(3) $$y_n = y(x_0 + hn),$$

we may form such a table as

(4)

x	x_0	x_1	x_2	$\cdots$	x_n	$\cdots$
y	y_0	y_1	y_2	$\cdots$	y_n	$\cdots$
y'	y_0'	y_1'	y_2'	$\cdots$	y_n'	$\cdots$

636

in which y_0 is given and $y_0' = f(x_0, y_0)$ is known. The last row is added for convenience in checking the table.

Since the formulas used have truncation errors and the numbers involved have roundoff errors, all the tabulated values are more or less inaccurate. To increase accuracy we may:

1°. Use formulas with low truncation errors;
2°. Use numbers with more decimal places than are required in the final result to counteract roundoff;
3°. Use a small mesh h.

Thus accuracy is achieved at the expense of additional work; because

1°. Low truncation error means a more elaborate formula;
2°. High decimal computations are very laborious, at least by hand;
3°. Decreasing the mesh increases the number of steps to attain a desired goal. Thus halving the mesh h doubles the number of steps to reach $y(x)$ for a given x.

If the calculation is rounded off at the nth decimal place, the roundoff error may be as large as 5 in the next place, that is $\pm \frac{1}{2} 10^{-n}$, and after k steps may be as large as $\pm \frac{1}{2} k 10^{-n}$. This amount is extremely improbable because, in general, roundoff errors of opposite sign are equally probable and some cancellation of errors is likely. However, if we halve the mesh to increase accuracy, k is doubled to reach a certain point, and the roundoff error may actually increase and partially offset the increase in accuracy.

Finally, we must cope with the question: How accurate is table (4)? If we halve the mesh and obtain a new table with twice as many entries (with double the work) and half of the new entries agree with the old ones, we may assume the correctness of the table.

A less laborious plan is to use a simple quadrature formula, such as Weddle's rule, as a check. From (1)

$$y_6 - y_0 = \int_{x_0}^{x_6} y' \, dx, \qquad y_i' = f(x_i, y_i),$$

and hence from Weddle's rule (170.11),

(5) $$y_6 - y_0 \simeq \frac{3h}{10} [y_0' + 5y_1' + y_2' + 6y_3' + y_4' + 5y_5' + y_6'].$$

If this checks, we may assume that the entries from y_0 to y_6 are correct.

In any really complicated problem the assistance of an electronic computer is needed to effect a satisfactory solution in a reasonable length of time.

PROBLEMS

1. In the problem $y' = \log(x + y^2)$, $y(0) = 1$, what is the Picard y_1 if $y_0 = 1$. How about y_2?

2. Find the Taylor expansion for y in Problem 1 up to the term in x^4

177. EULER-CAUCHY METHOD

The simplest method of obtaining an approximate numerical solution of the initial value problem

$$(1) \qquad \frac{dy}{dx} = f(x, y), \qquad y(x_0) = y_0,$$

consists in assuming that the slope in any interval $[x_n, x_n + h]$ is constant. Thus in the interval $[x_0, x_0 + h]$, we assume that the slope maintains its value at x_0, namely, $f(x_0, y_0)$; hence

$$\frac{y_1 - y_0}{h} = f(x_0, y_0)$$

or

$$y_1 = y_0 + hf(x_0, y_0).$$

At the point (x_1, y_1) the slope given by (1) is $f(x_1, y_1)$ and we find as before

$$y_2 = y_1 + hf(x_1, y_1).$$

Thus, step by step, we can construct an approximate tabular solution by means of the recursion formula

$$(2) \qquad y_{n+1} = y_n + hf(x_n, y_n).$$

This method approximates the solution curve through (x_0, y_0) by a broken line or *Cauchy polygon* (Fig. 177), and it is plausible that this polygonal approximation will approach the exact solution as the mesh $h \to 0$. Cauchy, assuming the continuity of $f(x, y)$ and $f_y(x, y)$, was the first to prove this (1828).* Euler, however, had used such "polygons" a hundred years earlier; hence the name Euler-Cauchy applied to this method.

---

* The continuity of $f_y(x, y)$ implies that $f(x, y)$ satisfies a Lipschitz condition (§ 153), but the latter is a less restrictive condition since it may hold even when $f_y(x, y)$ is discontinuous.

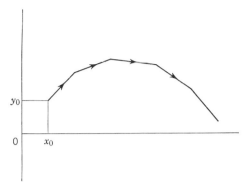

Fig. 177 Cauchy polygon.

Unless h is very small, this method is rather crude and substantial errors may rapidly accumulate. To estimate the error in formula (2), assume that $y(x)$ is twice differentiable and write the Taylor expansion*

$$y(x_n + h) = y(x_n) + hy'(x_n) + \frac{h^2}{2} y''(\xi)$$

$$= y_{n+1} + \frac{h^2}{2} y''(\xi), \qquad x_n < \xi < x_{n+1}.$$

Hence the one-step error

$$E_n(h) = y(x_n + h) - y_{n+1} = \tfrac{1}{2}h^2 y''(\xi).$$

If we reduce h to $\tfrac{1}{2}h$, the one-step error

$$E_n(\tfrac{1}{2}h) = \frac{1}{2}\left(\frac{h}{2}\right)^2 y''(\bar{\xi}) = \frac{1}{8} h^2 y''(\bar{\xi}), \qquad x_n < \bar{\xi} < x_{n+1}.$$

Assuming that $y''(x)$ varies slowly, so that $y''(\xi) \simeq y''(\bar{\xi})$, we have

$$2E(\tfrac{1}{2}h) \simeq \tfrac{1}{2}E(h).$$

Thus the two-step error with mesh $\tfrac{1}{2}h$ is about half the one-step error with mesh h.

The accuracy of this method can be improved by first finding y_{n+1} from (2) and then computing an adjusted value

$$Y_{n+1} = y_n + \tfrac{1}{2}h[f(x_n, y_n) + f(x_{n+1}, y_{n+1})]$$

which in effect averages the slope at the beginning and end of the interval. This extra complication, however, is hardly worthwhile in view of better methods, such as that in § 179, which are available.

---

* *Advanced Calculus*, § 65.

Example. For the problem

$$y' = x + y, \qquad y(0) = 1,$$

the recurrence formula (2) becomes

$$y_{n+1} = y_n + h(x_n + y_n).$$

The calculation with $h = 0.1$ is shown in Table 177.

Table 177

n	x_n	y_n	$y_n' = x_n + y_n$	hy_n'	$y = 2e^x - x - 1$
0	0.0	1.00000	1.00000	0.10000	1.00000
1	0.1	1.10000	1.20000	0.12000	1.11034
2	0.2	1.22000	1.42000	0.14200	1.24281
3	0.3	1.36200	1.66200	0.!6620	1.39972
4	0.4	1.52820	1.92820	0.19282	1.58365
5	0.5	1.72102	2.22102	0.22210	1.79744
6	0.6	1.94312	2.54312	0.25431	2.04424
7	0.7	2.19743	2.89743	0.28974	2.32751
8	0.8	2.48717	3.28717	0.32872	2.65108
9	0.9	2.81589	3.71589	0.37159	3.01921
10	1.0	3.18748	———	———	3.43656

Since the problem has the exact solution

$$y = 2e^x - x - 1,$$

the computed values of y_n given in the second column may be compared with the exact values in the last column. The results are computed to five decimal places for comparison with the same problem in § 179.

178. PREDICTION AND CORRECTION

Suppose that, from a Taylor series or otherwise, we have found the first n values

$$y_0, y_1, \ldots, y_{n-1}$$

in the tabular solution of the problem

$$(1) \qquad y' = f(x, y), \qquad y(x_0) = y_0.$$

Then we also know the n corresponding values of y', namely

$$y_0' = f(x_0, y_0), \; y_1', \ldots, y_{n-1}'$$

from equation (1). Our problem is to find y_n.

One method that is widely used with excellent results is the method of prediction and correction. We first predict the value y_n by using an *open-end quadrature* that involves $y_1, y_2, \ldots, y_{n-1}$ to *predict* y_n:

$$y_n - y_0 = \int_{x_0}^{x_n} f(x, y) \, dx;$$

Then we may write (omitting y_0' and y_n')

$P \qquad\qquad y_n = y_0 + a_1 y_1' + \cdots + a_{n-1} y_{n-1}'$

with an error

$$E_p = p h^m y^{(m)}(\xi_1), \qquad [y^{(m)} = D^{m-1} y']$$

of order h^m with the constant p.

With this estimate of y_n we compute

$E \qquad\qquad y_n' = f(x_n, y_n)$

and use a *closed quadrature* of the same order h^m to *correct* y_n, say

$C \qquad\qquad y_n = y_k + b_k y_k' + \cdots + b_n y_n'$

with an error

$$E_c = c h^m y^{(m)}(\xi_2).$$

Call the predicted and corrected values of y_n simply P and C; then since the true value of y_n is

$$P + E_p = C + E_c,$$

$$C - P = E_p - E_c = E_c\left(\frac{E_p}{E_c} - 1\right) \simeq E_c\left(\frac{p}{c} - 1\right),$$

provided $y^{(m)}(\xi_1)$ and $y^{(m)}(\xi_2)$ are fairly close. Then we have the estimated error

(2) $$E_c \simeq \frac{c}{p - c}(C - P)$$

and may *adjust* the corrected value C by adding E_c:

$A \qquad\qquad y_n = C + \frac{c}{p - c}(C - P).$

This completes one cycle of operations in which we predict (P), equate (E), correct (C), and adjust (A)—a cycle condensed to the acronym *PECA*.

If the estimated error E_c in (2) is tolerable for the contemplated degree of accuracy, we may neglect the adjustment. When E_c is too large for tolerance we may use the corrected y_n to get y_n' from E and then recompute y_n from C. Such an iteration may be continued, if necessary, until y_n remains unchanged. Although this procedure is more time-consuming than the adjustment A, it is also more accurate.

179. A SIMPLE PREDICTOR-CORRECTOR METHOD

This method uses formulas (171.1) and (171.2).* For the first cycle these become

P $\qquad\qquad y_2 = y_0 + 2hy_1', \qquad E_p = \dfrac{h^3}{3} y'''(\xi_1),$

E $\qquad\qquad y_2' = f(x_2, y_2),$

C $\qquad\qquad y_2 = y_1 + \dfrac{h}{2}(y_1' + y_2'), \qquad E_c = -\dfrac{h^3}{12} y'''(\xi_2).$

For the adjustment of C we have

$$p = \frac{1}{3}, \qquad c = -\frac{1}{12}; \qquad \frac{c}{p-c} = -\frac{1}{5}; \qquad E_c \simeq -\frac{1}{5}(C - P),$$

A $\qquad\qquad\qquad y_2 = C - \dfrac{1}{5}(C - P).$

The starting value y_1, needed in P to get $y_1' = f(x_1, y_1)$, may be obtained from the Taylor expansion

$$y_1 = y(x_0 + h) = y_0 + hy_0' + \frac{h}{2!} y_0'' + \cdots$$

after computing an adequate number of derivatives y_0^j from $y' = f(x, y)$.

After y_2 is computed, the equations for the next cycle are obtained from P, E, C, A by increasing all subscripts by 1. Thus we compute $y_2, y_3, \ldots$ in turn until the desired terminal value y_n is reached. Weddle's rule (176.5) may be used as a check. (The stability of this method is discussed in Hamming, *op. cit.* A case in point is treated in Example 2.)

Example 1. $y' = x + y, y(0) = 1$. From the equation we find that $y'(0) = 1$, $y^{(n)}(0) = 2 \ (n > 1)$; hence

$$y(x) = 1 + x + x^2 + \tfrac{1}{3}x^3 + \tfrac{1}{12}x^4 + \tfrac{1}{60}x^5 + \cdots,$$

from which we find

$$y_1 = y(0.1) = 1.11 + 0.000333 + 0.000008 = 1.11034,$$
$$y_1' = y_1 + 0.1 = 1.21034.$$

We are now ready to start the process *PECA* where

E $\qquad\qquad\qquad y_n' = y_n + \dfrac{n}{10}.$

---

* Hamming, ref. 28, §§ 14.3–14.6.

The results of six cycles are given in Table 179.

Table 179

n	x	$y = C - \dfrac{C-P}{5}$	y'	P	C	$\tfrac{1}{5}(C - P)$	$y(\text{exact})$
0	0.0	1.00000	1.00000				1.00000
1	0.1	1.11034	1.21034				1.11034
2	0.2	1.24278	1.44278	1.24207	1.24296	0.00018	1.24281
3	0.3	1.39967	1.69967	1.39890	1.39986	0.00019	1.39972
4	0.4	1.58358	1.98358	1.58271	1.58379	0.00021	1.58365
5	0.5	1.79734	2.29734	1.79639	1.79758	0.00024	1.79744
6	0.6	2.04410	2.64410	2.04305	2.04436	0.00026	2.04424

Since
$$y''' = y'' = 1 + y' = 1 + x + y > 0,$$
$$E_p > 0, \qquad E_c < 0, \qquad P < y < C.$$

Compare the computed values in Table 179 with the values computed from the solution
$$y = 2e^x - 1 - x$$
given in the last column of Table 179.

Weddle's rule (176.5) is used to make an overall check to four decimal places.

$$y_0' = 1.0000$$
$$y_2' = 1.4428$$
$$y_4' = 1.9836$$
$$y_6' = 2.6441$$
$$5y_1' = 6.0515$$
$$5y_5' = 11.4865$$
$$6y_3' = 10.1982$$

$$y_6 = 2.0441$$
$$y_0 = 1.0000$$
$$\overline{}$$
$$y_6 - y_0 = 1.0441$$

$$\overline{}$$
$$39.8067 \times 0.03 = 1.0442$$

Example 2. Consider the problem
$$y' + y = 0, \qquad y(0) = 1$$
whose solution is e^{-x}.

If the predictor P alone is used, y_n is a solution of the difference equation

(i) $\qquad\qquad y_{n+2} + 2hy_{n+1} - y_n = 0, \qquad\qquad (y_n' = -y_n)$

whose characteristic equation
$$r^2 + 2hr - 1 = 0$$
has the roots
$$r_1 = -h + \sqrt{1 + h^2} = 1 - h + \tfrac{1}{2}h^2 - \cdots,$$
$$r_2 = -h - \sqrt{1 + h^2} = -1 - h - \tfrac{1}{2}h^2 + \cdots.$$

The solution of (i) is
$$y_n = Ar_1{}^n + Br_2{}^n,$$

where $A + B = 1$ in view of $y_0 = 1$. Now fix $x = nh$ and let $n \to \infty$; then

$$r_1{}^n \to \lim \left(1 - \frac{x}{n}\right)^n = e^{-x},$$

$$r_2{}^n \to \lim (-1)^n \left(1 + \frac{x}{n}\right)^n = \pm e^x.$$

Thus, if $A \simeq 1$, the part $A r_1{}^n$ approaches the solution e^{-x}, but the part $B r_2{}^n$ approaches a spurious or "parasitic" solution $\pm B e^x$ which changes sign at each cycle and increases exponentially no matter how small the constant B.

Examine now the effect of the corrector C which here corresponds to the difference equation

$$y_{n+1} = y_n - \frac{h}{2}(y_n + y_{n+1}),$$

(ii) $$\qquad\qquad (2 + h)y_{n+1} - (2 - h)y_n = 0.$$

Its characteristic equation has the root

$$r = \frac{1 - h/2}{1 + h/2} = 1 - h + \tfrac{1}{2}h^2 - \cdots$$

and yields the solution $y_n = r^n$. If $x = nh$ is fixed, then as $n \to \infty$,

$$y_n \to \lim \left(1 - \frac{x}{n}\right)^n = e^{-x}$$

is the exact solution. The corrector thus neutralizes the instability of the predictor. Note that for small h, $|r| < 1$ and ensures stability (§ 101).

PROBLEMS

Solve numerically with $h = 0.1$ up to y_6:
1. $y' = x - y$, $\qquad y(0) = 1$.
2. $y' = 1 + y^2$, $\qquad y(0) = 0$.

180. MILNE'S METHOD

A widely used method of prediction and correction is due to Milne.* This uses the open-end quadrature (171.3) as predictor and Simpson's rule (170.7) as corrector. Four starting values are needed and these are usually taken as y_{-1}, y_0, y_1, y_2. These may be computed from a Taylor expansion

---

* W. E. Milne, *Numerical Calculus*, Princeton University Press, 1949; *Am. Math. Monthly.* **33** (1926) pp. 455–460.

or a Runge-Kutta process. The Milne formulas are

$$P \qquad y_4 = y_0 + \frac{4h}{3}(2y_1' - y_2' + 2y_3'), \qquad E_p = \tfrac{28}{90}h^5 y^{V}(\xi_1),$$

$$E \qquad y_4' = f(x_4, y_4),$$

$$C \qquad y_4 = y_2 + \frac{h}{3}(y_2' + 4y_3' + y_4'), \qquad E_c = -\tfrac{1}{90}h^5 y^{V}(\xi_2).$$

For the adjustment of C we have

$$p = \frac{28}{90}, \qquad c = -\frac{1}{90}, \qquad \frac{c}{p-c} = -\frac{1}{29}; \qquad E_c \simeq -\frac{1}{29}(C - P);$$

$$A \qquad\qquad\qquad y_4 = C - \frac{1}{29}(C - P).$$

Of course all subscripts may be advanced or diminished by the same amount. Thus, for the starting values above,

$$P \qquad\qquad y_3 = y_{-1} + \frac{4h}{3}(2y_0' - y_1' + 2y_2'),$$

$$C \qquad\qquad y_3 = y_1 + \frac{h}{3}(y_1' + 4y_2' + y_3').$$

The value y_{-1} is chosen at the start because it can be computed more accurately than y_3.

Example 1. Using the problem of Example 178,

$$y' = x + y, \qquad y(0) = 1,$$

we assume the starting values computed from the series in Example 179.1.

Table 180

n	x	$y = C - \dfrac{C-P}{29}$	$y' = x + y$	P	C	$\tfrac{1}{29}(C-P)$
-1	-0.1	0.90967	0.80967			
0	0.0	1.00000	1.00000			
1	0.1	1.11034	1.21034			
2	0.2	1.24280	1.44278			
3	0.3	1.39971	1.69971	1.39970	0.39971	—
4	0.4	1.58364	2.98364	1.58364	1.58364	—

Predict $y_3 = y_{-1} + \dfrac{4h}{3}(2y_0' - y_1' + 2y_2')$:

$$P \qquad\qquad y_3 = 0.90967 + \frac{0.4}{3}(2 - 1.21034 + 2.88556)$$

$$= 0.90967 + 0.49003 = 1.39970.$$

Find $y_3' = x_3 + y_3$:

E
$$y_3' = 0.3 + 1.39970 = 1.69970.$$

Correct $y_3 = y_1 + \dfrac{h}{3}(y_1' + 4y_2' + y_3')$:

C
$$y_3 = 1.11034 + \frac{0.1}{3}(1.21034 + 5.77112 + 1.69970)$$
$$= 1.11034 + 0.28937 = 1.39971.$$

No adjustment is necessary for 5-place accuracy.

Predict $y_4 = y_0 + \dfrac{4h}{3}(2y_1' - y_2' + 2y_3')$:

P
$$y_4 = 1.00000 + \frac{0.4}{3}(2.42068 - 1.44278 + 3.39942)$$
$$= 1.00000 + 0.58364 = 1.58364.$$

Find $y_4' = x_4 + y_4$:

E
$$y_4' = 0.4 + 1.58364 = 1.98364.$$

Correct y_4:

C
$$y_4 = 1.24280 + \frac{0.1}{3}(1.44278 + 6.79880 + 1.98364)$$
$$= 1.24280 + 0.34084 = 1.58364.$$

Predicted and corrected values agree.

Example 2. We again examine the equation
$$y' + y = 0, \qquad y(0) = 1$$
for stability, this time using only the Milne corrector. Here it corresponds to the difference equation
$$y_{n+2} = y_n - \frac{h}{3}(y_n + 4y_{n+1} + y_{n+2}),$$
$$(3 + h)y_{n+2} + 4hy_{n+1} - (3 - h)y_n = 0.$$

Its characteristic equation

(i)
$$(3 + h)r^2 + 4hr - (3 - h) = 0$$

has the roots

$$r_1 = \frac{-\frac{2}{3}h + \sqrt{1 + \frac{1}{3}h^2}}{1 + \frac{1}{3}h} = (1 - \tfrac{2}{3}h + \tfrac{1}{6}h^2 - \cdots)(1 - \tfrac{1}{3}h + \tfrac{1}{9}h^2 - \cdots)$$
$$= 1 - h + \tfrac{1}{2}h^2 - \cdots,$$

$$r_2 = \frac{-\frac{2}{3}h - \sqrt{1 + \frac{1}{3}h^2}}{1 + \frac{1}{3}h} = (-1 - \tfrac{2}{3}h - \tfrac{1}{6}h^2 - \cdots)(1 - \tfrac{1}{3}h + \tfrac{1}{9}h^2 - \cdots)$$
$$= -1 - h - \tfrac{1}{18}h^2 + \cdots.$$

The solution of (i) is now

$$y_n = Ar_1{}^n + Br_2{}^n, \qquad A + B = 1.$$

Now fix $x = nh$ and let $n \to \infty$ $(h \to 0)$; then

$$r_1{}^n \to \lim \left(1 - \frac{x}{n}\right)^n = e^{-x},$$

$$r_2{}^n \to \lim (-1)^n \left(1 + \frac{x}{n}\right)^n = \pm e^x.$$

Thus if $A \simeq 1$, the part Ae^{-x} approaches the actual solution, but the part $\pm Be^x$ is a spurious solution that changes sign at each cycle due to $(-1)^n$, and at the same time increases exponentially. Thus no matter how small the constant B, the spurious part of the Milne solution will ultimately swamp the actual solution Ae^{-x} and oscillate more and more wildly if the table of values for $y(x)$ is extended far enough. Computers often attribute such oscillations to roundoff errors, but here they are an intrinsic effect of the method itself. The culprit is the root r_2 whose absolute value exceeds 1 (§ 101).

181. RUNGE-KUTTA METHODS

These are designed to avoid the computation of the first few derivatives in a Taylor expansion. Given the equation

$$y' = f(x, y), \qquad y(x_0) = y_0,$$

we have

$$y''(x) = f_x + f_y y' = f_x + f f_y,$$

$$y'''(x) = f_{xx} + f_{xy} y' + f_x f_y + f_y f_y y' + f f_{yx} + f f_{yy} y'$$

$$= f_{xx} + 2 f f_{xy} + f^2 f_{yy} + f_x f_y + f f_y{}^2.$$

Now

$$\Delta y = y(x_0 + h) - y(x_0)$$

$$= h y'(x_0) + \tfrac{1}{2} h^2 y''(x_0) + \tfrac{1}{6} h^3 y'''(x_0),$$

if we neglect terms of higher order; and on substituting the foregoing values of y', y'', y''', we have

(1) $$\Delta y = h f + \tfrac{1}{2} h^2 (f_x + f f_y)$$

$$+ \tfrac{1}{6} h^3 (f_{xx} + 2 f f_{xy} + f^2 f_{yy} + f_x f_y + f f_y{}^2)$$

where f and its partial derivatives are all computed at (x_0, y_0).

In a *second-order* Runge-Kutta process we write

(2) $$\Delta y = w_1 k_1 + w_2 k_2,$$

(3) $$\begin{cases} k_1 = h f(x_0, y_0), \\ k_2 = h f(x_0 + \alpha h, y_0 + \beta k_1). \end{cases}$$

The numbers α and β and the weights w_1, w_2 are then determined so that (2) agrees with (1) up to the term in h^2. In k_2, expand the function in a Taylor series:

$$f(x_0 + \alpha h, y_0 + \beta k) = f + \alpha h f_x + \beta k_1 f_y + \cdots$$
$$= f + h(\alpha f_x + \beta f f_y) + \cdots,$$

stopping at the terms in h. Then from (3),

(3)′ $\qquad\qquad k_1 = hf, \qquad k_2 = hf + h^2(\alpha f_x + \beta f f_y),$

and (2) becomes

(2)′ $\qquad\qquad \Delta y = (w_1 + w_2)hf + w_2 h^2(\alpha f_x + \beta f f_y).$

If (2)′ is the same as the first line of (1),

$$\begin{array}{c|c} w_1 + w_2 = 1 & hf \\ \alpha w_2 = \tfrac{1}{2} & h^2 f_x \\ \beta w_2 = \tfrac{1}{2} & h^2 f f_y, \end{array}$$

where the quantities on the right are the common coefficients. Then $\alpha = \beta$, but the two equations in three unknowns

$$w_1 + w_2 = 1, \qquad \alpha w_2 = \tfrac{1}{2}$$

may be variously satisfied. The solutions

$$w_1 = 0, \; w_2 = 1, \qquad \alpha = \beta = \tfrac{1}{2} \qquad \text{(Runge)}$$
$$w_1 = w_2 = \tfrac{1}{2}, \qquad \alpha = \beta = 1 \qquad \text{(Heun)}$$

are the simplest. Hence from (2) and (3),

R_2 $\qquad\qquad \Delta y = hf(x_0 + \tfrac{1}{2}h, y_0 + \tfrac{1}{2}hf),$

H_2 $\qquad\qquad \Delta y = \tfrac{1}{2}h[f(x_0, y_0) + f(x_0 + h, y_0 + hf)].$

For the equation $y' = f(x)$ these yield simple rules of quadrature, H_2 being the trapezoid rule. To find $y_1 = y(x_0 + h)$, they are usually written

R_2 $\qquad \begin{cases} k_1 = hf(x_0, y_0) \\ k_2 = hf(x_0 + \tfrac{1}{2}h, y_0 + \tfrac{1}{2}k_1) \\ y_1 = y_0 + k_2; \end{cases}$

H_2 $\qquad \begin{cases} k_1 = hf(x_0, y_0) \\ k_2 = hf(x_0 + h, y_0 + k_1) \\ y_1 = y_0 + \tfrac{1}{2}(k_1 + k_2). \end{cases}$

Both R_2 and H_2 reproduce equation (1) up to terms in h^2.

In the *third order* Runge-Kutta process, we write

(5) $$\Delta y = w_1 k_1 + w_2 k_2 + w_3 k_3,$$

(6) $$\begin{cases} k_1 = hf(x_0, y_0) \\ k_2 = hf(x_0 + \alpha h, y_0 + \beta k_1) \\ k_3 = hf(x_0 + \alpha_1 h, y_0 + \beta_1 k_1 + \gamma_1 k_2) \end{cases}$$

and force agreement with (1) up to the term in h^3 by suitably choosing the weights w_1, w_2, w_3 and the numbers α, β, α_1, β_1, γ_1. The functions in (6) are replaced by the Taylor expansions up to second degree terms:

$$f(x + a, y + b) = f(x, y) + af_x + bf_y + \tfrac{1}{2}a^2 f_{xx} + abf_{xy} + \tfrac{1}{2}b^2 f_{yy}.*$$

Then a comparison of (5) with (1) yields eight equations:

	$w_1 + \quad w_2 + \qquad\qquad w_3 = 1$		hf
I	$\begin{cases} \alpha w_2 + \qquad\qquad \alpha_1 w_3 = \tfrac{1}{2} \\ \beta w_2 + \quad (\beta_1 + \gamma_1)w_3 = \tfrac{1}{2} \end{cases}$		$\begin{matrix} h^2 f_x \\ h^2 f f_y \end{matrix}$
II	$\begin{cases} \tfrac{1}{2}\alpha^2 w_2 + \qquad\qquad \tfrac{1}{2}\alpha_1{}^2 w_3 = \tfrac{1}{6} \\ \alpha\beta w_2 + \alpha_1(\beta_1 + \gamma_1)w_3 = \tfrac{1}{3} \\ \tfrac{1}{2}\beta^2 w_2 + \tfrac{1}{2}(\beta_1 + \gamma_1)^2 w_3 = \tfrac{1}{6} \end{cases}$		$\begin{matrix} h^3 f_{xx} \\ h^3 f_x f_y \\ h^3 f^2 f_{yy} \end{matrix}$
III	$\begin{cases} \alpha\gamma_1 w_3 = \tfrac{1}{6} \\ \beta\gamma_1 w_3 = \tfrac{1}{6} \end{cases}$		$\begin{matrix} h^3 f_x f_y \\ h^3 f f_y{}^2 \end{matrix}$

where the quantities on the right are the common coefficients. From groups III and I we have

(7) $$\alpha = \beta, \qquad \alpha_1 = \beta_1 + \gamma_1;$$

then groups I, II, III collapse into their first equations and the set of eight reduces to four equations in six unknowns:

(8) $$\begin{cases} w_1 + \quad w_2 + \qquad w_3 = 1 \\ \alpha w_2 + \quad \alpha_1 w_3 = \tfrac{1}{2} \\ \alpha^2 w_2 + \quad \alpha_1{}^2 w_3 = \tfrac{1}{3} \\ \alpha\gamma_1 w_3 = \tfrac{1}{6}. \end{cases}$$

If we choose $\alpha = \tfrac{1}{2}$, $\alpha_1 = 1$, we find the weights $w_1 = w_3 = \tfrac{1}{6}$, $w_2 = \tfrac{4}{6}$; then $\gamma_1 = 2$ and from (7), $\beta = \tfrac{1}{2}$, $\beta_1 = -1$, and we obtain the formulas

---

* *Advanced Calculus*, § 91.

of Kutta's third-order process:

$$K_3 \quad \begin{cases} k_1 = hf(x_0, y_0) \\ k_2 = hf(x_0 + \tfrac{1}{2}h, y_0 + \tfrac{1}{2}k_1) \\ k_3 = hf(x_0 + h, y_0 - k_1 + 2k_2) \\ k = \tfrac{1}{6}(k_1 + 4k_2 + k_3) \\ y_1 = y_0 + k. \end{cases}$$

When $f(x, y)$ is independent of y, the process reduces to Simpson's rule, which validates the choice of α and α_1.

We spare the reader the derivation of the fourth-order process of Kutta. This accurate and widely used method employs the formulas:

$$K_4 \quad \begin{cases} k_1 = hf(x_0, y_0) \\ k_2 = hf(x_0 + \tfrac{1}{2}h, y_0 + \tfrac{1}{2}k_1) \\ k_3 = hf(x_0 + \tfrac{1}{2}h, y_0 + \tfrac{1}{2}k_2) \\ k_4 = hf(x_0 + h, y_0 + k_3) \\ k = \tfrac{1}{6}(k_1 + 2k_2 + 2k_3 + k_4) \\ y = y_0 + k. \end{cases}$$

This also reduces to Simpson's rule when $f(x, y)$ is independent of y. Note that k_{i+1} depends only on k_i.

Runge-Kutta procedures are often used as starting methods to obtain one or more values for a continuing method such as Milne's. Of course, they may also be used as continuing methods, but the calculations are more numerous than in other methods of comparable accuracy. One advantage they all share is that the mesh h may be changed at any stage of the process.

Example. We again consider the problem

$$y' = x + y, \qquad y(0) = 1.$$

With $h = 0.1$, we use K to find y_1 and y_2.
First cycle with $x_0 = 0$, $y_0 = 1$.

$k_1 = 0.1(0 + 1) = 0.1$ $\qquad\qquad$ $y_0 + \tfrac{1}{2}k_1 = 1.05$
$k_2 = 0.1(0.05 + 1.05) = 0.11$ $\qquad$ $y_0 + \tfrac{1}{2}k_2 = 1.055$
$k_3 = 0.1(0.05 + 1.055) = 0.1105$ $\quad$ $y_0 + k_3 = 1.1105$
$k_4 = 0.1(0.1 + 1.1105) = 0.12105$
$k = \tfrac{1}{6}(0.1 + 0.22 + 0.221 + 0.12105) = 0.1103417$
$y_1 = y_0 + 1 = 1.1103417.$

Second cycle with $x_1 = 0.1$, $y_1 = 1.1103417$.

$k_1 = 0.1(0.1 + 1.1103417) = 0.1210342$ $y_1 + \tfrac{1}{2}k_1 = 1.1708588$
$k_2 = 0.1(0.15 + 1.1708588) = 0.1320859$ $y_1 + \tfrac{1}{2}k_2 = 1.1763847$
$k_3 = 0.1(0.15 + 1.1763847) = 0.1326385$ $y_1 + k_3 \;\; = 1.2429802$
$k_4 = 0.1(0.20 + 1.2429802) = 0.1442980$
$\;\; k = \tfrac{1}{6}(0.1210342 + 0.2641718 + 0.2652770 + 0.1442980)$
$\;\;\;\; = \tfrac{1}{6}(0.7947810) = 0.1324635$
$y_2 = y_1 + k = 1.2428052.$

Compare y_1 and y_2 with their values in the brief table below computed from the solution (Table 181).

Table 181

x	$y = 2e^x - 1 - x$
−0.1	0.90967 48
0.0	1.00000 00
0.1	1.11034 18
0.2	1.24280 55
0.3	1.39971 76
0.4	1.58364 94
0.5	1.79744 25
0.6	2.04423 76

PROBLEMS

1. Deduce Heun's formulas:

$$k_1 = hf(x_0, y_0)$$
$$k_2 = hf(x_0 + \tfrac{1}{3}h, y_0 + \tfrac{1}{3}k_1)$$
$$k_3 = hf(x_0 + \tfrac{2}{3}h, y_0 + \tfrac{2}{3}k_3)$$
$$k = \tfrac{1}{4}(k_1 + 3k_3)$$
$$y = y_0 + k$$

by choosing $\alpha = \tfrac{1}{3}$, $\alpha_1 = \tfrac{2}{3}$ in (7) and (8).

The following problems refer to the equation in the example.

2. Use K_3 to compute y_1 and y_2.
3. Use H_3 to compute y_1 and y_2.
4. Use K_4 to compute y_3 and y_4.

182. ADAMS' METHOD

When a starting method has provided $n + 1$ values, $y_0, y_1, \ldots, y_n$ of the solution of the equation

$$y' = f(x, y), \qquad y(x_0) = y_0,$$

we can compute the $n + 1$ derivatives

$$y_j' = f(x_j, y_j), \qquad j = 0, 1, \ldots, n$$

and construct from them a difference table that will include the n backward differences $\nabla y_n', \nabla^2 y_n', \ldots, \nabla^n y_n'$. Since

$$y_{n+1} = y_n + \int_{nh}^{(n+1)h} y' \, dx,$$

we can use the open Gregory formula (173.9)

$$\int_{nh}^{(n+1)h} y' \, dx = h\left[1 + \frac{1}{2}\nabla + \frac{5}{12}\nabla^2 + \frac{3}{8}\nabla^3 + \frac{251}{720}\nabla^4 + \frac{95}{288}\nabla^5 + \cdots\right]y_n'$$

to find y_{n+1}. Then $y_{n+1}' = f(x_{n+1}, y_{n+1})$ and with the backward differences of y_{n+1}', we can use the closed Gregory formula (173.8)

$$\int_{nh}^{(n+1)h} y' \, dx = h\left[1 - \frac{1}{2}\nabla - \frac{1}{12}\nabla^2 - \frac{1}{24}\nabla^3 - \frac{19}{720}\nabla^4 - \frac{3}{160}\nabla^5 - \cdots\right]y_{n+1}'$$

to correct y_{n+1}.

If the starting values y_0, y_1, y_2, y_3 are known, and we truncate the series at ∇^3, then

P $\qquad\qquad y_4 = y_3 + h\left[1 + \frac{1}{2}\nabla + \frac{5}{12}\nabla^2 + \frac{3}{8}\nabla^3\right]y_3',$

E $\qquad\qquad y_4' = f(x_4, y_4),$

C $\qquad\qquad y_4 = y_3 + h\left[1 - \frac{1}{2}\nabla - \frac{1}{12}\nabla^2 - \frac{1}{24}\nabla^3\right]y_4'.$

If $C - P$ is not within the error tolerance, recompute y_4' from E and again apply the corrector C to obtain an adjusted value. This procedure can be repeated until y_4 is stable.

Example. Given y_0, y_1, y_2, y_3 in the problem $y' = x + y$, compute y_0', y_1', y_2', y_3', and form a difference table for y' as shown in Table 182.

Table 182

x	y	$y' = x + y$	$\nabla y'$	$\nabla^2 y'$	$\nabla^3 y'$
0.0	1.00000	1.00000			
			0.21034		
0.1	1.11034	1.21034		0.02212	
			0.23246		0.00234
0.2	1.24280	1.44280		0.02446	
			0.25692		0.00255
0.3	1.39972	1.69972		0.02701	
			0.28393		
0.4	1.58365	1.98365			

Predict y_4:

$P \qquad y_4 = 1.39972 + 0.1(1.69972 + \tfrac{1}{2}0.25692 + \tfrac{5}{12}0.02446 + \tfrac{3}{8}0.00234)$

$\qquad\qquad = 1.39972 + 0.16997 + 0.01285 + 0.00102 + 0.00009$

$\qquad\qquad = 1.58365$

$E \qquad$ Compute $y_4' = x_4 + y_4 = 1.98365.$

$\qquad$ Correct y_4:

$C \qquad y_4 = 1.39972 + 0.1[1.98365 - \tfrac{1}{2}0.28393 - \tfrac{1}{12}0.02701 - \tfrac{1}{24}0.00255]$

$\qquad\qquad = 1.39972 + 0.19836 - 0.01420 - 0.00022 - 0.00001$

$\qquad\qquad = 1.58365.$

Since $C = P$, no adjustment is needed. Now find the differences of y_4' and proceed to the next cycle.

183. TWO EQUATIONS OF THE FIRST ORDER

The system

$$y' = f(x, y, z), \qquad y(x_0) = y_0$$
$$z' = g(x, y, z), \qquad z(x_0) = z_0$$

may be solved by the method of prediction and correction when an adequate number of starting values of y and z are known. For example, the Milne formulas of § 180 apply to both y and z when the values of y_0, y_1, y_2, y_3 and z_0, z_1, z_2, z_3 are known.

The starting values are obtained from a series expansion if possible. Runge-Kutta methods are also available but are more laborious. There are now two sets of K_4 formulas of identical structure:

(2f)
$$\begin{cases} k_1 = hf(x_0, y_0, z_0) \\ k_2 = hf(x_0 + \tfrac{1}{2}h, y_0 + \tfrac{1}{2}k_1, z_0 + \tfrac{1}{2}m_1) \\ k_3 = hf(x_0 + \tfrac{1}{2}h, y_0 + \tfrac{1}{2}k_2, z_0 + \tfrac{1}{2}m_2) \\ k_4 = hf(x_0 + h, y_0 + k_3, z_0 + m_3), \end{cases}$$

(2g)
$$\begin{cases} m_1 = hg(x_0, y_0, z_0) \\ m_2 = hg(x_0 + \tfrac{1}{2}h, y_0 + \tfrac{1}{2}k_1, z_0 + \tfrac{1}{2}m_1) \\ m_3 = hg(x_0 + \tfrac{1}{2}h, y_0 + \tfrac{1}{2}k_2, z_0 + \tfrac{1}{2}m_2) \\ m_4 = hg(x_0 + h, y_0 + k_3, z_0 + m_3). \end{cases}$$

Then

(3)
$$\begin{cases} y_1 = y_0 + \tfrac{1}{6}(k_1 + 2k_2 + 2k_3 + k_4) \\ z_1 = z_0 + \tfrac{1}{6}(m_1 + 2m_2 + 2m_3 + m_4). \end{cases}$$

The Milne method is illustrated in the next article. When the Adams method is used, difference tables for both y' and z' must be constructed.

184. SECOND-ORDER EQUATION

The initial value problem

(1) $$y'' = g(x, y, y'), \qquad y(x_0) = y_0, \qquad y'(x_0) = y_0'$$

may be replaced by the first-order system

$$y' = z, \qquad y(x_0) = y_0$$
$$z' = g(x, y, z), \qquad z(x_0) = y_0'.$$

If Runge-Kutta method K_4 is used to find starting values, the k_i and m_i are computed from formulas (183.2). Since $z = y'$, these become

(2)
$$\begin{cases} k_1 = hy_0' & m_1 = g(x_0, y_0, y_0') \\ k_2 = h(y_0' + \tfrac{1}{2}m_1) & m_2 = g(x_0 + \tfrac{1}{2}h, y_0 + \tfrac{1}{2}k_1, y_0' + \tfrac{1}{2}m_1) \\ k_3 = h(y_0' + \tfrac{1}{2}m_2) & m_3 = g(x_0 + \tfrac{1}{2}h, y_0 + \tfrac{1}{2}k_2, y_0' + \tfrac{1}{2}m_2) \\ k_4 = h(y_0' + m_3) & m_4 = g(x_0 + h, y_0 + k_3, y_0' + m_3). \end{cases}$$

Formulas (183.3) then yield

(3)
$$\begin{cases} y_1 = y_0 + hy_0' + \tfrac{1}{6}h(m_1 + m_2 + m_3) \\ y_1' = y_0' + \tfrac{1}{6}(m_1 + 2m_2 + 2m_3 + m_4) \end{cases}$$

with errors of order h^5.

If the derivatives are readily obtained from the given equation, we may save labor by using the Taylor expansion

$$y(x_0 + nh) = y_0 + y_0'nh + \frac{y_0''}{2!} n^2h^2 + \cdots$$

to obtain an adequate number of starting values.

When Adams' method is used, a difference table that includes backward differences of y_n' and y_n'' is needed to predict y_{n+1} and y_{n+1}':

P $\qquad y_{n+1} = y_n + h[1 + \tfrac{1}{2}\nabla + \tfrac{5}{12}\nabla + \cdots]y_n'$,

P' $\qquad y_{n+1}' = y_n' + h[1 + \tfrac{1}{2}\nabla + \tfrac{5}{12}\nabla_2 + \cdots]y_n''$.

Then

E $\qquad y_{n+1}'' = g(x_{n+1}, y_{n+1}, y_{n+1}')$.

Find backward differences for y_{n+1}' and y_{n+1}'' and apply the correctors

C $\qquad y_{n+1} = y_n + h[1 - \tfrac{1}{2}\nabla - \tfrac{1}{12}\nabla^2 - \cdots]y_{n+1}'$,

C' $\qquad y_{n+1}' = y_n' + h[1 - \tfrac{1}{2}\nabla - \tfrac{1}{12}\nabla_2 - \cdots]y_{n+1}''$.

If the difference $C - P$ is tolerable, proceed to the next cycle; if $C - P$ is too large, recompute y_{n+1}'' and correct again until a stable value is obtained.

Example. We shall consider the special case of Weber's equation (Prob. 124.1)

(i) $\qquad y'' - xy' - y = 0, \qquad y(0) = 1, \qquad y'(0) = 0.$

Its theta form

$$\vartheta(\vartheta - 1)y - x^2(\vartheta + 1)y = 0$$

rapidly gives the solution of index 0:

$$y = \sum_{n=0}^{\infty} \frac{1}{n!}\left(\frac{x^2}{2}\right)^n = e^{x^2/2}.$$

Suppose now that we only know a few terms of the foregoing series, say

$$y = 1 + \tfrac{1}{2}x^2 + \tfrac{1}{8}x^4 + \tfrac{1}{48}x^6,$$
$$y' = x + \tfrac{1}{2}x^3 + \tfrac{1}{8}x^5,$$

from which we compute y and y' and then $y'' = y + xy'$ to give four rows of Table 184.

Table 184

x	Cy	Cy'	$y'' = y + xy'$	Py	Py'
−0.1	1.00501	−0.10050	1.01506		
0.0	1.00000	0.00000	1.00000		
0.1	1.00501	0.10050	1.01506		
0.2	1.02020	0.20404	1.06101		
0.3	1.04602	0.31381	1.14016	1.04602	0.31376
0.4	1.08328	0.43331	1.25658	1.08328	0.04326
0.5	1.13314	0.56657	1.41638	1.13313	0.56650

We now apply Milne's method to find y_3 and y_3':

$P \qquad y_3 = y_{-1} + \dfrac{4h}{3}(2y_0' - y_1' + 2y_2')$

$\qquad\qquad = 1.00501 + \dfrac{0.4}{3}(0 - 0.10050 + 0.40808)$

$\qquad\qquad = 1.04602.$

$P' \qquad y_3' = y_{-1}' + \dfrac{4h}{3}(2y_0'' - y_1'' + 2y_2'')$

$\qquad\qquad = -0.10050 + \dfrac{0.4}{3}(2 - 1.01506 + 2.12202)$

$\qquad\qquad = 0.31376.$

$E \qquad y_3'' = y_3 + 0.3y_3' = 1.04602 + 0.09413 = 1.14015.$

$C \qquad y_3 = y_1 + \dfrac{h}{3}(y_1' + 4y_2' + y_3')$

$\qquad\qquad = 1.00501 + \dfrac{0.1}{3}(0.10050 + 0.81616 + 0.31376)$

$\qquad\qquad = 1.04602 \text{ (check)}.$

$C' \qquad y_3' = y_1' + \dfrac{h}{3}(y_1'' + 4y_2'' + y_3'')$

$\qquad\qquad = 0.10050 + \dfrac{0.1}{3}(1.01506 + 4.24404 + 1.14015)$

$\qquad\qquad = 0.31381.$

$E \qquad y_3'' = 1.04602 + 0.3(0.31381) = 1.14016.$

These results are entered in row $x = 0.3$.

For the second cycle, advance all subscripts in the preceding calculation by 1. Enter the results in row $x = 0.4$.

For the third cycle, again advance subscripts by 1 and enter the results in row $x = 0.5$.

The agreement of C and P is satisfactory, but a double overall check can now be made by Weddle's rule:

$$y_5 - y_{-1} = 0.03[y_{-1}' + 5y_0' + y_1' + 6y_2' + y_3' + 5y_4' + y_5']$$

gives $0.12813 = 0.12813$; and

$$y_5' - y_{-1}' = 0.03[y_{-1}'' + 5y_0'' + y_1'' + 6y_2'' + y_3'' + 5y_4'' + y_5'']$$

gives $0.66707 = 0.66707.$

PROBLEMS

1. Compute the starting values of Table 184 from the K_4 formulas (2).

2. Form a table like Table 184 for the problem

$$y'' = xy' - y = 0, \qquad y(0) = 0, \qquad y'(0) = 1.$$

3. In the problem of the example, assume starting values up to $x = 0.3$ and compute y_4 and y_5 by Adams' method.

Appendix 1

Table A Laplace Transforms: Special Functions

	$f(t)$ $(t \geqq 0)$	$F(s)$ $(s > \sigma)$	σ
1	1 or $h(t)$	$\dfrac{1}{s}$	0
2	e^{at}	$\dfrac{1}{s-a}$	a
3	t^n $(n > -1)$	$\dfrac{\Gamma(n+1)}{s^{n+1}}$ (§ 66)	0
	$t,\quad t^2$	$\dfrac{1}{s^2},\quad \dfrac{2}{s^3}$	
4	$t^n e^{at}$	$\dfrac{\Gamma(n+1)}{(s-a)^{n+1}}$	a
	$te^{at},\quad t^2 e^{at}$	$\dfrac{1}{(s-a)^2},\quad \dfrac{2}{(s-a)^3}$	
5	$\cosh bt$	$\dfrac{s}{s^2-b^2}$	$\lvert b \rvert$
6	$\sinh bt$	$\dfrac{b}{s^2-b^2}$	$\lvert b \rvert$
7	$\cos bt$	$\dfrac{s}{s^2+b^2}$	0
8	$\sin bt$	$\dfrac{b}{s^2+b^2}$	0
9	$e^{-at}\cos bt$	$\dfrac{s+a}{(s+a)^2+b^2}$	$-a$
10	$e^{-at}\sin bt$	$\dfrac{b}{(s+a)^2+b^2}$	$-a$
11	$t\cos bt$	$\dfrac{s^2-b^2}{(s^2+b^2)^2}$	0

657

Table A (*Continued*)

	$f(t)$ $(t \geqq 0)$	$F(s)$ $(s > \sigma)$	σ
12	$t \sin bt$	$\dfrac{2bs}{(s^2 + b^2)^2}$	0
13	$\dfrac{1}{2b} \sin bt - \dfrac{t}{2} \cos bt$	$\dfrac{b^2}{(s^2 + b^2)^2}$	0
14	$\dfrac{1}{2b} \sin bt + \dfrac{t}{2} \cos bt$	$\dfrac{s^2}{(s^2 + b^2)^2}$	0
15	$h(t - a)$ $\quad a \geqq 0$	$\dfrac{e^{-as}}{s}$ $\quad$ (§ 71)	0
16	$\delta(t - a)$ $\quad a \geqq 0$	e^{-as} $\quad$ (§ 73)	0
	$\delta(t)$	1	
17	$\mathrm{Si}(at)$	$\dfrac{1}{s} \cot^{-1} \dfrac{s}{a}$	Prob. 68.6
18	$\mathrm{Ci}(at)$	$-\dfrac{1}{2s} \log \left(1 + \dfrac{s^2}{a^2} \right)$	Prob. 68.7
19	$-\mathrm{Ei}(-at)$	$\dfrac{1}{s} \log \left(1 + \dfrac{s}{a} \right)$ $\quad (a > 0)$	Prob. 68.8
20	$\mathrm{erf}\,(a\sqrt{t})$	$\dfrac{a}{s\sqrt{s + a^2}}$	Ex. 68
21	$L_n(at)$	$\dfrac{(s - a)^n}{s^{n+1}}$	Ex. 123
22	$e^{-at} L_n(a - b)t$	$\dfrac{(s + b)^n}{(s + a)^{n+1}}$	Ex. 123
23	$J_n(at$	$\dfrac{[\sqrt{a^2 + s^2} - s]^n}{a^n \sqrt{a^2 + s^2}}$	Ex. 127.4
	$J_0(at)$	$\dfrac{1}{\sqrt{a^2 + s^2}}$	

See ref. 4, 24, or 45 for more extensive tables.

Table B   Laplace Transforms: Operations

No.	$f(t)$ $(t \geqq 0)$		$F(s) = \int_0^\infty e^{-st}f(t)\,dt$
I	$\begin{cases} f'(t) \\ f''(t) \\ f^{(n)}(t) \end{cases}$		$sF(s) - f(0)$ $s^2F(s) - sf(0) - f0'()$ $s^nF(s) - s^{n-1}f(0) - s^{n-2}f'(0) - \cdots - f^{(n-1)}(0)$
II	$\int_0^t f(x)\,dx$		$\dfrac{F(s)}{s}$
III	$\begin{cases} tf(t) \\ t^2f(t) \\ t^nf(t) \end{cases}$		$-F'(s)$ $F''(s)$ $(-1)^n D^n F(s)$
IV	$\dfrac{f(t)}{t}$		$\int_s^\infty F(x)\,dx$
V	$f(at)$	Change of scale	$\dfrac{1}{a}F\left(\dfrac{s}{a}\right)$
VI	$e^{-at}f(t)$	Damping factor	$F(s + a)$
VII	$f(t - a)h(t - a)$	Shift and cutoff	$e^{-as}F(s)$
VIII	$f(t) * g(t)$	Convolution	$F(s)G(s)$
IX	$f(t + a) = f(t)$	Period a	$F(s) = \dfrac{\int_0^a e^{-st}f(t)\,dt}{1 - e^{-as}}$
X	$f(t + a) = -f(t)$	Period $2a$	$F(s) = \dfrac{\int_0^a e^{-st}f(t)\,dt}{1 + e^{-as}}$

Table C Laplace Transforms of Periodic Functions

Square Wave: amp = 1, p = 2a

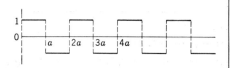

$f_1(t) = h(t) - 2h(t - a) + 2h(t - 2a) - \cdots$

$$F_1(s) = \frac{1}{s} + \frac{2}{s}\sum_{j=1}^{\infty}(-1)^j e^{-jas}$$

$$= \frac{1}{s}\frac{1 - e^{-as}}{1 + e^{-as}}$$

$$= \frac{1}{s}\tanh\frac{as}{2}$$

Rectified Triangular Wave: amp = 1,
p = 2a

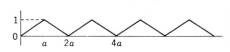

$$f_2(t) = \frac{1}{a}\int_0^t f_1(t)\,dt$$

$$F_2(s) = \frac{1}{as}F_1(s)$$

$$= \frac{1}{as^2} + \frac{2}{as^2}\sum_{j=1}^{\infty}(-1)^j e^{-jas}$$

$$= \frac{1}{as^2}\tanh\frac{as}{2}$$

Morse Dot Function: amp = 1, p = 2a

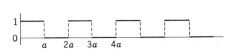

$$f_3(t) = \tfrac{1}{2}[h(t) + f_1(t)] = \sum_{j=0}^{\infty}(-1)^j h(t - ja)$$

$$F_3(s) = \frac{1}{2}\left[\frac{1}{s} + F_1(s)\right]$$

$$= \frac{1}{s}\sum_{j=0}^{\infty}(-1)^j e^{-jas}$$

$$= \frac{1}{s}\frac{1}{1 + e^{-as}}$$

Sawtooth Function: amp = 1, p = a

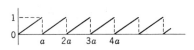

$$f_4(t) = \frac{t}{a} - \sum_{j=1}^{\infty}h(t - ja)$$

$$F_4(s) = \frac{1}{as^2} - \frac{1}{s}\sum_{j=1}^{\infty}e^{-jas}$$

$$= \frac{1 - (1 + as)e^{-as}}{as^2(1 - e^{-as})}$$

Table C (*Continued*)

Rectified Sine Wave: amp $= 1$, p $= \dfrac{\pi}{b}$

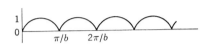

$f_5(t) = |\sin bt|$

$\qquad = \sin bt + 2 \displaystyle\sum_{j=1}^{\infty} h\left(t - \frac{j\pi}{b}\right) \sin\left(t - \frac{j\pi}{b}\right)$

$F_5(s) = \dfrac{b}{s^2 + b^2}\left[1 + 2 \displaystyle\sum_{j=1}^{\infty} e^{-j\pi s/b}\right]$

$\qquad = \dfrac{b}{s^2 + b^2}\dfrac{1 + e^{-\pi s/b}}{1 - e^{-\pi s/b}}$

$\qquad = \dfrac{b}{s^2 + b^2} \coth \dfrac{\pi s}{2b}$

Rectified Sine Half-wave: amp $= 1$, p $= \dfrac{2\pi}{b}$

$f_6(t) = \dfrac{1}{2}[\sin bt + |\sin bt|]$

$\qquad = \displaystyle\sum_{j=0}^{\infty} h\left(t - \frac{j\pi}{b}\right) \sin\left(t - \frac{j\pi}{b}\right)$

$F_6(s) = \dfrac{b}{s^2 + b^2} \displaystyle\sum_{j=0}^{\infty} e^{-j\pi s/b}$

$\qquad = \dfrac{b}{s^2 + b^2}\dfrac{1}{1 - e^{2\pi s/b}}$

Series of Unit Impulses: mag $= 1$, p $= a$

$f_7(t) = \displaystyle\sum_{j=1}^{\infty} \delta(j - at)$

$F_7(s) = \displaystyle\sum_{j=1}^{\infty} e^{-jas}$

$\qquad = \dfrac{e^{-as}}{1 - e^{-as}}$

Appendix 2

*The Solution of Linear Algebraic Equations**

A1. COEFFICIENT MATRIX

The rank of the coefficient matrix plays a dominant role in the theory of linear algebraic equations. It is not surprising, therefore, that a test for the rank of a matrix, that was a by-product of some work in dimensional analysis,† proves to be an admirable tool in this theory. With its aid the consistency requirement assumes a simple and effective form, and the solution of both homogeneous and non-homogeneous systems is given explicitly in terms of submatrices. The test for rank is given in the

Theorem. *A partitioned $m \times n$ matrix $\begin{pmatrix} P & Q \\ R & S \end{pmatrix}$, in which P is a non-singular $r \times r$ matrix, will be of rank r when and only when*

$$(1) \qquad\qquad RP^{-1}Q = S.$$

PROOF. Let $m = r + j$, $n = r + k$; then the submatrices P, Q, R, S are respectively $r \times r$, $r \times k$, $j \times r$, $j \times k$. When the matrix is of rank r, the last j rows (R, S) will be linear combinations of the first r rows (P, Q); hence there exists a $j \times r$ matrix C such that

$$CP = R, \qquad CQ = S;$$

hence $C = RP^{-1}$ and $RP^{-1}Q = S$. Conversely when this condition holds the matrix is of rank r; for on putting $C = RP^{-1}$, we have $CP = R$, $CQ = S$, showing that the last j rows are linearly dependent on the first r.

---

* Reprinted by permission from the *Mathematical Gazette*, vol. 46, no. 357, October, 1962.

† L. Brand, *The Pi Theorem in Dimensional Analysis*, Archive for Rational Mechanics and Analysis, vol. 1, 1957, pp. 35–45.

663

Note 1. The matrix RP^{-1} gives the precise constants for expressing the linear dependence of (R, S) on (P, Q).

Note 2. If the given matrix has only r columns ($k = 0$) the above partitioning becomes $\begin{pmatrix} P \\ R \end{pmatrix}$ and the matrix is then of rank r since $\det P \neq 0$ and there are *no* determinants of higher order.

Note 3. If the matrix is enlarged to $\begin{pmatrix} P & Q & U \\ R & S & V \end{pmatrix}$, this augmented matrix will be of rank r if

$$CP = R, \qquad CQ = S, \qquad CU = V;$$

then $C = RP^{-1}$ and we have the two conditions

$$(2) \qquad\qquad RP^{-1}Q = S, \qquad RP^{-1}U = V.$$

These tests, applied to the coefficient matrix of a linear system, lead readily to the general solution and indeed to all the relevant theorems appertaining thereto.*

A2. HOMOGENEOUS SYSTEMS

Consider the set of $m = r + j$ equations in $n = r + k$ variables ($x_1, x_2, \ldots, x_r$; $y_1, y_2, \ldots, y_k$):

$$(3) \qquad\qquad \begin{pmatrix} P & Q \\ R & S \end{pmatrix} \begin{pmatrix} x \\ y \end{pmatrix} = \begin{pmatrix} O_r \\ O_j \end{pmatrix}, \qquad \det P \neq 0,$$

where O_i denotes a column of i zeros. Here $\det P$ is of order r and the coefficient matrix, partitioned as in § A1, is of rank r, so that relation (1) holds good. Equations (3) are equivalent to

$$Px + Qy = O_r, \qquad Rx + Sy = O_j;$$

hence

$$(4) \qquad\qquad x = -P^{-1}Qy;$$

and substituting this in the second equation,

$$(S - RP^{-1}Q)y = O_j.$$

By virtue of (1) this is satisfied by an *arbitrary* $k \times 1$ column vector y; and after y is chosen at pleasure, the $r \times 1$ column vector x is uniquely determined by (4).

---

* See Bôcher, M., *Introduction to Higher Algebra*, Macmillan, New York, 1922, Chap. 4.

A3. NON-HOMOGENEOUS SYSTEMS

Consider the non-homogeneous linear system

$$(5) \qquad \begin{pmatrix} P & Q \\ R & S \end{pmatrix} \begin{pmatrix} x \\ y \end{pmatrix} = \begin{pmatrix} a \\ b \end{pmatrix}, \qquad \det P \neq 0,$$

where a and b denote $(r \times 1)$ and $(j \times 1)$ column vectors respectively, and the coefficient matrix is partitioned as before. The system (5) is equivalent to the homogeneous system

$$(5') \qquad \begin{pmatrix} P & Q & a \\ R & S & b \end{pmatrix} \begin{pmatrix} x \\ y \\ -1 \end{pmatrix} = \begin{pmatrix} O_r \\ O_{j+1} \end{pmatrix}.$$

This may be solved as in § A2 provided the augmented matrix on the left has the rank r.

But a direct treatment of (5) is actually more illuminating. For (5) is equivalent to the two equations

$$Px + Qy = a, \qquad Rx + Sy = b;$$

hence if the coefficient matrix is of rank r,

$$(6) \qquad x = P^{-1}a - P^{-1}Qy,$$

$$RP^{-1}a + (S - RP^{-1}Q)y = b.$$

With an arbitrary choice for y, the last equation becomes

$$(7) \qquad RP^{-1}a = b$$

in view of (1). *This is the necessary and sufficient condition that the system* (5) *be consistent.* With reference to Note 3 above we see that conditions (1) and (7) together imply that the rank of the coefficient matrix and the augmented matrix, namely

$$\begin{pmatrix} P & Q \\ R & S \end{pmatrix} \quad \text{and} \quad \begin{pmatrix} P & Q & a \\ R & S & b \end{pmatrix},$$

must be the same. But there is no need to form the augmented matrix for nothing could be simpler or more practical in computation, than the sharp condition for consistency given in (7).

The general solution (6) may be written $x = X_0 + X_y$; here

(8) $$X_0 = P^{-1}a$$

is the solution of (5) for the choice $y = 0$ and is free of arbitrary constants, whereas

(9) $$X_y = -P^{-1}Qy$$

is the solution of the corresponding *homogeneous system* with the k arbitrary constants in y. Note that when $a = O_r$, consistency requires $b = O_j$ also. The number of arbitrary constants in the general solution is equal to the nullity $n - r = k$ of the coefficient matrix.

A4. COMPUTATION PROCEDURE

The method is illustrated in the solution of the following system:

(10)
$$\begin{aligned}
2x_1 + 2x_2 + 5y_1 + 3y_2 &= 5 \\
6x_1 + x_2 + 5y_1 + 4y_2 &= 5 \\
4x_1 - x_2 \qquad + y_2 &= 2 \\
2x_1 \qquad + y_1 + y_2 &= 1.
\end{aligned}$$

The coefficient matrix

$$\left(\begin{array}{cc|cc}
2 & 2 & 5 & 3 \\
6 & 1 & 5 & 4 \\
\hline
4 & -1 & 0 & 1 \\
2 & 0 & 1 & 1
\end{array}\right) = \begin{pmatrix} P & Q \\ R & S \end{pmatrix}$$

is of rank 2; for $\det P = -10$ and $RP^{-1}Q = S$. But since

$$RP^{-1}a = \begin{pmatrix} -1 & 1 \\ -\frac{1}{5} & \frac{2}{5} \end{pmatrix}\begin{pmatrix} 5 \\ 5 \end{pmatrix} = \begin{pmatrix} 0 \\ 1 \end{pmatrix} \neq b$$

the equations are *not consistent*. But if we replace the 2 on the right side of (10) by 0 we obtain a consistent system with $b = \begin{pmatrix} 0 \\ 1 \end{pmatrix}$. For *this* system x is given by (6) for an arbitrary choice by y. Now

$$X_0 = P^{-1}a = -\frac{1}{10}\begin{pmatrix} 1 & -2 \\ -6 & 2 \end{pmatrix}\begin{pmatrix} 5 \\ 5 \end{pmatrix} = -\frac{1}{10}\begin{pmatrix} -5 \\ -20 \end{pmatrix} = \begin{pmatrix} \frac{1}{2} \\ 2 \end{pmatrix},$$

$$X_y = -P^{-1}Qy = \frac{1}{10}\begin{pmatrix} 1 & -2 \\ -6 & 2 \end{pmatrix}\begin{pmatrix} 5 & 3 \\ 5 & 4 \end{pmatrix}\begin{pmatrix} y_1 \\ y_2 \end{pmatrix} = -\begin{pmatrix} \frac{1}{2} & \frac{1}{2} \\ 2 & 1 \end{pmatrix}\begin{pmatrix} y_1 \\ y_2 \end{pmatrix},$$

and

$$\begin{pmatrix} x_1 \\ x_2 \end{pmatrix} = \begin{pmatrix} \frac{1}{2} - \frac{1}{2}y_1 - \frac{1}{2}y_2 \\ 2 - 2y_1 - y_2 \end{pmatrix}.$$

A5. FUNDAMENTAL THEOREM

The preceding developments show that any system of linear algebraic equations may be tested for consistency and solved when consistent by means of the following

Theorem. *Let the system of* $m = r + j$ *linear equations in* $n = r + k$ *variables* $x_1, x_2, \ldots, x_r, y_1, y_2, \ldots, y_k$ *be written*

$$\begin{pmatrix} P & Q \\ R & S \end{pmatrix} \begin{pmatrix} x \\ y \end{pmatrix} = \begin{pmatrix} a \\ b \end{pmatrix}, \qquad \det P \neq 0;$$

the $r \times r$ *submatrix* P *is non-singular and* a, b *are respectively* $r \times 1$ *and* $j \times 1$ *column vectors. The partitioned* $(r + j) \times (r + k)$ *coefficient matrix will be of rank* r *iff*

(r) $RP^{-1}Q = S.$

The equations will be consistent iff

(c) $RP^{-1}a = b.$

When both conditions are fulfilled the general solution is

(s) $x = P^{-1}a - P^{-1}Qy, \qquad y$ *arbitrary.*

Special cases:

1, If $m = r, (j = 0)$ the system becomes

$$(P, Q)\begin{pmatrix} x \\ y \end{pmatrix} = (a), \qquad \det P \neq 0.$$

The rank of (P, Q) is r, the equations are consistent and the solution is given by (s). The general case reduces to case 1 when R and S form a row of zeros and $b = 0$.

2, If $n = r, (k = 0)$, the system becomes

$$\begin{pmatrix} P \\ R \end{pmatrix}(x) = \begin{pmatrix} a \\ b \end{pmatrix}, \qquad \det P \neq 0.$$

The rank of $\begin{pmatrix} P \\ R \end{pmatrix}$ is r and when condition (c) is fulfilled the solution $x = P^{-1}a$ is unique. The general case reduces to case 2 when Q and S form a column of zeros and $y = 0$.

3, When $a = O_r, b = O_j$ the homogeneous system

$$\begin{pmatrix} P & Q \\ R & S \end{pmatrix} \begin{pmatrix} x \\ y \end{pmatrix} = \begin{pmatrix} O_r \\ O_j \end{pmatrix}, \qquad \det P \neq 0,$$

is always consistent, and when the rank of $\begin{pmatrix} P & Q \\ R & S \end{pmatrix}$ is r, has the general solution $x = -P^{-1}Qy$.

In the important case $m = n = r + 1$, Q, $P^{-1}Q$ and $x = -P^{-1}Qy$ are all $r \times 1$ vectors; y is an arbitrary scalar and the general solution x is an arbitrary multiple of the vector $P^{-1}Q$.

PROBLEMS

Find the general solution of the following systems:

1. $\begin{aligned} x_1 + 2x_2 - x_3 + 3x_4 &= 2, \\ 3x_1 + 4x_2 \quad - x_4 &= 1, \\ -x_1 \quad - 2x_3 + 7x_4 &= 3. \end{aligned}$

2. $\begin{aligned} 2x_1 + 2x_2 - 2x_3 \quad &= 3, \\ 2x_1 + x_2 - 2x_3 + 2x_4 &= 1, \\ -2x_1 - 2x_2 + 2x_3 \quad &= -3, \\ 2x_2 \quad - 4x_4 &= 4. \end{aligned}$

3. Find the rank of the matrix

$$A = \begin{pmatrix} 2 & -2 & 4 & 1 \\ 2 & 3 & 2 & 2 \\ -1 & 1 & -1 & 3 \\ -3 & -2 & -1 & 8 \\ 2 & 3 & 0 & -5 \end{pmatrix}.$$

Solve the system: $A \begin{pmatrix} x_1 \\ x_2 \\ x_3 \\ x_4 \end{pmatrix} = \begin{pmatrix} 1 \\ 2 \\ 0 \\ -1 \\ 1 \end{pmatrix}.$

4. Find the rank of the matrix A and then solve the system $Ax = 0$:

$$A = \begin{pmatrix} 1 & -2 & 1 & -3 \\ 2 & 1 & -3 & 1 \\ 3 & 3 & -2 & 1 \\ 2 & -3 & -3 & -2 \end{pmatrix}.$$

Appendix 3

Periodic Solutions of Linear Difference Equations

Consider the linear difference equation

(1) $$P(E)x(t) = f(t)$$

in which

(2) $$P(E) = a_0 E^n + a_1 E^{n-1} + \cdots + a_n$$

is a polynomial of degree n, and $\{f(t)\} \neq \{0\}$ is a sequence of period p on the set of non-negative integers: $f(t + p) = f(t)$. We shall obtain conditions under which (1) admits a solution of period p and find the precise set of initial values

(3) $$x(0) = x_0, \quad x(1) = x_1, \ldots, \quad x(n-1) = x_{n-1},$$

which yield this periodic solution.

In terms of the shift operator $s = \{0, 1, 0, 0, \ldots\}$ of §148, we have (cf. §150)

$$s\{Ex\} = \{x\} - x_0, \quad s^2\{E^2x\} = \{x\} - x_0 - sx_1,$$

and, in general,

(4) $$s^n\{E^nx\} = \{x\} - x_0 - sx_1 - \cdots - s^{n-1}x_{n-1}.$$

If (4) is applied to the periodic sequence $\{f(t)\}$, with $n = p$, we have $E^p f = f$, and

(5) $$\{f(t)\} = \frac{f_0 + sf_1 + \cdots + s^{p-1}f_{p-1}}{1 - s^p}$$

For example, $\{\sin \pi t/2\} = \{0, 1, 0, -1\}_4$ of period 4, has the operator

$$\left\{\sin \frac{\pi}{2} t\right\} = \frac{s - s^3}{1 - s^4} = \frac{s}{1 + s^2};$$
(149.15)

669

and for the constant sequence $\{k\}$ of period 1,

$$\{k\} = \frac{k}{1-s}. \tag{149.4}$$

We now introduce the operator $r = 1/s$; although r is not a sequence on the non-negative integers, it yields results more suitable for our purpose. In terms of r, (4) and (5) become

(4)′ $$\{E^n x\} = r^n\{x\} - r^n x_0 - r^{n-1} x_1 + \cdots + r x_{n-1},$$

(5)′ $$\{f(t)\} = \frac{f_0 r^p + f_1 r^{p-1} + \cdots + f_{p-1} r}{r^p - 1} = F(r).$$

Equation (1) now transforms into

(6) $$P(r)\{x\} = Q(r) + F(r),$$

where $Q(r)$ is a polynomial of degree n whose coefficients are linear functions of the initial values $x_0, x_1, \ldots, x_{n-1}$; and when $Q(r)$ is known, these initial values are uniquely determined by a set of n linear equations.

If (1) admits a solution $x(t)$ of period p, it must have the operational form

$$\{x\} = \frac{x_0 r^p + x_1 r^{p-1} + \cdots + x_{p-1} r}{r^p - 1} = \frac{X_p(r)}{r^p - 1}.$$

Then (6) becomes

(7) $$P(r) \frac{X_p(r)}{r^p - 1} = Q(r) + \frac{F_p(r)}{r^p - 1}.$$

If the zeros of $P(r)$ are not poles of $F(r) = F_p(r)/(r^p - 1)$, and hence not poles of $X_p(r)/(r^p - 1)$, the left member of (7) will vanish when $P(r) = 0$. Then

(8) $$Q^{(i)}(r) + F^{(i)}(r) = 0, \qquad i = 0, 1, \ldots, m_j - 1,$$

for every zero r_j of $P(r)$ of multiplicity m_j. The n zeros of $P(r)$, simple or multiple, thus yield n equations (8) which may be solved uniquely for the initial values $x_0, x_1, \ldots, x_{n-1}$, so that one period of $\{x\}$ is known. To prove this, multiply (7) by $r^p - 1$:

$$P(r) X_p(r) = Q(r)(r^p - 1) + F_p(r).$$

In this polynomial equation of degree $n + p$, the right member vanishes with $P(r)$ and is therefore divisible by $P(r)$. The quotient obtained is a polynomial $X_p(r)$ of degree p or less, and $X_p(r)/(r^p - 1)$ is the operator for the desired periodic solution. We state this result in the

Theorem. *Let the initial value problem*

$$P(E)x(t) = f(t), \qquad x(0) = x_0, \qquad x(1) = x_1, \ldots, x(n-1) = x_{n-1},$$

in which $P(E)$ is a polynomial of degree n and $\{f(t)\}$ a sequence of period p, have the transform

$$P(r)\{x(t)\} = Q(r) + F(r).$$

Then the problem has a unique solution of period p if the zeros of $P(r)$ are not poles of $F(r)$, and the initial values that yield $\{x(t)\}$ are determined by equations (8).

Example 1. $(E^3 + E^2 - E - 1)x(t) = \{1, 0, -1\}_3$. The zeros of $P(r) = (r+1)^2(r-1)$ are $1, -1, -1$; and

$$F(r) = \frac{r^3 - r}{r^3 - 1} = \frac{r^2 + r}{r^2 + r + 1}, \qquad F'(r) = \frac{2r + 1}{(r^2 + r + 1)^2};$$

$$Q(r) = x_0(r^3 + r^2 - r) + x_1(r^2 + r) + x_2 r,$$

$$Q'(r) = x_0(3r^2 + 2r - 1) + x_1(2r + 1) + x_2.$$

Equations (8) are now

$$Q(1) + F(1) = 0: \qquad x_0 + 2x_1 + x_2 + \tfrac{2}{3} = 0$$

$$Q(-1) + F(-1) = 0: \qquad x_0 + 0 - x_2 + 0 = 0$$

$$Q'(-1) + F'(-1) = 0: \qquad -x_1 + x_2 - 1 = 0;$$

hence $x_0 = \tfrac{1}{3}$, $x_1 = -\tfrac{2}{3}$, $x_2 = \tfrac{1}{3}$ is the periodic solution. To verify, compute x_3, x_4, x_5 from the equation.

Example 2. $(E^2 - 2E + 2)x(t) = \{0, 1, 0, -1\}_4$. The zeros of $P(r) = r^2 - 2r - 2$ are $1 \pm i$; and

$$F(r) = \frac{r^3 - r}{r^4 - 1} = \frac{r}{r^2 + 1}; \qquad Q(r) = x_0 r^2 + x_1 r - 2x_0 r = x_0(r^2 - 2r) + x_1 r.$$

From (8), $Q(i + 1) + F(i + 1) = 0$ gives

$$(1 + i)x_1 - 2x_0 + \frac{1 + i}{2i + 1} = (1 + i)x_1 - 2x_0 + \frac{3 - i}{5} = 0.$$

On equationing real and imaginary parts, we have

$$x_1 - 2x_0 + \tfrac{3}{5} = 0, \qquad x_1 - \tfrac{1}{5} = 0.$$

Hence $x_0 = \tfrac{2}{5}$, $x_1 = \tfrac{1}{5}$; and from the equation, $x_2 = -\tfrac{2}{5}$, $x_3 = -\tfrac{1}{5}$. The periodicity is readily verified. As always, in the case of conjugate complex zeros, one zero serves for two.

If $S = \sum\limits_{i=0}^{p-1} f_i$, it is easily shown that

$$(9) \qquad\qquad s = \sum\limits_{i=0}^{p-1} x_1 = S/P(1).$$

In this example, $P(1) = 1$, and $s = S = 0$. Indeed, even when $P(1) = 0$, $S = 0$ implies $s = 0$ (cf. Example 1).

PROBLEMS

Find the periodic solution, verify periodicity, and also equation (9).

1. $(E^2 + 1)x(t) = \{1, 2, 3\}_3$.

2. $(2E^2 - 2E + 1)x(t) = \{1, 0\}_2$.

3. $(E^2 + 4)x(t) = \{1, 2, 3, 2\}_4$.

4. $(E^2 - 4)x(t) = \{1, 2, 3, 2\}_4$.

5. $(E^2 + 1)^2 x(t) = \{1, 2, 3, 4, 5\}_5$.

6. $(E^2 + 1)^2 x(t) = \{10, 1\}_2$.

7. $(E^2 - 4)x(t) = \{1, -2, 1, 0\}_4$.

8. Prove equation (9) when $f(1) \neq 0$. If $f(1) = 0$ and $S = 0$, show that $s = 0$ (cf. Ex. 1).

Bibliography

General Reference

1. Birkhoff, G. and S. MacLane, *A Survey of Modern Algebra*, second edition, Macmillan, New York, 1953.
2. Brand, L., *Advanced Calculus*, Wiley, New York, 1955.
3. Courant, R., *Differential and Integral Calculus*, 2 vols., Interscience, New York, 1937–36: vol. 1, second edition; vol. 2, first edition.
4. *C.R.C. Standard Mathematical Tables*, fourteenth edition, Chemical Rubber Publishing Co., 1964.
5. Erdélyi, A., *Operational Calculus and Generalized Functions*, Holt, Rinehart and Winston, New York, 1962.
6. Gantmacher, F. R., *The Theory of Matrices*, 2 vols., Chelsea, New York, 1959.
7. Goursat, E., *Cours d'Analyse Mathématique*, fifth edition, 3 vols., Gauthier-Villars Paris, 1927.
8. Hildebrand, F. B., *Introduction to Numerical Analysis*, McGraw-Hill, New York, 1956.
9. Jahnke-Emde-Lösch, *Tables of Higher Functions*, sixth edition, Teubner, Stuttgart, 1960.
10. Knopp, K., *Theory and Application of Infinite Series*, Blackie, London, 1928.
11. Kopal, Z., *Numerical Analysis*, second edition, Wiley, New York, 1961.
12. Mikusiński, J., *Operational Calculus*, Pergamon, New York, 1959.
13. Peirce, B. O. and R. M. Foster, *A Short Table of Integrals*, fourth edition, Ginn 1956.
14. Picard, E., *Traité d'Analyses*, second edition, 3 vols., Gauthier-Villars, Paris, 1922–1928.
15. Taylor, A. E., *Advanced Calculus*, Ginn, Boston, 1957.
16. Tolstov, G., *Fourier Series*, Prentice-Hall, Englewood Cliffs, N.J., 1962.
17. Vallée-Poussin, Ch.-J., *Cours d'Analyse Infinitésimale*, eighth edition, 2 vols., Gauthier-Villars, Paris, 1938.
18. Watson, G. N., *A Treatise on the Theory of Bessel Functions*, second edition, Macmillan, New York, 1962.
19. Widder, D. V., *The Laplace Transform*, Princeton University Press, Princeton, 1941.
20. Widder, D. V., *Advanced Calculus*, second edition, Prentice-Hall, Englewood Cliffs, N.J., 1961.

Differential Equations

21. Bellman, R., *Stability Theory of Differential Equations*, McGraw-Hill, New York, 1953.
22. Bieberbach, L., *Einführung in die Theorie der Differentialgleichungen im Reellen Gibiet*, Springer, Berlin, 1956.
23. Bôcher, M., *Leçons sur les méthodes de Sturm*, Gauthier-Villars, Paris, 1917.

24. Churchill, R. V., *Operational Mathematics*, second edition, McGraw-Hill, New York, 1955.
25. Coddington, E. A., and N. Levinson, *Theory of Ordinary Differential Equations*, McGraw-Hill, New York, 1955.
26. Forsyth, A. R., *A Treatise on Differential Equations*, sixth edition, Macmillan London, 1961.
27. Fox, L., *Numerical Solution of Ordinary and Partial Differential Equations*, Addison-Wesley, Reading, Mass., 1962.
28. Hamming, R. W., *Numerical Methods for Scientists and Engineers*, McGraw-Hill, New York, 1962.
29. Ince, E. L., *Ordinary Differential Equations*, Dover, New York, 1944.
30. Kamke, E., *Differentialgleichungen Reeller Functionen*, Akademische Verlagsgesellschaft, Leipzig, 1930. (A standard work.)
31. Kamke, E., *Differentialgleichungen: Lösungsmethoden und Lösungen*, I. *Gewöhnliche Differentialgleichungen*, fourth edition, Akademische Verlagsgesellschaft, Leipzig, 1951. (Contains systematic lists of differential equations and their solutions.)
32. LaSalle, J., and S. Lefschetz, *Stability by Liapunov's Direct Method*, Academic, New York, 1961.
33. Lefschetz, S., *Differential Equations: Geometric Theory*, second edition, Interscience, New York, 1962.
34. Levy, H., and E. A. Baggott, *Numerical Solutions of Differential Equations*, Dover, New York, 1950.
35. Minorsky, N., *Introduction to Non-Linear Mechanics*, Edwards Brothers, Ann Arbor, 1947.
36. Nemytskii, V. V. and V. V. Stepanov, *Qualitative Theory of Differential Equations*, Princeton University Press, Princeton, 1961.
37. Sansone, G. and R. Conti, *Non-linear Differential Equations*, Pergamon, New York, 1964.
38. Struble, R. A., *Nonlinear Differential Equations*, McGraw-Hill, New York, 1962.

Difference Equations

39. Fort, T., *Finite Differences and Difference Equations in the Real Domain*, Clarendon Press, Oxford, 1948.
40. Jordan, C., *Calculus of Finite Differences*, second edition, Dover, New York, 1964.
41. Levy, H., and F. Lessman, *Finite Difference Equations*, Macmillan, New York, 1961.
42. Milne-Thompson, C. B. E., *The Calculus of Finite Differences*, Macmillan, London, 1960.
43. Nörlund, N. E., *Leçons sur les équations linéares aux différences finies*, Gauthier-Villars, Paris, 1929.

Integral Transforms

44. Ditkin, V. A., and A. P. Prudnikov, *Integral Transforms and Operational Calculus*, Pergamon, New York, 1966.
45. Erdélyi et al., *Tables of Integral Transforms*, Bateman Manuscript Project, 2 vols., McGraw-Hill, New York, 1954.

Answers to Odd-Numbered Problems

Chapter 1

<small>SECTION</small> 3

1. $2xy' - y = 0.$
3. $xy' = y + \frac{1}{4}y^2.$
5. $(x^2 - y^2 - 1)y' - 2xy = 0, \quad \frac{1}{4}y = 0.$
7. $fy' - f'y = fg' - gf'.$
9. $(gh - fk)y' + (gh' - g'h + kf' - fk')y + (hk' - h'k)y^2$
$$+ fg' - f'g = 0.$$

<small>SECTION</small> 4

5. Isoclines: $y/x = (p - 1)/(p + 1).$
7. $X + Y = -1; \quad Y = (X + 1)^2.$

<small>SECTION</small> 6

1. $\frac{1}{3}x^3 - xy^2 + \frac{1}{4}y^4 = C.$
3. $7r^3 - 4r\cos\theta = C.$
5. $x + \sqrt{x^2 + y^2} = C.$
7. $(x + y)/(1 - xy) = C.$
9. $y^2 - x^2 - e^{xy} = 3.$
11. $3x^2 + y^4 = 4y.$
13. $\frac{1}{2}y^2 + yx^{-1} - x^{-2} = \frac{3}{4}$

<small>SECTION</small> 7

1. $y = Ce^{2x}/x.$
3. $k = (a - b)/ab; \quad y = ab/[(a - b)t + b].$
5. $y = Cxe^x.$
7. $y(1 + x^2) = C(1 - y^2).$
9. $x + y = C(1 + xy).$
11. $y/\sqrt{1 + y^2} = (x + C)/(1 - Cx).$
13. $y = \frac{1}{2}(5 - e^{-2x}).$
15. $y = Cxe^{1/x}.$
17. $y = 1, y = x.$

<small>SECTION</small> 9

1. $4x^3y + 3y^4 + 6y^2 = C.$
3. $y = Cx^2 - x^{-1}.$
5. $y = 1/(1 + Cx).$
7. $x^2y^4 + y^6 = Cx^4.$

<small>675</small>

9. $X = (1 - n) \exp \int p \, dx$, $Y = y^{-n}$.

11. $x + y = C(1 + xy)$.

13. $y + x^3 + 3 = Ce^{x^3/3}$.

15. (a) $x^2y + \frac{1}{3}y^3 = Ce^{-x}$; (b) $y = x^2/(Cx - 1)$.

SECTION 11

1. \$148.02; \$148.59; \$148.88; \$149.18.

3. 115.13 years.

5. 27.1 min.

7. $r_0t_1/(r_0 - r_1)$ days.

9. $y_0t_1/(y_0 - y_1)$ days.

13. 16.77 years.

SECTION 12

1. 139.76 lb.   **3.** 50 min.

5. 24 min.   **7.** 60 min.

9. 22.9 min.; 8.208 ft.

SECTION 13

1. 4.85 hours.

3. $k = \frac{1}{60}$; $x = \frac{4}{3}$.

5. $k_1 = 0.14 \log 1.75$; $k_2 = 0.06 \log 1.75$.

7. $k_2 = 0.001314$, $k_1 = 4k_2$; 209 days.

9. $k_1 = 0.0125 \log 1.5$; 54.2 days; $\xi = \frac{3}{2}$, $k_1 = \frac{1}{60} \log 3$.

SECTION 15

1. $3x^2y + y^3 = c$.

3. $x^2 - y^2 = c$.

5. $y = ce^x$.

7. $r = c(1 + \cos \theta)$.

9. $r = c \exp(-\theta \tan \alpha)$.

11. $r^2 = c(1 + \cos^2 \theta)$.

17. $r = c \exp(\alpha \cot \theta)$.

Chapter 2

SECTION 16

1. (a) $\exp x^2$; (b) x^{-2}; (c) $\sec^2 x$; (d) 1; (e) $x^{-3} \exp(-1/x)$; (f) $\exp(e^{-x} - x)$; (g) t^{-1}; (h) $y^{-2} \exp(1/y)$.

3. $y = \frac{3}{2}e^{-x} + \frac{1}{2}(\sin x - \cos x)$.

5. $y = 5 - 5x + 2x^2 - x^3 - 4e^{-x}$.

7. $y = \sqrt{\dfrac{1 + x}{1 - x}}$, $|x| < 1$.

9. $y = x/3$.

11. $y = x^2 - 1$.

13. (i) $y = ae^{-x}$, $y = 0$;

(ii) $y = ae^{-x}/\sqrt{1 - a^2 + a^2e^{-2x}}$; $y = 0, y = 1, y = -1$.

15. $X = 0$, $Y = \sqrt{x}$; $y = x - 2\sqrt{x}$.

17. $\mu = \cos y/\sin^3 y$, $\lambda = 1/(x + 2) \tan y$; $\sin^2 y = C(x + 2)$.

SECTION 17

1. $1/y = Cx - \frac{1}{2}x^3$.

3. $x^4 = y^2 + Cy$.

5. $y^2 = x^2/(2e^x + C)$.

7. $1/y = C\sqrt{1 - x^2} - 1$.

9. $(x + 1)y = \frac{1}{3}x^3 + \frac{1}{2}x^2 + C$.

SECTION 18

1. $y = (e^{3x} + Ce^x)/(e^{2x} - C)$.

3. $(xy - 1)/(xy + 1) = Ce^{-2x}$.

5. $(y - 1)/(y + 1) = C(1 - x)/(1 + x)$.

7. $\mu = \exp(2x - \frac{1}{2}x^2)/(x + y - 1)^2$.

9. $(y - 1)/(y - 2) = Ce^{-x}$.

13. $y = x + \left[e^{x^2} \middle/ \left(1 - \int_0^x e^{t^2}\, dt \right) \right]$.

15. $y = (Ce^x - 1)^{-1} - x$.

SECTION 19

1. $x^2(x^2 + 2y^2) = C$.

3. $(x + y)^3 = C(y - x)$.

5. $(x + y)^2(y - x) = C$.

7. $\log|x| + \exp(-y/x) = C$.

9. $y^3(y^2 - x^2) = Cx$.

11. $y = x \log|x| - x$.

SECTION 20

1. $\log|x| + y^3/x^2 = C$.

3. $y^2(y - x^2) = C$.

5. $7x^3 - x^7y = Cy$.

7. $x(xy + 1)/(xy - 1) = C$.

9. $2x^2y + x^4 + y^2 = C$.

11. $y = x^2/(Cx - 1)$.

13. $\log|x| + \int \frac{g(u)}{f(u) - g(u)} \frac{du}{u} = C$, $(u = xy)$.

15. $\mu = x/(ax^2y^2 - xy - b)$; $y = (x^3 + C)/(x^4 - 2Cx)$.

SECTION 21

1. $x^2 + 4xy - y^2 + 4x - 12y = C$.

3. $\log[(x + 2)^2 + (y - 1)^2] + 8 \tan^{-1} \dfrac{x + 2}{y - 1} = C$.

5. $(x - y)^2 + 2\log|x - y + 2| + 8x = C$.

7. $r = C\exp(b\theta/a)$.

SECTION 22

1. $y = 1 - x + x^2 - \frac{2}{3}x^3 + \frac{5}{6}x^4 - \frac{4}{5}x^5 + \frac{23}{30}x^6 - \cdots$.

3. $y = 1 + \sum\limits_{n=1}^{\infty} \frac{n+2}{n!} x^n$.

5. $y = x - \frac{3}{4}x^4 + \frac{9}{28}x^7 - \frac{27}{280}x^{10} + \frac{81}{3640}x^{13} - \cdots$.

9. $a_0 = 1$, $a_n = (2n)!!/(2n+1)!!$.

SECTION 23

1. $y = C_1 - \log |x|$, $y^2 = C_2 - 2x$.

3. $C^2 y + Cxy + 1 = 0$; $x^2 y = 4$.

5. $x = \frac{2}{3}p + \dfrac{C}{p^2}$, $y = \dfrac{p^2}{3} + \dfrac{2C}{p}$; $y = 0$.

7. $x^2 + (y - C)^2 = a^2$.

9. $(x + C^2) - y^2 = 1$.

11. $x = t^{-1} - 2\tan^{-1} t + C$, $y = a/(t^3 + t)$. [Put $p = ty$.]

SECTION 24

1. $y = Cx + \sqrt{C^2 - 1}$; $x^2 - y^2 = 1$.

3. $y = Cx + \dfrac{aC}{\sqrt{1 + C^2}}$; $x^{2/3} + y^{2/3} = a^{2/3}$.

5. $x^2 + y^2 = a^2$.

7. $xy = k^2/2$.

9. $F(y - Cx, C) = 0$.

11. $y = Cx^2 + f(2C)$.

13. $y^2 = 2Cx + C^2$; point union at $(0, 0)$.

Chapter 3

SECTION 27

1. xe^{2x}.

3. -2.

5. $e^{(a+b+c)x}(a - b)(b - c)(c - a)$.

SECTION 28

1. $v = x \log |x|$.

3. $v = e^x \log |x|$.

5. $v = \sqrt{1 - x^2}$.

7. $v = (1 + x)^{-3} (\log |x| + 2x + \frac{1}{2}x^2)$.

9. $v = x^2(1 + x)^{-1}$ or $(x^2 - 1)/(x + 1) = x - 1$.

11. (a) $x^2 y'' - 2xy' + 2y = 0$;

(b) $(x^2 + 2x - 1)y'' - 2(1 + x)y' + 2y = 0$;

(c) $(2x - 1)y'' - 4xy' + 4y = 0$.

SECTION 29

1. $y_1 = \frac{1}{2}(\sec x - \cos x)$.

3. $y_1 = \frac{1}{4}x^2 e^{-x}(2 \log |x| - 3) + (x - \frac{1}{4})e^{-x}$.

5. $y_1 = x \sin x + \cos x \log \cos x$.

SECTION 31

1. $y = 1 - \cos x - \sin x;$ $G(x, t) = \begin{cases} -\sin t \cos x, \, 0 \leqq t \leqq x, \\ -\cos t \sin x, \, x \leqq t \leqq \frac{1}{2}\pi. \end{cases}$

3. $b = \frac{1}{2}\pi.$

5. $y(a) = \frac{1}{3}a^2 b^2 P / cEI;$ $c^3/48EI.$

9. $G(x, t) = \begin{cases} \dfrac{\sinh (t - a) \sinh (x - b)}{\sinh (b - a)}, \, a \leqq t \leqq x, \\[2mm] \dfrac{\sinh (t - b) \sinh (x - a)}{\sinh (b - a)}, \, x \leqq t \leqq b. \end{cases}$

SECTION 32

1. $u = (x + 1)^{-1}, v = x^2(x + 1)^{-1}$ or $x - 1.$

3. $u = e^x(1 - x)^2, v = u \int e^{-x}(1 - x)^{-3} \, dx.$

7. $(x^3 + 1)y = x^3 + C_1 x + C_2.$

9. $y = x^4 + C_1 \log |x| + C_2.$

SECTION 33

1. Self-adjoint; $\sigma = 1.$

3. $y = x^{-2}(C_1 e^{-x} + C_2 e^{-2x}).$

7. $(y' \sec x)' + y = 0.$

SECTION 34

1. $y = e^{-x^2/2}(C_1 + C_2 \int e^{x^2} \, dx).$

Chapter 4

SECTION 35

1. $1, \frac{1}{2}(-1 \pm i\sqrt{3}).$

3. $\pm \frac{1}{2}(1 + i)\sqrt{2}, \pm\frac{1}{2}(-1 + i)\sqrt{2}.$

5. $1, \frac{1}{2}(1 \pm i\sqrt{7}).$

7. $-2, 1 \pm \sqrt{2}.$

9. $\pm i, \pm \sqrt{2}\,i.$

SECTION 36

1. $y = c_1 e^x + c_2 e^{2x}.$

3. $y = (c_1 + c_2 x)e^{-x}.$

5. $y = c_1 e^{-x} + c_2 e^{-2x} + \frac{1}{2}.$

7. $y = (c_1 + c_2 x)e^{2x} + \frac{1}{2}x^2 e^{2x}.$

9. $y = (c_1 + c_2 x)e^x + xe^x \log |x|.$

11. $y = (c_1 + c_2 x + c_3 x^2)e^x + e^{2x} + \frac{1}{6}x^3 e^x.$

13. $y = (c_1 + c_2 x + c_3 x^2)e^{-x} + \frac{1}{8}e^x + \frac{1}{6}x^3 e^{-x}.$

15. $y = (c_1 + c_2 x)e^x + \frac{1}{4}x^2 e^x(2 \log |x| - 3).$

SECTION 37

1. $y = c_1 e^x + e^{-x/2}\left(c_2 \cos \dfrac{\sqrt{3}}{2} x + c_3 \sin \dfrac{\sqrt{3}}{2} x\right).$

3. $y = e^{x/\sqrt{2}}(c_1 \cos x/\sqrt{2} + c_2 \sin x/\sqrt{2}) + e^{-x/\sqrt{2}}(c_3 \cos x/\sqrt{2} + c_4 \sin x/\sqrt{2}).$

5. $y = c_1 e^x + e^{x/2}\left(c_2 \cos \dfrac{\sqrt{7}}{2} x + c_3 \sin \dfrac{\sqrt{7}}{2} x\right)$.

7. $y = c_1 e^{-2x} + e^x(c_2 e^{\sqrt{2}x} + c_3 e^{-\sqrt{2}x})$.

9. $y = c_1 \cos x + c_2 \sin x + c_3 \cos \sqrt{2}\, x + c \sin \sqrt{2}\, x$.

11. $y = c_1 + (c_2 + c_3 x)e^{-x} + c_4 \cos x + c_5 \sin x + e^{-x}(c_6 \cos x + c_7 \sin x)$.

13. $(D - 3)^3 (D^2 + 1)^4 D^2$.

15. $D^4(D + 2)^3 (D^2 + 4)$.

SECTION 39

1. $v = x; \ y_1 = x \displaystyle\int_0^x e^{-t^2}\, dt + \tfrac{1}{2}(e^{-x^2} - 1)$.

3. $v = \tfrac{1}{2} \sinh 2x; \ y_1 = \tfrac{1}{2}(\cosh 2x - 1)$.

5. $v = e^{-x} \sin x; \ y_1 = e^{-x}(1 - \cos x)$.

7. $v = \dfrac{e^{ax} - e^{bx}}{a - b}; \ y_1 = \dfrac{e^{ax}}{a - b} \displaystyle\int_0^x e^{-at}\varphi(t)\, dt - \dfrac{e^{bx}}{a - b} \displaystyle\int_0^x e^{-bt}\varphi(t)\, dt$.

SECTION 40

1. $y = (c_1 + c_2 x)e^x - \tfrac{1}{2} \sin x$.

3. $y = c_1 e^x + c_2 e^{-x} + x^4 + 12x^2 + x + 23$.

5. $(c_1 + c_2 x + c_3 x^2)e^x - \tfrac{1}{8}e^{-x}$.

7. $y = c_1 \cos x + c_2 \sin x + \tfrac{1}{2}x \sin x$.

9. $y = c_1 e^x + c_2 e^{-x} - \tfrac{1}{4}(x - x^2)e^x$.

11. $y = c_1 e^x + c_2 e^{-x} - \tfrac{1}{4}(x + x^2)e^{-x}$.

13. $y = c_1 e^x + c_2 e^{-x} + \cos x - x^2 - 2$.

15. $y = c_1 \cos x + c_2 \sin x + \tfrac{1}{4}(x \sin x - x^2 \cos x)$.

17. $y = e^{-2t} \cos 3t - \cos t$.

SECTION 41

1. $y_1 = -1 + \tfrac{1}{6}x^3 e^x + e^{2x} + \tfrac{1}{8}e^{-x}$.

3. $y_1 = \tfrac{1}{2}(\cos x + \sin x)$.

5. $y_1 = \tfrac{1}{2}xe^x \sin x$.

7. $y_1 = x + \tfrac{1}{10}e^{2x} - \tfrac{1}{2}x \cos x$.

9. $y_1 = \tfrac{1}{2}x^4 e^{2x}$.

11. $y_1 = 1 - \tfrac{1}{3} \cos 2x$.

13. $y_1 = -\tfrac{1}{4}x \sin x$.

15. $y_1 = \tfrac{1}{25}e^{-x}[(5x + 2) \cos x - (10x + 14) \sin x]$.

17. $y_1 = x^6 - 6x^5 + 120x^3 - 360x^2 + 720$.

19. $y_1 = \tfrac{1}{6}x^3 e^{-x} + x^2 - 6x + 12$.

SECTION 42

3. Metastable.

5. Unstable.

SECTION 43

1. x, x^{-1}.

3. $\cos \log |x|, \sin \log |x|$.

5. x^{-1}, $x^{-1} \log |x|$.

7. $x^{-2} \cos (3 \log |x|)$, $x^{-2} \sin (3 \log |x|)$.

9. $y = x + x^{-1}$.

11. $y = c_1(-x)^{1/2} + c_2(-x)^{3/2} + 1 - x$.

13. $y = x^{-1}(c_1 \cos \log |x| + c_2 \sin \log |x|) + \frac{1}{2}(\log |x| - 1)$.

15. $y_1 = -\frac{1}{12}(2 + 3x + 2x^{-1})$.

Chapter 5

SECTION 45

1. $x = c_1 e^t + c_2 e^{-t} - t - 1$,
$\quad y = c_1 e^t - c_2 e^{-t} - t - 1$.

3. $y = c_1 e^t + c_2 e^{-2t} + \frac{1}{2}t + \frac{1}{4}$,
$\quad x = \frac{1}{2}c_1 e^t - \frac{2}{5}e^{-2t} + c_3 e^{3t} - \frac{1}{3}(t^2 + \frac{2}{3}t - \frac{5}{18})$.

5. $x = c_1 + c_2 \cos t + c_3 \sin t + t - \frac{1}{2}t^2$,
$\quad y = c_1 - c_3 \cos t + c_2 \sin t + t + \frac{1}{2}t^2 - 2$.

7. $x = c_1 \cos t + c_2 \sin t + c_3 \cos 2t + c_4 \sin 2t$,
$\quad y = \frac{5}{2}c_2 \cos t - \frac{5}{2}c_1 \sin t + 2c_4 \cos 2t - 2c_3 \sin 2t - t$.

9. $x = c_1 + c_2 e^{4t}$, $y = -2c_2 e^{4t}$.

11. $x = c_1 e^t + c_2 e^{-2t} + 3e^{-t} - \frac{1}{2}t - \frac{7}{4}$,
$\quad y = -\frac{3}{4}c_1 e^t - \frac{3}{5}c_2 e^{-2t} - 2e^{-t} + \frac{1}{2}t + \frac{5}{4}$.

13. $x = c_1 + c_2 t + c_3 e^t + c_4 e^{-t} - \frac{1}{6}t^3$,
$\quad y = -(c_1 + c_2 + 1) - c_2 t - c_3 e^t + \frac{1}{2}t^2 + \frac{1}{6}t^3$.

SECTION 46

3. $x = c_1 e^t + \quad c_2 e^{\omega t} + \quad c_3 e^{\omega^2 t}$, $(\omega = -\frac{1}{2} + \frac{1}{2}i\sqrt{3})$.
$\quad y = c_1 e^t + \omega c_2 e^{\omega t} + \omega^2 c_3 e^{\omega^2 t}$.
$\quad z = c_1 e^t + \omega^2 c_2 e^{\omega t} + \omega c_3 e^{\omega^2 t}$.

5. $z = 0$, $y = c_1 \cos t + c_2 \sin t$,
$\quad x = c_1 \cos t + c_2 \sin t + c_3 t + c_4$.

7. $x = c_1 e^{-t} - t^2 + 4t - 3$,
$\quad y = c_1 e^{-t} + c_2 + \frac{1}{3}t^3 - \frac{1}{2}t^2 + 4t$,
$\quad z = 1 + t + t^2$.

SECTION 48

1. $x = c_1 e^t + c_2 e^{-t}$, $y = c_1 e^t + \frac{5}{3}c_2 e^{-t}$; saddle-point (un).

3. $x = c_1 e^{2t}$, $y = 2c_1 e^{2t} + c_2 e^t$; node (un).

5. $x = -2c_1 e^t + 2c_2 e^{5t}$, $y = c_1 e^t + c_2 e^{5t}$; node (un).

7. $x = 3c_1 e^{3t} + c_2 e^{10t}$, $y = -4c_1 e^{3t} + c_2 e^{10t}$; node (un.)

9. $x = c_1 + c_2 e^{2t}$, $y = c_1 - c_2 e^{2t}$; parallel lines (un), $x + y = 0$ in
$\qquad\qquad\qquad\qquad\qquad\qquad\qquad\qquad$ equilibrium.

SECTION 49

1. $\lambda_1 = \lambda_2 = -3$; $\mathbf{e}_1 = (1, -1)$, $\mathbf{e}_2 = \mathbf{e}_1' = (0, 1)$.

3. $\lambda_1 = 1$, $\lambda_2 = -1$; $\mathbf{e}_1 = (1, -1)$, $\mathbf{e}_2 = (1, -3)$.

5. $\lambda_1 = 0$, $\lambda_2 = 1$, $\lambda_3 = -2$: $\mathbf{e}_1 = (1, 0, 1)$, $\mathbf{e}_2 = (1, -1, -1)$, $\mathbf{e}_3 = (1, 2, -1)$.

7. $\lambda_1 = 9$, $\lambda_2 = \lambda_3 = -9$; $\mathbf{e}_1 = (4, 1, -1)$, $\mathbf{e}_2, \mathbf{e}_3 \perp \mathbf{e}_1$,
$\qquad\qquad\qquad$ e.g., $\mathbf{e}_2 = (0, 1, 1)$, $\mathbf{e}_3 = (1, -2, 2)$.

9. $\lambda_1 = 4$, $\lambda_2 = 5$, $\lambda_3 = 9$; $\mathbf{e}_1 = (1, 1, -3)$, $\mathbf{e}_2 = (1, -1, 0)$, $\mathbf{e}_3 = (1, 1, 2)$.

11. $\lambda_1 = \lambda_2 = 1$, $\lambda_3 = 2$; $e_1 = (1, 1, 1)$, $e_2 = e_1' = (0, 1, 2)$, $e_3 = (1, 2, 4)$.

13. $\lambda_1 = 2$, $\lambda_2 = \lambda_3 = -1$; $e_1 = (1, 1, 1)$, $e_2, e_3 \perp e_1$,

$$\text{e.g., } e_2 = (1, 0, -1), \; e_3 = (0, 1, -1).$$

19. $\begin{pmatrix} 0 & 1 & 0 \\ 0 & 0 & 1 \\ 1 & -1 & 1 \end{pmatrix}$; $e_1 = (1, 1, 1)$, $e_2 = (1, i, -1)$, $e_3 = (1, -i, -1)$.

26. $\frac{1}{2}\begin{pmatrix} \beta + \gamma & \gamma - \beta & \beta - \gamma \\ \gamma - \alpha & \gamma + \alpha & \alpha - \gamma \\ \beta - \alpha & \alpha - \beta & \alpha + \beta \end{pmatrix}$.

27. $\begin{pmatrix} 3 & 2 & -1 \\ -3 & -2 & 2 \\ -1 & -1 & 2 \end{pmatrix}$.

28. $\frac{1}{2}\begin{pmatrix} 0 & -18 & 8 & 12 \\ 0 & 2 & 0 & 0 \\ 1 & 1 & 2 & -2 \\ -1 & -5 & 2 & 6 \end{pmatrix}$.

SECTION 50

1. $x = (c_1 + c_2 t)e^{-3t}$, $y = (c_2 - c_1 - c_2 t)e^{-3t}$.

3. $x = c_1 e^t + c_2 e^{-t}$, $y = -c_1 e^t - 3c_2 e^{-t}$.

5. $x = c_1 + c_2 e^t + c_3 e^{-2t}$, $y = -c_2 e^t + 2c_3 e^{-2t}$, $z = c_1 - c_2 e^t - c_3 e^{-2t}$.

7. $x = 4c_1 e^{9t} + c_3 e^{-9t}$, $y = c_1 e^{9t} + (c_2 - 2c_3)e^{-9t}$,

$$z = -c_1 e^{9t} + (c_2 + 2c_3)e^{-9t}.$$

9. $x = c_1 e^{4t} + c_2 e^{5t} + c_3 e^{9t}$, $y = c_1 e^{4t} - c_2 e^{5t} + c_3 e^{9t}$,

$$z = -3c_1 e^{4t} + 2c_3 e^{9t}.$$

11. $x = c_1 e^t + c_2 t e^t + c_3 e^{2t}$, $y = c_1 e^t + c_2(t + 1)e^t + 2c_3 e^{2t}$,

$$z = c_1 e^t + c_2(t + 2)e^t + 4c_3 e^{2t}.$$

13. $x = c_1 e^{2t} + c_2 e^{-t}$, $y = c_1 e^{2t} + c_3 e^{-t}$, $z = c_1 e^{2t} - (c_2 + c_3)e^{-t}$.

SECTION 52

1. $(0, 0)$, node (ss); $(4, 2)$, saddle point (un).

3. $(0, 0)$, focus (ss); $(-2, 0)$, saddle point (un).

5. $(1, 1)$, focus (un); $(-1, -1)$, node (un).

SECTION 53

1. (a) $(0, 0)$, node (ss); $(-2, 0)$, saddle point (un).

(b) $(0, 0)$, focus (ss); $(-1, 0)$, saddle point (un).

(c) $(0, 0)$, focus (ss); $(-2, 0)$, saddle point (un).

Chapter 6

SECTION 54

1. $x = c \log [(c + \sqrt{c^2 - y^2})/y] - \sqrt{c^2 - y^2}$.

SECTION 55

1. $y = \frac{1}{2}(x^2 - 1) + (x + 1)e^{-(x+1)}$.

3. (a) $y = 1$; (b) $y = 2 \tan^{-1} x$; (c) $y = \log \dfrac{1 - x}{1 + x}$, $|x| < 1$;

(d) $y = 2 - 2/x$, $x \neq 0$.

5. $(x - a)^2 + (y - b)^2 = 1.$
7. $y = -2 \log (1 - \frac{1}{2}x), \; x < 2.$
9. $y = 4/(x + 2)^2, \; x > -2.$

SECTION 56

1. $\mathbf{a} = (\mathbf{v}_2 - \mathbf{v}_1)/(t_2 - t_1).$
3. $\mathbf{a} = n^2 \mathbf{r}.$

SECTION 57

3. (a) 80 ft/sec; (b) 69.2 ft/sec, 227 ft.
5. $v = v_0 e^{-kt}, \; x = v_0(1 - e^{-kt})/k.$

7. $h = \dfrac{1}{2k} \log (1 + k v_0^2/g).$

9. $x = a \cosh \sqrt{gt/L}; \quad V^2 = g(L^2 - a^2)/L.$
11. $V^2 = g(L^2 - a^2)/L.$
13. $\frac{1}{2}y^2 = k(C - x \operatorname{sgn} y), \; y = x'.$

SECTION 58

1. $\tau = 0.393$ sec.
3. 2.81 ft.
5. $\tau = \pi\sqrt{2\varepsilon/g}.$
7. $\tau = \pi/4$ sec.
11. 60°.

13. $\tau = \dfrac{2\sqrt{2}}{a} K(\frac{1}{2}\sqrt{2}) = 5.243/a.$

SECTION 59

3. $b = \frac{1}{10} \log 2; \; \tau = 2.0005$ sec.
5. $x = 0.175 \cos 2t + 0.05, \; 0 \leqq t \leqq \pi/2$ sec;
$x = 0.075 \cos 2t - 0.05, \; \pi/2 \leqq t \leqq \pi$ sec.

SECTION 60

1. $x = \frac{1}{3} \sin 3t - t \cos 3t, \; v = t \sin 3t.$

SECTION 61

1. $Q = e^{-\alpha t}(A \cosh \beta t + B \sinh \beta t), \qquad Q = e^{-\alpha t}(A + Bt),$
$Q = e^{-\alpha t}(A \cos \beta t + B \sin \beta t).$

SECTION 63

3. Max $r = \left(\dfrac{1}{r_0} - \dfrac{v_0^2}{2\gamma M} \right)^{-1}$

SECTION 64

1. $v = -gt - b \log \dfrac{M + m_0 - at}{M + m_0},$

$x = -\frac{1}{2}gt^2 + bt + \dfrac{b}{a}(M + m_0 - at) \log \dfrac{M + m_0 - at}{M + m_0}.$

Chapter 7

SECTION 65

11. $\pounds\{t \cosh t\} = \dfrac{s^2 + b^2}{(s^2 - b^2)^2}$, $\pounds\{t \sinh t\} = \dfrac{2bs}{(s^2 - b^2)^2}$.

SECTION 67

1. $(1 - 2t)e^{-2t}$.

3. $(\cos at - \cos bt)/(b^2 - a^2)$.

5. $e^{-at}\left(c \cos bt + \dfrac{d - ac}{b} \sin bt\right)$.

7. $\frac{1}{3}(\cos t + 2 \sin t - \cos 2t - \sin 2t)$.

SECTION 68

9. See Table A, nos. 17, 18, 19.

SECTION 69

1. $y = \frac{1}{2}(5 - e^{-2t})$.

3. $y = 2e^t - te^t - e^{2t}$.

5. $y = -\frac{1}{3} + \frac{8}{15}e^{3t} + \frac{4}{5}e^{-2t}$.

7. $y = t(\sin t + \cos t)$.

9. $x = e^t, y = t - e^t$.

11. $x = 4 - 2e^t, y = e^t$.

13. $x = \frac{1}{3}t^3 + 2t^2 - 2e^t, y = e^t - 2t$.

15. $i = (E/R)e^{-t/RC}$.

SECTION 70

13. $y(t) = e^t - 1$.

SECTION 71

9. $y(t) = te^t - (t - 1)e^{-(t-1)}h(t - 1)$.

Chapter 8

SECTION 78

1. $2x^{(4)} + 4x^{(3)}$; $2x^{(4)}$.

3. $-(2x + 3)/2x(x + 1)$.

5. $y = 0^{(x)} - 1/\Gamma(1 - x)$. From Fig. 66 we see that the curve crosses the x-axis at 1, 2, 3, $\cdots$ and the waves increase without limit as $x \to +\infty$; $y = 1$ at $x = 0$ and -1 and has a local maximum between, and $y \to 0$ as $x \to -\infty$.

SECTION 82

1. $y = a^x$.

3. $y = (x - 1)!$

5. $y = \dbinom{n + x - 1}{x} = \dbinom{n + x - 1}{n - 1}$.

7. $y = x2^x/(x - 1)!$

9. $y = \dfrac{b}{1-a} + \omega a^x.$

11. $y = \dfrac{\cos n(x-1) - a \cos nx}{1 - 2a \cos n + a^2} + \omega a^x.$

13. $y = 2^x + \omega x!$

SECTION 83

1. $\lambda = \dfrac{(-1)^{x+1}}{\Gamma(x)\Gamma(x+2)};\ y = \omega(-1)^x\, \Gamma(x-1)\Gamma(x+1).$

3. $\lambda = \dfrac{1}{2^{x+1}\Gamma(x+2)};\ y = \omega\, \dfrac{2^x\Gamma(x+1)}{x+2}.$

5. $y = \dfrac{2(-1)^x - 4}{x - 2}.$

7. $y(5) = 5,\ y(6) = 16.$

9. $(-1)^x\Gamma(x+1)y(x) = \omega_1 \sum\limits_{t=\alpha}^{x-1} (-1)^{t+1}\Gamma(t+1) + \omega_2.$

SECTION 86

3. $v = x2^x.$
5. $v = x\Delta^{-1}x^{-1} = x\Psi(x)$ (cf. Table 81, 14).
7. From Ex. 2, $y(50)/50! \simeq 1/e.$

SECTION 87

1. $y = \omega_1 + \omega_2 6^x + \frac{1}{50}(3x - 5x^2).$

Chapter 9

SECTION 90

3. $y = \frac14 x - \frac{1}{16} + \frac{17}{16}(-3)^x.$
5. $y = \frac16 x3^x + c_1 + c_2 3^x.$
9. $y(x+1) = y(x) + 2x,\ \ y(1) = 2.$

SECTION 91

1. $y = c_1 + c_2 \cos \dfrac{2\pi}{3} x + c_3 \sin \dfrac{2\pi}{3} x.$

3. $y = c_1 \cos \dfrac{\pi}{4} x + c_2 \sin \dfrac{\pi}{4} x + c_3 \cos \dfrac{3\pi}{4} x + c_4 \sin \dfrac{3\pi}{4} x.$

5. $y = c_1 + 2^{x/2}(c_1 \cos \tan^{-1} \sqrt{7}x + c_3 \sin \tan^{-1} \sqrt{7}x).$

7. $y = c_1(-2)^x + c_2(1 + \sqrt{2})^x + c_3(1 - \sqrt{2})^x.$

9. $y = c_1 \cos \dfrac{\pi}{2} x + c_2 \sin \dfrac{\pi}{2} x + 2^{x/2}\left(c_3 \cos \dfrac{\pi}{2} x + c_4 \sin \dfrac{\pi}{2} x\right).$

11. $y = (c_1 + c_2 x)(-1)^x + c_3 \cos \dfrac{\pi}{2} x + c_4 \sin \dfrac{\pi}{2} x$

$$+ 2^{x/2}\left(c_5 \cos \dfrac{\pi}{4} x + c_6 \sin \dfrac{\pi}{4} x\right).$$

13. $f(E) = (E - 3)^2(E - 1)^2[E^2 - 2(\cos 1)E + 1]^4.$

15. $f(E) = (E - 1)^4(E + 2)^2[E^2 - 2(\cos 2)E + 1].$

17. $y(n) = \left(\dfrac{1 + \sqrt{5}}{2}\right)^n + \left(\dfrac{1 - \sqrt{5}}{2}\right)^n.$

SECTION 93

1. $y_1 = 2^x - x - 1.$

3. $y_1 = \frac{1}{12}x^{(4)} + \frac{1}{6}x^{(3)}.$

5. $y_1 = \frac{1}{4}[2x + (-1)^x - 1].$

SECTION 94

1. $y = c_1 + c_2 6^x + \frac{1}{50}(3x - 5x^2).$

3. $y = (c_1 - \frac{1}{2}x) \cos \dfrac{\pi}{2} x + c_2 \sin \dfrac{\pi}{2} x.$

5. $y = c_1 2^x + c_3 3^x + \frac{1}{2}(x^2 + 3x + 5).$

SECTION 95

1. $y = c3^x + \dfrac{\sin 2(x - 1) - 3 \sin 2x}{5 - 3 \cos 2}.$

3. $y = c_1 2^x + c_2 3^x + \frac{1}{4}(2x + 5).$

5. $y = (c_1 + c_2 x + c_3 x^2)2^x - 2x^{(3)} - 18x^{(2)} - 69x - 111.$

7. $y = c_1(3 + \sqrt{5})^x + c_2(3 - \sqrt{5})^x - 10.$

9. $y = 5^{x/2}(c_1 \sin \alpha x + c_2 \cos \alpha x) + \frac{1}{32}(20x^2 + 12x + 3), \ \alpha = -\tan^{-1} 2.$

11. $y = c_1 \cos \dfrac{\pi}{2} x + c_2 \sin \dfrac{\pi}{2} x + \dfrac{\cos (x - 2) - \cos x}{2(1 + \cos 2)}.$

13. $y = (c_1 + c_2 x + \frac{1}{8}x^2)2^x + \frac{1}{9}(-1)^x + 1.$

15. $y = c_1 \cos \dfrac{\pi}{2} x + (c_2 - \frac{1}{2}x) \sin \dfrac{\pi}{2} x.$

17. $y = c_1 + c_2 \left(-1 - \dfrac{b}{a}\right)^x + \dfrac{kx}{2a + b}.$

SECTION 96

1. $y = \frac{1}{2} - \dfrac{\sqrt{3}}{2} \tan \left(\dfrac{\pi}{3} x - \gamma\right);$ period 3.

3. $y = \dfrac{3}{2} - \dfrac{\sqrt{3}}{2} \tan \left(\dfrac{\pi}{3} x - \gamma\right);$ period 6.

5. $y = 2 - \dfrac{4(-1)^x}{3^x + (-1)^x}$ if $y(0) = 0.$

7. $y = x \dfrac{2x - 5}{2x - 3}.$

SECTION 100

1. $y = (-1)^t$.

3. $y = \left(\dfrac{1 + \sqrt{5}}{2}\right)^t + \left(\dfrac{1 - \sqrt{5}}{2}\right)^t$.

5. $y = \frac{1}{110}[10 \cdot 2^t + (-9)^t - 11]$.

7. $y = -2^t + \frac{1}{4}3^t + \frac{1}{2}t + \frac{3}{4}$.

9. $y = \frac{1}{9}\left[3t^2 + 3t + 1 - \cos\dfrac{2\pi}{3}t + 5\sqrt{3}\sin\dfrac{2\pi}{3}t\right]$.

11. $y = \sin\frac{1}{3}\pi(t + 1)/\sin\frac{1}{3}\pi = \{1, 1, 0, -1, -1, 0\}_6$.

13. $y = \frac{1}{2} + \frac{1}{10}(-1)^t + \frac{2}{5}\left(\dfrac{1}{\sqrt{2}}\right)^t\left[\cos\dfrac{\pi}{4}t - 3\sin\dfrac{\pi}{4}t\right]$.

Chapter 10

SECTION 106

3. $0, 1, \infty$.

SECTION 109

1. $y_1 = 1 + \displaystyle\sum_{n=1}^{\infty} \dfrac{x^{3n}}{3^n n!\, 2 \cdot 5 \cdot 8 \cdots (3n - 1)} \qquad (\lambda = 0)$,

$y_2 = \displaystyle\sum_{n=0}^{\infty} \dfrac{x^{3n+1}}{3^n n!\, 1 \cdot 4 \cdot 7 \cdots (3n + 1)} \qquad (\lambda = 1)$.

3. $y_1 = \displaystyle\sum_{n=0}^{\infty} (-1)^n \dfrac{2n + 1}{(2n)!!} x^{2n} \qquad (\lambda = 0)$,

$y_2 = \displaystyle\sum_{n=0}^{\infty} (-1)^n \dfrac{n + 1}{(2n + 1)!!} x^{2n+1} \qquad (\lambda = 1)$.

5. $y_1 = 1 + 4x^2 + \frac{4}{3}x^4 \qquad (\lambda = 0)$

$y_2 = \displaystyle\sum_{n=0}^{\infty} (-1)^n \dfrac{3x^{2n+1}}{(2n + 1)(2n - 1)(2n - 3)n!} \qquad (\lambda = 1)$.

7. $y_1 = \exp\left(-\frac{3}{2}x^2\right) \quad (\lambda = 0)$,

$y_2 = \displaystyle\sum_{n=0}^{\infty} (-1)^n \dfrac{3^n x^{2n+1}}{(2n + 1)!!} \qquad (\lambda = 1)$,

9. $y_1 = \displaystyle\sum_{n=0}^{\infty} \dfrac{3x^{2n}}{(2n - 1)(2n - 3)n!} \qquad (\lambda = 0)$,

$y_2 = x - \frac{2}{3}x^3 \quad (\lambda = 1)$.

12. $y_1 = 1 + \sum\limits_{n=1}^{\infty} (-1)^n \dfrac{x^{3n}}{2 \cdot 5 \cdot 8 \cdots (3n-1)}$ $(\lambda = 0)$,

$\qquad y_2 = \sum\limits_{n=0}^{\infty} (-1)^n \dfrac{x^{3n+1}}{3^n n!}$ $(\lambda = 1)$,

$\qquad y_3 = \sum\limits_{n=0}^{\infty} (-1)^n \dfrac{x^{3n+2}}{4 \cdot 7 \cdot 10 \cdots (2n+1)}$ $(\lambda = 2)$.

13. $y = x + \dfrac{x^3}{1 \cdot 3} + \dfrac{x^5}{1 \cdot 2 \cdot 5} + \cdots$.

SECTION 110

1. $y_1 = \cosh x^2$, $y_2 = \sinh x^2$.

3. $y_1 = x^{-1} \cosh x$, $y_2 = x^{-1} \sinh x$.

5. $y_1 = 1 - \tfrac{1}{2}x^2$, $y_2 = \exp(-x^2/2)$.

7. $y = 1 - x^{-1}$.

9. $y = \sinh x^2$.

SECTION 113

1. $y_1 = \tfrac{1}{4} \sum\limits_{n=1}^{\infty} (n+4)x^{-(n+1)}$, $y_2 = x^2 + 2x + 3$, $y_3 = x^4(x-1)^{-2}$.

3. $y_1 = x^{-1}$, $y_2 = -\dfrac{1}{\sqrt{x}} \sum\limits_{n=0}^{\infty} \dfrac{x^{-n}}{2n-1} = \dfrac{1}{\sqrt{x}} - \dfrac{1}{2x} \log \dfrac{\sqrt{x}+1}{\sqrt{x}-1}$.

5. $y = 1 - \tfrac{1}{4}x^{-2} - \sum\limits_{n=2}^{\infty} \dfrac{(2n-3)!!}{2^{2n}(n!)^2} x^{-2n}$.

SECTION 115

1. $y_1 = 1 + x \tan^{-1} x$, $y_2 = x$; $y_3 = y_2$, no y_4;
$\quad y_5 = -x^{-2} F(1, \tfrac{3}{2}; \tfrac{5}{2}; -x^{-2}) = 3(x \tan^{-1} x^{-1} - 1)$, $y_6 = y_2$.

3. $y_1 = \sqrt{1-x^2}$, $y_2 = x^4 F(1, \tfrac{3}{2}; 3; x^2) = 2x^4/(2-x^2)$; $y_3 = 2 - x^2$,
$\quad y_4 = y_1$; $y_5 = -y_3$, $y_6 = \sqrt{x^2-1}$.

5. $y_1 = (1-x^2)^{-3/2}$, $y_2 = x F(1, 2; \tfrac{3}{2}; x^2)$; $y_3 = F(\tfrac{1}{2}, \tfrac{3}{2}; \tfrac{5}{2}; 1-x^2)$,
$\quad y_4 = y_1$; no y_5; $y_6 = (x^2-1)^{-3/2}$

7. $y_1 = 1 - x^2$, $y_2 = x F(1, -\tfrac{1}{2}; \tfrac{3}{2}; x^2)$; no y_3, $y_4 = y_1$;
$\quad y_5 = x^{-1} F(\tfrac{1}{2}, 1; \tfrac{5}{2}; x^{-2})$, $y_6 = x^2 - 1$.

9. $y_1 = 1 - \tfrac{1}{2}x$, $y_2 = x^{-1}$; $y_3 = y_2$, $y_4 = y_2 - 2y_1$;
$\quad y_5 = y_2$, $y_6 = y_4$.

11. $y_1 = -x^{-1} \log(1-x)$, $y_2 = x^{-1} = y_3 = y_4 = y_5 = y_6$.

13. $y_1 = 1 - 3x^2$, $y_2 = \tfrac{1}{3}i(3x - x^3)$; $y_3 = \tfrac{1}{4}y_1$,
$\quad y_4 = (1+x^2)^3 F(2, \tfrac{3}{2}; 4; 1+x^2)$, $y_5 = \tfrac{1}{3}y_1$, $y_6 = 3x - x^3$.

SECTION 116

11. (a) $f(t) = \tfrac{1}{2} + \dfrac{4}{\pi^2} \sum\limits_{n=0}^{\infty} \dfrac{\cos(2n+1)\pi t}{(2n+1)^2}$.

$\qquad$ (b) $f(t) = \dfrac{2}{\pi} \sum\limits_{n=1}^{\infty} \dfrac{\sin n\pi t}{n}$.

SECTION 118

5. $T_5(x) = 5x - 20x^2 + 16x^4$.

SECTION 121

3. $3x^2 = 2P_2 + P_0$, $5x^3 = 2P_3 + 3P_1$, $35x^4 = 8P_4 + 20P_2 + 7P_0$.

SECTION 122

5. $y_1 = 1 + \frac{1}{2}x + \frac{1}{12}x^2$, $y_2 = x^5 F(3; 6; x)$.

7. $y_1 = (e^{-x} - 1 + x)/x$, $y_2 = e^{-x}/x$, $y_3 = y_2 - y_1 = (1 - x)/x$.

9. $y_1 = \exp(-\frac{3}{2}x^2)$, $y_2 = CxF(1; \frac{3}{2}; -\frac{3}{2}x^2)$.

SECTION 129

1. $y = (A \cos x + B \sin x)/\sqrt{x}$.

3. $y = \sqrt{x}[A J_3(2x^{3/2}) + B Y_3(2x^{3/2})]$.

5. $y = \sqrt{x}[A J_{1/4}(\frac{1}{2}kx^2) + B J_{-1/4}(\frac{1}{2}kx^2)]$.

7. $y = \sqrt{x}[A J_{1/2}(nx) + B J_{-1/2}(nx)]$.

SECTION 135

3. $y_1 = x - x^2 + \frac{3}{4}x^3 - \frac{23}{60}x^4 + \frac{19}{120}x^5 + \cdots$ $(c_0 = 1, c_1 = -1)$.

$y_2 = x^{-1} + 1 + \frac{2}{3}x^2 - \frac{1}{3}x^3 + \frac{1}{5}x^4 - \frac{7}{90}x^5 + \cdots$ $(c_0 = c_1 = 1, c_2 = 0)$.

5. $y = x^{-1} - \frac{1}{4}x + \frac{1}{18}x^2 + \frac{1}{192}x^3 + \cdots$ $(c_0 = 1, c_1 = 0)$.

6. $b_n = 1, 0, -1, -1, -1, -2, -7, -33, \ldots$;

$b_n = 0, 1, 0, -1, -2, -5, -18, -85, \ldots$.

Chapter 11

SECTION 144

1. $f = \dfrac{1}{s}(h_2 - 2h_3 + 3h_4 - 2h_5)$.

2. $f = \dfrac{1}{s^2}(\frac{1}{2} - \frac{3}{2}h_2 + \frac{3}{2}h_5 - \frac{3}{2}h_8 + \frac{1}{2}h_{10})$.

SECTION 145

1. $y(t) = \dfrac{1}{a}(e^{at} - 1)$.

3. $y(t) = \sin at$.

5. $y(t) = \cos 4t$.

SECTION 150

7. $y(t) = \frac{2}{3}(-1)^t + \frac{1}{3}2^t$.

9. $y(t) = \frac{1}{2}(2\sqrt{2})^t \sin \dfrac{\pi}{4} t$.

11. $y(t) = \frac{1}{2}(3 - t) \sin \dfrac{\pi}{2} t$.

13. $y(t) = \frac{1}{5}\left(\sin \dfrac{\pi}{2} t + 2 \cos \dfrac{\pi}{2} t\right) + \frac{3}{5}\left(2^{t/2} \cos \dfrac{\pi}{4} t\right) - \frac{4}{5}\left(2^{t/2} \sin \dfrac{\pi}{4} t\right)$.

Chapter 12

SECTION 151

1. (a) No solution; (b) $y = \sqrt{1 - x^2}$, $|x| < 1$; (c) $y = -\sqrt{1 - x^2}$, $|x| < 1$;
   (d) no solution for $y'(1)$ does not exist, but both $y = \pm\sqrt{1 - x^2}$ satisfy
   equation when $|x| < 1$, and $y \to 0$ as $x \to 1$.

3. (a) Infinitely many solutions $y = x/(1 + cx)$;
   (b) no solution; (c) one solution $y = x$;
   (d) one solution $y = x/(1 + x)$, continuous when $x > -1$.

5. (a) No solution; (b) one solution $y = 1/x$, continuous when $x > 0$.

7. Two continuous solutions $y = (2 \pm 5)x$.

SECTION 152

1. (a) $y_n = 1 + x + 2\left(\dfrac{x^2}{2!} + \dfrac{x^3}{3!} + \cdots + \dfrac{x^{n+1}}{(n + 1)!}\right) \to 2e^x - x - 1$.

3. y_4 agrees with the series in Ex. 22.1.

5. (a) $y_n \to x$; (b) $y_n = x$, $n \geq 1$.

8. $y_n = \displaystyle\sum_{j=1}^{n} \frac{x^{2j-1}}{(2j - 1)!!}$.

SECTION 156

1. $y_n \to \cosh x$, $z_n \to \sinh x$.

5. $x_5 = \displaystyle\sum_{j=0}^{6} \frac{t^j}{j!}$, $y_5 = -1 - \displaystyle\sum_{j=2}^{5} \frac{t^j}{j!}$; $x_n \to e^t$, $y_n \to t - e^t$.

SECTION 157

1. $y = (1 + \frac{1}{2}\log x)/\sqrt{x}$, $z = -\sqrt{x}\log x$.

3. $y_3 = 1 + x + x^2 + x^3 + \cdots \to (1 - x)^{-1}$.
   $z_3 = 1 + 2x + 3x^2 + 4x^3 + \cdots \to (1 - x)^{-2}$.

SECTION 158

1. $y = \displaystyle\int_0^x e^{t^2}\, dt$.

3. $y = \log\cosh x$.

SECTION 159

1. $\lambda^2 = 4n^2$, $y_n = \pm\sin nx^2$.

Chapter 13

SECTION 168

1. $J_1(1.1) = J_1(1.0) + \frac{1}{2}\Delta J_1 - \frac{1}{8}\Delta^2 J_1 = 0.4710$;
   $J_1(1.3) = J_1(1.0) + \frac{3}{2}\Delta J_1 + \frac{3}{8}\Delta^2 J_1 = 0.5219$.

7. $f(x) = 2 + 4x + 3x^{(2)} + x^{(3)}$.

SECTION 170

1. $C_{40} = C_{44} = 7/90$, $C_{42} = 12/90$, $C_{41} = C_{43} = 32/90$.

3. erf $(1) = 0.8427$.

SECTION 172

5. 31/5 (exact).

7. 17/4 (exact).

Appendices 2 and 3

SECTION A2

1. $x_1 = -3 - 2y_1 + 7y_2$, $x_2 = \frac{5}{2} + \frac{3}{2}y_1 - 5y_2$, $x_3 = y_1$, $x_4 = y_2$.

2. $x_1 = -\frac{1}{2} + y_1 - 2y_2$, $x_2 = 2 + 2y_2$, $x_3 = y_1$, $x_4 = y_2$.

3. $x_1 = -\frac{1}{10} + 49y$, $x_2 = \frac{4}{10} - 16y$, $x_3 = \frac{5}{10} - 35y$, $x_4 = 10y$.

4. $x_1 = 17y$, $x_2 = -15y$, $x_3 = 13y$, $x_4 = 20y$.

SECTION A3

1. $\{0, 2. 1\}_3$.

2. $\{3/5, 2/5\}_2$.

3. $\{1/15, 6/15, 11/15, 6/15\}_4$.

4. $-\{7/15, 10/15, 13/15, 10/15\}_4$.

5. $\{19/4, 15/4, -9/4, -13/4, 3/4\}_5$.

6. $\{5/2, 1/4\}_2$.

7. $\{-1/3, 8/15, -1/3, 2/15\}_4$.

Errata

Page 4:   Line 8 (from bottom): change y to y'.

Page 61:   Problem 6: read e^{t^2}.

               Problem 13 (ii): read $-y^3$.

Page 64:   Problem 1: change x^2y^2 to x^3y^2.

Page 100:   Line 8: read $v(x)$.

Page 117:   Figure 31: delete crosshatch on left of beam.

Page 217:   Line 12: read Lefschetz.

Page 239:   Equation (8): place $\frac{1}{2}$ before first π.

Page 241:   Line 3: replace (iii), (i), (ii) by (iv), (ii), (iii).

Page 246:   Last line: place $\frac{1}{2}$ before second integral.

Page 291:   Equation (14): replace π by $\sqrt{\pi}$.

Page 294:   Table: space between t and t^2.

Page 300:   Line 6 (from bottom): replace third $+$ by $=$.

Page 332:   Line 9 (from bottom): read $-\lim F(s)$.

               Line 6 (from bottom): read $x'(0) = 0$.

Page 342:   Equation (7): delete first (after $=$.

Page 355:   Line 6: replace (2) by (5).

Page 394:   Problem 5: read $y(0) = 0$.

Page 396:   Line 9 (from bottom): replace e^{ax} by e^{at}.

Page 423:   Line 2 of Example: replace i by 1.

Page 438:   Last line: change y_1 to y_2.

Index

Page numbers with asterisks locate definitions or defining equations.

693